W9-CSD-358

Management information systems handbook

Volume 1 : Introduction
Volume 2 : Project management
Volume 3 : Feasibility study;
System analysis & design
Volume 4 : System development
Volume 5 : System implementation
& evalation
Volume 6 : Techniques & standards

Management Information Systems Handbook

Analysis

Requirements determination

Design and development

Implementation and evaluation

W. Hartman

H. Matthes

A. Proeme

Universal Data Systems

McGRAW-HILL BOOK COMPANY

New York St. Louis San Francisco Toronto Mexico Panama

MANAGEMENT INFORMATION SYSTEMS HANDBOOK

Library of Congress Catalog Card Number 75-91966

26957

Second Printing

Printed in The Netherlands

PREFACE

The Management Information Systems Handbook has the subtitle "ARDI". This subtitle is an acronym derived from the names of the activities:

Analysis;
Requirements determination;
Design and development;
Implementation and evaluation,

which are pivotal points in the methods advocated. We feel that the name ARDI serves as a reminder, expressing the thought processes which occur not only in the activities represented, but also at a very detailed level throughout a project.

In writing ARDI, we felt that we could contribute to the state of the art of systems engineering by organizing the description of the systems effort in the form of a planning network. Each activity of the network is separately described, and in its description are provided the considerations, techniques and methods necessary for its execution.

Documentation standards appropriate to the detail work performed during the systems effort are associated with the major milestones of the network. The formalised approach to a project file contributes to the integration of the systems effort. Moreover, the project file is designed to grow ultimately into a comprehensive user documentation.

In complement to the systems engineering side of a project, the management aspects are discussed in relation to the organization, guidance and evaluation of an integrated systems effort. The importance of management's role in requirements determination is emphasized, as is the necessity for continuity of top management commitment and control throughout, from the decision to pursue the systems effort to implementation and evaluation. An information system must fully recognize both the organization's strategic goals and its managerial and operational control requirements; only by achieving a balance between these factors it is possible to create a successful system.

The first volume of ARDI is introductory. Volume 2 deals with project management and Volumes 3 to 5 detail the systems engineering activities. Volume 6 comprises a collection of authoritative papers on techniques and standards specific to systems engineering, or on subjects associated with other relevant disciplines such as organization theory, psychology, operations research and mathematics.

The material of this book has grown out of a decade and a half of computer experience in the PHILIPS organization, a period in which the organization experienced a rapid and widespread expansion of computer-based information systems. With the entry of PHILIPS into the computer manufacturing field, it became necessary for us to consolidate the experience of many people over many years, and to present it in a compact and readily available form. The result was ARDI.

We wish to acknowledge fully the assistance and cooperation of all our colleagues in the various departments of Philips-Electrologica, Apeldoorn; of the Applications Group of the Information Systems and Automation (ISA) division of Philips' Gloeilampenfabrieken in Eindhoven; and of all those in others parts of the Philips organization who shared their thoughts with us, freely offered us the benefit of their experience, and made available to us the testing ground where the feasibility of the ARDI approach was proved. Without their support ARDI could not have been written.

W. Hartman

H. Matthes

A. Proeme

May 1968

To the second printing

For this new printing some corrections have been made. In volume 6 chapters dealing with conversion and forms design have been added.

W.H. H.M. A.P.

Contents

Activity 3-3: Identify system requirements and constraints

- Step 3-3.1: Define the performance of new system
- Step 3-3.2: Identify organizational requirements and constraints of a new system
- Step 3-3.3: Determine information and control requirements and constraints
- Step 3-3.4: Determine general design requirements and constraints

Activity 3-4: Design new system

- Step 3-4.1: Design new information flow
- Step 3-4.2: Prepare system file design
- Step 3-4.3: Study data processing aspects
- Step 3-4.4: Prepare hardware and software requirements

Activity 3-5: Divide system into subsystems

- Step 3-5.1: Identify possible divisions into subsystems
- Step 3-5.2: Select division into subsystems
- Step 3-5.3: Prepare subsystem requirements

Activity 3-6: Review system specification and prepare master plan

Volume 4 : System development

General

Activity 4-1: Develop subsystem

- Step 4-1.1: Review subsystem requirements
- Step 4-1.2: Develop subsystem flow
- Step 4-1.3: Develop subsystem files
- Step 4-1.4: Review hardware and software requirements

Activity 4-2: Specify program requirements

Activity 4-3: Specify procedure and forms requirements

- Step 4-3.1: Specify procedure requirements
- Step 4-3.2: Specify forms requirements

Activity 4-4: Preparation for conversion

- Step 4-4.1: Prepare file conversion
- Step 4-4.2: Prepare program conversion

Activity 4-5: Develop programs

- Step 4-5.1: Flowchart programs
- Step 4-5.2: Code programs
- Step 4-5.3: Prepare first compilation
- Step 4-5.4: Test programs
- Step 4-5.5: Prepare program description
- Step 4-5.6: Prepare instructions for the computer centre

Activity 4-6: Develop procedures and forms
Step 4-6.1: Develop procedures
Step 4-6.2: Develop forms
Step 4-6.3: Try out the procedure
Step 4-6.4: Prepare procedure description

Activity 4-7: Prepare system description

Activity 4-8: Test subsystem

Activity 4-9: Complete user documentation

Volume 5 : System implementation & evaluation

General

Activity 5-1: Conduct training programme
Step 5-1.1: Management orientation
Step 5-1.2: Train users
Step 5-1.3: Train programmers
Step 5-1.4: Train operators

Activity 5-2: Install equipment
Step 5-2.1: Site preparation
Step 5-2.2: Install data processing equipment
Step 5-2.3: Hardware and software check-out

Activity 5-3: Prepare operating schedules

Activity 5-4: Convert programs and files
Step 5-4.1: Perform program conversion
Step 5-4.2: Gather file conversion data
Step 5-4.3: Perform file conversion
Step 5-4.4: Check converted files
Step 5-4.5: Maintain converted files

Activity 5-5: Begin new operations
Step 5-5.1: Start operations of new system
Step 5-5.2: Evaluate early results
Step 5-5.3: Turn over (sub)system to user
Step 5-5.4: Maintain implemented system

Activity 5-6: Evaluate information system

Volume 6 : Techniques & standards

Activity 6-1: Management techniques
- Technique 6-1.1: Network planning
- Technique 6-1.2: Human engineering
- Technique 6-1.3: Presentation techniques

Actiuity 6-2: Documentation
- Technique 6-2.1: Technical writing
- Technique 6-2.2: Charting techniques
- Technique 6-2.3: Gridcharting
- Technique 6-2.4: Decision tables
- Technique 6-2.5: Forms Design

Activity 6-3: Data gathering
- Technique 6-3.1: Interview
- Technique 6-3.2: Measuring and estimating

Activity 6-4: Design and development
- Technique 6-4.1: Identification of system elements and data objects
- Technique 6-4.2: Data organization
- Technique 6-4.3: Application software
- Technique 6-4.4: Data transmission

Activity 6-5: Control techniques

Activity 6-6: Programming
- Technique 6-6.1: Methods for computer programming
- Technique 6-6.2: Programming language selection
- Technique 6-6.3: Practical rules for COBOL programming
- Technique 6-6.4: Record key transformation
- Technique 6-6.5: Program conversion

Volume 1: Introduction

Contents

Chapter 1-1: The concept of an organization

Any organization — a government agency, a public service, a business company, or any association of people united by a common interest — can be typified by its structure; its combination of men, machines, and rules of behaviour. In the more dynamic "systems" concept, however, we learn to think of an organization as a complex of channels through which products, services, resources and information flow from point to point within the organization, and between the organization and its environment.

This complex is usually the outcome of a long process of growth, of the acquisition of experience, and of the need to meet the changing demands imposed by recurring changes in the policies and goals of the organization.

Since acceptance of its products and services by its environment is vital for the organization, it must adopt only those policies and goals which are compatible with both its current environment and its strategically planned change of environment and must adapt its channels and flows accordingly.

It is of the utmost importance to an organization to have a flow-structure which is efficient internally, and which is capable of rapid and appropriate response to all relevant factors in a constantly changing environment.

In industry and commerce, the growth of the need for information races ahead of the actual growth in complexity of the organization. There is thus an ever-increasing demand on the flow-structure in respect to the volume and rate at which information must be supplied to management for decision-making purposes. Managers can make correct decisions only on the basis of reliable, timely and relevant information, many of them are becoming daily more keenly aware that, under modern conditions, only modern systems can supply it to them. The time is long past when information handling could be considered a trivial recording task; the impossibility of controlling any enterprise without a properly organized information system is now universally recognized.

The demands for a higher degree of flexibility give rise to coordinating policies such as centralization and integration of management and operating controls.

To enable managers to concentrate on those aspects of the conduct of an organization which are properly the concern of management, the field covered by information processing is being gradually extended.
To give three examples:

- information of certain pre-selected types can be furnished at critical moments without the necessity of making a specific request in each particular instance (exception reporting falls into this category);
- additional computations can be performed on the normal information output, such as the calculation of ratios with respect to corresponding figures for previous periods;

- in a "decision situation", all possible courses of action can be delineated, together with the consequences which will flow from them ("programmed decisions").

It is many years since data-handling equipment came into use in offices of all kinds; and the introduction of the first integrated machines — computers with a wide range of peripheral equipment — must be considered a milestone in technological history. But computer technology does not stand still; and the information demands of business organizations do not pause in their growth. The great challenge lies in bringing these two giants amicably together; in satisfying the gargantuan appetites of the one by the proper utilization of the enormous potential of the other.

Chapter 1-2: The purpose of ARDI

ARDI is a guide to all personnel involved in the field of systems engineering; managers, systems personnel and trainees.

To management ARDI offers an overall picture which is nevertheless sufficiently detailed to promote real understanding of all aspects of the systems effort. The relevant parts of the work for this purpose are: volumes 1 and 2, and the general parts of volumes 3 to 5.

To the professional practitioner in systems engineering ARDI is a source and reference book covering the whole field of project management, system creation and system maintenance.

To the ADP trainee, ARDI is a comprehensive training guide. For later stages of training, and for the deeper pursuit of specialist interests, adequate bibliographies are provided.

In addition, ARDI serves to generate ideas for solving problems in those situations where, due to the present state of professional knowledge and experience, no specific methods can be advocated.

ARDI serves to generate ideas for solving problems in those situations where no specific methods are advocated. However. ARDI does not claim to provide a concise receipt which, when followed, will result in the most appropriate system for an organization. For that purpose objectives, methods and procedures specific for the organization should be selected and added.

If ARDI is planned to be applied as a basis for systems engineering of "stand-alone", non-integrated systems, the organizational structure to accomplish the effort and the system design phase will certainly be too heavy. In such cases the responsible personnel of the areas involved will work together with a relatively small group of systems analysts/programmers, while consultants from outside the organization will often provide for the specialist knowledge required. Then, volume 4 and 5 will discribe the most essential activities to performed.

Chapter 1-3: The scope of ARDI

The systems effort is divided into phases. Each phase is dealt with by specifying the activities which it comprises; where necessary, activities are further subdivided into steps. In the interests of readability and logical layout, each phase is described as a straightforward process. It should be understood, however, that in practice iteration may be necessary. Where this is so, it will be indicated in the activity concerned.
The phases of the systems effort are dealt with in volumes 3, 4 and 5, which may be referred to as the "phase volumes".
Apart from the phase volumes separate volumes deal with project management and techniques & standards generally applicable to the systems effort.

Feasibility study

In this phase, a comprehensive study is made of the user organization in order to determine requirements for a new system. The existing system is studied only in sufficient depth to determine whether significant benefits are to be expected from the use of computers. If they are, the feasibility study will result in a design concept leading to recommendations for further efforts.
It is not always necessary to have a feasibility study; the decision to implement a system may be taken directly by management as a strategic decision (volume 3).

System analysis & design

This phase covers a wide range of activities; three major ones are defined here. Analysis in this context covers a study for the purpose of understanding the present structure, operations, and goals of the organization; systematic analysis of the findings of the study, and the creation of an explicit specification of the problem areas.
The next important activity involves the definition of the requirements and constraints which have to be met in the design of the new information system. Design involves determining what kind of system will best meet these requirements and constraints. In this activity, once the appropriate system concept has been generated, the modular approach is utilized. The proposed system is broken down into a structure of subsystems adapted to deal efficiently with the required information flows, and the hardware and software requirements are specified (volume 3).

System development

In this phase, the system, already divided into subsystems, is brought to realization. The general approach is to elaborate further on the subsystems, breaking them into programs and procedures (volume 4); and by detailed design of these programs and procedures, to prepare the subsystems for implementation.

System implementation & evaluation

In this phase, the system is introduced into the organization and set in motion. This process includes not only the installation of the necessary equipment, but also the training of personnel. Post-implementation evaluation comprises the determination of the effectiveness of the system in operation.
Collateral with these activities is that of maintenance. In this context, system maintenance means a continuous process of re-evaluation, whereby it is ensured that the system, within the limits of its inherent flexibility, is enabled to meet new and changed demands (volume 5).

Project management

Project management is dealt with in volume 2, which is concerned with the composition of the steering committee, the information systems department, the project team and other teams; job specifications; project planning and budgeting; progress and cost control; cost and benefit calculations; project documentation; and change control.

Techniques & standards

Techniques and standards form the subject matter of volume 6. In this volume are provided particulars of the methods and techniques used in the execution of all phases of the systems effort, together with detailed descriptions of individual management techniques, e.g. project planning and presentation techniques.

Chapter 1-4: The ARDI approach to the systems effort

The rapidly changing environment in which most modern organizations must operate makes exacting demands in respect of reaction times and internal control measures. These demands can be met only when timely, accurate and relevant information is available.

In the past decade, many organizations have implemented "operational control" systems, which use card or medium sized tape/disc computers, and are employed mainly for routine functions such as salaries or stock recording. The technical concept of such systems leads generally to the creation of a number of more or less independant automated procedures, with a large number of process-oriented files and a large-scale maintenance problem. It contributes little to the actual control of the processes involved, and still less to the overall control of the organization.

The necessity of effecting such control, and of creating an integrated system capable of supporting decision-type functions as well as those which are purely routine, has radically altered the requirements which must be met by the systems effort. The new requirements can be satisfied only by the development of a new technical concept, and by the employment of the most modern third-generation hardware and software.

An up-to-date management information system must be control-oriented. It must embody a variety of related functions in such a way as to exercise effective control over the performance of selected processes. To achieve this, it is necessary to change the level of abstraction employed during system analysis and design. Instead of thinking in terms of programs and runs, the first step must be to produce a control-oriented design at the functional level.
ARDI is geared to the design of such management information systems, and embodies as a subset the methodology for the design of partial or operational control systems (volume 4).

Basic to the ARDI approach to the systems effort are the recognition of project management as a dominating and stimulating force, which has to operate from the start to control effectively the entire range of activities; the central position of the determination of requirements and constraints in all phases; and finally, the interfacing of the elements of the information system to establish an integrated system which permits the subsequent implementation of sub-systems.

At the commencement of a systems effort, it is necessary to take appropriate steps to achieve a good appreciation of the existing system of the organization. This will involve obtaining effective knowledge of the goals of the organization, and making a study of its present material-, money-, product- and information-

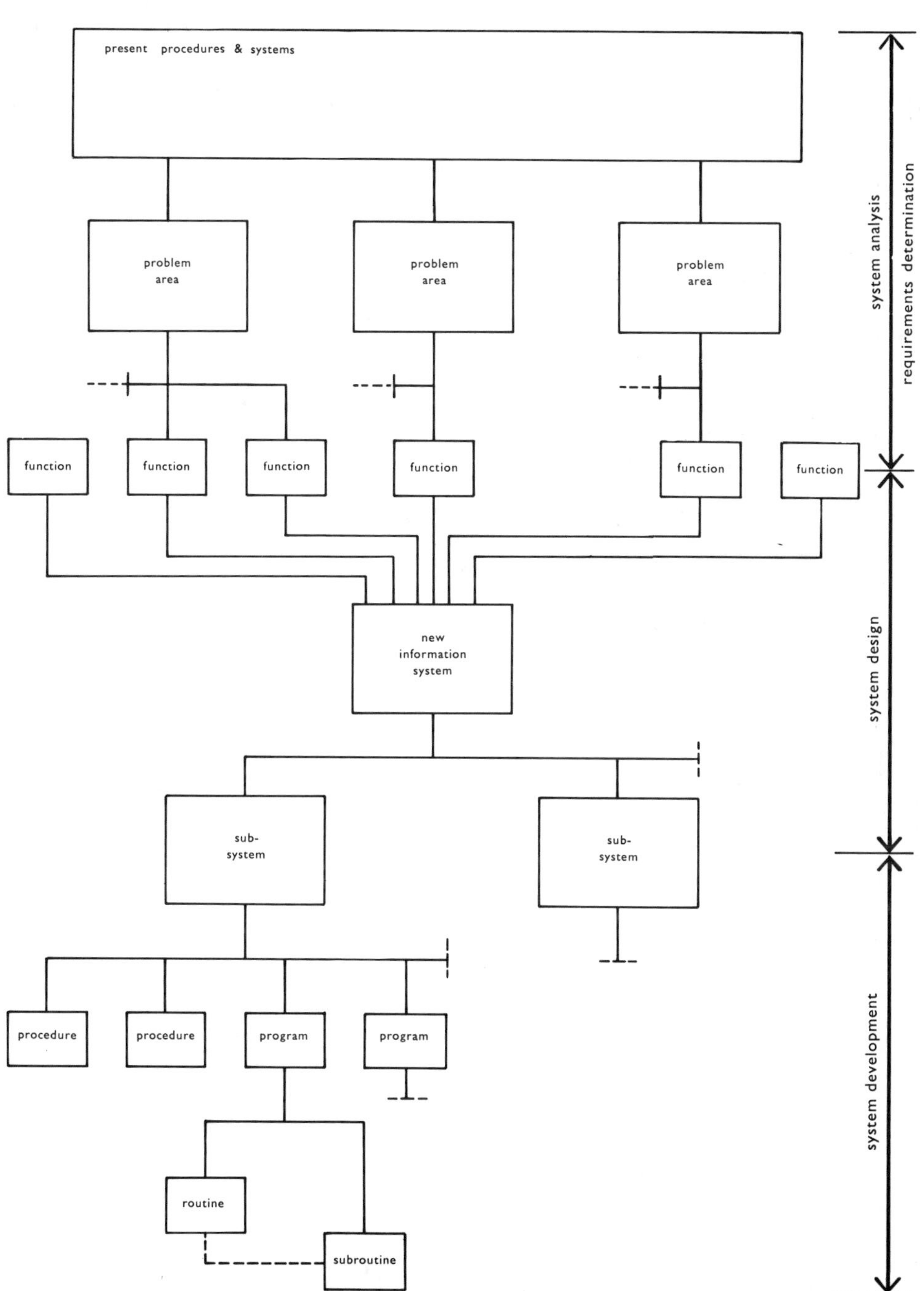

Structure of a system

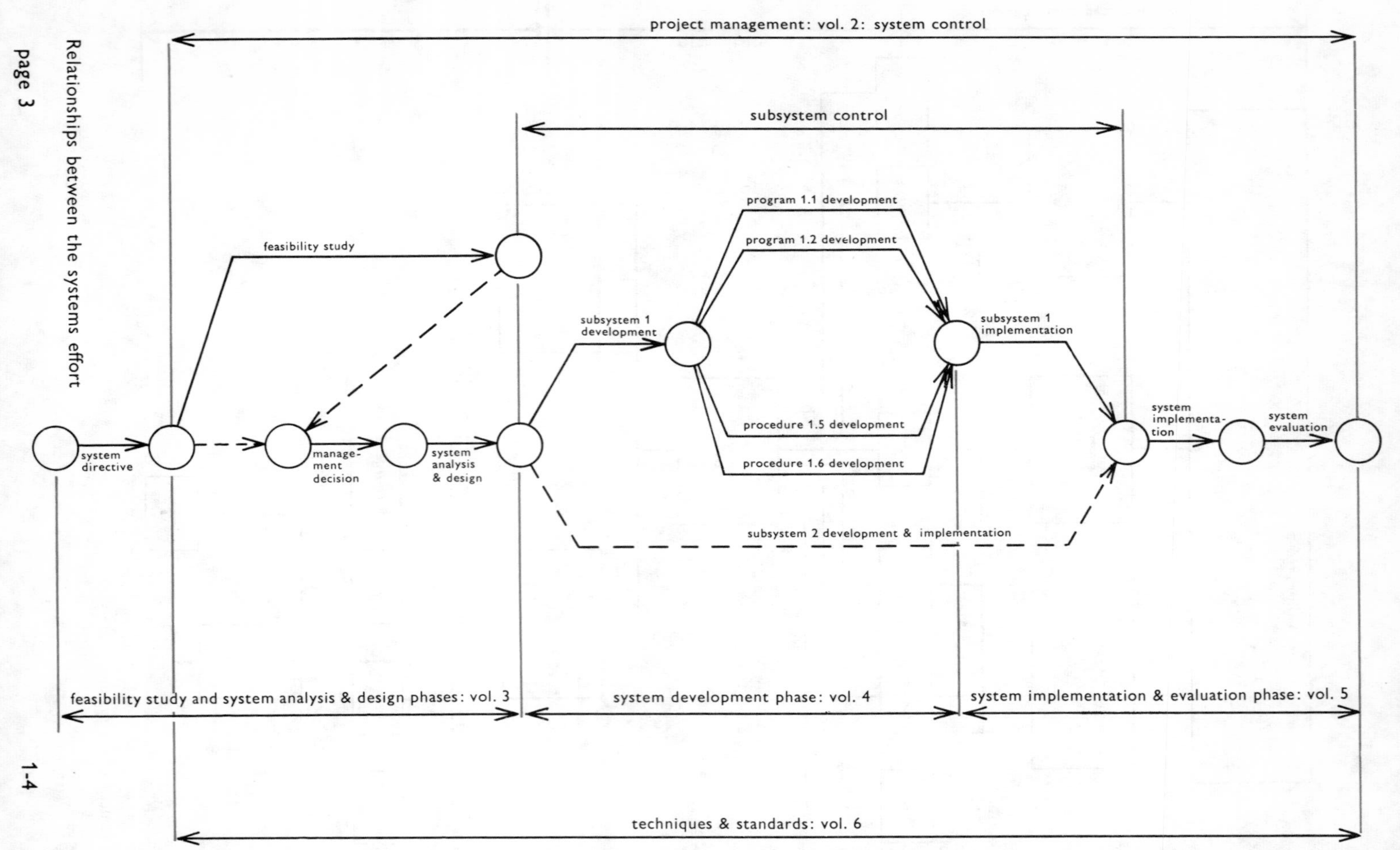

Relationships between the systems effort

flows. It is believed, however, that it is unnecessary to attempt a total detailed description of the existing system in order to be able to proceed with the requirements determination.

The preparation of such a description could take an uneconomically long time, and could tend to bias the later phases of the systems effort towards an automated perpetuation of the old system, thus failing to make intelligent use of the potential of computers within the organization.

The ARDI approach is best explained by reference to the figures on pages 2 and 3 of this chapter, the standard activity diagram in 2-2.1, and the activity network in 2-2.1.

Structure of a system

In the ARDI approach an existing system which is the subject of evaluation and redesign is divided into areas to which the efforts are directed; these are called problem areas. In these areas, functions are identified which are essential to the realization of the organization's goals. Design of the new system consists of synthesizing the functions thus characterized, without resolving detail problems which can be dealt with later. The design process is continued by breaking the new system down into subsystems. These subsystems do not necessarily correspond to the functions of a problem area. A subsystem is a structure of programs and procedures which serve a group of related functions in the organization; it can be developed independently, although its implementation may depend upon the implementation of other subsystems. For the purposes of development and maintenance, the programs are built up as a modular arrangement of routines and subroutines (figure on page 2).

Relationships between the phases of the systems effort

The figure on page 3 is a generalized network, accompanied by additional lines showing the applicability of the various volumes of ARDI at any stage during the systems effort. A vertical line drawn across the diagram to intersect any particular phase or activity will show what other phases or activities, if any, are going on concurrently; and which volumes are applicable to these phases or activities.

Chapter 1-5: Subdivision and updating

Subdivision

Volumes 3, 4 and 5 of the ARDI handbook are subdivided on the following plan:

Phase volumes

GENERAL
- Purpose and scope
- Results
- Methodology

ACTIVITIES
- 1 Activity "A"
  - 1.1 First step within activity "A"
  - 1.2 etc.

Project management

Because of the difference in the nature of the subject matter, the subdivision of volume 2 is slightly different:

GENERAL
- Purpose and scope
- Methodology

CHAPTERS
- 1 First chapter
  - 1.1 First section within chapter 1
  - 1.2 etc.

Techniques & standards

In volume 6, the subdivision is also into chapters, one chapter for each group of techniques or set of standards. Each chapter is divided into sections for the individual techniques or standards.

Updating

The handbook is issued in loose-leaf binders, in order to facilitate the insertion of new pages or chapters as required. In volumes 2 to 6, the pages are sequentially numbered from 1 in each GENERAL part, and again in each chapter, activity, or technique. Thus the insertion of new material does not interfere with the pagination.

References

References in the text are given in two ways:

- within a section or step to specific pages or points, indicated by page number;
- to other sections or steps only by volume and chapter, activity or step number, not mentioning the specific page.

Examples:

2-1.3 means volume 2
chapter 1
section 3

4-3.1 means volume 4
activity 3
step 1

6-1.2 means volume 6
chapter 1
technique 2

Chapter 1-6: Terminology

ARDI uses many terms which, though familiar to the initiate, may well be unknown to the newcomer in the field of systems engineering. It is not the purpose of this chapter to provide a detailed glossary of all these terms; the reader is referred to the standard publications, e.g. USAS X3. 12-1966: USA Standard Vocabulary for Information Processing; and IFIP-ICC Vocabulary of Information Processing (first English language edition 1966; other language editions forthcoming).

In this chapter those terms are defined which are used in ARDI with restricted or somewhat altered meanings as compared with those given in the above publications. The departures are made for increased clarity and precision in the expression of the ARDI approach.

The words which are italicized are themselves defined in this chapter.

activity	A subdivision of *phase*.
analysis (system)	The methodical investigation and evaluation of the existing situation.
constraints	The *specification* of the restrictions which an information *system* must obey and take account of.
conversion	The *activity* of translating data and/or files into formats and representations in conformity with the *requirements* of the new information (*sub*)*system*.
design (system)	The creative process of translating *requirements* and *constraints* into an information *system*, and of specifying the working relationships between its elements.
development (system)	The creative process of accomplishing in practice the results of the *design* by translating it into *programs* and *procedures* ready for *implementation*.
function	The accomplishment of specific purposes or *requirements*.
history file	An ordered collection of outdated documents produced or collected during the *systems effort*.
implementation (system)	The process of bringing developed (*sub*)*systems* into operation.
objective	The purpose and scope of an information *system* in terms of impact upon the effectiveness of the control of an organization.

phase One of the stages into which the *systems effort* can be subdivided.

problem area A field of action within the organization towards which the *systems effort* will be directed.

procedure An ordered collection of instructions, specifying operations to perform a desired task outside the computer.

program (computer) A modular arrangement of one or more *routines* and *subroutines* to execute *functions* or parts of *functions* within a *subsystem*.

project The *systems effort* as a whole.

project file An ordered collection of current documents produced or collected during the *systems effort*.

requirements The *specification* of what an information *system* or part of it must perform. ARDI distinguishes e.g.:
- *system* requirements;
- *subsystem* requirements;
- *program* requirements;
- *procedure* requirements;
- hardware and software requirements.

routine A set of instructions arranged in proper sequence to cause a computer to perform a desired task (ASA).
In ARDI, a routine is regarded as one of the modular elements of a *program*.

run A single continuous performance of one *program*, or of an ordered set of more than one *program*, on a computer.

specification Documentation representing the consolidated status of a *project* at appropriate points in time.

standard An accepted criterion or an established measure for performance, practice, *design*, terminology, size, etc.; a rule by which something is evaluated.

step A subdivision of *activity*.

subroutine A *routine* that can be part of another routine (ASA). In ARDI, the modular concept is here again employed.

subsystem A part of a *system* for the performance of one or more *functions* within the *system*.
Comments:
(1) A subsystem must be interfaced with one or more other subsystems.
(2) Examples of subsystems within a Production control system are:
- raw materials inventory;

- work in process inventory;
- materials allocation;
- production scheduling.

system (information) — An organized collection of men, machines, *programs* and *procedures* to perform *functions* accomplishing specific *objectives.*

systems effort — A general term to describe the work performed in creating a *system*, from the time of the initiating directive to the moment of turnover.

technique — A method employed for the accomplishment of an *activity* or for the control of the *project.*

Volume 2: Project management

Contents

General

This volume deals with the management of an information systems effort. To be effective, a new information system must become an integral part of the organization; and the costs and benefits involved are such as to call for the application of high-investment management techniques. For these reasons, it is clear that the top management of the organization must be involved in all phases of the systems effort.

The fulfilment of a systems effort in accordance with preplanned time schedules is termed a project. This volume advocates methods of project management which utilize and integrate the work of a number of teams whose members are drawn largely from the existing staff of the organization, and each of which may regard its own contribution as, in a limited sense, a project. While some of these personal efforts may continue throughout the systems effort, others might be only the conversion of a set of files, or the implementation of a subsystem. Such methods familiarize a wide range of personnel with the new system at an early stage.

The description of management methods in this volume is closely related to that of the actual systems effort in volumes 3, 4 and 5.

Purpose and scope

The purpose of project management is to initiate, administer, direct and control the activities associated with the systems effort, in order to achieve the best results possible in the given circumstances and environment, giving due attention to the constraints of time, capacity and budget. The scope of project management includes:

- definition of the boundaries of the project, with respect to both the departments involved and the business operations served;
- determination and quantification of the objectives for system performance;
- progressive delegation of project management responsibilities throughout the systems effort, from the breakdown of the system into subsystems through the parallel development efforts, to eventually independent implementation of subsystems;
- overall planning and scheduling of manpower and other resources;
- measurement of the cost and progress of the effort; comparison with budgets and schedules;
- evaluation of performance of the new system against objectives.

Methodology

Project management is concerned with both the systems and subsystems efforts. The overall management of the systems effort is the responsibility of the steering committee. The day to day guidance and control is delegated to the manager of the information systems department, who will direct the activities of specialists in various disciplines (systems engineers, systems analysts, programmers, etc.) drawn from his department.

For the execution and coordination of the systems effort a project team should be formed comprising users from departments involved in the systems effort, a systems engineer, and one or more systems analysts. Systems analysts and programmers will either be assigned to work with, or be incorporated in, the project team. The chairman of the project team should preferably be either a user representative, or a systems engineer who has a solid knowledge of the operations of the organization. The project team is responsible for the quality and effectiveness of the system.

Management of the subsystems efforts is the responsibility of the project team and the subsystem teams, and is concerned with the planning and coordination required in the parallel development efforts. The chairman of each subsystem team is responsible for the guidance and control of his team, and for ensuring proper communication between it and the project team.

In this volume are discussed subjects applicable to all levels in project management; steering committee, information systems department, project team and other teams. In discussing these subjects the appropriate levels of application are indicated.

The management techniques chapter of ARDI (6-1) provides more detailed information on planning techniques, and offers a number of papers on relevant subjects such as presentation techniques.

Chapter 2-1: Organization of the systems effort

A fundamental concept in the organization of a systems effort is that of forming teams within the organization (figure on page 2). The membership of a team should combine operational experience in performing line functions with specialist knowledge, in order to encourage interdepartmental and interdisciplinary thinking. If sufficient expertise is not available within the organization, external consultants, or the organization/application specialists of a hardware supplier, should be called upon at an early stage of the project.

Each team should acknowledge its share in the common responsibility for realizing an efficient information system. Although there has to exist a hierarchical relationship between these teams, expressed by formal reporting lines, e.g. via the chairman, the team members should continue to communicate with, and feel themselves members of, that part of the organization which they represent.

The percentage of members' time devoted to the systems effort fluctuates, both for the project team and for such other teams as may be set up to perform specific tasks. The steering committee, the information systems department, the project and other ad hoc teams are more fully described below.

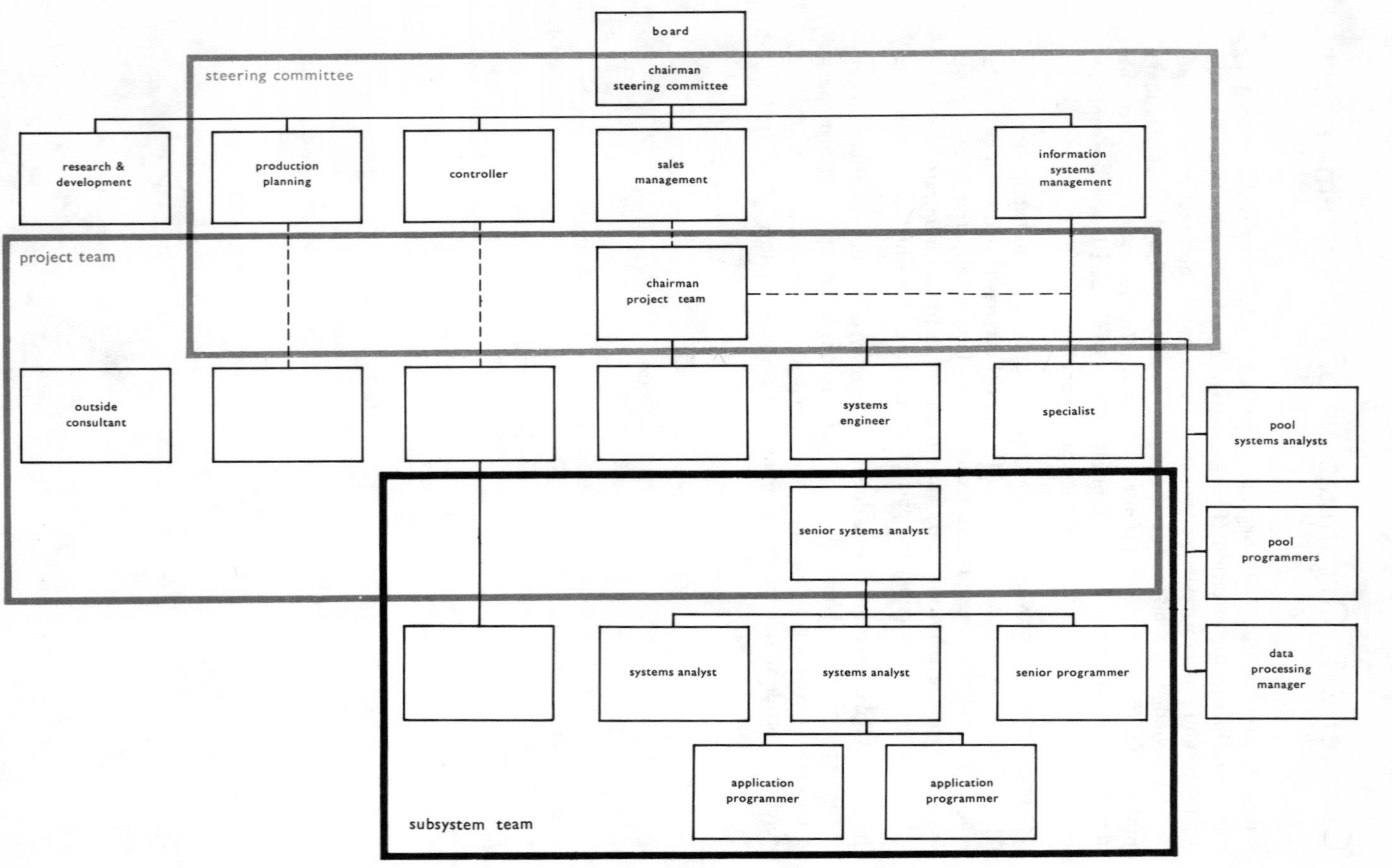

The organization of the systems effort

2-1

Section 2-1.1: Steering committee

In the creation of an information system, one of the first responsibilities of top management is to propound its aims and philosophy; to state its business goals, and to investigate the objectives of the information system which will best serve these goals. The continued active participation of top management — in defining objectives, enabling their realization, provisioning of all kinds, and in exercising throughout a lively and positive control — is essential if the system is to succeed in its ambitious purpose of supporting the overall control of the organization's operations.

In any organization there can be identified certain areas of potential difficulty — maintaining delivery dates, response rate to changing market conditions, maintaining service levels with minimum stock — which have a strong effect on efficiency and profitability. To deal effectively with these areas requires an effective information system.

The increasing information demands of a growing organization inevitably cut across existing departmental boundaries, giving rise to organizational and psychological problems. These problems can be resolved only if they are considered in the context of the organization's management aims and philosophy.

Composition

A steering committee, combining management insight and operational experience of user representatives with the expertise of available staff or outside consultants, should be formed to direct the systems effort. The participation of those senior managers whose departments will be involved must be secured from the start. The steering committee should be presided over by a member of top management, and its secretariat should be provided by the information systems department.

The composition of a steering committee should be limited to as few people as possible. Those who are specially assigned for the feasibility study should be regarded as "associate" or co-opted members. The steering committee should be appropriately enlarged as the areas involved in continuing efforts are identified.

Tasks

The following tasks could be considered as terms of reference for the steering committee:

- issue directive for the feasibility study (3-1);
- guide and participate in the feasibility study phase (volume 3);
- decide whether or not to continue the systems efforts (3-6);
- define, qualitatively and quantitatively, objectives for further systems efforts (3-3.1);

- approve hardware order (3-4.4);
- assign people to the project team, relieve them from other tasks, arrange necessary training (2-1.3);
- approve initiation of ad hoc teams by the project team (2-1.3);
- introduce the systems effort in the organization (5-1.2);
- settle reporting lines for teams (2-2.4);
- install planning and control procedures (2-2.4);
- support and authorize project schedules (2-2.4, 6-1.1);
- approve budgets (2-2.3);
- define priorities, consider and evaluate if objectives are fulfilled (3-5, 5-6);
- approve cost and benefit calculation (2-3);
- approve and authorize new system design (3-6);
- perform ultimate control on progress, quality, cost and realization of the project (2-2.4);
- introduce and promote the new system in the organization (5-1);
- arrange introductions to similar applications to secure efficient system development;
- perform post-implementation evaluation (5-6).

Feasibility study

The purpose of the steering committee during the feasibility study is to define the policy concerning systems efforts; to formulate and approve the objectives and to provide the means to realize these objectives.

Associate members of the steering committee participating in the feasibility study should be briefed at the start on the purpose and scope of the study, the lines and manner of reporting, the time schedule for the study and the minimum set of people to be contacted.

The feasibility study (volume 3) should provide adequate qualitative (structural) and quantitative information to decide whether or not to continue the systems effort (2-3); what objectives, stated in terms of performance ratios, have to be met by the new information system (3-3.1); what organizational constraints must be considered (3-3.2); and what hardware and software is required (3-4.4). The result of the feasibility study should be consolidated in a master plan for the new information system.

The steering committee must make the decision whether or not to continue further systems efforts; and, having received recommendations from the information systems department, should decide what available hardware should be used, or what preliminary hardware configuration should be ordered. They should set up a project team, and ensure that all concerned understand the purpose and scope of the project, and specifically of the system analysis & design phase.

The steering committee, which may assemble only at intervals of about a month, depending on the progress of the project, must nevertheless be in continuous communication with the project team. For this purpose, the manager of the information systems department, who is a member of the steering committee, should be available for day to day coordination with the project team; if necessary, he will arrange for intermediate reporting, and for joint discussions of specific problems with the steering committee.

Reporting

In order to give information on the consolidated status of the work to date, and to obtain approval for proposed plans and budgets, scheduled formal reporting to the steering committee should occur at least at the moments specified below.

System analysis & design

At the start of the system analysis & design phase, the items to report on are:
- composition of the project team (2-1.3);
- masterplan and estimated budgets required for analysis & design, development and implementation of the new information system (3-6);
- schedule of system analysis & design (3-5);
- approach to be taken in the system analysis & design phase (volume 3);
- training requirements (5-1);
- standards for reporting and documentation (2-1.2, 2-2.4);
- equipment delivery schedule (2-2.2, 3-4.4, 6-1.1).

At the end of the system analysis & design phase:
- system requirements and constraints (3-3);
- specification of the system design (3-6);
- system solution selected by the project team, showing the allocation of system requirements to the various subsystems (3-6), giving reasons for the selection, and explaining the resulting consequences for the organization;
- cost incurred up to the end of the phase (2-2.4);
- cost and benefit reports (2-4);
- detailed hardware and software requirements (3-3.4);
- schedules for system development and implementation (2-2.2).

The steering committee should approve the solution to be developed and implemented; approve schedules and budgets; and approve the hardware order with the supplier as adapted and detailed by the information systems department.

System development

At the start of the system development phase:
- system development schedule and, if appropriate, the revised budgets for system development and implementation (2-2.2, 3-5, 6-1.1);
- composition of subsystem teams (2-1.3);
- plans for conversion (2-2.2, 5-4);

- equipment delivery schedule (2-2.2, 5-2);
- required training and introduction measures (5-1).

At the end of the system development phase:
- the final user documentation (4-4.5, 4-5.5, 4-6.3, 4-7 and 4-9);
- result of subsystem tests and simulation of procedures (4-8);
- cost incurred up to the end of the phase (2-2.4);
- organizational measures to be taken for the implementation of the new information system (3-3.2).

Implementation & evaluation

At the start of the implementation:
- composition of teams in charge of conversion and implementation (2-1.3);
- plans and budgets, revised if necessary, for the implementation phase (2-2.3);
- implementation, conversion, and turnover schedule (2-2.2).

The steering committee should evaluate the implementation plans, consider the original objectives in relation to budgets applied for, and, if necessary, set new priorities for the implementation of subsystems.
During and after implementation the steering committee should follow if, and how well, the new information system meets the original objectives. The post-implementation evaluation, which could start up to six months after turnover, will make clear whether the system brings the estimated benefits to the organization. If necessary, the steering committee should take appropriate action to procure the satisfaction of the objectives. It should ensure that appropriate measures are taken to maintain the newly implemented information system.

Section 2-1.2: Information systems department

The purpose of the information systems department is to combine all the disciplines necessary to support the creation of information systems, and to bring together the skills required for the introduction of advanced scientific methods and management techniques.
The manager of the information systems department, who is a permanent delegate from the board, is responsible for the day to day coordination of the systems efforts. He or personnel from his department should perform the secretarial work for both the steering committee and for the teams.

Skills and knowledge

The manpower resources available in the information systems department, e.g. systems analysts and programmers, can be assigned to teams in a project as necessary. A survey of the skills and knowledge of such specialists is presented in the table below.

skills and knowledge	systems engineer	senior systems analyst	systems analyst	senior program-mer	program-mer
company/system					
knowledge of the organization	T	A	E		
problem areas involved	T	T	A	E	
objectives of the system	T	T	T	E	
hardware					
capabilities for application	T	A	A	A	E
characteristics	E	E	A	T	T
operating		E	A	T	T
software					
standard	A	E	A	T	T
languages	A	E	A	T	T
file organization	T	T	T	T	T
addressing techniques	E	A	A	T	T
applications	T	T	A	T	E
general					
human relations	T	T	A	E	E
leadership	T	T	A	T	
standards and procedures	T	T	T	T	T
programming	E	E	A	T	T
logical thinking	T	T	T	T	T
ability to convince	T	T	A	A	E
ability to synthesize	T	T	A	A	A

Legend: T = thorough
A = average
E = elementary

Standards and control

Among the responsibilities of the information systems department which are of major importance to the systems effort are the establishment and maintenance of standards and procedures; and the enforcement and control of the use of forms. This task is performed by a standards group. One of the line responsibilities of the information systems department, data processing itself, is outside the scope of ARDI and is therefore not discussed.

The employment of uniform standards of method and performance by all systems personnel in the organization is necessary to understanding and communication, and lays the basis for control of the work.
Standards — in relation to systems efforts — can be divided into two classes viz. method standards and performance standards.

Method standards dictate methods of operation and provide a basis for a formal control over the quality of the efforts.
Performance standards permit an amount of work to be related to usage of resources.

Method standards and quality control

The reasons for establishing method standards centrally are:

- uniformity in terminology, identifications and documentation reduces the impact of personnel turnover on the systems effort and facilitates maintenance and change control;
- uniform methods of planning, budgeting, status and progress reporting improve communication with management, assure completeness, and reduce the costs of the effort;
- the availability of method standards is a prerequisite for the establishment of performance standards.

In volume 2 a number of methods are given which are relevant to project management. Volumes 3, 4 and 5 describe, under "activities", the work to be done in a systems effort in a methodical way. Although it is not proposed that the activities described should become part of an organization's method standards, the uniform adaption of the methods advocated has the same advantages.

A number of techniques in volume 6 indicate methods of working and of documenting the work performance. They can be of help in the establishment of standards if such are not yet available in the organization. A checklist of some subjects for the establishment of method standards follows:

- planning (2-2.2, 6-1.1);
- budgeting (2-2.3);
- status reporting (2-2.4);
- progress reporting (2-2.4);
- documentation of project history (2-4.1);
- change control (2-4.2);

- documentation of system, programs, procedures and instructions for the computer centre (4-5.5, 4-5.6, 4-6.4, 4-7);
- flowcharting symbols and techniques (4-5.1, 6-2.2);
- configuration description (6-2.2);
- programming languages (6-2, 6-3);
- preferred sets of instructions and statements in a prescribed notation (6-2.2, 6-3);
- identification of system elements and data objects such as files, records, fields (6-4.1);
- labels (6-4.1);
- testing and documenting test results (4-5.4);
- tape/disk filing.

To obtain the full benefit of the adoption of method standards a procedure (method standard) should be established to permit the exercise of control over the method standards by representatives from the information systems department, e.g. the standards group.

Performance standards and project planning and control

Performance standards can be developed only by analyzing performance in earlier efforts similar in kind and circumstance. This fact makes it clear that performance standards will never be as rigorous as method standards, and therefore call for much more understanding and experience in their application.

The availability of performance standards can be of help in making realistic plans and schedules for the systems effort and in estimating expected costs. Performance standards are the yardstick for measuring the performance of teams executing scheduled tasks.

The recording or allowances, costs, and the actual usage of resources, related to the activities defined in the volumes 3, 4 and 5, offer a method of building up performance standards. The project status report and the planning and progress control chart are useful aids to this end (2-2.4).

Section 2-1.3: Teams on a project

Project team

The purpose of the project team is to bring personnel from departments affected by the project together with specialists, to contribute to and to coordinate the accomplishment of the objectives of the system. The composition of the project team can be adapted during the systems effort to keep departmental involvement in line with the actual progress of the systems effort. However, the project team as such continues to function from the start of the project until implementation and evaluation of the new information system and, as a team, carries the primary responsibility for the effectiveness and quality of the systems effort. The project team should enforce the employment of established standards, and ensure that the appropriate group in the information systems department is made responsible for formal quality control. The project team is also responsible for the completion of the systems effort in accordance with schedules and budgets, and for striking a balance between quality of work, cost and slippage of schedules.

Other teams

To execute specific tasks the project team can initiate the ad hoc formation of other teams. The tasks to be performed by ad hoc teams depend upon the situation encountered; however, these tasks have in ARDI defined starting points and end results. For example, teams could be formed for system analysis and requirements determination in identified problem areas, for subsystem development, for hardware and software selection, for conversion and for implementation. Also, a team should be formed to handle (sub)system maintenance after implementation has been completed, if this task is too complex to be handled by an individual.

Formation of teams

The most capable personnel should be made available to participate in the systems effort. They should be relieved from their normal duties, and if necessary, given suitable training. It is important to ensure that all team members have a clear understanding of the purpose and scope of their assignment. They must be familiar with the schedules and constraints of the systems effort which are applicable to their work. They must know how their team is organized, its relationship to other teams, the manner in which they are expected to contribute, the standards of documentation to be applied, and the methods of progress reporting. Sources of background information should be presented to them, and new team members should be informed of the work accomplished to date on the basis of the project file (2-4).

The ad hoc teams will generally be guided by a member of the project team and, as in the project team, many of them will possess different skills and specializations. The composition of such a team depends on the type of charter given by the project team, and on the activities to be performed. The table on page 10 shows the composition of the teams in the different phases. In long-term projects, it may not be desirable to assign all personnel at the time of formation of a team.

Sufficient and appropriate user personnel should be phased in during implementation as the system nears operational status. Too often systems analysts and other specialists find themselves caught in system operation after implementation has been completed, when user personnel should actually be running the system.

Effectiveness and output are significantly reduced if personnel are transferred during the course of the project. Transfer of know-how and indoctrination gathered earlier in the project may become significant enough to delay the execution of schedules.

	feasibility study	system analysis & design	system development		system implementation & evaluation
			programs	procedures	
manager of the information systems department	×	×	×	×	×
project team		×	×	×	×
user representative	×	×		×	×
systems engineer	×	×			×
senior systems analyst		×	×	×	×
systems analyst			×	×	×
senior programmer		×	×		
programmer			×		×
specialist	×	×	×		
subsystem team			×	×	×
conversion team			×	×	×
maintenance team					×

N.B. At every stage specialists can be consulted e.g. for data communication, auditing, industrial engineering, operations research, personnel relations, etc.

Teams and personnel involved during the phases of the systems effort

Tasks and responsibilities of team members

A detailed description of the activities to be performed during a project is given in volumes 3, 4 and 5. A survey of the involvement of personnel in the activities, including references to where the activities are described in detail, is given in page 12 tasks in a systems effort. Although not mentioned in this survey,

tasks, activities and steps	reference to text	steering comm. and/or manager info. syst. dept.	chairman project team	user representatives	systems engineer	senior systems analyst	systems analyst	senior programmer	programmer
• state business goals	2–1.1	×							
• define objectives for feasibility study	2–1.1	×							
• define the problem	3–1	×		×					
• perform feasibility study	3	×		×	×				
• prepare schedules for further efforts	2–2.2	×		×	×				
• prepare budgets for further efforts	2–2.3	×		×	×				
• prepare cost and benefit report	2–3	×		×	×				
• constitute master plan	3–6	×		×	×				
• decide about continuation of the systems effort	2–1.1	×							
• order preliminary hardware configuration	2–1.1 2–2.2	×							
• formation of project team	2–1.3	×	×						
• introduce standards for reporting and documentation	2–1.2 2–4	×	×		×			×	
• check training requirements	5–1		×		×				
• complete analysis of present system	3–2		×	×	×	×	×		
• identify system requirements and constraints	3–2		×	×	×	×	×		
• design new system	3–4		×	×	×	×		×	
• divide system into subsystems	3–5		×	×	×	×		×	
• prepare schedule for system development	2–2.2		×		×	×	×	×	
• review budgets for further efforts	2–2.3		×		×			×	
• review system specification	3–6		×	×	×				
• review cost and benefit report	2–3		×	×	×				
• report system analysis & design phase to steering committee	2–1.1	×	×						
• confirm system to be implemented	2–1.1	×	×						
• approve budgets and schedules	2–1.1	×	×						
• schedule installation and site preparation	2–2.2	×	×						

• plan conversion and implementation	2–2.2		×	×	×	×	×	×	
• review training requirements	5–1		×	×	×			×	
• site preparation	5–2.1	×							
• develop subsystem	4–1				×	×	×	×	×
• assign conversion teams	2–1.3		×		×			×	
• adjust hardware and software order	4–1.4	×	×						
• specify program requirements	4–2					×	×	×	
• specify procedure and forms requirements	4–3				×	×	×		
• preparation for conversion	4–4			×	×	×		×	
• develop programs	4–5							×	×
• develop procedures and forms	4–6					×	×		
• train users	5–1.2	×	×	×	×	×	×		
• train operators	5–1.4		×						
• install data processing equipment	5–2.2	×							
• equipment check out	5–2.3	×						×	
• prepare system description	4–7					×	×	×	
• test subsystem	4–8		×		×	×	×	×	×
• prepare operating schedules	5–3		×	×	×			×	
• adjust implementation schedule	2–2.2		×	×	×				
• report system development phase to steering committee	2–1.1	×	×						
• decide about start new operations and turnover	2–1.1	×	×	×					
• approve budgets and schedules	2–1.1	×							
• assign implementation teams	2–1.3	×	×	×					
• gather file conversion data	5–4.2			×		×	×		
• perform file conversion	5–4.3			×		×	×	×	×
• check out converted files	5–4.4			×			×		×
• maintain converted files	5–4.5			×			×		×
• start operation new system	5–5.1		×	×	×	×			
• evaluate early results	5–5.2		×	×	×			×	
• turn over subsystem to user	5–5.3	×	×	×					
• assign maintenance team	2–1.3	×	×	×					
• maintain implemented system	5–5.4			×			×		×
• evaluate implemented system	5–6	×	×	×					

Tasks in a systems effort

it is a responsibility of the members of the project team to meet each other regularly, to coordinate the parallel efforts of the team members and to discuss, evaluate and approve the results of the work of other teams. The other teams should meet regularly and whenever necessary. However, it should be borne in mind that the teams have work to do; meetings should not be too frequent or too long.

Chairman of a team

The chairman of a team has the responsibility for planning, coordinating, and reporting the execution of the tasks assigned to the team. He has the same responsibility as the other team members for the quality of this contribution.

Secretary of a team

The secretary of a team in most cases will be a systems engineer or a systems analyst assigned to the team from the information systems department. In addition to his function as a normal team member, he is responsible for planning and organizing meetings, recording agreements and action points, for creating and maintaining the project file and ensuring that reports are distributed to all those concerned.

User representative

The representatives of the user are essential members of the project team. They should always be included in any stage of the systems effort, not only because they can provide details which might otherwise be difficult and time-consuming to obtain, but also because they are most directly concerned with the results of the systems effort; their participation can make it easier to "sell" the system to the organization. To be most effective, they should preferably be relieved of their normal responsibilities in order to spend their time with the project team. It is usually advisable to have several user representatives on such a full-time basis, while others should be available part-time to contribute as appropriate.

The user representative has specific responsibilities in the project team. He assists in arranging and conducting interviews and investigations in order to determine and document the present methods of operation. He represents his organization when the team is determining and evaluating requirements and constraints for the new system. He is particularly valuable here in placing relative values on the requirements and constraints. He must represent the user organization in meetings where alternative system designs are evaluated. He helps to identify the need for new or modified procedures and forms, and assists in their preparation. He assists in the development of data used in testing programs and subsystems, and helps evaluate the results. He participates in conducting training classes for personnel who will use the system.

Effectively to represent his organization, the user representative should be either a line supervisor or a member of the line manager's staff. He must possess a thorough understanding of his organization, its functions, its relationship to other units in the company, its goals and objectives, and the "informal organization" (i.e., who has the real authority in the organization regardless of position). He should be familiar with, or know how to identify and locate, the various legal and internal policies which impose restrictions upon the operation of his organization. It would be very desirable if he had participated in previous projects, so that he is familiar with computer applications.

Systems engineer, senior systems analyst, systems analyst

These team members are responsible for the objective separation of fact from assumption. They must interpret facts logically, and evaluate organizational relationships and operations, in order to achieve the isolation of real system requirements from those incorrectly considered necessary by the user. They are with other team members responsible for:

- the effectiveness and efficiency with which the information system design meets the system requirements;
- the specification of program requirements;
- the development, in collaboration with the user representatives, of user documentation, including procedures;
- the training necessary for the introduction of the system into the organization.

Senior programmer, programmer

These team members are responsible for the translation of program requirements into effective and efficient programs, the design of programs in a form easy to maintain, program documentation, and the testing of programs and subsystems.

Specialists

Specialized or more detailed knowledge than that possessed by members of the project team may be required during the systems effort. Knowledge or experience of such a diverse nature may be required at such unpredictable and infrequent intervals that it is not practical to attempt to satisfy all requirements by enlarging the project team. A better solution is to make use of specialists for short periods of time, to advise, or to develop solutions to specific problems. When called in, the specialist reports to the project team if the problem involves several subsystems, or otherwise to the senior systems analyst requiring his services. He is responsible for the quality of the assistance provided.

Examples of the kinds of specialists which might be required in a systems effort are below. This list is not intended to be exhaustive:

- computer specialists to advise on hardware capabilities, peculiar configurations and special optional features;
- data communication specialists to advise on the types of special equipment or transmission techniques available to meet the system requirements;
- software specialists to advise on operating systems, software packages, unique software potentials or special processing techniques;
- auditing specialists to review systems data protection schemes, data control techniques, and financial system audit trails;
- labour relations and personnel specialists to advise on the impact of proposed system techniques which affect personnel (e.g., new methods of collecting labour data and establishing time standards in the factory);
- industrial engineers to advise on the impact of, or assist in the development of, new materials handling techniques, production scheduling, etc.;
- forms designer.

These specialisms will not always be available in the smaller organization: neither can a larger organization always afford the specialization of different people in all directions. The combination of specialisms and the use of external consultants or a manufacturer's advice should then be considered a necessary approach to warrant quality.

Chapter 2-2: Project planning and control

Purpose and scope

The purpose of project planning is to prepare time schedules for the activities to be performed in an actual project, to establish which resources are required, and when, and to ensure that these resources are obtained. Project planning includes the conversion of time schedules and the planned use of resources into budgets. The control of a systems effort assumes the availability of a plan and established standards for performance. Project control consists of the appraisal of the performance; the execution of plans in accordance with the established standards; and the initiation of corrective action if required. Examples of circumstances in which project control should ensure that corrective actions are taken are:

- change detected in resources needed;
- slippage of schedules;
- deviations from accepted working standards.

A thorough job of planning may not ensure a successful project; however, the lack of planning will definitely increase the difficulties involved in accomplishing the activities, and will probably result in wasted time and effort, and in incurring excessive costs before the required results are achieved. Planning is not a process which may be accomplished once and then forgotten; to be effective, it must be a dynamic, continuing process. Planning should be done early in the project. The schedules developed should be progressively refined to take advantage of the knowledge gained during the course of the project. The schedules and needs of resources should be reviewed frequently, and updated if:

- objectives are formulated differently or changed;
- unforeseen complications occur, e.g. in system design;
- deviations from authorized schedules are detected.

Planning responsibility

In the chapter organization of the systems effort (2-1) it has been stated that top management of the organization, and the steering committee, are concerned with the long term planning aspects of an information systems effort. They determine the objectives of the organization and of the information system, the policies for acquisition and use of resources, and the disposition of these resources.

The teams assigned to perform the activities in a systems effort should participate in drawing up the schedules relevant to these activities. Although the actual budgets may be prepared by others, e.g. the accounting department, the team should be aware of the costs of the effort. The control of the project is executed by the project team, being supervised by the steering committee and the information systems department. The latter exerts a formal control, e.g. on the uses of standards.

Section 2-2.1: Planning

The methodology for making schedules consists of 5 actions. Although these actions are given as straightforward procedures, actions 4 and 5 have to be re-iterated in order to accommodate to existing constraints.

1. Identification of the activities which have to be performed to obtain a defined end-result. The standard activity diagram on page 2A presents the activities normally found in the systems effort in summary form. If detailed plans have to be developed the text of volumes 3, 4 and 5 should be read in relation to the referenced activities and steps in this diagram, in order to compose a list of tasks to be done applicable to a specific project.
2. Identification of the relationship between the activities. The standard activity diagram on page 2A gives only the activities categorized within phases. Circumstances in an actual project dictate the logical relationships between the activities, and therefore this relationship cannot be given as a standard.
   Network planning and barcharting are very useful aids in planning a systems effort. They require well defined tasks in logical relationship. Network planning helps to identify which activities or steps are critical in the execution of the project, and thus provides a means to direct special efforts and attention to these activities and steps. Technique 6-1.1 provides more detailed information concerning the use of barcharting and network planning techniques in the systems effort. Pages 2B and 2C give examples of activity networks, showing the relationship of activities and steps in a specific project for a feasibility study and for the systems effort as a whole.
3. Determination of the type and magnitude of the resources required for the performance of each activity. Examples of such resources are personnel with specific experience or skills, equipment, materials and space. There are no hard and fast rules for estimating the magnitude of the resources required for the performance of the activities and phases in the systems effort. Experience gathered in similar projects by people involved in the effort provides one of the most important references for estimating. The figure below gives broad time estimates for project phases based on efforts spent in previous systems.
4. Determination of major milestones and target dates in the systems effort, including turnover dates of subsystems to the user; and identification of activities which are critical in meeting the time constraints presented by the major milestones. If possible, completion of projects should not be planned to occur when personnel are likely to request vacation. Schedules should take into account any major vacations where the effectiveness of the group is drastically reduced.
   Schedules should not be made concurrent in all phases since this will tend to peak e.g. the requirements for computer time and delay the project.

phase of systems effort	systems effort in manmonths	
	manufacturing	non manufacturing
feasibility study	4-10	3-6
analysis of present system (for each problem area)	3-10	2-8
determination of requirements for new system	5-12	4-10
design and development (for each subsystem)	6-48	6-36
implementation (for each subsystem)	4-8	3-6

Time estimates for project phases based on effort spent on previous systems

5. The preparation of time schedules for the use of resources corresponding to the time constraints on each activity as given in the activity network. It must be decided what kind of action, if any, has to be taken if insufficient capacity is available in some time period; e.g. acquire additional resources, or change the date of the milestones and repeat the procedure. The manpower usage chart on page 4 is useful in establishing the load, and in evaluating alternative solutions if appropriate.

MANPOWER USAGE CHART

system : *Production planning & control system*
subsystem :
prev. issue: *june 16th ; '65*

project no. : X 1000
chapter/sect.: 1·2
page : 10
issued : aug. 15th ; '65

activity	personnel	periods 1965/1966															total
		jan.	feb.	mar.	apr.	may	jun.	jul.	aug.	sept.	oct.	nov.	dec.	jan	feb.	mar	manmonths
basic project	sr. syst. analyst	2	2	2	2	2	2	2	2	2	2	2	2	1	1	1	27
	systems analyst		2	2	2	2	2	2	2	2	2	2	2				22
	sr. programmer							1	1	1	1	1	1				6
	programmer																
	user		1	1	1	1	1	1	1	1							8
product information subsystem	sr. syst. analyst										½	½	½	½	½	–	2½
	systems analyst										1	1	1	2	2	1	8
	sr. programmer													1	1	1	3
	programmer															2	2
	user										½	½	½	½	½		2½
main planning subsystem	sr. syst. analyst										½	½	½	½	½	1	3½
	systems analyst										1	1	1	2	2	1	8
	sr. programmer													1	1	1	3
	programmer														1	3	4
	user										½	½	½	½	½	½	2½
materials control subsystem	sr. syst. analyst																
	systems analyst																
	sr. programmer																
	programmer																
	user																
purchasing subsystem	sr. syst. analyst																
	systems analyst																
	sr. programmer																
	programmer																
	user																
total	sr. syst. analyst	2	2	2	2	2	2	2	2	2	3	3	3	3	2	2	33
	systems analyst		2	2	2	2	2	2	2	2	4	4	4	4	4	2	38
	sr. programmer							1	1	1	1	1	1	2	2	2	12
	programmer														1	5	6
	user		1	1	1	1	1	1	1	1	1	1	1	1	1		13

Section 2-2.2: Types of schedule

From the start of the systems effort schedules should be developed and, as the project progresses, should be detailed and updated. Schedules, together with derived budgets and specifications of the system should be included in each plan for a phase of the systems effort. Hardware and software specifications and a cost and benefit report, should be added if any change has occurred in these areas. Details of the schedules can be enlarged in accordance with assignments to teams. Examples of schedules to be developed are discussed below.

Schedule for feasibility study

The activities to be performed in a feasibility study are described in volume 3. The feasibility study is virtually a preliminary system design, but will not give enough detailed information for the final division of the system into subsystems. The activities and steps which apply to the feasibility study are given in the activity network on page 2B of 2-2.1.

Overall schedule of the systems effort as part of the project master plan

The activity network in 2-2.1 gives the relationships between the activities and phases. The business operations and the departments to be involved in further efforts are the other variables of which knowledge is necessary in order to develop a specific schedule (3-5.3). The overall schedule of the project covers all areas to be included in the systems effort, throughout all of its phases. This schedule should be developed at the end of the feasibility study, and should illustrate in the masterplan the recommended approach to be taken and the major milestones in the project. The overall schedule should be updated at least at the start of each new phase, or when major changes, e.g. in system objectives, occur.

Schedule of system analysis & design

There are three different approaches to system analysis & design, viz.:

- the steering committee which performed the feasibility study continues, and takes care of the design of the system;
- at the end of the feasibility study a project team is formed for the design of the system;
- at the end of the feasibility study, besides a project team, special teams are formed to work in parallel through the system analysis and requirements determination activities.

In the first approach, the members of the steering committee must be aware of all the details in every problem area. To obtain an overall view is therefore more difficult, and the throughput time will be longer. In the third approach, the steering committee assigns teams to each of a number of problem areas, for the investigation and definition of information and control requirements. Up to the end of the requirements definition stage, the activities of these teams are scheduled in parallel, while the project team takes care of coordination. After this stage, the project team takes over for system design and the definition of subsystems.

The design activity is a creative one and consequently very difficult to schedule. The schedule for the system analysis & design phase should provide for sufficient time to:

- make alternative designs;
- train new people;
- obtain cooperation of the user;
- specify design;
- establish cooperation with the manufacturer of equipment.

Schedule for system development

By the end of the system analysis & design phase the system will be divided into subsystems. The system development schedule should be based upon this subdivision, and on the measures to be taken in order to make the subsystems operational. Activity 3-5 gives information on the division of the system into subsystems, and on the determination of the sequence in which the subsystems must be implemented.

The methodology for producing the system development schedule is:

- determine the sequence and stages in which the subsystem will be developed and implemented;
- show the relationship between partially developed and implemented subsystems;
- determine temporary measures to operate partially implemented or single subsystems;
- determine the activities and steps to be performed, ranging from review of subsystem requirements; program, procedure and form development; preparing conversion requirements; to preparing user documentation.

An example of such a situation is the development of a production control system comprising subsystems, such as an item and parts list file creation and maintenance subsystem (called file creation subsystem), and a materials planning subsystem. The materials planning subsystem must be designed in such detail that all interfaces relevant to the file creation and maintenance subsystem are defined. It is a logical requirement that the file creation subsystem should be partly implemented before materials requirements can be calculated.

The materials planning subsystem, however, requires data such as production lead times, which might not be available when implementing the file creation subsystem.

Equipment delivery schedule

Provisions for installation have to be related to the other activities to be performed, and with the progress of the project. The equipment delivery schedule should provide for checkout of the equipment and testing of the software. The requirements of hardware delivery scheduling vary according to the situation:

- upgrading of existing computer hardware;
- installation of first computer based system, replacing manual systems;
- replacement of unit-record equipment.

In the first situation the process is easier because much information and many facilities are already available. In the second and third situations, where computer equipment is to be used for the first time, the hardware planning process will begin with a feasibility study and end just before implementation, allowing only for normal delivery lead time. The following phases are distinguished:

- *Feasibility*: It is decided whether a computer will be installed. An affirmative decision will lead to the ordering of a provisional equipment configuration.
- *System analysis & design*: After selection of the system to be implemented, the hardware requirements will be refined, and the order adapted and detailed for specific equipment.
- *System development*: Detailed study of the available software and application packages may cause minor changes in hardware requirements. The order with the supplier should be modified accordingly.
- *System implementation*: Installation and site preparation must be scheduled.

The site preparation, including such provisions as space, airconditioning, special floors, storage of files, etc., is the responsibility of the manager of the information systems department. Requirements raised by the system study, such as file retention requirements and paperhandling capacity, should be specified by the project team. It is good practice to contact the supplier for specialist support in defining the equipment configuration and other preparations to be made for the hardware installation.

Implementation schedule

A provisional implementation schedule should be worked out at the start of the system development phase. This schedule should be updated to include latest changes for implementation, based on the results of the system development effort.

A major part of the implementation schedule is the conversion schedule, because to implement any subsystem it is necessary that both the user organization and the files, are brought into the form needed by the subsystem.

The conversion schedule comprises:

- preparation of conversion procedures;
- user training in conversion and new procedures;
- performing program conversion;

- file conversion programming;
- testing file conversion programs;
- file conversion processing and checkout.

When both the conversion and, if applicable, the parallel operation have been scheduled, the scheduling of the turnover of the subsystem or system to the user must be undertaken. In this, the following checks and steps are important:

- description of conversion procedures;
- forms availability;
- reorganization and staffing of user and data processing departments;
- preparing user documentation;
- conversion and initial exercising of new information system;
- turnover to user.

Section 2-2.3: Budgeting

Project budget

Budgeting is the translation of the planned use of resources into financial data. Budgets should be related to sets of activities which form logical charters to teams. The budgets for the systems effort are one of the inputs for making a cost and benefit report; they should be updated when schedules or use of resources are changed, to enable the feasibility of the effort to be monitored.
Budgets and recorded expenditures of previous projects can facilitate the estimating of costs of the systems effort. It is therefore advisable to install a labour reporting procedure for the project (see 3-2.3 for a daily job report), in order to maintain records of time spent and costs incurred for the execution of each set of activities. This registration provides also the basis for project control.

Page10gives an example of a project budget which is useful in budgeting the systems effort.

PROJECT BUDGET

system : *Production planning & control system*
subsystem :
prev. issue: *may 24th; '65*

project no. : *X 1000*
chapter/sect.: *1·3*
page : *3*
issued : *aug. 15th; '65*

task or activity	cost element	periods 1 Q 65	2Q	3Q	4Q	1 Q 66	2 Q	3Q	4Q	1 Q 67	2Q	3Q	4Q	1 Q 68	2 Q	3 Q	total $
basic project systemanalysis and general system design	personnel	20	25	30	25	5	5	5	5	5	5	5	5	5			145.000
	computer												5	6			11.000
	other																
product information subsystem development and implementation	personnel				10	20	20	25	15	10	5						105.000
	computer						2	2	4	4	2						14.000
	other																
main planning subsystem development and implementation	personnel				10	25	25	20	15	15	10	5					125.000
	computer							4	6	6	4	4					24.000
	other																
materials control subsystem development and implementation	personnel						5	10	20	25	20	10	5	5			100.000
	computer									2	2	4	2	1			11.000
	other																
purchasing subsystem development and implementation	personnel						5	10	15	15	15	10	5				75.000
	computer									3	3	2	1				9.000
	other																
total $																	619.000
	personnel	20	25	30	45	50	60	70	70	70	55	30	15	10			550.000
	computer						2	6	10	15	11	10	8	7			69.000
	other																

Section 2-2.4: Control of the project

One of the responsibilities of the project team is to ensure that the steering committee is kept informed of project status. A certain amount of informal verbal reporting may exist, but a standard periodic reporting procedure should be followed which will provide written reports that can be distributed to the steering committee, and which record the systems effort.

A progress report should consist of two parts. The first is a narrative which summarizes the status of the project in terms of accomplishment, and details problems which are not easily expressed in quantitative terms. The second relates the current status of each task to schedules and cost estimates, and presents revised project estimates where necessary.

Two types of form which can be used for progress reporting are:

- project status report (page 12);
- planning and progress control chart (page 13).

Narrative report

The narrative report should have as a minimum the following sections:

- work accomplished: Identify the significant accomplishments achieved since submission of the last report. Any changes in scope, schedules, or agreed costs should be summarized in this section ;
- problems encountered: Those problems which have been encountered in the project, and anything which has caused a deviation from the plan, schedule of activity, or estimated cost, should be discussed. Also, situations which present potential problems should be identified. The report should indicate what actions have been initiated or are necessary to correct the situation as well as naming the team member who has authority to take these actions.

Project status report

Status reporting provides a method for a team to present the current status of the project tasks relative to schedules and budgets.

The project status report (page 12) gives this information under three main headings; costs, resource usage, and dates. Each heading is further subdivided into original estimate, previous estimate, to date, and current to complete (with the exception that the date heading has no to date subdivision). This arrangement permits rapid and easy comparison between the original estimates, the previous estimates and the current estimates. The current estimates can be calculated in the costs and resource usage sections, by adding corresponding figures in the to date and current to complete columns.

The original estimates figures provide a reference level for the schedule. They should not be altered unless the scope of the tasks referred to is changed.

Previous estimate is the figure derived from the immediately preceding status

PROJECT STATUS REPORT

system : *Production planning & control system*
subsystem :
prev. issue: *june 16th ; '65*

project no. : *X 1000*
chapter/sect.: *1·5*
page : *2*
issued : *aug. 15th '65*

task or activity	cost				completion date			manmonths			
	original estimates	estimate prev. stat. report	to-date	current estimate completion	original estimates	estimate prev. stat. report	current estimate completion	orig. est.	est. pr. st. rep.	to-date	curr. estim. compl.
basic project	125.000 11.000	145.000 11.000	55.000 –	99.000 11.000	dec.'67	march '68	march 68	75	85	33	52
product information subsystem	80.000 10.000	90.000 12.000	– –	105.000 14.000	feb. '67	feb. '67	april '67	50	56	–	65
mainplanning subsystem	125.000 24.000	125.000 24.000	– –	125.000 24.000	sept. '67	sept. 67	sept. '67	75	75	–	75
materials control subsystem	90.000 10.000	100.000 11.000	– –	100.000 11.000	nov. '67	dec. '67	feb. '68	55	60	–	60
purchasing subsystem	75.000 9.000	75.000 9.000	– –	75.000 9.000	sept. '67	sept. '67	dec. '67	50	50	–	50
total	559.000	602.000	55.000	564.000	dec. '67	march 68	march '68	305	326	33	302

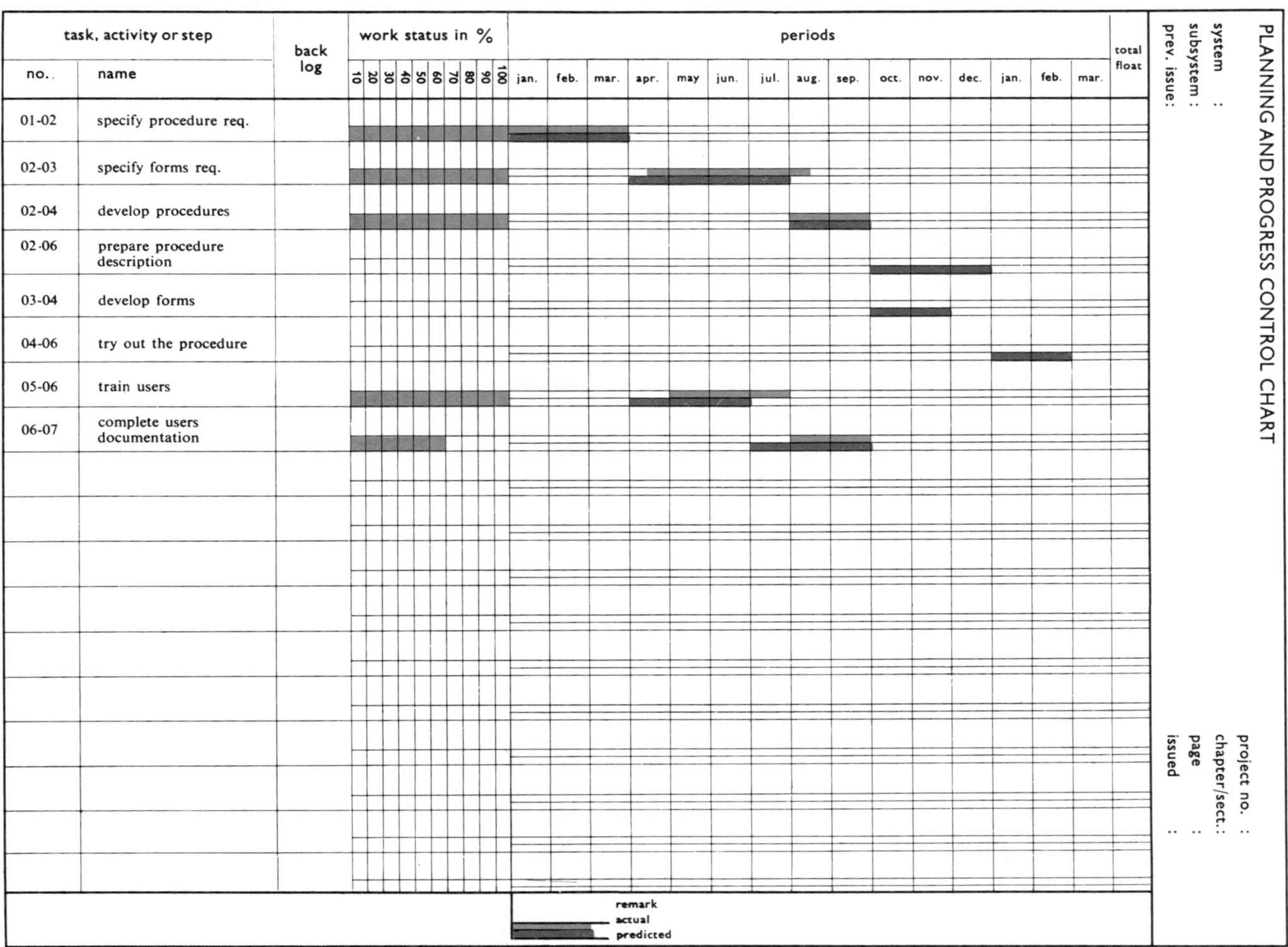

PLANNING AND PROGRESS CONTROL CHART
system :
subsystem :
prev. issue:
project no. :
chapter/sect.:
page :
issued :
task, activity or step
no.
name
back log
work status in %
10
20
30
40
50
60
70
80
90
100
periods
jan.
feb.
mar.
apr.
may
jun.
jul.
aug.
sep.
oct.
nov.
dec.
jan.
feb.
mar.
total float
01-02 specify procedure req.
02-03 specify forms req.
02-04 develop procedures
02-06 prepare procedure description
03-04 develop forms
04-06 try out the procedure
05-06 train users
06-07 complete users documentation
remark
actual
predicted

report on the same group of tasks, by adding corresponding figures in the to date and current to complete columns of that report.

To date means the actual effort and costs charged to each task from inception to the date of reporting. This information should be available from the regular accounting system.

Current to complete. This column should contain the best available estimates of effort, associated cost, and time to complete in respect of each task listed.

Planning and progress control chart

The planning and progress control chart (page 13) is a bar-chart in which the tasks to be performed are displayed by lines relative to time periods. The actual execution can be represented by a second line for each task, while the work status in % of accomplishment can be displayed in a column for each task. The backlog column draws special attention to those tasks where corrective actions may be required.

Chapter 2-3: Costs and benefits of an information system

Purpose and scope

The cost and benefit report is a management tool for use in guiding the systems effort. It provides a means for:

- evaluating the profitability of the new system and the necessary investment for it;
- ranking priorities of the objectives, on the basis of profitability of partial efforts.

The cost and benefit report provides basic information:

- for deciding whether or not to continue the systems effort at the end of the feasibility study;
- for adjustment or confirmation of the priorities at the end of the system analysis & design phase;
- for supporting crucial decisions during the course of the project;
- for evaluating the new information system after implementation and turnover to the user — the post implementation evaluation.

Although cost and benefit reporting is dealt with for the case of a new information system, the same method can be applied if only hardware replacement is under consideration.

Preparation of cost and benefit report

For the preparation of a cost and benefit report, the following information has first to be made available:

- objectives for the new information system defined in performance ratios (3-3.1);
- overall schedule for design, development and implementation (2-2.2);
- project budget (2-2.3);
- changes in the organization (3-3.2);
- appraisal of the existing system (3-2.4);
- new system design, including hardware and software requirements (3-4).

Cost and benefit specification form

The cost and benefit specification form in page 2 is laid out for recording any cost element applicable to the project calculation. A specification form should be used for each line in the project calculation form.

COST AND BENEFIT SPECIFICATION FORM
line number in project calculation form: 20
system : Production planning & control system
subsystem :
prev. issue: —

project no. : X 1000
chapter/sect.: 1·4
page : 3
issued : aug. 15th; '65

description	19	19	1967	1968	total
· decreased no of un-productive machine hours			25.000	55.000	80.000
· decrease in boarding-out costs			15.000	35.000	50.000
· reduction of interest of work in process inventory			—	40.000	40.000
total			40.000	130.000	170.000

PROJECT CALCULATION FORM

system : *Production planning & control system*
subsystem :
prev. issue: *dec. '64*

project no. : *X 1000*
chapter/sect.: *1.4*
page : *2*
issued : *aug. 15th; '65*

initial costs	1965	1966	1967	1968	TOTAL
1 feasibility study	PM				
2 system analysis & design	100.000	20.000	20.000	5.000	145.000
3 system development	20.000	160.000	110.000		290.000
4 cost of outside programming		70.000	–		70.000
5 machine cost - program tests		18.000	44.000	7.000	69.000
6 system implementation & evaluation			40.000	5.000	45.000
7 installation/test cost					
8 miscellaneous					
A TOTAL INITIAL COSTS —/—	120.000	268.000	214.000	17.000	619.000
additional costs in operating new system					
9 user personnel					
10 computer centre hardware			40.000	85.000	125.000
11 computer centre personnel			7.000	12.000	19.000
12 in plant terminal units			2.000	2.500	4.500
13 maintenance			5.000	15.000	20.000
14 miscellaneous			1.000	3.000	4.000
B TOTAL ADDITIONAL COSTS IN OPERATING —/—			55.000	117.500	172.500
costs omitted by operating new system					
15 user personnel		3.000	8.000	29.000	40.000
16 computer centre hardware					
17 computer centre personnel					
18 in plant equipment			500	500	1.000
19 miscellaneous			1.000	1.500	2.500
C TOTAL COSTS OMITTED IN OPERATING +		3.000	9.500	31.000	43.500
impact on performance *(see 3-3 ; 1)*					
20 *better shop performance*			40.000	150.000	190.000
21 *improved end stock product mix*			20.000	55.000	75.000
22 *miscellaneous*			10.000	35.000	45.000
D TOTAL IMPACT ON PERFORMANCE +			70.000	240.000	310.000
E SAVINGS / YEAR ON RECURRING COSTS —/— B + C + D		3.000	24.500	153.500	181.000
F TOTAL SAVINGS / YEAR —/—A + E	./. 120.000	./. 265.000	./. 139.500	./. 136.500	./. 438.000
G CUMULATIVE TOTAL SAVINGS					

(See cost and benefit specification forms)

Project calculation form

The project calculation form on page 3 is subdivided as follows:

- initial costs;
- additional costs in operating new system; under this heading are included all costs whose occurrence is directly attributable to the operation of the new system;
- costs omitted by operating new system; under this heading are included all costs which were applicable to the old system, but which are no longer incurred under the new system;
- impact on performance;
- savings/year on recurring costs; this is the influence on the economy of the organization effected by operating the new system;
- total savings/year; this demonstrates the influence of the initial costs, and of the operation of the new system, on the company results;
- cumulative total savings; the sum of the total savings over a number of years.

The project calculation should be prepared over a number of years; benefits should be proven after a period of 3-6 years, depending on the planned life time of the system.

Initial costs

Initial costs are all those costs which result from the systems effort itself. The costs of the feasibility study should be considered as initial costs if it is decided to continue the project. The activities given in ARDI, together with the techniques and aids in project planning and control (2-2), provide a basis for calculating the costs which can be expected. Detailed cost information is given on the project budget form in 2-2.3, and can be summarized in the cost and benefit specification form. The total in each specification form should be transferred to the lines 1 up to 8 of the project calculation form.

The temporary increase in operating costs during the start-up of the new system, (i.e. the cost incurred in parallel running, or whatever method is chosen for turnover of the new system) has to be considered as a once-only initial cost under the cost element "implementation".

Operating costs

In determining the relative operating costs of the old and new systems, it is necessary to compare situations which are equivalent. It is not correct to compare a badly organized system, which can be improved by rather simple measures, with a new system developed as a result of a significant systems effort. In such a case, the improvements which would result from the simple measures should not be assessed as benefits of the new system.

In making the comparison, it is necessary to take into account the values at the time of implementation of such quantities as number of articles, number of orders, number of customers, number of stock-keeping items, and turnover.

In a project calculation only those operating costs should be taken into account which will be affected by the implementation of the new information system. Cost elements which might be affected are costs of personnel, equipment, space and supplies. In such areas, the costs of the changed situation should be entered on the specification forms, and summarized in lines 9 to 14 of the project calculation form.

As the new system becomes operational, certain costs no longer occur. These costs must be summarized under the heading costs omitted by operating the new system on lines 15 to 19 of the project calculation form.

Impact on performance
Under the heading impact on performance, on the lines 20 and following the measurable objectives should be listed.
In determine the performance of the new system (3-3.1) the development of performance ratios from detailed quantifiable objectives is discussed. These performance ratios serve to measure the influence of the improvement of the organizational control arising from the implementation of the new information system.

Illustrations of such improvements are cost reduction in stockkeeping, or by increased capital turnover; better performance in the form of shorter delivery times or better mix of products in stock; improved commercial revenue by reason of having new products on the market earlier than competitors, or because of shorter delivery times for capital goods; and ability to maintain sales levels in the face of improving customer service in the industry.

The translation of measurable objectives into financial data should be undertaken in close cooperation with, and under the responsibility of, the financial manager or controller of the organization.

Evaluation of the costs and benefits

After collecting all cost and benefit items and arranging them according to the breakdown of the project calculation form, an evaluation of the project can be made. A major consideration is the time span. For an adequate evaluation, the time-span chosen should fall between a minimum which includes the total time spent on the systems effort and the first normal year of execution of the information system, and a maximum not exceeding the sum of the total time spent on the systems effort and the expected economic life time of the information system.
The economic life time of the new system is of special importance when the impact of the system on the user organization is expected to make itself manifest gradually, and not directly in the first year of operation of the system.

The project calculation for the selected time-span should take into account the initial or nonrecurring costs connected with the systems effort, with the installing of new hardware, and with the implementation of new procedures and runs. This method permits either upward or downward adjustment of the expected operating or recurring costs over the years of actual operation of the system, to meet respectively growth, or increase in efficiency and experience. It permits also an integrated evaluation of all costs and benefits concerned, irrespective of the year in which they occur or are realized.

The minimal requirement imposed on the accounting department of the organization is that it shall keep accurate separate records of all items for each project. The final result of the evaluation is a summing up of all costs and benefits over the chosen time span. This figure must show a favourable balance of benefits and costs omitted over new costs before the project can be considered successful.

Chapter 2-4: Project documentation and change control

In the course of creating an integrated information system, a very large quantity of data becomes available. Systems personnel must not only understand the individual items, but must also appreciate the problems implicit in the complex of relationships which links them. When, in such an environment, creative people are working in parallel towards a common goal, the preparation and maintenance of comprehensive up-to-date documentation is essential to success. Such documentation provides also the information and instruction for those who join teams during the course of the systems effort and, when implementation is achieved, presents an overall picture of the accomplishment which is of value both as a record and as a tool for future efforts.

Purpose

The purposes of project documentation are therefore:

- to set down the data discovered in a full and logical manner, demonstrating relationships;
- to facilitate communication between teams and between members within a team;
- to provide a complete and accurate picture of the work accomplished;
- to offer, at implementation, a complete set of user documentation enabling maintenance and post-implementation evaluation;
- to present a record of efforts and costs in relation to activities and solutions, for reference and research in similar systems efforts.

Documentation standards

If these purposes are to be adequately fulfilled, the production, filing, and maintenance of documentation must be controlled by fixed standards. The standards advocated and exemplified throughout this work are eminently suitable, although it is not suggested that they are the only ones possible. The standards to be used must be set up at the start of the systems effort; the same standards must be used consistently throughout the system and all of its subsystems, and also in all other systems in the same organization. The enforcement of the use of these standards is the duty of the standards group of the information systems department.

Change control

Since it calls for the responsible exercise of judgement, change control is an executive rather than an administrative procedure. Nevertheless, when the effect of a proposed change has been evaluated, and a solution found and approved, these decisions must be recorded and formally incorporated in the project documentation.

Section 2-4.1: Project documentation

The project documentation consists of the project file, the history file and the user documentation. The first two should be kept by the project team, while the latter is distributed as mentioned below.

Project file

The project file contains frozen documents, the latest version of approved documents (e.g. schedules), and since it is a working file, drafts, concepts, and preliminary documentation of work in progress. It thus represents the current state of the systems effort, and provides a medium of communication between teams.

Systematic subdivision of the project file, one chapter or section to each specific subject or aspect, is essential for efficient filing and maintenance. Thus the project file must be organized in advance of the work, in order to accomodate under appropriate headings the documentation which will be prepared for it. This will also ensure a logical growth from dynamic project documentation into user documentation.

As the systems effort proceeds, the content of the project file will change. Provisional documents will be replaced by later, and ultimately by finalized versions; periodic reports by later issues; changes will be requested and implemented. When, for whatever reason, a document is removed from the project file, it is refiled in the history file, which will thus contain copies of all outdated documents.

As in the case of the project file, the history file is maintained centrally, and only a single copy is necessary. When a document is placed in the history file, the front page of the appropriate section or chapter of the project file must be updated accordingly; see example below.

chapter and section no.	document name	date issue	edition number	date replaced	edition number
4-4.1	subsystem requirements for production information	1.6.67	1	15.9.67	2
4-4.2	subsystem requirements for materials requir. calcul.	3.8.67	1		
4-4.1	subsystem requirements for production information	5.11.67	2		

Number of copies

In principle, and apart from protection rules, one copy of the project file is sufficient. However, in a project where many teams are working in parallel, this may prove unpractical. In these circumstances, duplicates should be made of those portions of the project file applicable to the work of each team. These "subsets" of the project file should be used mainly for filing material under development, and for ensuring communication within a team. All material filed in such a subset should be filed also in the centrally maintained project file, which should be regarded as the master. The last activity in each of the phase volumes is directed towards the preparation of project file documentation of the activities dealt with in the volume.

History file

The history file may be organized either in date order or in correspondence with the project file, whichever is found more convenient for retrieval.

Protection

In view of the cost and the importance of the systems effort, it is desirable to protect the documentation against loss. A duplicate of both files should therefore be kept in a separate location in the information systems department.

User documentation

The user documentation of the information system is derived from the content of the project file by reorganizing and rewriting as necessary to adapt it to specific needs. The following table shows the documentation to be prepared for different people in the organization.

type of user documentation	ref. to specification of contents	user management	inform. syst. dept.	maintenance team	computer centre	auditing dept.	user personnel
system description	4-7	x	x	x	x	x	x
instructions for computer centre	4-5.6		x	x	x	x	
program description	4-5.5		x	x		x	
procedures	4-6.3	x	x	x		x	x

When the new information system is turned over to the user, all project documentation should be filed in the history file. This file should be stored in the information systems department.
The user documentation will be maintained by a maintenance employee or team assigned for the purpose.

Updating

Both project and user documentation should be assembled in loose leaf or file binders to facilitate updating. Additions to or changes in user documentation will be issued in page form. For control purposes, each page should be identified by:

- system/subsystem name;
- project number;
- chapter and section number;
- page number within the section;
- date of issue;
- date of issue replaced.

The total number of pages should be indicated in the first page of any report or section as a check on completeness.
When distributed, documentation should be accompanied by:

- a mailing list; during the systems effort this permits a formal check on lines of communication;
- instructions for:
  — filing of additions;
  — replacement of earlier documentation;
  — removal of earlier documentation;
  — alterations of the total indicated number of pages per section.

Subdivision of the project file

The following is an example of the subdivision of a project file.

Chapter 1 Project management

This chapter should contain all documents concerned with the conduct of the project itself.

1. *Personnel* (2-1):
   — team formation;
   — assignments to individuals.
2. *Planning and schedules* (2-2.2):
   — overal schedule of the systems effort (barchart) or activity network for the project;
   — schedules for each phase of the systems effort;
   — detailed schedules for subsystem development and implementation;
   — manpower usage chart allocating personnel by number and type throughout the project.
3. *Budgets* (2-2.3)
4. *Cost and benefit report* (2-3)
5. *Project control reports* (2-2.4):
   — project status reports;
   — progress reports;

— planning and progress control chart.

6. *Change control, only for changes during the systems effort* (2-4.2):
   — change requests and dispositions;
   — change request summaries.
7. *Correspondence*
8. *Minutes of meetings of each committee or team*

Chapter 2 General company information

This chapter should contain general information about the company (3-2.1):

1. *Characteristics of the company*
2. *Company organization charts*
3. *Product, market and production information*
4. *Glossary of terms and abbreviations used in the company*

Chapter 3 Analysis

This chapter should contain all the data collected and prepared during system analysis (3-2), such as:

1. *Record of all personnel contacted*
2. *Notes on interviews*
3. *Notes on collected suggestions from line personnel and staff*
   The same type of form can be used for these notes as for change request summaries.
4. *Description of present system*
   This section includes flowcharts of product and information flow, procedures etc.
5. *Cost and effectiveness reports on the present system*

Documentation prepared during the system analysis stage is subdivided by problem area or function. It does not follow that future work in the system design activity will be concentrated on the same areas or functions, or indeed that the subdivision into, or scope of the problem areas will be the same.

Chapter 4 Design

In this chapter the following documentation should be filed:

1. *System objectives* (3-1 and 3-3.1):
   — original problem definition;
   — defined system objectives.
2. *System requirements and constraints* (3-3, 3-4):
   — organizational requirements and constraints;
   — information and control requirements;
   — general design requirements and constraints;
   — information flow;
   — function worksheets;
   — function evaluation charts;
   — file usage charts;

— file evaluation charts;
— data usage charts.

3. *Subsystem requirements* (3-5.3)
4. *System specification* (3-6)

Chapter 5 Development

This chapter should be divided into sections in a manner corresponding to the division of the system into subsystems. Each section should contain the appropriate system requirements, the system specification including flowcharts and files; and interface information relating the subsystem to the system specification, the subsystem requirements, and the hardware and software.

In addition the chapter should contain:

1. *Subsystem specification:*
   — subsystem flow (4-1.2);
   — subsystem files (4-1.3).
2. *For each program:*
   — program requirements (4-2);
   — program description (4-5.5).
3. *For each procedure:*
   — procedure requirements (4-3.1);
   — procedure description (4-6.3).
4. *Documentation concerning conversion* (4-4)
5. *Instructions for the computer centre* (4-5.6)
6. *System description* (4-7)

Chapter 6 Implementation

This chapter should contain all documentation relevant to the implementation of subsystems, such as:

1. *Training programs* (5-1)
2. *Operating schedules* (5-3)
3. *Error reports* (5-5.4)
4. *File conversion* (5-4.3)
5. *Program conversion* (5-4.1)

Chapter 7 Hardware and software

This chapter should include information about:

1. *Proposals* (3-4.4)
2. *Selected hardware and software* (3-4.4)
3. *Installation of hardware and software*
4. *Hardware and software evaluation reports* (3-4.4, 4-1.4)

Chapter 8 Maintenance

This chapter should include:

1. *Post-implementation evaluation reports* (5-6)
2. *Change requests* (2-4.2)
3. *Change request summaries*

Section 2-4.2: Change control

The primary purpose of a change control procedure is to establish a standard method of initiating, evaluating, and monitoring changes requested during and after the systems effort. Due to the nature of the systems effort, many changes may be expected. These changes cannot always be avoided; they should be regarded as a necessary factor in systems work. They arise from the many alternatives to be considered, the requirements from different areas which must be satisfied, and, in some cases, decisions which must be based on incomplete information. Until decisions are made and considered final, these changes do not require any special control. However, as the project progresses it may become desirable to reconsider some of the decisions already made and "frozen". These changes must be considered in a systematic manner, and implemented on a well regulated basis, so as to avoid unnecessary confusion, wasted effort in other parts of the system, and accidental violation of some of the design requirements.
The acceptance of changes should lead to updating of the project documentation in the project file, and, if appropriate, of the user documentation.

Reasons for change

Changes to the project's scope, schedules or programs may arise for a number of reasons. Some of these are:

- to add new requirements to the system;
- to expand the system to other areas in the organization;
- to modify design specifications in order to add or delete capabilities;
- to meet a new or changed request for a report;
- to modify requirements in order to resolve an inconsistency;
- to change specifications in order to allow more economical use of equipment;
- to correct deficiencies in subsystem or program specifications;
- to correct any incompatability between subsystem design specifications and hardware capabilities, or between subsystem and subsystem, or between programs;
- to accelerate the development of a subsystem to accommodate a more rapidly increasing workload than earlier anticipated.

Change request

The first step in changing any part of a system, from definition of requirements to implementation procedures, is the initiation of the change request. A change request form describes and requests the proposed change, and is used also in the evaluation and disposal of the request (see page 8).

Initiation
A change request may be initiated by any member of the project team, by personnel in the organization where the system will be or is used, by the steering committee, or by management. For an example of a change request see page 8.

CHANGE REQUEST

system : *Production planning & control system*
subsystem :
prev. issue:

project no. : *X 1000*
chapter/sect.: *1·6*
page : *3*
issued : *july 7th; '65*

submitted by *John labels*
name :
department :

change request no:

title of change: *Alternative production methods*

description of change:

Basic system design should allow for short term selection of alternative production method. This means that altenatives should be stored similarly to preferred production methods

justification of change:

Provision should be made for future expansion of system. The job dispatching function will become more flexible

interface implicating:

Requirements should be rediscussed with user management. Available source data should be checked for completeness, consistency and upto-dateness

actions to be taken:

Review at forthcoming system design meeting; detailed report is attached.

disposition

CHANGE REQUEST SUMMARY

system : *Production planning & control system*
subsystem :
prev. issue:

project no.: : *X 1000*
chapter/sect.: *1·6*
page : *1*
issued : *july 7th; 65*

change number	title of change	date of issue	date of action	status*
1	*sequential indentification coding system*	*june 9; '65*		*O*
2	*alternate production methods*	*july 7; '65*		*O*

* status: O = open, received but no disposition
A = approved for implementation
D = deferred
I = implemented
P = approved but postponed
R = rejected

Review
The description and justification of the change will be reviewed by the project team, in order to arrive at a possible solution. When the implementation of the system is realized this task is done by the maintenance team or employee. After the preliminary review, the team will either make a decision if the change is straightforward and desirable, or convene a discussion meeting for further investigation. The discussion meeting should be composed of personnel who are directly concerned with the change request.
Any difficulties or ambiguities arising from the change request should be resolved in this discussion. Recommandations for alternative solutions may be suggested and explored. An assessment of the worth of the improvement should be made in terms of cost effectiveness, and according to the justification given. The change request summary (see example on page 9) records all pending requests.

Disposal
An important question which must be answered prior to disposal is whether or not the change can be installed within the available manpower resources without affecting the project schedule. If the schedule is affected, the possibility of deleting less important features in the system in order to implement the change request should be investigated. "Disposal" can include acceptance for implementation; rejection as unnecessary or undesirable; or deferment for further consideration. If the meeting is unable to reach a decision acceptable to all parties concerned they may refer the matter, provided that it is of a suitable level, to the steering committee. If a change is accepted, a work statement for implementation should be prepared and schedules should be adapted accordingly.

Implementation

The final and most important aspect of change processing is the actual implementation of approved changes. This may involve the modification of the system specification as recorded in the project file and user documentation. The change is not considered to be fully implemented until both the documentation and the programs or procedures are modified.

Volume 3: System analysis & design

Contents

General

In ARDI, the term "analysis" covers a much wider field than the mere collection and ordering of data on the existing system. It involves an examination of the relationships between the user organization and its environment; a critical comparison of the organization with other, similar entities; and the identification, appraisal, and, if necessary, restatement of the goals of the organization. Only in this way it is possible to make an intelligent assessment of the future behaviour which will be required of the organization, and to design an integrated information system having the appropriate capacity and flexibility to deal with it.

In the design activity, we are concerned not merely with programs and runs, but with the total impact of the system on the organization. Thus an integrated system design is concerned with functions to be executed by procedures as well as by programs, and must recognize and solve the psychological problems raised by any organizational changes called for.

The feasibility study phase and the system analysis & design phase are brought together in this volume because of their similarity in method. They differ, however, in purpose and scope. The feasibility study provides the information which management requires in order to take a decision whether or not to start a systems effort. In the system analysis & design phase, deeper analysis leads to the detailed determination of the requirements of the new system, and a system is designed to meet these requirements.

Feasibility study

There are three basic approaches to the feasibility study. A general appraisal of the user organization may be made, in order to obtain notional justification for the use of computers; a study of specific areas of the organization, such as payroll or customer billing may be undertaken, for the purpose of demonstrating that automation, even if confined to these areas, would be significantly beneficial; or the organization may be studied comprehensively.

Purpose and scope

In the last case, which is the approach recommended in ARDI, preliminary analysis and requirements determination must be carried out in sufficient depth to allow a technical and economic evaluation of a proposed new system to be made. Due attention must be paid to the possible existence of problem areas and trouble spots in the existing system; to the user organization's level of experience in the use of computers; to the type of improvements which user management will expect from a new system; and to future organizational changes which will be called for by the implementation of a new system.

Results

The results of the feasibility study can be presented in the form of a masterplan for the new system, which will provide a sound basis for further systems effort. Throughout the study, however, it must be borne in mind that the end sought is a decision by user management. The masterplan and its presentation are to be regarded primarily as means to this end. The presentation should therefore be designed to emphasize those aspects of the plan which most clearly assist the making of the decision.

The contents of a typical masterplan might be:

- a general statement of system objectives (3-1);
- a brief description of the user organization (3-2);
- a preliminary requirements definition (3-3);
- a general outline for a system design with possible alternatives (3-4.1);
- a preliminary hardware and software specification (3-4.4);
- an overall schedule for the systems effort (3-5, 2-2, 6-1.1);
- a cost and benefit report (2-3);
- a recommendation to management whether or not to start a systems effort, and if positive a description of measures to be taken (3-6).

System analysis & design

If the management decision is favourable, the systems effort enters the system analysis & design phase.

Purpose and scope

In this phase, the collection and analysis of data on the existing system and the investigation of its position and attitude in relation to its environment are carried sufficiently far to enable the requirements and constraints of the new system to be fully determined. A system meeting these requirements and constraints is then defined; the information flow is specified, the files designed, and the hardware and software selected. At the end of this phase, the system is divided into subsystems capable of being developed and implemented separately, and the system specification is drawn up.

Results

The system specification embodies the results of the system analysis & design phase, and provides the baseline for further effort. It should clearly present solutions to all detail problems. At the end of the system analysis & design phase, the content of the project file will be:

- system directive (3-1);
- description of present system (3-2);

- system requirements (3-3):
  - — objectives of the system, in detail (3-3.1);
  - — organizational requirements and constraints (3-3.2);
  - — information and control requirements and constraints (3-3.3);
  - — general design requirements and constraints (3-3.4);
- system design (3-4):
  - — information flow (3-4.1);
  - — function work sheets (3-4.1);
  - — function evaluation charts;
  - — file evaluation charts;
  - — file usage charts;
  - — system file definitions (3-4.2);
  - — hardware and software requirements (3-4.4);
- subsystem requirements (3-5):
  - — input definitions (3.5.3);
  - — output definitions (3-5.3);
  - — file design (3-5.3);
  - — processing logic for each function in the subsystem flow (3-5.3);
- calculations of cost and benefits of the new system (2-3);
- schedules for system development and implementation (2-2.2, 3-5.2);
- assignment of a subsystem team to each subsystem for the next phases (2-1.3);
- documentation standards for the system development phase (2.1.2).

Methodology

The chart on page 5 displays the relationship between the activities described in this volume, and is applicable to both the feasibility study and the system analysis & design phases.
Activity 3-2, analyze present system, is shown as optional. This activity can safely be omitted when the organization has an effective information systems or organization & methods department capable of supplying all the necessary data. Where an organization has a large data flow whose individual items are simple and of only a few types, activity 3-2 will be so abbreviated that it can no longer be considered a major part of the phase.
This activity will be initially bypassed when a new organization and a system are being created together. When activity 3-2 is wholly or partially bypassed, the collateral aspects of analysis described in the first paragraph of this volume (page 1) retain their importance. They are never omitted.

It is sometimes stated, in support of bypassing the analysis activity, that a detailed study would take too long, and would be at least partly out of date before it could be used; and that the delay caused would impede the ultimate transfer of work to the computer. The reasons given for these supposed effects are lack of manpower, complexity of the organization, and high rates of growth or change. Where the manpower available is inadequate, the alternatives are either to provide more, or to restate the immediate aims. But where the ARDI approach is employed, complexity, growth, and change are anticipated, and methods are given to overcome the difficulties encountered.

Types of inadequacy

Where the analysis has been incorrectly omitted or unduly abridged, the following types of inadequacy and failing can be expected:

- the wrong type of information is prepared;
- the equipment capacity is incorrect;
- due to faulty data organization, required information is difficult of access;
- unrelated solutions for related problem areas impede ultimate integration;
- goals are missed because of inadequate definition, lack of key information, or unrecognized weaknesses in the existing structure of the organization;
- the systems effort grows too long and too costly, because inherently good design work has to be discarded and repeated when it is found to have been based upon imperfect information;
- if the system eventually reaches implementation, it is unacceptable to line personnel, who feel that they have not been sufficiently consulted.

Trigger to system analysis & design

The activities which comprise system analysis & design are set in motion, at the feasibility study level, when the management of the organization identifies one or more problem areas, and calls a meeting of the department managers concerned to discuss the matter. After top management approval, and assignment of the steering committee (2-1.1), the latter will take the decision of this meeting as a directive, and will seek such assistance from both inside and outside the organization as they require.

Depth of analysis

To this committee at this stage, and to the project team as constituted at the end of the feasibility study, falls the responsibility of deciding in each case the depth to which the present system should be studied.

In making their decision, they should consider the following points:

- sufficient knowledge of all relevant present operations must be acquired to permit correct requirements definition;
- the response behaviour of the organization must be understood; in particular, where the response behaviour is inadequate, it must be determined whether the inadequacy is inherent in the present structure or due to malfunction;
- the study should produce enough information to permit the preparation of comparative cost and benefit reports relating the existing and proposed new systems.

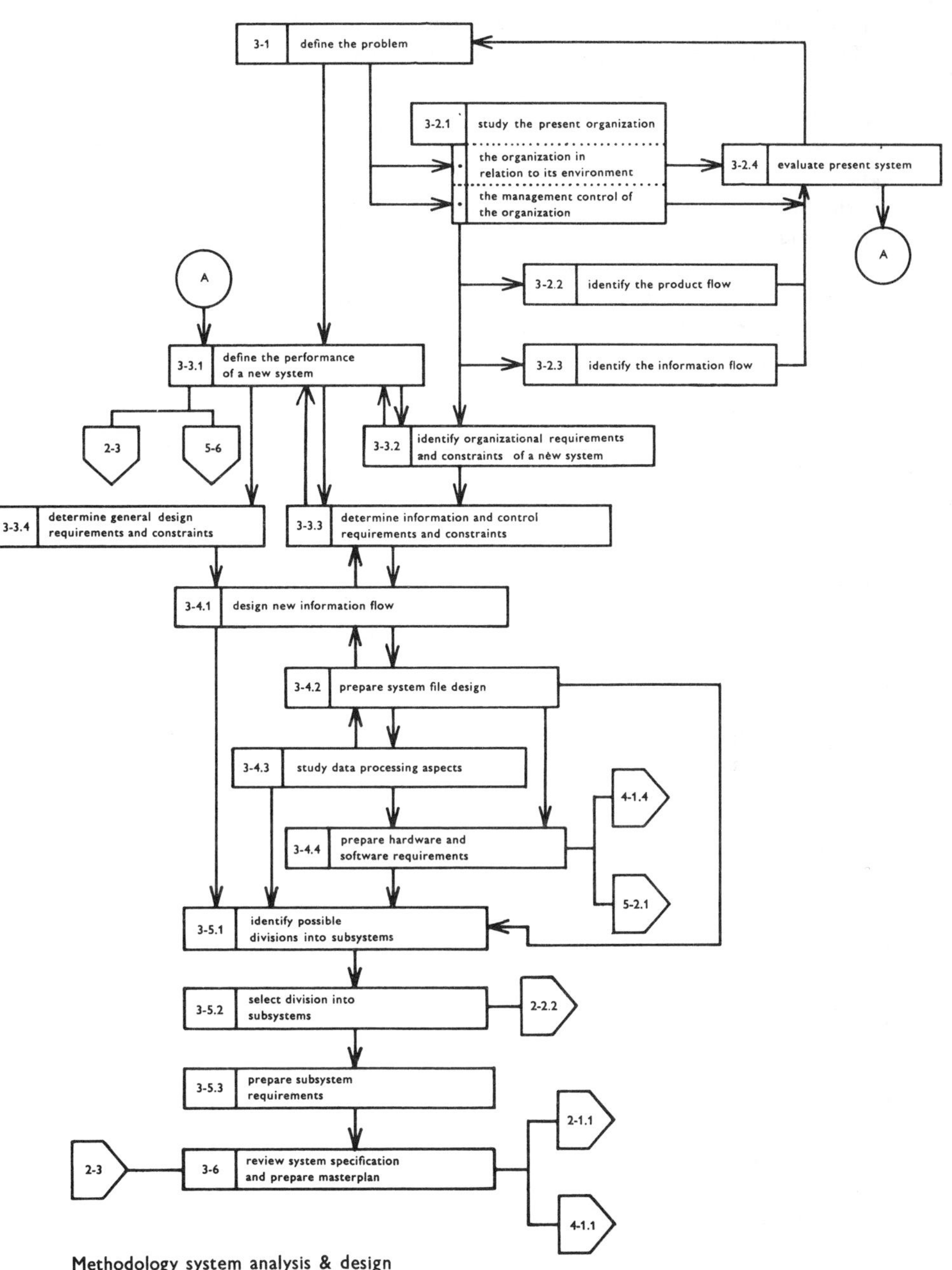

Methodology system analysis & design

Aim of analysis

In analyzing the present system, whether at the level of the feasibility study or subsequently during the system analysis & design phase proper, it should be constantly borne in mind that the purpose in gathering data is not, in ARDI, to build up a total picture of the existing organization. It is to provide a firm basis for the identification of problem areas, the discovery of inadequacies in the present system, the statement, evaluation and possible restatement of the goals of the organization, and the determination of the requirements and constraints applicable to the new system.

It is a tenet of the ARDI approach that a total depiction of the existing system is neither necessary nor desirable for the accomplishment of these purposes. Analysis in accordance with the steps of activity 3-2 is shorter, more direct, and of much greater value.

Activity 3-1: Define the problem

The management directive which initiates the feasibility study seldom presents a sufficient definition of the problem to be solved. It can be too general — "Increase profitability by improving production flow" — or too specific — "Provide weekly production status reports".

The first task of the steering committee and the project team is therefore to make such a definition, clearly stating the proposed objectives of the project. This definition must receive management approval before any further work is done. During the course of the feasibility study, improved or additional objectives may come to light. These will arise not only from a direct study of the existing organization, but also from an assessment of its future potential, and an evaluation of the performance of other similar organizations.

When the objectives have been identified, they should be recorded, preferably on a systems directive form (page 2). This form carries a brief description of the objectives; a summary of the motives which prompted management to initiate the project, with any necessary background material; and general remarks relevant to the planning and organization of the project (3-2.1, 2-2.1, 2-2.2). One purpose of the form is to present an explicit statement of the objectives, which can be seen and understood by management, steering committee and project team. Without such understanding, failure is probable. The form provides an agreed documentation of objectives in sufficient detail and context. It is filed in the project file (2-4).

In defining the problem, the following questions must be answered:

- What are the main objectives of management in calling for this study?
- Is it possible to quantify these objectives?
- Into what specific requirements can the objectives be broken down?
- Will management require an assurance of immediate cost savings before they approve a proposal, or would they accept evidence of potential long-range benefits?
- What budgetary limitations will be placed on the systems effort?
- What time limitations will be placed on the feasibility study and on the whole systems effort?
- How will the effort be organized; what manpower is available for the performance of the effort?
- What is the attitude of management towards centralization or decentralization of control over business operations?
- What is the attitude of management towards centralization or decentralization of computer equipment?
- Which departments will be involved?
- Have the managers of these departments been informed and asked to cooperate?
- Is the present study part of an overall plan?
- Will the systems effort be integrated with other efforts?

SYSTEM DIRECTIVE FORM

system : *Production planning & control system*
subsystem :
prev. issue:

project no. : *X 1000*
chapter/sect.: *4·1*
page :
issued : *June '64*

objectives/problem definition:

Analyze present situation in organization and make proposal for future actions as to the introduction of automation, preferably using present equipment applied in the commercial area.

motivation for initiating project:

Capital tied-up in stocks and work in process is increasing faster than turn-over. Ratio

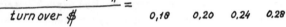

$\frac{\text{stock + work in process \$}}{\text{turn over \$}} =$	1962	1963	1964	1965
	0,18	0,20	0,24	0,28

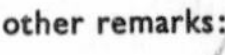

other remarks:

User representatives from construction, materials management, production and accounting department will participate in the feasibility study. They will be available on a part-time basis.

Systems people will become available in the second half of 1965, due to the finalization of the commercial project.

project start date:	date first reporting:	date decision:	date budget approval:	date of acceptance by steering committee
aug 15th	*sept 15th*	*dec '64*		

Activity 3-2: Analyze present system

This activity consists of four steps:
3-2.1; study the present organization
3-2.2; identify the product flow
3-2.3; identify the information flow
3-2.4; evaluate the present system.

Reasons

There are three main reasons for analyzing the present system of the organization:

- to obtain an overall picture, and an understanding of the position of the company, the structure of the organization and the relationships between the various functions involved (3-2.1, 3-2.2, 3-2.3);
- to evaluate the present system by determining its effectiveness and cost (3-2.4);
- to investigate specific operations in detail (3-2.3).

Types of analysis

Each reason leads to a different type of analysis. The first type gives a broad picture, and is best suited to the feasibility study or to a first system analysis & design effort. The second type is a follow-up to the first; it provides as a part of a feasibility study the means for making a cost comparison between the existing and proposed systems. The third type of investigation probes deeply into individual problem areas and functions and details of the present operations to gather, for example, quantitative data essential for the determination of requirements (3-3,) or for the continuation of the design activity (3-4).
The nature of the investigation depends upon the current needs of the systems effort. The purpose for which the analysis is being undertaken will determine which of the steps of this activity are to be performed in any given case. Appropriate indications are given in the description of each step. In all cases, the systems analyst or team member must concern himself with the exact nature of the problem area or function he is investigating, as well as with its purpose; the "what" as well as the "why". Only in this way will the requirements of the new system be successively determined and refined.

Introduction in the organization

Systems analysts, or other team members who are to undertake this activity, should arrange to be introduced to each department by the appropriate department manager, who should explain the purpose of the investigation. This will help in securing cooperation and assistance from user personnel.

Techniques

The following techniques, described in volume 6, are applicable to this activity and will be referred to where applicable:

- data gathering techniques:
  - — interview (6-3.1);
  - — measuring and estimating (6-3.2);
- documentation techniques:
  - — technical writing (6-2.1);
  - — charting techniques (6-2.2);
  - — grid charting (6-2.3);
  - — decision tables (6-2.4);
- design and development techniques:
  - — identification of system elements and data objects (6-4.1).

Step 3-2.1: Study the present organization

If the study of the present system is to be effective, it must paint a picture of the organization which, although broad, is sufficiently accurate to permit the identification of problem areas and the evaluation of the present system. To this end, the present step is divided into two substeps.

The first deals with the organization in relation to its environment. Major considerations which arise are growth potential, new product and market prospects, and competition. The information obtained in the pursuit of this substep will assist in defining the technological and economic characteristics of the industry and will bring to light any statutory obligations and benefits which apply to it, thus enabling the project team to anticipate the possible directions of future development.

The second is concerned with the structure of the organization. Here, major considerations are general business goals, management strategies, and operating policies. The information collected gives the members of the project team an understanding of the functions of the various departments studied, and of the aspects of the business goals which they serve. The interviewing technique (6-3.1) is particularly applicable to this substep.

The organization in relation to its environment

When the systems directive formulated in 3-1 indicates that the feasibility study should not be restricted to a specific area within the organization, but should include an evaluation of the present organization and system, it is good practice to start with a study of the company's position within its industry.

The industry to which the organization belongs must be considered not only as it exists in the present, but also historically. A dynamic view is thus obtained, giving a picture of areas of growth and decay, and permitting intelligent extrapolation.

Specific items of interest include:

- technologies used in the industry:
  - — historical development of the industry, its products, and its services;
  - — current pattern of research and development activities within the industry;
  - — practices, patterns, and problems characteristic of the industry in its response to new technologies;
  - — types of diversification common in the industry;
- economic structure of the industry;
  - — evolution of the industry in respect of number and size of companies;
  - — characteristic demand patterns for the industry's products;
  - — characteristic supply patterns for the resources used in the industry, including personnel;
  - — investment and earning patterns characteristic of the industry;
  - — historical development of the company, including mergers and spin-offs;

- — product, customer, and product-demand patterns, and degree of market penetration of the subject company;
  - — resource usage and payment practices characteristic of the company;
  - — investment and earning patterns of the company;
  - — assessment of the company's overall competitive position within the industry;
- government regulations:
  - — restrictions upon, and assistance to, the industry as a whole;
  - — restrictions upon, and assistance to, individual companies in the industry;
  - — legal factors affecting the operation of individual companies;
- future developments:
  - — expansion plans, including new organizational structures, new products, new markets, new engineering and production techniques and facilities.

Sources of Information

Management and the Marketing-research department can provide information on the environment in which the organization operates, and on the position of the organization within its industry. Sources of background information are many and varied. Local chambers of commerce often maintain a file of annual reports of companies in the area, and usually subscribe to a number of industrial and trade journals. Some of the sources and types of information available are discussed in the following paragraphs.

Annual reports, new issues and prospectuses

Annual reports present a financial statement of the organization's operating results for the previous year, and often outline its future intentions in broad product categories, sales highlights, and expansion plans, with an explanation of any particular circumstances which affected sales or profits during the year. Due to their general character and to the lack of mandatory standards, the picture of company growth and profitability offered by annual reports is usually incomplete, and is not an accurate yardstick for comparisons between companies. In many countries the statements made in connection with new issues and prospectuses are subject to strict legal regulations.

Thus, although limited in scope, the information obtained from these publications is often accurate. In particular, the reasons given for requiring to raise capital, and the amount of capital needed for specific purposes, are likely to be informative.

Industry or trade journals

These journals and magazines usually contain articles of general interest to companies in a specific industry. Many journals publish articles on automation as it typically affects companies in the industry; some have a column devoted exclusively to industry-specialized developments in automation.

These journals are an excellent source of background material on the industry, such as general trends, statistics, useful production or marketing techniques, and effective new methods of operation.

Case studies
The documentation of theoretical or practical problems, at varying levels of depth and detail, may provide helpful background information for all phases of the systems effort. The case studies published in all types of business and industrial periodicals, journals and house organs can give valuable background material either on an entire industry, or on typical companies within it.

Business periodicals
There are many publications, such as "Fortune", "Business" or "Economisch-Statistische Berichten" which publish in-depth studies for industries and companies. These studies are required reading, since they distil the results of many hours of background research into a few pages.

Industry, systems and other specialists
The members of the steering committee and the project team may find it sufficiently difficult to keep up-to-date in their own professions, without having to maintain similarly current knowledge in other fields.
As a consequence, it is always wise for them to seek out specialists who can advise on the latest industry trends, system design approaches, operating techniques, etc., and who can refer them to the most reliable experts, books, or periodicals.

General information concerning the organization

The purpose of this substep is to gain a general understanding of the management policies and strategies, and to investigate the present organization. When the system directive does not require such a broad study as described in this step, the steering committee should have indicated in the system directive specific policies, strategies and parts of the organization to which attention should be directed.
After this step has been performed and its results evaluated as described in 3-2.4, the steering committee and the project team should be able jointly to determine the objectives of a new system in more detail, and should be able to identify possible organizational changes, and to express them in terms of requirements and constraints.

Management control
The management control system of a company is the structure of planning, staffing, coordination and control practices whose purpose it is to ensure the efficient acquisition and use of resources in pursuit of the organization's business goals. In this substep, management control is considered under the two headings of strategy and policy, and organization.

Strategy and policy
The strategic planning system of a company is the established network of management practices whose purpose is the control of product planning and develop-

ment, resource planning, markets to be served, and of the administration of the complex of products and services from which the company derives its income.

The project team must achieve a good knowledge of this aspect in order to be able not only to identify present and future goals, and the manner in which present policies contribute to them, but also to form a critical appraisal of these goals and policies as a preparation for the determination of system objectives.

Organization

An understanding of the company's organizational structure will enable the members of the project team to see clearly the divisions into which the organization falls; to determine the information processing needs of the divisions; and to decide which officials and other employees of the organization should be consulted in respect of those needs. Items to be studied are:

- organizational and functional relationships;
- responsibility and reporting patterns within and between the research, planning, production, marketing and administration divisions of the company;
- organization chart; in cases where the organization involved is part of a larger organization, also a general overall organization chart;
- a framework of geographical locations, if decentralization exists or is contemplated;
- legal considerations, where the organization comprises a number of units of different statutory types (holding company, parent and subsidiary, affiliated company, etc.).

Sources of information

Although some of the information sought in this substep may be obtained from existing documents (e.g. charts and records), it will be derived chiefly from interviews with the personnel involved. In some cases, for example in a rapidly expanding or changing organization, it will be difficult to obtain reliable data. In these instances, the project team must be alert to the nature of the situation, and must exercise careful judgement in interpreting the data collected. It will sometimes occur that questions raised during this substep will not be fully answered until 3-2.2 or 3-2.3 is being performed.

Study strategy and policy

In studying these aspects the project team should collect all relevant published material concerning company strategy and policy, such as management directives, company regulations, memos and standard reporting procedures. The best method of obtaining this information, however, is by interviewing company officials.

Records submitted to the interviewer should be actual company records which existed before the investigation began: "fixed up" records are often unreliable and misleading. The interviewer, however, should record any favourable and unfavourable impression he gains. Such notes should be kept separately, and should be used to substantiate findings rather than as primary source material.

The following sections and checklists deal with subjects applicable to the collection of the information required in this substep. The paragraphs on personnel and workload are not normally required in a feasibility study. In using the checklist, it is not always essential to probe to the depth implied by certain of the questions; the application of the lists is not a mechanical exercise, but requires skill and discretion on the part of the interviewer. Although the questions are appropriate to a manufacturing organization, they can be of assistance in the preparation of interviews for other types of organization as well.

General company strategy and policy

- What share does the company have in the industry and territory in which it operates? Can supporting figures or statistics be supplied? Who are national, European Common Market and international competitors?
- What is the opinion of top management on the trend of business within the industry, and especially of the company within the industry? What figures and statistics can be supplied to support theories advanced?
- What are the company's policies in respect of profit and return on investment?
- What are the company's pricing policies, and what formulae are used to arrive at a selling price?
- What are the company's budgeting and calculation policies?
- What are the company's policies with respect to sales of finished goods and composition of product range?
- Are products protected by patents? If so, who owns the patents?
- What are the company's policies with respect to customer service, including after sales service?
- How are "make or buy" decisions taken for important components?
- What is company policy towards the production method (flow or batch production), and on making products for stock or for order?
- What is the ratio of working capital to total assets? Compare this ratio with the average value in the industry (see preceding section).
- Establish and appraise the "operation ratio" (the ratio of total running expenses, including all staff-departments, to gross sales value), expressed as a percentage. A high operating ratio indicates instability, because under these conditions a profit can easily be transformed into a loss.
- If possible, establish the ratio of value of physical product volume to money invested in plant and equipment. If this is not possible, use sales figures and eliminate the effects of price changes.
- Establish and appraise the work in progress ratio; this is the ratio of total production stock value to gross sales value expressed as a percentage.

Marketing strategy and policy

- Are written sales policies obtainable? If not, obtain letters, memos and directions issued by management to sales personnel indicating management's intentions with regard to sales policies, and interview the sales-manager and a number of selected salesmen in order to establish principal sales policies actually employed.
- Obtain particulars of products sold. What is the share of each product in the annual gross sales value?
- What are the sales costs for each type of product, and how do these figures deviate from the average sales cost? (Sales cost should include cost of market-research, advertising sales activities, commercial inventories and after sales service).
- Do some products prove to be money-makers, and others money-losers?
- Why are the money-losers kept in the product range?
- What is the discount policy?
- Obtain information on the number, type and geographical distribution of customers. List according to type (wholesale, retail, products purchased etc.).
- Are there any customers who individually account for over 5% of sales volume? Describe any condition which might indicate that a large portion of the sales volume falls within a specific grouping of products or customers.
- What is the advertising program? Check on present program and future commitments.
- What is the policy in respect to product planning?
- How are actual and historic sales figures used to initiate the development of new products?
- What is the company's market research program, and how are the collected figures used?
- What is the research program of the company and how is the cost of the general research related to product-oriented research?

Production strategy and policy

- How frequently and in what manner are production objectives determined? Collect a production programme or a customer oriented production order, depending upon the type of company.
- Is the equipment general or special purpose?
- Does the company anticipate modernizing its equipment, or does it feel that the existing equipment is adequate for efficient manufacturing?
- What is the extent of subcontracting, and who furnishes tooling and materials?
- Is production flow, batch or mixed?
- How is the control of the production organized, and what type of system is foreseen for the future?
  — determination of production method;
  — making to stock or to order;
  — size of manufacturing order;
  — determination of throughput time and planning;

  — materials requirements calculations;
  — shop floor control and data collection.
- What are the company policies in respect to product quality?
- How is resource levelling effected?
- What is the main constraint in production control?
  — throughput time, resource load, quality of the product?

Purchasing strategy and policy

- Is speculative buying practiced? If so, to what extent of gross sales value, and who is responsible for this kind of purchasing?
- How are the following expenses spread over the different product groups, and how are they distributed within each group?
  — the subcontracting of work;
  — the purchasing of raw materials;
  — the purchasing of components;
  — the purchasing of individual products incorporated in the sales mix.
- How many suppliers serve the company? What is the average number per item and what is the smallest number used for any item?
- What percentage of the gross sales value is expenditure on manufacture items?
- Has one specific supplier a major share in the expenditure on manufactured items? If so, for what reason?
  — a technical specialization not available elsewhere;
  — a financial relationship, based on a common interest; between the company and the supplier;
  — a tradition;
  — special discounts based on long-term contract;
  — any other reason.
- Are purchasing policies stated in writing? If so, obtain an up-to-date copy and investigate whether the policies described are those actually followed:
  — How is a purchase action triggered in the different situations encountered e.g. by a customer order, by a minimum inventory level, by a sales forecast?
  — How is the order quantity determined?
  — Which selection criteria are considered to be most important for each type of product; price, quality, delivery time, reliability of the supplier with respect to delivery dates?
- How are purchasing policies coordinated with sales and production policies?
- To what amount are the buyers authorized to buy, and what are the average and maximum sizes of a purchase order?
- How are purchase price arrangements settled, and what are the general purchasing conditions. In what circumstances are these conditions not observed?

Accounting strategy and policy

- Obtain balance sheets and profit and loss statements for the last five years.

- Does the company have an accounting manual?
  - How are new projects budgeted and cost prices of new products calculated?
  - How are prices of resources calculated and how are overheads taken into account? Are "indirect" hours calculated and budgeted separately?
  - What is the policy with respect to the depreciation of investments?
  - What degree of profitability must be demonstrated in order to get approval for expenditure on new projects?
- What is the policy with respect to post-calculation?
  - Is a post-calculation for each order required, based on post-calculated prices for development projects?
  - Is a statistical comparison of post- and pre-calculated prices possible?
  - Is a post-calculation effected for each production stage or department?
  - Are pre-calculated prices used for price setting?
- Is the sale price of the product based on the market price, or primarily dictated by the pre-calculated price?
- How are costs of work in progress and current inventories taken into account?
- What financial reports are prepared, and how frequently, to inform management about the financial position of the company.
- What is the company's policy with respect to:
  - Financing of long term investments?
  - Liquidity?
  - Solvency?
  - Profitability?
- Are performance ratios used for the evaluation of the financial position of the company?
  - What ratios are employed?
  - How frequently are they measured?
- Some examples of performance ratios are:
  - borrowed capital to share capital;
  - working capital to total assets;
  - amounts of sales to outstanding accounts receivable;
  - gross sales value to value of plant and equipment;
  - gross sales value to total capital;
  - operating expenses (production, selling, development, accounting) to gross sales value;
  - value of revenue to total share capital;
  - composition of borrowing (supplier credit, long term loans, short term loans, advance payments on customers orders);
  - "yield" of shares.

Study organization

The project team should obtain a reliable current organization chart of the user company. The chart should be sufficiently detailed to include the lowest eche-

ions affected by the systems effort, and can be annotated in respect of each group or division chosen with function, actual and planned number of employees, and costs. The cost entries might with advantage be broken down in an appropriate manner, say into wages, overheads, fixed equipment costs, and material costs. If no suitable chart exists, the project team must draw up one. It should then be submitted to the steering committee for verification. However obtained, the copy of the chart held by the project team should be checked initially, and maintained thereafter in an up-to-date condition, by the information systems department (2-1.2).
The following checklists assist in obtaining necessary information on the organizational structure.

Organization of marketing

- Chart and describe the marketing organization.
- How are sales, advertising, customer engineering and after sales service coordinated?
- Which responsibilities are decentralized and which are centralized?
- Are separate sales and distribution facilities provided for different classes of products, types of customers or territories?
- How are sales, pricing and distribution controlled?
- To which department is the pricing function delegated?
- Who has authority to determine the discount policies?

Organizational pattern

- What type of organizational structure is predominant in the company; line, functional, line and staff, committee, etc.?
- Does a management committee exist? If so, describe its responsibility and authority.
- How frequently do top executives meet for discussion of current problems and adjustment of company policies?
- Does any overlapping exist of basic managerial functions such as finance, sales and production?
- Does any overlapping exist of operational functions? If so, which departments are involved and what are their sizes?
- In every company one function seems to be given preference above others. Which functions are given respectively the most and least importance?
- Authority does not always go with responsibility, but may follow seniority or personality rather than principal functions. Determine who is responsible to whom, and determine whether responsibility is coupled with authority; who cracks the whip in this company?

Organization of production

- What is the structure of the organization in respect of main production and work preparation functions?

— Parts fabrication;
— assembly;
— testing and quality control;
— tool design and fabrication;
— materials handling;
— maintenance of equipment;
— replacement and extension of production facilities;
— technical work preparation and work methods studies;
— materials requirements calculation;
— production scheduling;
— work allocation ("dispatching");
— process control.

- How are interrelationships between production, accounting, purchasing, sales and development engineering effected?
- How are the production facilities organized? (identify the product flow, 3-2.2.)
- How is production controlled (3-2.3)?
- To what extent are production planning and control centralized or decentralized?
- Is there a clear distinction between different product lines in the organization? If so, how does this affect the organization?
- What number of products are produced in each period?
- What is the amount of work in progress?

Purchasing organization

- What departments within the organization are empowered to authorize contracts, or to purchase items such as:
  — raw materials;
  — components;
  — individual products incorporated in the product flow;
  — outside resources required for the subcontracting of work;
  — contracts for specialist assistance?
- How is (are) the purchasing department(s) related to the rest of the organization? Is purchasing considered to be part of the production or the accounting activities of the company?
- To what extent is purchasing functionalized or centralized?
- Is the purchasing department organized according to type of supplier or according to end products produced by the company?
- Who is responsible for supplier selection?
- Who is responsible for order-quantity and order point determination?
- How is the responsibility for making decisions in respect of purchasing divided between the marketing, production, engineering, accounting and purchasing departments?
- Does this division correspond with stated policies?
- How many products are purchased in each period?
- What is the ratio of value purchased to gross sales value?
- How many suppliers do serve the company?

Accounting organization

- How are the main accounting functions, (budgeting, cost estimating and post-calculation) embodied in the organization?
- Who prepares the financial status reports?
- How are the interfaces with marketing, production and purchasing departments effected?
- Who is responsible for inventory management?
- Does the company have an auditing department?
- Who is the independent auditor?

Personnel

The actual personnel complement devoted to the performance of a given function within the organization is a useful measure of a part of the current cost of that function. Comparison of actual with planned future complements indicates those parts of the organization where increases or decreases of cost are expected. Comparison of both actual and planned complements with the proposed manning of the same function in the new system is an essential step in the preparation of cost and benefit reports referring to the date of implementation and to specific subsequent dates (2-3).

In entering actual and planned manning figures into the organization chart, great care must be taken to avoid double counts. Entries should be made only once, at the lowest level possible. In this way the number of employees, for example in a division of a company, can be determined by adding up the figures stated in all boxes referring to that division.

Management-labour relations

Amongst the reasons which may be quoted for the study of labour relations, the most important are the effect of the systems effort in causing organizational changes, and the influence exerted by flexibility of personnel assignment under new circumstances. A number of the following questions are for the purpose of gaining an appreciation of the social climate within the organization, and an understanding of its readiness to participate in the implementation of a new system.

- Does the company have a labour relations department? If not, who takes care of the labour relations?
- What is the local labour situation?
- Are there any work stoppages, slow-downs or manpower wastes which can be attributed to poor labour relations?
- What is the company's record for industrial relations?
- Does a bonus plan or any other incentive pay system exist?
- How are labour rates established?
- Does the company have a labour contract? If so, attach a copy.
- Is a suggestion system used?
- Is an employee rating system used?
- Is a job evaluation system used?
- What schemes does the company have for pensions, sickness benefits, hospitalization, group insurance, etc.?

Workload

For the purpose of system analysis & design, workload information is in its most useful form when it relates a specific quantity of work to the discharge of a particular task or set of tasks. In many cases, it may not be directly available in this form. It then becomes necessary to investigate the workload under the categories in which the data is available in the organization, and to organize the information in a form suitable for use in the systems effort.

For this purpose, workload can be investigated under two headings; departmental and individual.

- Departmental.

  The investigation of a departmental workload must be undertaken in close cooperation with the head of the department concerned. A clear picture must be obtained of the tasks performed within the department, and of the manpower available for their performance. This can be done by drawing up a workload distribution table and introducing ranking into the task columns and into the personnel roster (page 15). Effective use of manpower is indicated by positive correlation.

- Individual.

  The most effective tool for the investigation of individual workload is the daily job report. A standard form should be used (page 16); by suitable preprinting, the filling in can be made very simple. The form should clearly distinguish between productive work, non-productive work, and time off.

  It is important that the form should be filled in during the day, and not from memory at the end of the day or week. If every employee concerned fills in a daily job report for, say, one month, adequate material is then available, not only for the purpose of investigating individual workload, but also, by combining and summarizing, for obtaining an overall view of the utilization of manpower in the organization. To aid in summarizing, it is worth considering the possibility of working in decimal units (deci-days) instead of quarter hours. Any period of about 45-50 minutes can, with sufficient accuracy, be considered as 0.1 days. For reporting purposes this representation lends itself to an easy summarization in units of days worked by shifting the decimal point.

  Only regular working days should be accounted for; in case of official closing days, the period concerned should be omitted.

WORKLOAD DISTRIBUTION TABLE (in hrs. per week)

system :
subsystem :
prev. issue:

project no. :
chapter/sect.:
page :
issued :

cost calculation dept.	employee						
tasks	head of calc. dept. mr. P	calculator mr. A	calculator mr. Z	assistent calculator mr. C	assistent calculator miss S	typing clerk miss D	total
meetings with factory management	10	5	2	—	—	—	17
meetings with product committee	3	5	2	3	—	—	13
calculating	10	15	3	5	—	—	33
writing price contracts	—	2	5	15	—	4	26
verifying calculations	5	—	8	5	—	—	18
retrieval of prices	5	6	10	4	5	7	37
arithmetical operations (adding, multiplying)	3	3	6	2	15	7	36
file updating & records keeping	—	4	3	1	10	10	28
typing	—	—	—	3	5	10	18
other	4	—	1	2	5	2	14
(specify)	personnel affairs		training	literature study	updating product docu-mentation	birthday fund	
	40	40	40	40	40	40	240

DAILY JOB REPORT

	1		2	3		5
cardcode				weekno.:		
	6		11	13		16
wageno.:				dept. no.:		

Name ....

dept. .... tel. no. ....

week from: .... to: ....

	task description	task code 17 18 24	total 25 27	M	T	W	Th	F	Sa/Su
direct time		D							
		D							
		D							
		D							
		D							
		D							
		D							
		D							
		D							
		D							
		D							
		D							
		D							
indirect time:	illnes	I							
	holiday	I							
	training	I							
	courses	I							
	waiting time	I							
	library	I							
		I							
		I							
		I							
	miscellaneous	I							
		total deci days		10	10	10	10	10	
overtime		Ø							
		Ø							
		Ø							
		Ø							
		Ø							
		Ø							
		Ø							
		total overtime							

remarks

Step 3-2.2: Identify the product flow

General aspects

This step in the analysis of the present system familiarizes the project team with the production processes involved in the company's operations, and assists in discovering specific strengths and weaknesses in the flow of products.

The principal method employed in this step is the plant tour. A plant tour makes clear to the user that the systems analyst is interested in the actual operations of the organization, and demonstrates that the project team bases the study on personal observation rather than second-hand information. When undertaking a plant tour, a team member must constantly keep the time factor in mind, and must remain alert to the relationship between the product and information flows.

In respect of the time factor, it is not enough merely to determine the overall time for each set of operations, although this is, of course, essential. Under this heading due attention must be paid also to production delays, to the quantity of work in progress, and to the levels of central, buffer, and commercial stocks. The stock levels are necessary for a consideration of the time factor, since they determine the lead times permissible in respect of purchase orders. Only if the product flow is considered in relation to the information flow will full benefit be obtained from the plant tour, because only in this way can problem areas be satisfactorily identified and the interaction between product and information flow be studied.

Although the information flow must be duly considered during the plant tour, the order of the tour must be determined by the sequence of the product flow, and not by that of the information flow.
Sufficient time must be allowed to make all necessary observations. A morning's casual observation is not a plant tour. To do the job properly may require days, or even weeks of effort. Typical jobs must be followed step by step through the plant; key processes must be carefully monitored, and communication links checked.
If the outcome is to be satisfactory, the tour must be well planned and adequately performed.

Practical rules

Practical rules in this connection are:

- Acquire some familiarity with the product flow in advance. Request a summary of the operations beforehand.
- Arrange to be accompanied on the tour by a person familiar with the operations.
- See that the tour conductor and line personnel are informed of the purpose of the tour. This will prevent them from drawing wrong conclusions.
- Proceed through the flow in a logical manner. Obvious as this may seem, some

systems analysts skip from process to process without logical sequence, thus obtaining only a confused impression of the overall flow.

- Make notes or draw rough flowcharts to assist in understanding the flow. Indicate areas for subsequent examination in greater detail.
- Observe organizational patterns in the control of goods:
  - — Which functions in the organization are responsible for the flow of goods? How are they concerned with the control of inventories for raw material, supplies, assemblies, work in progress and finished products?
  - — Which inventories exist which are not controlled?
  - — How is control over inventories secured; open or closed stocks? Check of materials usage against production output and waste, or are materials used charged to jobs when issued from stock?
  - — Are perpetual inventory records maintained independently of the employees who have physical custody and who control quantities?
  - — How often are physical inventories taken?
  - — Are physical facilities adequate to protect goods?
  - — Are goods subject to depreciation?
  - — Describe the inspection program applied at goods inwards. Are quantities verified by counting and comparison with vendor's invoice and order?
  - — Describe quality control procedures at receiving production and shipping.
- Pay particular attention to the production organization in respect of such matters as plant layout, work scheduling, task setting and materials control in order that a subsequent evaluation can be made. Insofar as these are at least in part industrial engineering matters, which can nevertheless greatly influence information requirements, it will be necessary to contact management and the organization's industrial engineers (if any) in order to investigate any proposed changes.

  In most cases, these organizational problems will have been already identified during the preceding step — study the present organization — and are always closely related to the organization of the production department itself.
- Detect the points where trigger actions occur in the product flow.
- Record the results of the investigation by means of the charting technique of 6-2.2. See the chart presenting the product flow on page 20.
- The information obtained may also be transformed into a process model of the organization (page 21). [1]) Such a model presents in graphic terms the framework of the product flow (the broad arrows) and the communication pattern (narrow arrows).

  This diagram is a gross approximation of the overall system in a real organization, but is still a useful analytic tool when developed in terms of cycle times. Individual descriptions of each function or flow are by this means graphically interrelated, and the basic processes of the firm are clearly highlighted.
- The product flow performance checklist will assist in the evaluation of the efficiency and usefulness of the individual processes incorporated in the product flow.

---

[1]) The model shown is adapted from: Churchman, Ackoff, and Arnoff, *Introduction to operations research*, Wiley, New York, 1957, page 99.

PRODUCT FLOW PERFORMANCE CHECKLIST

Check on:	*Examples of detailed questions:*
Timelines	• What is the throughput time of the process involved? • What is the relationship between process delays and process times? • What is the volume of work in progress in relation to the amount of the total production? • What is the relationship between transportation time and process time? • Are some components or raw materials available before others arrive for processing?
Accuracy	• What percentage of items is shipped to the wrong destination? • What percentage of work has to be reworked? • Is production task setting accurate? • Is there 100% inspection and quality control? Would sampling be acceptable?
Usefulness	• Are all transportations involved necessary? • Are products stocked apparently over a long period? • Are articles kept in stock which are used only after one or more production cycles have been performed? • Is the manufacturing equipment suitable for its purpose? • Are products with uncertain sales value being made?
Necessity	• Is work done twice e.g. when leaving and arriving in a department? • Is work broken down into very small jobs which can be profitably combined?
Completeness	• Are all elements, components and raw materials available when necessary? • Does production get enough information to enable it to produce efficiently? • Is floorspace sufficient?
Cost	• Are product inspections made during the production process, or only after significant amounts of labour have been added to the material costs?
Efficiency	• Does the forwarding department select products for customers order in a logical sequence? Does backtracking occur?

PRODUCT FLOWCHART

system : manufacturing control
subsystem: dispatching
prev. issue:

project no. :
chapter/sect.:
page :
issued :

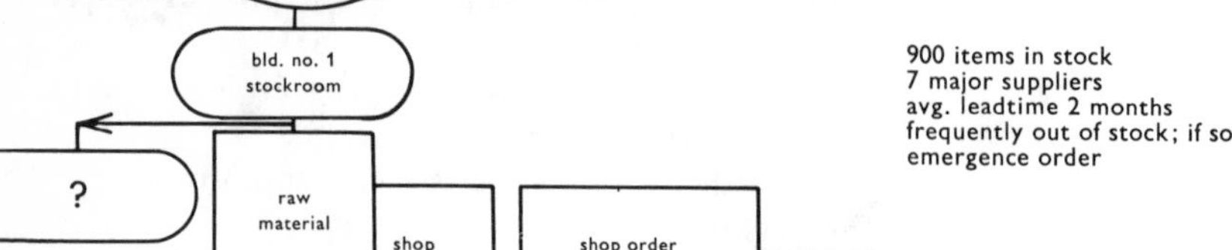

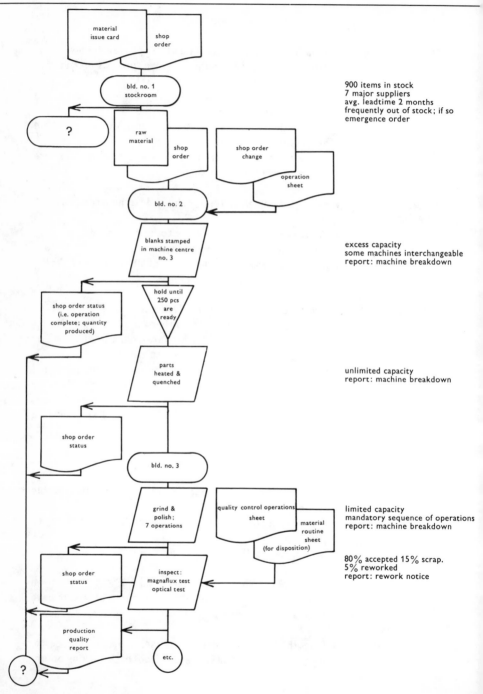

900 items in stock
7 major suppliers
avg. leadtime 2 months
frequently out of stock; if so emergence order

excess capacity
some machines interchangeable
report: machine breakdown

unlimited capacity
report: machine breakdown

limited capacity
mandatory sequence of operations
report: machine breakdown

80% accepted 15% scrap.
5% reworked
report: rework notice

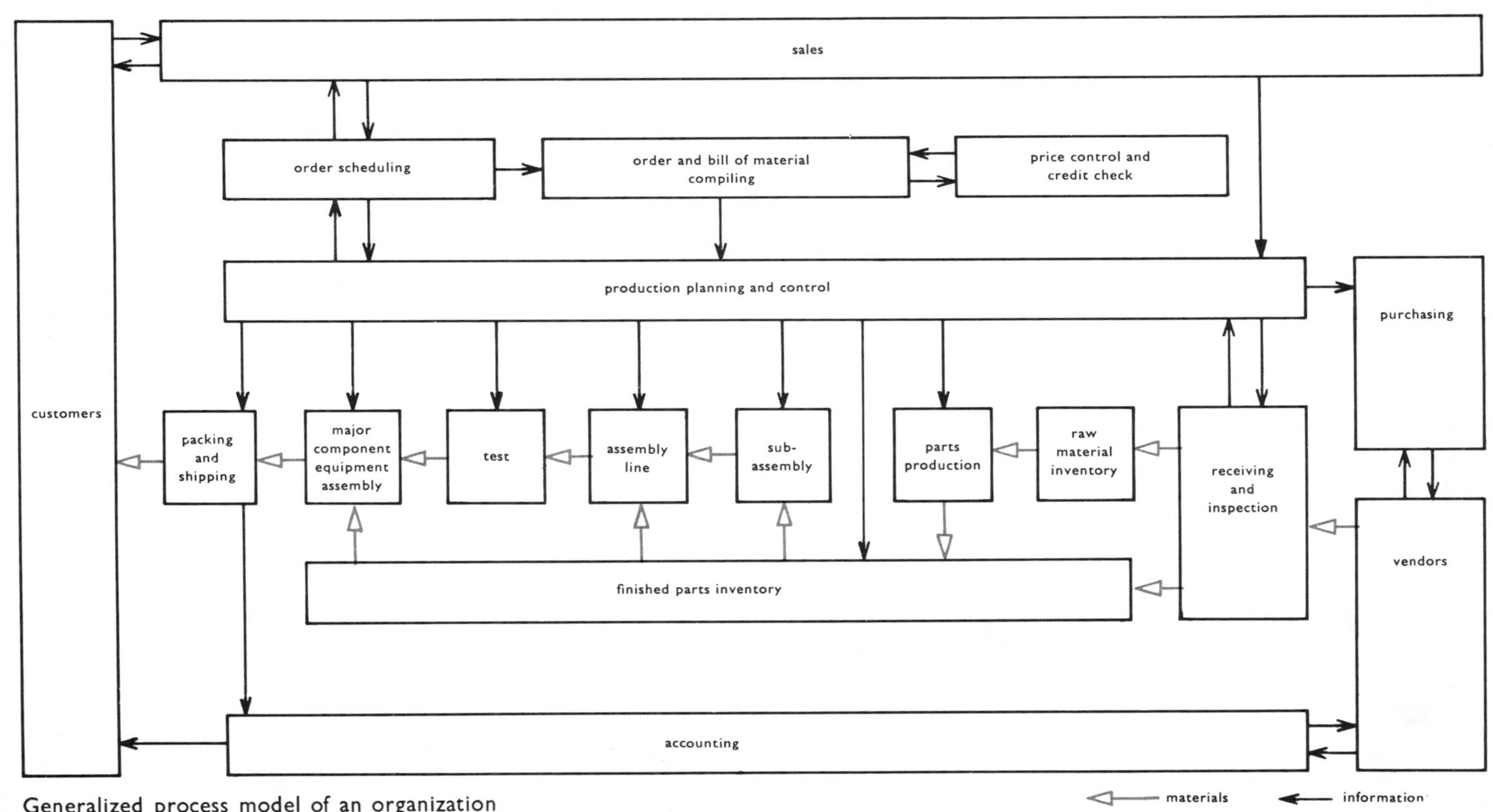

Generalized process model of an organization

Step 3-2.3: Identify the information flow

This step is performed for the purpose of understanding the information flow, including documents and other data carriers, which presently controls the operations of the organization. It is necessary when the existing system is complex, particularly in respect of its decision-making content; and when many problem areas are involved. Even when it is not proposed to automate a particular procedure, a study of the associated information flow will often reveal possibilities of simplification, combination, relocation, or even elimination with consequent benefit to the system.

Techniques used

The techniques of interviewing (6-3.1), flowcharting (6-2.2), grid charting (6.2-3) and decision tables (6-2.4) are widely applicable to the performance of this step. When interviewing, or when making any study requiring his appearance in a work area, the systems analyst or project team member must secure the permission and cooperation of the department manager concerned, and should arrange to have the purpose of the investigation explained, and any necessary introductions made, by an appropriate supervisory member of the organization.

A number of flowcharts will be prepared in the course of this step. It would be taking an oversimplified view to assume that a flowchart (or a portion of a flowchart) dealing with documents of a specific type represented the movements of a single document. Documents of the same type are often held up at a particular location, and the actual release may be determined by factors not genuinely relevant to the information flow.
Flowcharts, if they are comprehensively and accurately compiled, offer a basis for the comparison of the present and proposed systems. Step 3-4.1 provides an example of the charting of a complex information flow, while the documentation of a single procedure is illustrated in the charts of 4-6.4. Such representations, and the quantitative measurements associated with their preparations, assist in establishing the information and control requirements which lead to the design of a new system.

General approach

While studying the information flow, the project team should relate the work to that of the previous step (identify the product flow), and must pay particular attention to the decision (control and feedback,) points identified in the product flow during the course of that step. Adequate cross-referencing should be provided between the documentation of the two steps. The composite picture thus obtained must be assessed in the context of the results of step 3-2.1.

The project team must be aware that the existing system requirements are, in general, not those of the new system. E.g. they should be alert for "bootleg" records — files which are unofficially established by certain personnel for their own use. In addition, the project team must pay attention to those aspects of the information flow which are not included in the paper flow, such as meetings and telephone calls. Such verbal information exchanges are usually associated with needs for short response times. They are best assessed by means of interview and discussion meetings. Such "bootleg" records and unrecorded communications may indicate deficiencies in the present system, and thus represent genuine requirements; or they may be merely unnecessary duplication. They should be recorded for future evaluation.

It is essential that this step should be approached with an open mind; preconceived ideas must not be allowed to dictate the course of the investigation. The systems analyst should determine in advance the aspects of the organization in which he is interested; listen and observe without prejudice; avoid attempting to fit the facts into a predetermined framework; and finally, he should evaluate the facts in relation to the growing but as yet incompletely defined system concept.

Types of study

In studying an information flow [1]) which is not trivial, it is necessary to effect some kind of conceptual division of the organization.

Departmental method

The most obvious breakdown is into the existing departments. This method provides a complete understanding of the range of operations within a department in one investigation. However, care must be taken in observing the manner in which information passes between departments; the information interfaces are not always obvious.

Stimulus-response method

A method which eliminates this difficulty is to start with a stimulus or trigger (say a customer order) to which the organization must respond, and to follow the information flow associated with the response until the train of action comes to an end. In this method, if a complete picture is to be obtained, care must be taken to examine the response to each kind of stimulus to which the organization is required to respond — internal as well as external.

Action-oriented method

In association with either method it may be necessary, and is often profitable, to study the information required to initiate or control certain specific actions (preparation of a purchase order, delivery of goods, etc.).

---

[1]) See: A. B. Frielink, *Inleiding tot het organisatie-onderzoek ten behoeve van de toepassing van informaten bij de bestuurlijke informatiebehandeling*, Samson, Alphen aan den Rijn, 1965.

Object-information method

Another approach is to concentrate on the objects produced or controlled (products manufactured, customers served, etc.) by certain specific items of information.

Output analysis method

As a special aspect of the use of triggers, it is possible to start the analysis with the investigation of outputs. By working backwards through file updating, intermediate processing, etc. to the creation of source documents, an understanding of the information flow structure of the present system will be obtained.

Method selection

The third of these approaches can be useful in small scale applications, and in connection with independent procedures within a larger organization; the fourth is of service in determining file size and record length. Neither the third nor the fourth is in itself a complete method for studying a complex information flow. The stimulus-response method is the method best suited to the feasibility study, and to a preliminary system analysis & design stage. It stresses the relationship between processes, and gives a dynamic picture of the information flow. For the more detailed analysis, each of the five methods advocated is suitable. It should be noted, however, that the departmental method requires either that the systems analyst be familiar with the existing system, or that a preliminary study by the stimulus-response method has been made.
Only the first two methods are dealt with in detail.

Practical rules particular to the stimulus-response method

- Identify the stimuli to which that part of the organization relevant to the realization of the system objectives must respond. It is essential to the success of this method that a comprehensive set of internal and external stimuli is selected;
- identify the departments involved. This is necessary because the investigation will cut across departmental lines; but take care that the study is oriented towards functions and problem areas, and not towards departments. The information flow should be investigated only to the extent that it affects the stimulus-response under consideration;
- obtain copies of all documents bearing on current procedures which concern the response under investigation. Request completed examples of all relevant forms. The best method of collecting these forms is during interviews with the people who use them;
- proceed by following the main information stream. Note and record where conditional branches occur, identify the controlling conditions, and continue to follow the main stream. Do not attempt to get everything in one sweep; this will lead to confusion;

- wherever possible, obtain quantitative data. This permits the evaluation of exceptions from the general pattern;
- after the main stream has been understood and documented, go back to the branch points and follow the other streams.

Practical rules particular to the departmental method

- Obtain from the head of the department under investigation a description of the functions performed within the department, its boundaries, and its relationships with other departments;
- identify the tasks performed within the department;
- obtain description of each tasks from the appropriate supervisor before making actual observations;
- observe each task separately in detail. Pay particular attention to the information inputs required, the information outputs produced, the files used, and any decision making called for. Document the results of the observation by means of the function worksheet on page 33, gridcharts, decision tables, and flowcharts;
- obtain copies of all current procedures (flowcharts, written standard operating procedures, etc.);
- obtain completed copies of all forms used in the work of the department.

Practical rules common to both methods

Data usage chart

All documents collected must be evaluated in terms of content and usefulness. A document may contain too many data, or too few, or may cover the wrong data fields; or it may be unnecessary. All duplications, inadequacies and discrepancies must be determined and recorded. The data usage chart (example in page 26) is a suitable medium, and can serve also as a document checklist or summary.

Use of reports

The team members should investigate the answers given by the lower and middle management personnel concerning the uses they make of the reports, in order to determine if these answers are in conformity with reality.
In answering the following questions, emphasis must be laid upon specific actions taken by the recipient of the report, and not on repeating the content of the report itself. Questions which must be answered during interviews with managers and other officials of the user organization may cover the following:

- functional responsibility of the user;
- date on which report is received (to check with preparation date for consistency and lead time);
- usage of the information contained in the report:
  — for measuring performance of subordinates or operating departments;

DATA USAGE CHART

system :
subsystem :
prev. issue:

project no. :
chapter/sect.:
page :
issued :

data elements		output documents									
name	identi-fication	shipping label	inven-tory register	receiving report	invoice						
part number			x	x	x						
part description					x						
unit price					x						
customer name		x			x						
customer address		x			x						
date order recorded					x						
date due out		x									
quantity on hand			x								
quantity on order			x								
quantity recorded			x	x							
quantity issued			x		x						
stock location			x	x							
vendor no.				x							
purchase order no.				x							

— for evaluating operating results and expenditures, versus budgetary calculations;
— for evaluating status data or data concerning a period of time;
— for decision taking, in particular the initiation of corrective actions:
— for reference;
— for planning or progress control of activity schedules;

- requirements fulfilled by the report;
- any data checking which occurs on receipt of the report;
- use of the report by itself, or in conjunction with other reports (directed towards the possibility of combining reports);
- average time spent on each individual report, and number of references made to it;
- opinion on present layout of the report;
- opinion of the user on the present reporting period and the reporting delay after the end of the reporting period.

Report usage chart

The report usage chart is a gridchart (see page 28) to assist in the systematic analysis of the use made of existing reports. It lists the reports, and records code number or name, destination, frequency, number of pages, and time spent by each recipient in reading his copy. Reference numbers may be entered instead of "x's" to indicate the related procedure or computer run. It is thus possible to determine how many reports each executive receives, and the total time he spends in reviewing them.

The chart is therefore a valuable tool in interviewing an executive on the efficiency of present methods of providing him with information.

Time factor

Particular attention must be paid to the time of occurrence of significant events in the information flow. A significant event can be of a decision-making nature, or can be the execution of a set of straightforward operations. In both cases, the response time of the recipient is important in relation to the processing cycle of the system. In the latter case these times should be related to those when reports of the events reach the executives concerned, and to the times when the executives actually make the decisions or perform the operations required of them.

Performance evaluation

In order to be able to evaluate the performance of the information flow, all complaints, operational problems and suggestions proffered by respondents in the course of interviews must be recorded, and subsequently assessed. In addition, reasons must be sought for rush jobs, "bottlenecks", heavy fluctuations in workload, exception procedures, and overtime working.

Use the information flow performance checklist at the end of this step for the evaluation of individual procedures and operations.

REPORT USAGE CHART

system : *Production planning & control system*
subsystem : *Product information*
prev. issue: *jan 26th 1966*

project no. : *X 1000*
chapter/sect.: *4.2*
page : *12*
issued : *june 1st '66*

report identification	report freq.	report size lines	dept construction, name Smith	production preparation Johnson	time calculation Black	coding office Miller
100 D 11	D	70	222 P14	222 P18	222 P22	222 P10
100 D 12	D	10	222 P15			
100 D 13	D	15		222 P17		
100 D 14	M	300			222 P23	
100 D 15	D	5				222 P11
100 D 16	M	5000	222 P16			222 P16

Note: Instead of inserting "X's" reference numbers may be entered pointing at the related computer runs or procedures.

Volume figures

Volume figures obtained from people "on the job" may often prove unreliable. Such people seldom have an overall view, and tend to lay undue emphasis on peak loads or recent events. If no well-attested figures are available, they should be culled from various recording points, such as the accounting department, or by direct observation.

In the latter case, the general magnitude of the flow will indicate whether 100 % count is necessary, or whether sampling should be employed, and over what period the count should be made. For further details of this subject, see measuring and estimating (6-3.2).

When collecting volume data, care must be taken to distinguish categories and periods which possess special interest in evaluating the flow, and to remain alert for exception situations, some of which may be hitherto unknown.

The subdivision into relatively small periods gives insight into peaks and valleys of activities. Afterwards combining the figures is always possible, but not the opposite.

Internal control

The flowcharts prepared in the course of this step should include information on the internal control measures of the present system. Where for example the information flow is impeded by the holding up of documents until a release date determined, perhaps, by fixed time-periods, numbers accumulated, stock levels, or even by difficulty of handling, this must be clearly shown. Be alert for special internal control operations which are performed e.g. adding signatures for approval, making hash-totals. For a survey of control measures and techniques see 6-5. An assessment of the methods used for internal control is necessary in order to be able to evaluate, at the design stage, how best the control demands can be met in the new system.

Documentation of the information flow

Information flows can be drawn in different levels of detail. During the course of the investigation, the systems analyst will produce a detailed documentation of procedures and tasks. However, during the course of the investigation the project team should combine individual procedures and tasks with respect to functions.

Function worksheet

For the documentation of subsystems, problem areas or functions, the function worksheet can be used. Each function should be described in terms of:

- name and identification;
- purpose

- outputs and inputs:
  - — name and identification;
  - — volume average and peak;
  - — frequency;
  - — medium;
  - — destination or source;
- process:
  - — name and identification.

When the function worksheet is used for the documentation of a problem area or a subsystem it is possible to record also the names and identifications of the included functions.

Form and file description sheet

A form and file description sheet can be used to document each output or input in detail (see example on page 34).

Field description sheet

For each data field represented on the form and file description sheet, an individual field description sheet can be filled in. See example on page 35. Proceeding in this manner, the documentation is set out in levels in a way which clearly demonstrates its structure.

Process documentation

For each individual process to be performed, a separate description of the decision pattern involved can be made by means of a flowchart or decision table. Use straightforward, self explanatory verbs to represent the information handling actions concerned.

The principal method of documenting the information flow is flowcharting (6-2.2). The following details offer additional assistance in the use of this technique:

- to characterize the flow, it is recommended that the name of the department, and, where applicable, of the employee, engaged in specific operations, be entered in the appropriate symbol. This assists in illustrating the flow of data from point to point in the organization;
- to indicate the utilization of the charted flow, annotations should be made showing average and peak volume of documents processed per operation; average and peak number of operations; and average and maximum equipment usage time per operation;
- the symbol for a data-processing operation must be varied in such a way that the type of equipment represented can be seen at a glance.

Filing

All material collected and prepared during the analysis of the information flow should be documented in the project file according a methodology described in 2-4.1.

Document analysis and description

A document is a durable medium carrying information in the form of a recording of one or more data fields. The medium in this context is not necessarily paper, but may be any substance, such as punched cards, punched tape, magnetic tape, and the sleeves and disks of store units, on which a permanent recording can be made. The study of documents leads to a better understanding of the present information flow, and to the assessment of the forms requirements of the system.

Types of document

A possible method of document classification is into source documents, intermediate documents, records and reports.

- A source document is a document which introduces new data to the system. Generally speaking, data conversion will be necessary when a source document is used in conjunction with computers;
- an intermediate document is a document, such as a worksheet or a summary card, used mainly in manual or punched card systems to summarize a large quantity of source data ("data reduction"). Such documents find their chief application in non-integrated or step-by-step data processing. They can also be used to facilitate the editing of reports;
- a record is a document carrying recordings of a set of related data fields. It is usually part of a file which is regularly updated to permit the supply of current information for use in the preparation of reports;
- a report is a document carrying managerial or operational information. Such a document may call for a managerial decision, or may serve to initiate a necessary operation.
  Reports may be further subdivided into:
  — status reports, recording status at a given date — e.g. a balance sheet;
  — activity reports, recording activity over a given period — e.g. a profit and loss statement;
  — management reports, to enable managers to control and evaluate the performance of the functions under their control, and to assist them in decision-making;
  — operational documents or forms, which are communication links in the chain of operations. These documents express the results of completed operations, and initiate further operations. Even though they may be used by managers, they must be distinguished from management reports. An example is a production schedule.

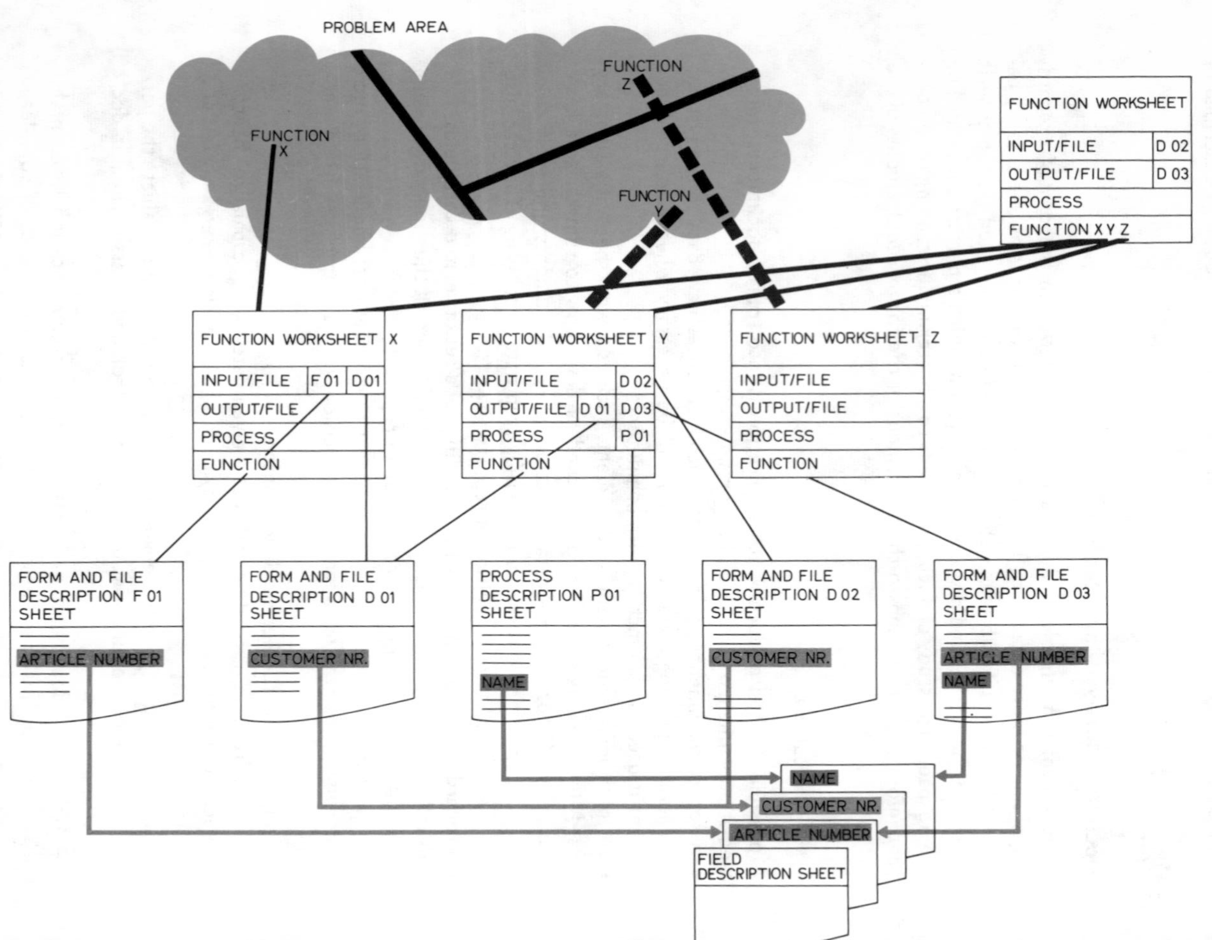

PROBLEM AREA
FUNCTION X
FUNCTION Z
FUNCTION Y
FUNCTION WORKSHEET
INPUT/FILE
D 02
OUTPUT/FILE
D 03
PROCESS
FUNCTION X Y Z
FUNCTION WORKSHEET X
INPUT/FILE
F 01
D 01
OUTPUT/FILE
PROCESS
FUNCTION
FUNCTION WORKSHEET Y
INPUT/FILE
D 02
OUTPUT/FILE
D 01
D 03
PROCESS
P 01
FUNCTION
FUNCTION WORKSHEET Z
INPUT/FILE
OUTPUT/FILE
PROCESS
FUNCTION
FORM AND FILE DESCRIPTION F 01 SHEET
ARTICLE NUMBER
FORM AND FILE DESCRIPTION D 01 SHEET
CUSTOMER NR.
PROCESS DESCRIPTION P 01 SHEET
NAME
FORM AND FILE DESCRIPTION D 02 SHEET
CUSTOMER NR.
FORM AND FILE DESCRIPTION D 03 SHEET
ARTICLE NUMBER
NAME
NAME
CUSTOMER NR.
ARTICLE NUMBER
FIELD DESCRIPTION SHEET

FUNCTION WORKSHEET

system : sales
subsystem : order processing
prev. issue:

project no. :
chapter/sect.:
page :
issued :

name demand registration

purpose to be able to create a survey of the demands, for each article subdivided into geographical areas

no. : OBA

INPUTS	1	2	3	4
name	order master	demand information		
identification	123D16	211D02		
volume/period	day	day		
average	100	3		
peak	200	10		
frequency	daily	random		
medium	A4 - paper	A5 - note		
source	order preparation	order preparation		

OUTPUTS	1	2	3	4
name	total demand in a period	total demand in a geographical area		
identification	121D11	121D23		
volume/period	month	month		
average	4	6		
peak	4	6		
frequency	monthly	monthly		
medium	printed paper	printed paper		
destination	article managers forecasting	sales managers		

PROCESSING	1	2	3	4
name	cumulation article	cumulation article		
identification	00A	for each geogr. area 00B		

This is a documentation of a: problem area ☒ subsystem ☐ Which functions are incorporated?				

comments:

FORM AND FILE DESCRIPTION SHEET

system : sales
subsystem : order processing
prev. issue:

project no. :
chapter/sect.:
page :
issued :

name: order master

form or file no. : 123D16

deprecated names :

purpose : converts various order forms used by customers to standard format for internal use

appearing in
function : demand registration, OBA
procedure :
run :
program :
form :

retention file
period : one year
sequence : random

label layout content
header :
trailer :

no. of copies : 4
usage volume p.: day
average : 100
peak : 200

issue date :

reporting delay : 1/2 day

size : A4
medium : paper

colour :

seq. no.	field name	field identification	line no.	number of characters maximum alph.	number of characters maximum num.	number of characters av.	usage freq.	comments
	Heading							
1	Customer no.	CUSN	1	6				Customer file
2	Salesman no.	SASN	1		2			Customer order
3	Order date	ORDN	1		6			do
4	Shipping date	SHPN	1		6			do
5	Customer Order no.	CUSO	2	(Max.	10)			do
7	Internal Order no.	IONR	2		6			Order clerk
	Line Items							
8	Item no.	ITNR	3/15		7			Cust. order or sales catalogue
9	Item name	ITNM	do	14				Customer order
10	Quantity ordered	QUNO	do		4			do
11	Unit of measure	UNME	do	2				do
12	Quantity shipped	QUSH	do		4			Shipping dept.
13	Unit price	UNPR	do		6			Pricing dept.

Comments

Note:
Contents of outputs, punched cards, punched- or magnetic tapes are specified on punched card layouts, record layouts or printer spacing charts.

FIELD DESCRIPTION SHEET

system :	project no. :
subsystem : sales	chapter/sect.:
prev. issue: orderprocessing	page :
	issued :

name: customer-no	abbreviation: cust.-no	field identification: CUSN
deprecated synonyms: account-no.	size av. / max.	responsible for updating:
characteristics:	av.: / max.: 6	

	picture	1	2	3	4	5	6	7	8	9	10	11	12	13	14	15	16	17	18	19	20	21	22	23	24	25	26	27	28	29	30
input	alphanum.	A	9	9	9	9	9																								
edition	picture	1	2	3	4	5	6	7	8	9	10	11	12	13	14	15	16	17	18	19	20	21	22	23	24	25	26	27	28	29	30

appearing in:

input	output	record layout	program	
customer order ordermaster	advice note invoice packing list	customer order record	invoicing	

comments:

Aspects of documentation

In analyzing the documentation of the present system, the points in the following list should be considered in respect of each document. In this connection, the form and file description sheet will prove useful (page 33) for those facts not yet documented in the flowchart.

• Identification	— Document number. — Official name. — Abbreviated name (for use in cross-indexing). — Secondary or deprecated names in use.
• Origin	— Originating department, person, procedure or agency. — Method and/or equipment used for preparation. — Stimulus for origination (will be shown in flowchart).
• Purpose	— Brief description of reasons for preparation. — Function of which it is an input.
• Distribution and use	— How many copies are prepared? — Who receives copies? Describe functions and responsibilities, and identify in flowchart. — Why is each copy required? — What particular data fields are used by each recipient? — What actions and/or decisions may be triggered by each copy? Make reference to all procedures which use this form.
• Retention	— Which retention measures exist for each copy of a document? — How does each recipient dispose of his copy? (The flowchart should follow each copy to eventual filing or destruction.)
• Frequency	— Is the document scheduled or produced on demand? — If scheduled, what is the reporting period, and do specific deadlines exist? — If on demand, who is authorized to request it? For what reasons? How frequently are demands likely?
• Volume	— Average and maximum number of documents used over a given period or for a run. — Average and maximum number of items per document (pages per report, lines per page, etc.). — Rate of growth.
• Timing	— Are timing demands reasonable with respect to data availability? — What is the reporting delay; state minimum, maximum, average.

- Medium — Punched card, punched tape, standard form, etc.
- Contents — What data fields are included; specify identifications and names.
  - — Which of these fields are used for the intended purpose?
  - — Which fields are used for other purposes?
  - — What is the frequency of usage of a field?
  - — If used, what is the average and maximum size of the field?
  - — What summaries or totals are given?
  - — Which rules for filling in exist?
  - — Which control measures are applied?
- Format — Size, paper quality and reproduction method of each document and its copies.
  - — Which names for data fields are preprinted in the case of a form?
  - — What are the average and maximum sizes of each entry?
  - — What are the average and maximum sizes of the document (lines per page, pages per issue)?
  - — Are the sequence and arrangement of the presentation efficient?

File analysis and description

A file is a collection of related records treated as a unit (ASA), and so organized that the data stored is accessible for reference and use. As employed in this section, the term "file" includes, inter alia, tub files, filing cabinets, loose-leaf notebooks, punched-card files, catalogues, black-book reference data, and rate tables. Special alertness must be exercised to discover the existence of "unofficial" files; all such should be noted for later evaluation.

In analyzing the present files, the following aspects should be considered in respect of each file:

- identification name and code;
- alternative names in use;
- purpose;
- type of data carrier;
- department or official responsible for maintenance;
- location;
- use; by whom, when, how often, and which sections;
- speed of access;
- types of enquiry made;
- response time to enquiries;
- unanswered enquiries;
  - — type of information;
  - — average number per period;

- contents:
  - — qualification and identification of the documents or records contained;
  - — sequencing method; description of keys;
  - — average and maximum number of records;
  - — average and maximum number of characters per record;
  - — average and maximum size;
  - — annual average growth in volume;
- frequency of updating;
- retention rules for each type of record;
- outputs using this file.

The form and file description sheet used for forms documentation can also be used as an aid for file documentation (see page 34).

Field analysis and description

The field description sheet should be used for the documentation of all information concerning a specific field. Each data field should be documented only once, regardless of the number of forms, files or programs using it. Thus a survey is made of all the data fields used in the system, while at the same time the usage of data fields is defined, facilitating maintenance.

INFORMATION FLOW PERFORMANCE CHECKLIST

Check on:	*Examples of detail questions:*
Timeliness	• Does any backlog of work exist? • Are personnel idle due to paper-processing delays? • Are reports produced too late to be of value to management? • Do reports come too late to permit operational feedback?
Accuracy	• Is too little or too much checking being performed? • Are too many corrective documents being prepared? • Are the figures or data presented too accurate for the intended purpose?
Usefulness	• Does the procedure provide the user with the information he requires? • Does the procedure contribute to profitability? • Does the procedure serve its intended purpose? • Is there an obviously better method? • If a computer is currently in use, does it support all functions or only a select few?

- Does the information have decision-making value?
- Are all copies of forms used?
- Are exceptions or items requiring special attention buried in the normal procedures?

Efficiency
- Must a clerk look in many places to answer a question?
- Could telephone sales, or mailing, be more economical (without substantial loss in effectiveness) than personal contacts?
- Is information supplied too frequently on slow-moving items?

Necessity
- Is work being duplicated?
- Are different people performing tasks which, because of basic similarities, could with advantage be combined?
- Are there reports which are prepared frequently but used only occasionally?

Completeness
- Are production problems, changes in customer buying habits, etc. reported?
- Are management provided with information which enables them to determine in advance the effect of their decisions, or of such factors as increased sales and market campaigns, upon production facilities and inventories?

Reliability
- Do management trust the facts with which they are supplied, or do they initiate their own private investigations?
- Do sales and production forecasts reflect actual sales trends?

Responsibility
- Are responsibilities clearly defined for each decision process within the information flow?
- Are the boundaries of the responsibilities defined?

Step 3-2.4: Evaluate present system

The purpose of this step is to bring together and review the information collected in the previous three steps, in which the present system was studied. As a result of this synthesis, a quantitative assessment of the organization is made in relation to its position in the industry, its business goals, its strategy and policy, its organizational structure, and its present system, and ideas are generated for effecting improvements.

When organizational or policy changes with important implications for the design of the new system are mooted by the project team, they should be discussed with the steering committee at the earliest possible time. In this way, the project team will achieve a detailed appreciation of the type of improvement management wants, and of what kind of changes management will or will not permit in order to achieve it. This process is, in effect, a return to the activity define the problem (3-1), but at a higher level. As a result of it, the present relative situation of the organization is clearly seen; the required direction of movement is clarified; and the project team is prepared to enter activity 3-3, identify system requirements and constraints.

In appraising the results obtained during steps 3-2.1, 3-2.2, and 3-2.3, the present system should be evaluated from the complementary viewpoints of effectiveness and cost. It is impossible to divorce these two aspects completely, since many of the best performance criteria have a financial basis. In this respect, it is important to observe that the project team should never enter into detailed consideration of any matter of company finance without first obtaining the cooperation and assistance of the accounting department. As professionals, this department will execute the necessary work with speed and accuracy; they are already in possession of detailed facts necessary for the work; they know the methods of cost presentation which are acceptable in the organization; and in such matters they enjoy the confidence of management.

Product and information flows

When studying the product and information flows, particular attention was paid to their points of contact (3-2.2, 3-2.3). The results of these investigations must now be considered in greater detail. The overall effectiveness of the product flow requires for its determination a clear understanding of the decision points at which the information flow impinges upon it; while in the evaluation of the information flow, attention must be given to its control aspects, and to the characteristics of the individual problem areas which it embodies.
The following questions should be answered:

- Does the present information system provide adequate control over the operation?

- Do relevant decision points exist?
- When deviations from planned processes occur, is the information feedback speedy enough to enable the right corrective actions to be taken?
- Is the feedback accurate enough?
- Is the feedback properly directed?

Models

Most of the techniques available for investigating the performance of a system or part of a system involve the construction of a model. The purpose of constructing and operating a model is to discover major inconsistencies and inefficiencies in the existing system. At this stage of analysis, thought should be mainly directed towards problem areas. A problem area is not necessarily one function, but is usually concerned with a number of related functions. For the further evaluation of problem areas, the product flow and information flow performance checklists can be used. In general, the systems analyst will employ the standard pattern — what, when, why, who, how and where, in relation to outputs, inputs, processes, and relationships between functions.
From the point of view of the control aspect, as well as for the detailed evaluation of problem areas, it is good practice to make comparison with other similar systems. Where no such systems are accessible, helpful comparisons may be drawn in respect of individual functions or problem areas. For the purpose of this step, mathematical models, simulators, and financial models are considered. The purpose of constructing any model is to facilitate the analysis of system behaviour. The system is conceptually divided into a number of aspects whose behaviour can be dealt with and manipulated [1]). The aspects, and their interrelationships, are always to some extent simplified; the practical value of a model is therefore highly dependent upon the degree of simplification employed. Unless this fact is borne in mind, the use of models, particularly of those taking the form of idealized pictorial representation, can mislead the user.

Mathematical models

A mathematical model expresses the behaviour of a system in terms of a set of equations. For any real system of even moderate complexity, the number of equations required for a good description is very high.
A study of chain linked (e.g. factory — warehouse — distributor — retailer) organizations was made in M.I.T.'s Project Dynamo [2]). The principles are applicable to a sequence of operations within an organization. Basically, Forrester showed that a link-structured organization has unstable characteristics unless the controlling feedbacks are suitably chosen and applied.

---

[1]) T. N. Naylor, J. L. Balintfy, D. S. Burdick & Kong Chu, *Computer simulation techniques*, Wiley, New York 1966.
[2]) J. W. Forrester, *Industrial dynamics*, Wiley, New York 1961.

Late feedback

If feedback is too late (too long a time-constant), or distorted (suffers a transformation), then the corrective action called up may cause disturbances more serious than the original trigger deviation.

As an example of late feedback, consider a machineshop suddenly faced by an overload (trigger deviation). As a result, it is decided to subcontract some work. For reasons of preparation, this work is commenced only after six weeks have elapsed. At the end of this period, some of the overload has already been dealt with; the machineshop, on sending out the work, begins to feel underload. More orders are accepted; with the result that, at the end of the subcontract, an even worse overload occurs. Here, throughout the cycle of operation, the true nature of the situation was appreciated too late.

Distorted feedback

As an example of distortion, consider what happens if a company officer in the planning department, on becoming aware of the approach of an overload on the machineshop, thinks to improve matters by making an over-demand. Even if no subcontracting is used, the resulting overproduction results in an over-high stock level, which in turn leads to a machineshop underload. The resultant oscillations if subcontracting is also employed can be very severe.

In cases such as this, corresponding to individual problem areas, pictorial or algebraic models may be of considerable use in determining appropriate feedbacks and their time-constants.

Simulators

A mathematical model enables us to predict the behaviour of a system, but does not itself imitate the structure of the system. A simulator represents as faithfully as possible the actual functions and relationships of the system, and is able accurately to reproduce its behaviour only insofar as the representation is accurate.

Simulator diagram

A simulator consisting of a diagram in which aspects of the information and material flows are represented by interconnecting arrows (see figure in 3-2.2) is of use in proportion to the accuracy with which it represents the factors relevant to the investigation. If drawn with care, such a simulator can give very useful results. If the results of the various trigger actions to which the organization must respond are followed out, many inconsistencies and inadequacies of the present system may be located.

Computer simulation

It has been said that "The best simulator of any system is the system itself". In later stages of the systems effort, and in particular during post-implementation evaluation, the availability of up-to-date files and programs and of the hardware-software configuration permits utilization of this fact.

Financial models

Financial matters enter, directly or indirectly, into most measurements of system effectiveness. In order to be able to identify what an improvement is, and to judge if improvements are possible, the project team must know what quantities are indications of effectiveness. It is impossible to assign a meaningful single value to the overall performance of a system. What is possible is to break down the system objectives into quantifiable elements. The units in which these elements are evaluated — their "dimensions" — should be time and money, or the names of objects having a clear relationship with time and/or money. The extent to which any objective is met in the system may now be determined by measuring the values of its elements, and by using these values to construct a quantified measure of performance.

Performance ratios

The ratios formed by selecting pairs or groups of elements to correspond with aspects of the system performance are called "performance ratios" [1]). By a judicious selection of aspects and elements, a "financial model" of the system is built up, and a quantitative assessment of the performance becomes possible. In constructing performance ratios, it must be borne in mind that only quantities which have the same dimensions may be added together (or subtracted); and that a ratio is a pure number, expressing the relationship between two quantities having the same dimensions, In many instances, it will be the rate of change of a ratio, rather than its absolute value at a particular time, which is of interest in assessing performance.

The following are examples of performance ratios which might well be of interest:

- value of work in progress : value of annual turnover;
- number of rush orders : total number of orders;
- number of outstanding orders: total number of orders;
- number of cancellations : total number of orders;
- value of finished stock : value of annual turnover;
- total processing time : total throughput time.

The selection, determination and use of performance ratios is never simple. The following hints should be of assistance:

- first identify the aspects of performance which exert major influence on achievement of the objectives, e.g. throughput time, customer service, production costs, stock levels;
- try to establish ratios which are independent of fluctuations in such quantities as turnover, number of customers, number of products, etc.;
- ensure that the quantites selected are capable of being measured, preferably by means of data available from the normal accounting and production records;

[1]) Spencer A. Tucker, *Successful Managerial Control by Ratio Analysis*, McGraw Hill, 1961.

- use ratios and combinations of ratios whose value and behaviour will indicate trends in performance which are of direct interest to management, in relation to system objectives and business goals (3-2.1) etc. In this way, the ratios can be related to significant improvements, and can be of use to management in decision making;
- ensure that the ratios selected cover the performance adequately. Measure them in a planned manner, and plan to measure them repeatedly, so that exceptional values can be identified and trends established.

Cost of the present system

In investigating the cost of the present system, the systems analyst must consider not only the direct data-processing costs, but also the costs incurred due to lack of reliable and sufficient information, and to inefficient control. A technique for dealing with these matters is that of cost and benefit calculations, and is equally applicable to the new and the present systems. This technique is described in 2-3.

Cost comparison

In addition to the material of 2-3, the following remarks should be noted.

Do not spend too much time on a determination of costs when management have indicated that they will not, in the first place, base their decision on whether or not to automate upon a cost comparison. In such cases performance ratios without translation into costs and benefits will give sufficient information.

When management require a complete cost comparison, it must be borne in mind that a direct comparison would be misleading if the proposed and present systems did not cover the same area. In such cases, the investigation of the present system must be extended to cover the appropriate areas, for cost determination purposes only. If the new system includes functions which are not performed in the existing system, then, of course, there is no basis for cost comparison in respect of these functions.

Do not attempt to display directly as a saving any reduction in resources required, unless the resources released can be given an alternative application. This applies to space, equipment, materials, and to employees who must be kept on the payroll.

Personnel cost factors

The workloads in office operations should be related to the cost of procedures. The cost of manual procedures tends to rise disproportionately to the rise in wage level, with little or no increase in the volume of production. In order to check this, the systems analyst should relate the volume of a number of years' manual work to the departmental cost over the years.

Equipment cost factors

For each piece of equipment the following information should be collected:

- type and model;
- data installed;
- if purchased:
  - — present value;
  - — salvage value;
  - — annual depreciation;
- the annual rental if rented;
- if leased:
  - — annual rental;
  - — contract termination date;
- annual service and maintenance costs;
- expected date and reason of replacement;
  - — wear and tear;
  - — insufficient capacity.

Activity 3-3: Identify system requirements and constraints

The main purpose of this activity is to produce a detailed specification of the requirements and constraints of a new system. It also produces a list of the general and detailed objectives of the new system together with estimates of the extent to which these objectives will be attained, and a complete specification of the organizational changes that are necessary to enable the new system to operate efficiently.
Much of the work to be carried out in this activity is based on the results of activities 3-1 (define the problem) and 3-2 (analyze present system). The requirements and constraints of a new system should not, however, be based completely on those of the existing system. It is essential to create an entirely separate concept for a new system, preferably one which is not merely a logical extension of the existing system. The comparison of the organization with others in the same industry will probably yield additional information on which to base the concept for a new system.

Subdivision

The identification of the system requirements and constraints can be broken down into four steps:
(3-3.1) define the performance of new system;
(3-3.2) identify organizational requirements and constraints of a new system;
(3-3.3) determine information and control requirements and constraints;
(3-3.4) determine general design requirements and constraints.

From the point of view of identifying system requirements and constraints, the first and second steps are mainly preparatory. They prepare the ground for carrying out the third step in which most of the requirements and constraints, expressed as inputs, processes and outputs of all the functions to be included in the new system are specified.
In addition, the first and second step produce outputs relating to the effect of the system on the organization it supports. The fourth step is entirely separate from the other steps; it deals with general design requirements and constraints for the system as a whole, unrelated to specific objectives.

Performance
The purpose of the first step is to define the performance expected of the new system in terms of its impact upon the effectiveness of the user organization. The output of this step is a list of the detailed objectives of the system arranged in order of priority, together with estimates, for a number of years ahead, of the extent to which these objectives can be achieved. These estimates provide the basis for the comparison of costs and benefits of the old and the new systems. As

far as the requirements and constraints definition is concerned, however, it is the degree of priority accorded to each objective that is important, in that it confers appropriate priorities on the requirements definitions of those system functions which contribute to the attainment of these objectives. The project team must bear these priorities constantly in mind during the whole of the requirements definition and design activities.

Organizational requirements and constraints

The second step involves determining how the existing or future organization will affect, or be affected by, the new system. Any changes that are to be made in the organization might entail changes in the system objectives formulated in the first step. If these changes are to take place when the new system is operational this will generate additional system requirements and constraints to ensure a smooth transfer. If it is found desirable to alter the organization in order to implement an effective system, then these alterations should be put forward for approval and implementation during this step of the requirements definition activity.

Information and control requirements and constraints

The third step contains the detailed work of specifying the requirements and constraints of the system. Using the results of 3-3.1, 3-3.2 and of 3-2.3 (identify the information flow) the system is broken down, first into problem areas and then into functions. The requirements and constraints of each function are then studied in respect of:

- requirements and constraints of the existing system;
- recommendations made by management;
- legal and corporate requirements and constraints;
- internal control requirements and constraints.

The requirements and constraints in terms of inputs, processes and outputs of each function, and of any additional functions that the studies reveal, are now finalized to produce a specification of the requirements and constraints of the complete system.

General design requirements and constraints

The purpose of the fourth step is to identify the general design requirements and constraints which set limitations and rules for the design of the new system in terms of maintainability, flexibility, compatibility, expandability, machine configuration, and efficiency of data processing operations within the system.

Step 3-3.1 : Define the performance of new system

The purpose of this step is to specify the objectives of a new system and to predict the extent to which these objectives can be achieved. The specification of the objectives is fundamentally the responsibility of the steering committee. In those cases where the steering committee does not start with a sufficiently clear idea of what is required, the project team can stimulate action by stating the objectives themselves and asking the steering committee for comments and approval.

It is necessary to predict the performance of a new system before any detailed design work is undertaken for three main reasons:

- to be able to compare the costs and benefits of the old and the new systems;
- to be able to determine, during post-implementation evaluation, whether the new system is satisfactory in terms of attaining the specified objectives;
- to be able to rank the objectives in order of importance. This forces the project team to place proper emphasis on the requirements definitions and design of each function according to its contribution to the realization of the system objectives.

It is suggested that the performance definition be carried out as follows:

- review the objectives of the system and list them in order of priority;
- break down each general objective into detailed objectives, each of which is quantifiable in such a manner that both an objective and the performance of the system in attaining it can be measured;
- define the manner in which each measurement is to be made;
- predict the performance of the system relevant to each objective for a number of years ahead.

Review objectives

The purpose of this substep is to review the objectives of a new system and to list them in order of priority. This involves refining, and in some cases reformulating the objectives defined in activity 3-1 (define the problem) in the light of the results obtained from activity 3-2 (study the present system). It is recommended, however, that the existing system alone is not regarded as the foundation on which to build the new system. It is better to attempt to define a required system and then to modify some of the objectives in order to arrive at a system that can be realized within budgetary limits, time schedules, etc. because this approach tends to produce a more integrated system. The comparison of the organization with others in the same industry, as carried out in step 3-2.1 will probably yield information which is useful in formulating a new system.

Define detailed objectives

The purpose of this substep is to define the objectives of the system in such a way that the performance of the system in terms of degree of attainment of these objectives can be measured. This implies that the objectives themselves must be capable of being quantified.
Usually, most of the objectives formulated in the previous substep will be general in nature, e.g. "improve flexibility", and not capable of being directly measured. It is therefore first necessary to break down each general objective into detailed objectives, each of which can be measured.
For example the objective "improve flexibility" can be broken down into the detailed objectives; decrease production throughput time, improve customer service, etc. The first of these can be measured (in terms of time) and is therefore acceptable, but the second is not and must be broken down further, until every element is measurable.

As each detailed objective is selected a method must be devised of quantifying and measuring the performance of the new system in attaining it. The best method of quantifying performance is by means of performance ratios (for a definition, see 3-2.4). For example a measure of system performance in attaining the objective "decrease production throughput time" might be the ratio:

$$\frac{\text{throughput time under new system}}{\text{throughput time under old system}} .$$

Of course, this simple ratio would be valid only if the organization makes a single type of product. Where there is more than one product there would need to be either as many ratios as there are products, or a single ratio of average throughput times. In this latter case a method of finding a statistically acceptable method of determining the average throughput time would have to be found.

In some cases it may not be possible to construct ratios which permit a direct measure of performance. It will usually be possible, however, to devise ratios whose rate of change with respect to another measurable quantity, e.g. time, is a measure of performance.

Determine method of measurement

When a set of ratios has been decided upon, it is necessary to lay down methods by which they will be measured. All ratios selected for use must be measured repeatedly; this will enable typical values to be identified and trends to be established. However, unless the actual method of measurement is carefully chosen, and made the subject of a written standard, there will be no guarantee that successive values are properly comparable.

Predict future performance

The purpose of this substep is to estimate the future performance of the new system in attaining the specified objectives by predicting the values of the corresponding performance ratios for a number of years ahead.

Documentation

It is recommended that the results of the performance definition be documented on a system objectives form of the type shown on the next page. The "objectives" column should contain the names of the detailed objectives of the system, grouped under the headings of the objectives to which they refer. Wherever possible the objectives should be listed in order of importance. The column measurable provides an indication of whether an objective is measurable. Every detailed objective must be measurable, and even if this measurement is not in money terms it must be capable of being translated into money terms for the purposes of the cost and benefit report. The next column contains the specification of the performance ratio measured in terms of the degree of attainment of the objective. The remaining columns provides space for entering the estimated initial values of all performance ratios and for predicting the values of the ratios for a number of years ahead.

Wherever possible the performance ratios should be the same as those specified in 3-2.4 for the measurement of the attainment of the corresponding objectives of the existing system. This facilitates direct comparison of the old and new systems.

It is good practice to allocate to each objective a unique identifier, in the form of a number or an alphanumeric mnemonic to facilitate cross-reference from other documents. A column is provided for this purpose.

SYSTEM OBJECTIVES FORM

system :
subsystem :
prev. issue:

project no. :
chapter/sect.:
page :
issued :

ref.	objectives		measurable		performance ratio's	performance predictions					
			yes	no.		1967	1968	1969	1970	19	19
A	improve customer service			x							
A-1	percentage of orders shipped				$\frac{\text{number of orders/period}}{\text{total number of orders/period}} \times 100$	20	30	60	75		
	- on schedule		x								
	- one week late		x		,,	40	30	10	5		
	- two weeks late		x		,,	20	20	10	0		
	- one week early		x		,,	15	15	15	15		
	- two weeks early		x		,,	5	5	5	5		
A-2	percentage of cancellations		x		$\frac{\text{number of cancellations/period}}{\text{total number of orders/period}} \times 100$	20	10	5	2,5		
A-3	number of back orders		x		$\frac{\text{number of back orders/period}}{\text{total number of orders/period}} \times 100$	15	10	5	2,5		
B	decrease of production throughput time			x							
B-1	total throughput time		x		in weeks	18	15	12	10		
B-2	- production preparation	% of B-1	x		$\frac{\text{production preparation time}}{\text{total throughput time}} \times 100$	20	20	10	10		
	- production	% of B-1	x		,,	60	60	80	85		
	- expedition	% of B-1	x		,,	20	20	10	5		
B-3	value of work in progress		x		$\frac{\text{value of work in progress}}{\text{value of annual turnover}} \times 100$	100	80	60	50		

Step 3-3.2: Identify organizational requirements and constraints of a new system

The purpose of this step is to predict the organizational requirements and constraints that will exist at the time the new system becomes operational and for as long as possible thereafter. These requirements and constraints are likely to change with time, as a result of changes in the organization of the company to meet external and/or internal needs.

Redefinition of policies and goals

In many companies the decision to start a systems effort is part of a long-term plan, which can sometimes include a partial redefinition of the company's policies and business goals, and which may result in some degree of re-organization of the company. The usual intention of this type of re-organization is to make the company more adaptable to the changing environment in which it operates. [1])

Any major changes contemplated must be allowed for in the design of the new system. For example, if a company with decentralized distribution points each holding significant stocks had decided upon a future policy of stock centralization, this would have a profound effect on the requirements and constraints of the new system. At least in its stock control aspects, the new system would be inappropriate to the present organization; it would be necessary either to time the policy change in relation to the implementation date of the new system, or to make interim modifications to the existing system.

Adaptation to system objectives

In some cases it will be necessary, or at least desirable, to change the organization of the company in order that the system objectives can be realized. By use of the checklist given in 3-2.1 the analysis of the existing system will have brought to light advantages which the new system will usually seek to retain and disadvantages which the new system will seek to eliminate. This may well be impossible, however, without changing the existing organization of the company. Any such changes will result in changes in the requirements and constraints of the new system.

Results

The results of this step will be a list of the organizational changes to be carried out, together with target dates by which they are to be implemented. Some of these changes might entail modifications to the system objectives defined in step 3-3.1, and generate additional requirements and constraints, which must be specified in detail in step 3-3.3.

[1]) For an extensive study in this field see W. W. Cooper, H. J. Leavitt and M. W. Shelley II (ed.), *New perspectives in organization research*, Wiley, New York, 1964.

Step 3-3.3: Determine information and control requirements and constraints

The purpose of this step is to determine the requirements and constraints that will be placed on the new system as a result of the information it must use or generate, due to recommendations made by management, to internal controls required or to legal and corporate policies to be followed. Only those information and control requirements and constraints which will be prerequisites of the new system need be determined at this stage; others may be set aside for consideration during the system design activity. Similarly, system' files are not considered at this stage since they are a means to an end and not an end in themselves.

It is recommended that the following method be adopted:

- identify every problem area to be included in the system, and divide each into functions. Then study, for each function, the requirements and constraints posed by:
- those parts of the existing system that are to be carried over into the new system;
- the various proposals put forward by all levels of management;
- corporate policies and legal considerations;
- the internal control measures that must be applied to the system.

Each of these topics is dealt with separately in this step.

Identify and divide problem areas into functions

A problem area is any field of action within the organization to which the systems effort will be directed. More specifically, a problem area is any function or group of inter-dependent functions which have identifiable boundaries or interfaces with other functions or groups of functions. These interfaces are usually distinguishable by the inputs or outputs that must cross them. Note that the word "problem" as used in the term "problem area" signifies that the area will pose a problem inasmuch as it entails expenditure of effort on the part of systems personnel. It does not necessarily signify that the area contains a "problem" in the sense of a "difficulty" or bottleneck within the organization.

The analysis of the existing system will have resulted in the identification of all existing problem areas. Some of these will be relevant to the new system and must be retained in it; others, particularly those which cause the shortcomings of the existing system, may require reformulation or redefinition for the purposes of the new system. In addition, the required performance of the new system will usually create a number of entirely new problem areas, each of which must now be defined. The problem areas and functions defined in 3-2 should now be related to the system objectives formulated in step 3-3.1.

Management cooperation

The project team should secure the cooperation of the managers of, or representatives from, any operating departments which are not already represented on the team, because these personnel are best qualified to identify the problem areas in their own departments. It should be borne in mind, however, that their approach will naturally be department-oriented, whereas problem areas must be defined in relation to system objectives, and this may well cut across traditional lines of the organization. The suggestions of departmental personnel should therefore be evaluated with respect to system objectives in order to avoid sub-optimization.

Documentation

It is recommended that the results of problem and function definition be documented as follows:

- make a list of all problem areas that are to be included in the new system and arrange them in order of importance;
- take each problem area in turn and list all the functions it contains, arranged in order of priority;
- describe each function on a separate function worksheet (example in 3-2.3). The description should be in terms of purpose, inputs, processes and outputs;
- where necessary, detailed specifications of inputs and outputs can be on form and file description sheets of the type shown in 3-2.3. Details of processes can, where necessary, be given in the form of decision tables, flowcharts, etc.

The documentation should in all cases be carried out as advocated in 3-2.3. Each separate document should bear a unique identification number to facilitate cross-reference to and from other documents.

Requirements and constraints posed by the existing system

The purpose of this topic is to determine the requirements and constraints in terms of inputs, processes and outputs that will be imposed on the new system as a result of incorporating problem areas and functions from the old system.
Most of the details required will be available from the analysis of the existing system (3-2). Because the present system has evolved over a number of years, however, some of its requirements and/or constraints may not be relevant even to the current situation, let alone the new system. All the requirements and constraints should therefore be scrutinized for relevance and the irrelevant ones discarded.
The incorporation of existing problem areas or functions may well impose additional requirements and constraints as a result of the design of the new information system, particularly if this entails the centralization of files. For example, under the existing system several departments hold similar files in order to be able to answer enquiries. In such a case the incorporation of these functions into the new system would create either a requirement for reports containing sufficient information to answer all expected enquiries, or a requirement for direct access to the appropriate data.

Recommendations made by management

The purpose of this topic is to convert all recommendations made by management into requirements and constraints in terms of inputs, processes and outputs of functions within the new system.
For the purposes of the feasibility study, a list of the requirements and constraints will normally be sufficient. For the purposes of system design, however, full details of the relevant inputs, processes and outputs are required. The project team should use cross-checking by interviewing different members of the organization on the same reporting needs.
Evaluate the reporting needs and synthesize these needs to obtain a limited number of types of report that will satisfy these needs.
Apply the considerations given in the section document analysis and description in 3-2.3.

Legal and corporate policy requirements and constraints

A knowledge of the requirements imposed by corporate policies or legal considerations guides the project team in determining what data must be made available for each function and how it must be processed and/or protected. This dictates some of the results the new system should produce.

Sources of information
The best sources for this information will be the corporate policy and procedures manuals if available. Additional information may be obtained through interviews with the controller, the company's legal counsel, the head of the personnel department, the contracts administrator, and Government officials.

Corporate constraints
An example of a corporate constraint would be a policy that all purchase requisitions in excess of a specified amount must be approved both by the purchasing manager and by the controller. This policy would be an important constraint in an automated purchasing system.

Legal requirements
An example of a legal requirement would be a law requiring employers to maintain records of employee earnings and deductions for tax purposes. This law would be a major design consideration in a payroll system.
Corporate policies which affect the system should be evaluated as to their effectiveness in present day operations. Some of them might be obsolete, due to the change in operations over the years. The project team should also be aware of proposed policies, not yet in effect, which may be pertinent. Managers responsible for establishing policies should be interviewed in order to ascertain if any policy changes are contemplated. The project team should take care to stipulate, well in advance of the system design activity, the need for new identification and/or classification codes for all kinds of data objects.

Internal control requirements and constraints

The operations carried out within an organization must be subject to an integrated interlocking network of internal controls to ensure reliability and to prevent waste and fraud. Due to the fact that these operations are to be included in the information system, then this system must also be subject to a similar integrated network of controls. This network of controls will impose additional requirements and constraints on the new system and it is the purpose of this topic to identify and specify them.
A start should be made by examining and evaluating the existing system of controls revealed by the study of the present system. If this system has evolved over a number of years, it will probably contain obsolete, duplicated and/or redundant controls which can be discarded in the new system. It will normally be possible to automate quite a number of controls, for example those concerned with the checking and comparing of input data. Other controls cannot be exercised by automatic means, and therefore some measure of manual control must be retained by the new system.
There are many aspects of internal control, a few of which are mentioned below, (these aspects are derived from: Felix Kaufman: *Electronic Data Processing and Auditing*).

Segregation of functional responsibility
Examples:
- cash registers must be cleared by employees from a department independent of the register clerks;
- the signing of receipts is a separate function from the receipt of the money, and should be registered independently of the cashiers' department.

Acting within the limits of authority
These are constraints put forward as management policies (3-3.4) and have to be audited under the heading of internal control. The following are examples:
- only a credit manager may approve sales to new customers;
- an assistant manager may not approve discount over 2% for sales exceeding an amount of $ 500.

Comparison with external data
Examples:
- debtors confirm their balance as per the end of a period;
- bank statements reflect the cheques issued by the organization.

Comparison with product flow
Examples:
- shipping papers against goods shipped;
- receiving reports against incoming materials.

Comparison with source data
Examples:
- prices on invoices against order confirmations;
- payroll clock cards against labour job reports.

Accuracy
Examples:
- checking prices on invoices against sales catalogue;
- verification of batch control totals.

Both the automatic and manual controls will impose requirements and constraints on the new system. It is a good practice in formulating these requirements and constraints not to specify the manner in which the control is to be carried out. This leaves the choice of control method open until the system design activity, when the available control techniques can be investigated.

A related set of controls should be implemented to guarantee an effective control network, covering the different problem areas. In 6-5 a survey is given of different control techniques which can be applied to the different types of information handling, and the problem of creating a control network throughout the system is discussed. It is emphasized that, in this growing field, the systems analyst should make every effort to keep up-to-date, and not place blind faith in traditional methods.

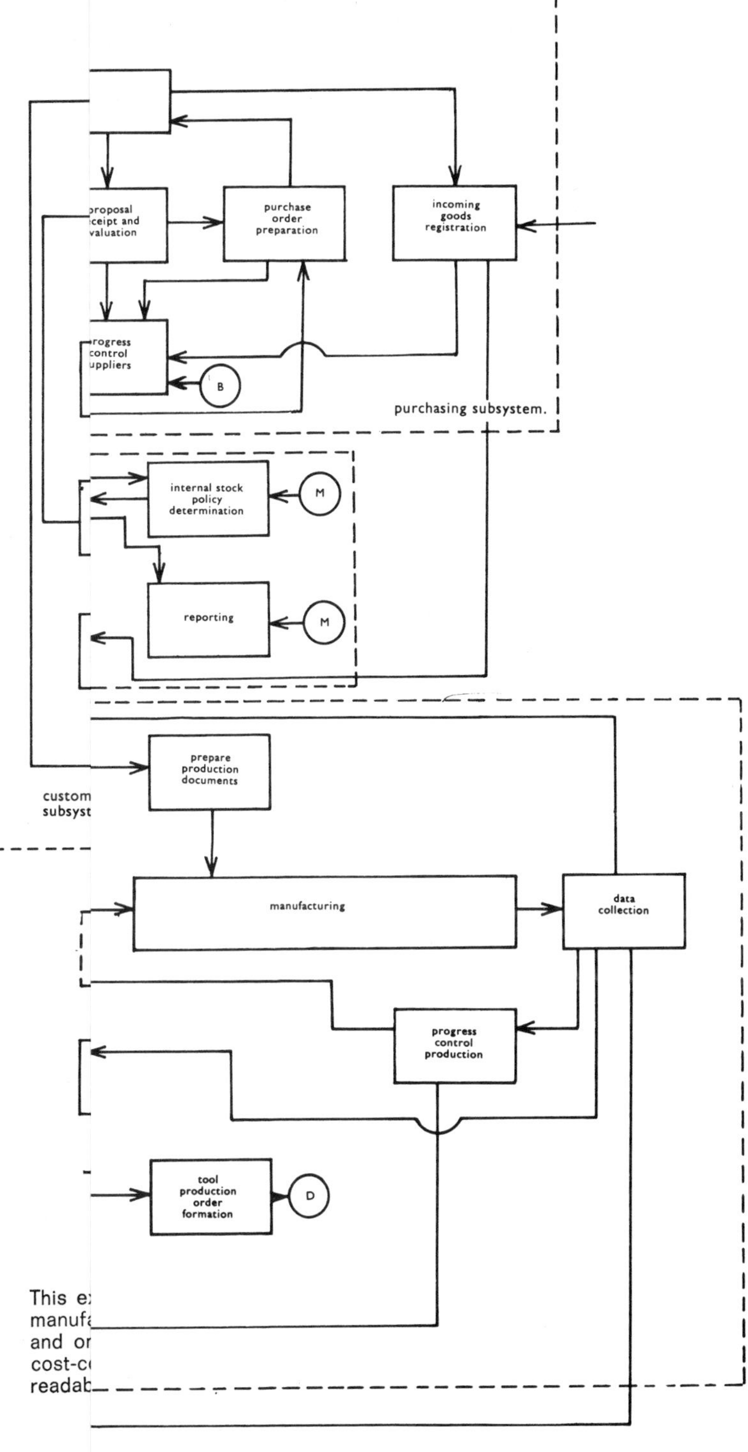

This e
manufa
and or
cost-c
readab

Step 3-3.4: Determine general design requirements and constraints

The purpose of this step is to determine the requirements and constraints that set limitations and rules for the design of the new information system. The parameters derived at this stage are essential to guide the project team during the system design effort. It is suggested that the requirements and constraints be evaluated with respect to maintainability, flexibility, compatibility, expandability, hardware and software configuration and efficiency of data processing.

Maintainability

Maintainability is the capacity of the system to accept changes ranging in severity from the initial debugging of programs to large-scale modifications to keep abreast of the latest techniques.

Flexibility

Flexibility is the capacity of a system to accept major changes in programs or procedures. For a business to be viable in a constantly changing environment, it must be capable of adapting to these changes e.g. by manufacturing new products. If the organization must be flexible, then so must the information system that supports it.

The best way to achieve both maintainability and flexibility is to make the system design modular. Changes can then be implemented, tested and evaluated on a single subsystem, procedure, program, routine or subroutine without disturbing the rest of the system. If the information and control requirements are dynamic, in that process and outputs are likely to change frequently, it might be desirable to direct the system design activity more specifically towards the creation and maintenance of a data base. This data base should contain all the information expected to be relevant to the new system in such a way that it is also ensured that information can be retrieved and processed by means of keys and rules as yet not determined.

Compatibility

Is the system intended to serve more than one user, and does this impose any special design constraints? If specific application software must be used for any function or subsystem, this will create additional requirements, and possibly constraints, for the new system.

Expandability

How can the system be made open-ended, in order that it can be expanded at a later date to accommodate problem areas not covered by the present systems effort?

Hardware and software configuration

If a hardware and software configuration is already in use, or if a particular manufacturer's hardware and/or software must be used, then this will impose requirements and constraints on the new system.
The situation can occur that a predetermined hard- and software configuration must be used, or that only additions to the present configuration can be considered, e.g. addition of external stores.

Efficiency of data processing

The design effort must result in a system which can be operated within the available budgets. This implies a certain performance of the data processing operations within the system. The determination of operating costs is treated in 3-2.4.

Results

Make a list of all requirements and constraints which direct the general design, and give a detailed description of each constraint or requirement e.g. computer configuration, available budgets, planned usage of application software, etc.

The impact of these requirements upon the design, and the methodology available to assist in the design of a system according the requirements, is described in the next activity, design new system.

Activity 3-4: Design new system

The purpose of this activity is to create a new information system, according to the requirements and constraints posed in 3-3.3 and 3-3.4. The subsequent development and implementation of this system must lead to the realization of the detailed objectives dealt with in 3-3.1. The overall approach advocated in this activity includes:

- a design of the information flow which emphasizes the control of the new system over the operations involved within the organization by identifying and detailing the different functions involved and the relationships between these functions;
- the transformation of this information flow into a data processing flow. The project team is at this stage oriented to questions such as:
  - For which functions do we need a computer?
  - Which data elements are required?
  - How do we organize the data in system files?
  - What kind of equipment is required?

The approach is divided into the following four steps:
3-4.1 design new information flow;
3-4.2 prepare system file design;
3-4.3 study data processing aspects;
3-4.4 prepare hardware and software requirements.

Because of the close relationship between file organization and the usage of files by the processing of data, it is recommended that steps 3-4.2 and 3-4.3 be performed concurrently.

In volume 6 a number of techniques are described which can be applied to system design. Some of the more important techniques are:

- charting technique (6-2.2);
- gridcharting (6-2.3);
- decision tables (6-2.4);
- identification of system elements and data objects (6-4.1);
- data organization (6-4.2);
- application packages (6-4.4);
- control techniques (6-5).

Step 3-4.1: Design new information flow

The purpose of this first step in system design is to present the new system graphically in the form of an information flow, and to define all the elements of the information flow. This information flow is the foundation of the new system, and its quality will directly affect the quality of system development as well as of system operation. This step can be explained by the following design check-list.

Construct information flow

Combine the functions identified and documented on function worksheet in 3-3.3 in one information flow, taking the following into consideration:

- start with the output of a function which directly controls the product flow and work backwards, thus going from the control and feedback points in the product flow to the controlling and administrative functions in the information flow;
- another approach often used is to start with trigger actions and work forwards as described in 3-2.3 for the analysis of the present information flow. Consequently the same methodology can be used, but the approach will be different;
- keep the flow as simple and straightforward as possible. When not all relationships can be viewed at the same time, select those functions which deal with one aspect of the business operations, e.g. planning and progress control, or budgeting and cost control.
  After having made an information flow depicting the relationships of the functions for one aspect, the same can be done for other aspects, either separately or by adding them to the information flow originally focused upon one aspect. This approach has the merit that the project team can deal with one aspect or one control parameter at a time;
- when the number of functions is too large to be handled conveniently, it can be useful to combine a number of functions, already specified in detail, in order to decrease the number of "boxes" to be dealt with. Afterwards, these individual boxes can be detailed and hooked into the overall information flow;
- yet another approach is to make a flow of the functions for each problem area, and to prepare the flow for the system by combining these flows. This approach is open to the danger of sub-optimization, due to the fact that the flow is not constructed from a systems point of view, but pays too much attention to the individual problem areas;
- do not be concerned at this stage with a selection of those functions which are best fitted for computer applications;
- beware of the differences in frequency between I/O's of the different functions. Detect the principal flow, i.e. the one with the highest demands in terms of frequency and/or volume;

- try to eliminate intermediate documents or similar products used in less integrated or in manual systems, by combining, in the flow, operations of more or less the same frequency;
- try to incorporate as many related operations as possible into the principal flow;
- investigate whether reports can be eliminated by adding some data fields to related reports, or by changing the frequency of the latter;
- plan carefully at what stage checks must be incorporated in the flow. Lay the utmost emphasis on input control directly at the data source. Checks can be effected more efficiently there than at a later stage, owing to knowledge of the content of the data, and to rapid correction possibilities;
- check if all requirements are covered, and if all relationships have been considered;
- use the standard flowcharting technique, 6-2.2.

To illustrate this step, an example at conceptual level of a socalled new information flow dealing with one aspect of a system is given on page 2A. This new information flow should be detailed by means of function worksheets for each function involved.

Develop alternative solutions

Develop alternative solutions; do not be satisfied with the first solution. The project team must find at least two or three possibilities for the new information flow.

Evaluate solutions

Evaluate the different solutions by comparing the results with the requirements defined in activity 3-3.
The methodology described for the evaluation of the present system, is useful, and the information flow performance checklist (3-2.3) can be of value. The use of models (3-2.4) can be applied to the evaluation of the design of the new system as well as to the evaluation of the present system.

What to do when stuck

When stuck, get out of the ivory tower. Use for example the brainstorming technique, to find different solutions and alternative approaches. Discuss the problems with other people from whom response and understanding can be expected. Try to take distance from a possible solution, and have a receptive ear for the comments of others. Be critical of your own ideas.

Keep the design on detail level

Time pressure must not seduce the team into keeping the design on a conceptual level. Leaving too many details for the system development phase will cause delays in the development of the system.

Step 3-4.2: Prepare system file design

It is the purpose of this step to design only the system files. A system file is a file which will be used by more than one subsystem. This distinction is made to obviate the necessity of creating intermediate files, such as input and output files. In general, each such file can be considered as a potential system file; however, when the functions concerned will be combined in one subsystem, the file is a subsystem file.

A general file design must be created in order to be able to:

- design a data processing flow (3-4.3). The reason for this is that for consolidated files, the file organization and structure is of paramount importance for the layout of the data processing flow;
- prepare hardware and software requirements (3-4.4). The design of file layout and file organization is closely related to the external stores upon which files will be stored. When specific hardware constraints exist, they are formulated under general design requirements and these constraints should be considered during this step;
- divide the system into subsystems which have as few information exchange interfaces as possible (3-5).

The grouping of data elements into files must be based upon the information flow, which shows the relationships between functions and defines the functions and data elements required.

Consolidated file approach

An approach, highly efficient considering the saving in operating costs and the reduction of the problems of file maintenance and file compatibility possible, is the consolidated file approach.

A consolidated file brings together all known and envisaged data fields or elements which can be related to a common denominator, file item or "information object", independently of its specific usage for a specific output, department, type of processing run or source; for example a product, a customer, a tool. This provides a real integrating force for the systems effort, as it makes the project team concentrate on the relationships throughout the whole system. A consolidated file can replace a number of relatively independent existing files which in the present situation may even belong to different departments. Thus a file is composed which will become the joint concern of a number of users. This stimulates integration as a result of shared responsibility for the quality of the file content. This approach imposes quite a heavy file clean-up task in order to re-establish consistency in the data derived from different sources.

The methodology described for this step is especially suited to the consolidated file approach, because this approach is the best one for the purpose of constructing the data base which must be considered as the backbone of an information system. Before following the methodology involved, a study in depth of the different data organization methods and techniques described in 6-4.2 is recommended.

Preliminary hardware and software selection

The latitude of the project team in file design is highly influenced by the type of external stores applied. The selection of hardware and software is discussed in 3-4.4, and before going into this step it is recommended that a rough selection of available hardware and software be made, taking budgetary limitations into account, in order to be able to take hardware constraints into consideration during file design. This results in a survey of the different types of store units available. Use this survey during the file design effort.

Design aids

The design of files means bridging the gap between functions which are to be performed by means of the computer and the data elements which are required for this execution.
The file design has two aspects:

- the allocation of data elements into the files;
- evaluation of the file usage in performing the functions.

In balancing these aspects many solutions are possible; however, the performance is highly dependent on the choice.

In the example below the relationships and their means of representation are depicted.

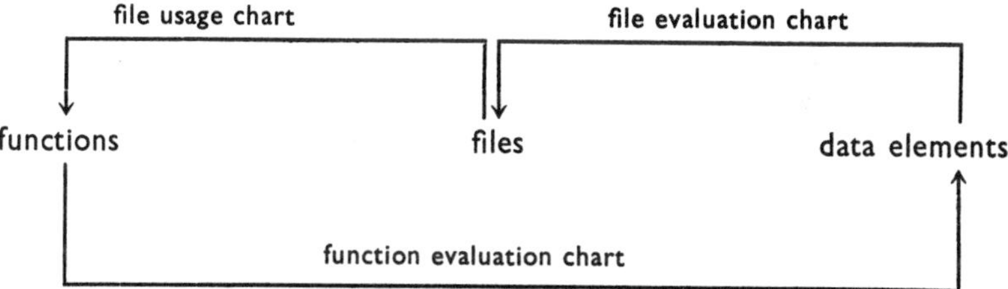

The file usage chart and file evaluation chart are helpful tools in evaluating the file design; they give a compact survey of the data concerned.

Function evaluation chart

Establish data relationships. The most important relationship between functions, in developing a file concept, is the use of common data. A gridchart of functions versus data fields should be prepared, using the function worksheets and form and file description sheets already prepared. An example of a function evaluation chart is shown in page 6.

File evaluation chart

In general, data elements belong to an object, such as a product, a tool or a supplier; or to a relationship between objects, such as a parts list, an order, or a transaction. These relationships can be of two different types: a relationship between objects of the same category, e.g. a parts list is a relationship between two

FUNCTION EVALUATION CHART

system : production control
subsystem : production planning
prev. issue:

project no. :
chapter/sect.:
page :
issued :

data elements	functions									
	cal-culation	detail planning	dis-patching	tool regi-stration	materials planning	report-ing	regis-tration			
part number	×	×	×	×	×	×	×			
part name	×	×	×	×	×	×	×			
number of operation	×	×	×			×				
cost machine group	×					×	×			
tool number	×			×						
etc.										

FILE EVALUATION CHART

system : production control
subsystem : production planning
prev. issue:

project no. :
chapter/sect.:
page :
issued :

data elements	files									
	product master	job order master	machine master	tool master	product struc-ture	product machine structure	job machine structure	job structure		
part number	×									
part name	×									
number of operation	×									
cost machine group			×							
tool number				×						
order number		×								
etc.										

FILE USAGE CHART

system : production control
subsystem : production planning
prev. issue:

project no. :
chapter/sect.:
page :
issued :

files	functions									
	cal-culation	detail planning	dis-patching	tool regis-tration	materials planning	reporting	regis-tration			
product master	×	×	×	×	×	×	×			
job order master	×	×	×							
machine master	×	×	×			×	×			
tool master	×			×						
etc.										

different products; or a relationship between objects of two different categories e.g. an order is a relationship between a customer and a product. These relationships are displayed in a file evaluation chart on page 6.

File usage chart

The relationship between functions and files is of the utmost importance for the division of the system into subsystems, and will be dealt with in more detail in activity 3-5.
See page 6 for an example of the file usage chart.

Master or relation file

It is necessary to identify the different objects, and the relationships between objects, and to determine which data elements of the function evaluation chart refer to which object or relationship.

Individual access
A file should be defined as an object or master file when individual access to the file items is required; relationships do not require independent access and should be stored in a separate file when (dynamic) multiple "where-used" relationships exist. For example in a product information file each product can be a component of an undefined number of higher assemblies; however in a resource file each item of resource is subordinated to only one higher level resource.

Multiple relations
The question of where to allocate data elements which can be assigned to more than one object or relationship is sometimes difficult to resolve. For example, the lead time of a product can be considered as a data element belonging to a product, but it can also be assigned to the relationship between products, because the lead time can be dependent on the assembly in which the product is used.

In these cases, apply the general rule to allocate data elements in the file which results in minimum total file size. In most cases, this will be the master file. Transfer data elements to the relation files only when there are very good arguments, based upon the fact that it is typical "condition" information, or upon frequency of usage.

Object or relation
The answer to the question whether a data field is an object or a relationship may seem obvious; however, in some cases it gives rise to problems. For example, in network planning, activities and events can each be considered both as objects and as relationships. In such cases, it is best to let minimum total file size prevail as a general rule. However, many other arguments effect the decision.

Functional system file design
Example based on the example of information flow shown in 3-4.1.

Examples of content of the files:

1 • SUPPLIER
- supplier identification
- address
- discount rules – General
- etc.

2 • SUPPLIER RELATION
- supplier reference
- product reference
- leadtime
- specific discount rules
- etc.

3 • MAIN-ORDER PRODUCTION RELATION
- product reference
- main-activity reference
- quantity
- time-frozen
- etc.

4 • MAIN ORDER RESOURCE RELATION
- resource reference
- main-activity reference
- capacity volume
- etc.

6 • JOB
- job identification
- job description
- start time
- etc.

5 • ROUTING
- product reference
- resource reference
- cycle time
- etc.

7 • PRODUCTION ORDER
- product reference
- due date
- order identification
- etc.

8 • RESOURCE
- resource identification
- capacity/period
- load/period
- etc.

9 • TOOL
- tool identification
- tool availability/period
- location
- etc.

10 • CUSTOMER
- customer identification
- customer name
- customer address
- customer general delivery conditions
- etc.

11 • ORDER
- order identification
- commercial delivery date
- status of order
- quantity for each product
- etc.

12 • MAIN ORDER ACTIVITY
- project-activity identification
- activity duration
- activity dates
- etc.

13 • INTER ACTIVITY RELATION
- event identification
- preceding activity
- following activity
- event times
- etc.

14 • PRODUCT
- product identification
- product name
- construction dept.
- etc.

15 • INTER PRODUCT RELATION
- quantity
- where in product
- consist of product
- etc.

16 • DETAIL ORDER
- order identification
- order quantity
- order due date
- etc.

17 • SUPPLIER ORDER
- supplier order identification
- due date
- contents
- etc.

18 • TOOL-ROUTING RELATION
- tool reference
- routing reference
- special conditions
- etc.

19 • JOB-TOOL RELATION
- job reference
- tool reference
- date required
- etc.

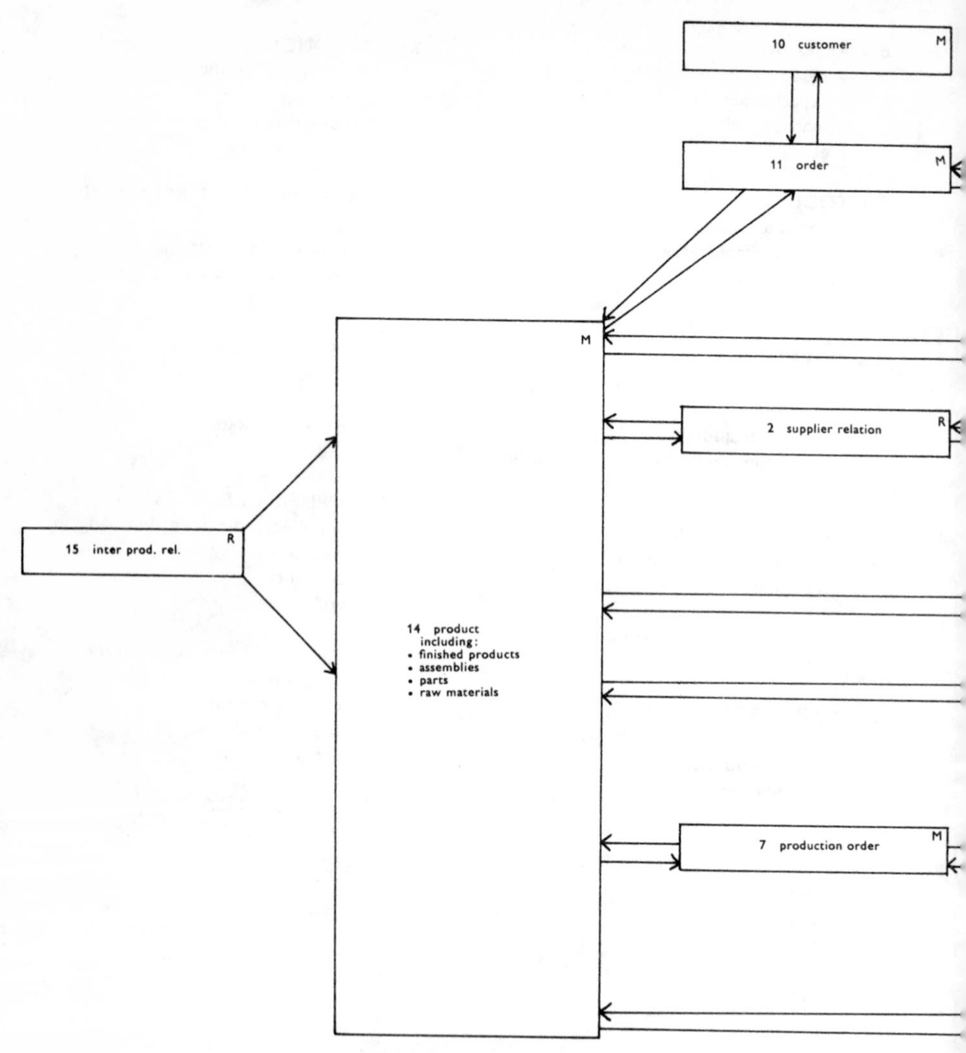

Functional system file design
Example based on the example of information flow shown in 3-4.1.

Legend:
M = Master
R = Relation or structure

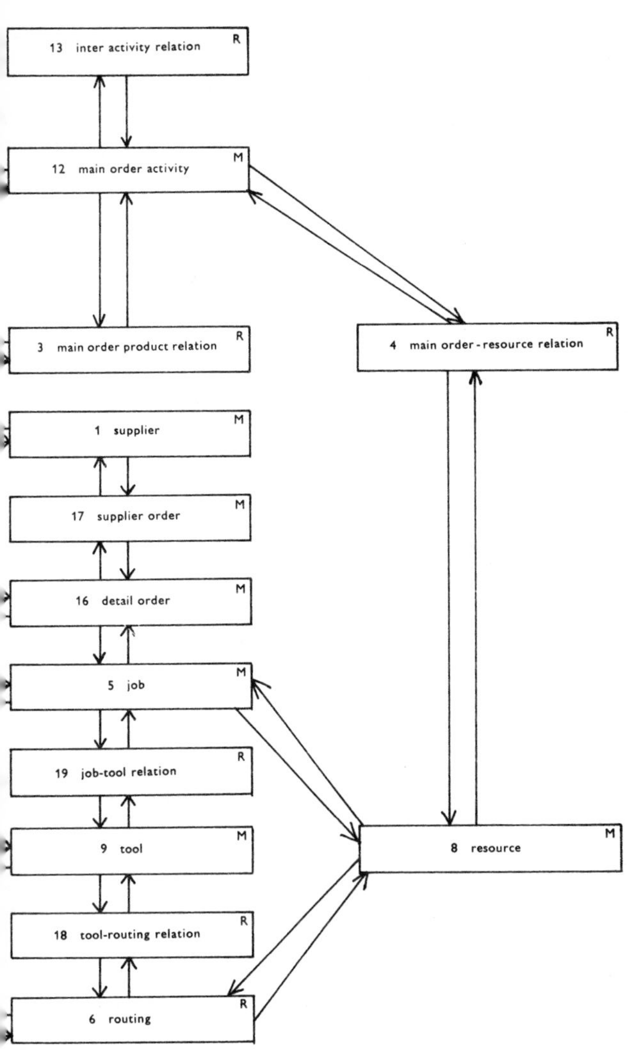

13 inter activity relation
R
12 main order activity
M
3 main order product relation
R
4 main order - resource relation
R
1 supplier
M
17 supplier order
M
16 detail order
M
5 job
M
19 job-tool relation
R
9 tool
M
8 resource
M
18 tool-routing relation
R
6 routing
R

For example:

- To which of the objects is direct access most frequently required?
- Is one of the two objects coded in such a manner that sequencing or record key transformation is facilitated? (6-6.4).
- Is it possible to combine the two objects into one file with a number of pointers, instead of using separate relationship files?

Documentation

The result is a list of all data elements for each file, by means of a form and file description sheet, and a file evaluation chart.

Functional file design

Combine all files in a functional file design which shows the relationships between them. An example is shown in page 10 and a limited number of data elements is given for each system file.

File structure chart

There is another method of defining the file organization, i.e. by means of a gridchart indicating for each relationship, whether it is a direct relationship or a chain. The figure in page 13 shows a file structure chart in which a file design is presented in this manner. This type of chart is especially recommended for very complex files with many chains, which could hardly be shown with the layout of page 10.

Detailed remarks

The following detailed remarks are instructive in relation to the text of 3-4.3:

- classify the information needed for the outputs into new and existing data, or in other words, into transaction data and file data. All new transaction data which will be needed later on must be temporarily stored;
- classify information needed for file(s) or to be deleted from file(s) into:
  — permanent data;
  — optional data (temporary storage of transaction data).
  (This classification into types of information gives an understanding of the organization of files and the structure of required inputs);
- be alert for additional information which will be required on source documents, e.g. transaction codes, record identification codes and check data. A transaction code is necessary to indicate the type of processing required; record identification codes might replace existing alphanumeric debtor or product codes: and finally, check data will be necessary for safeguarding the quality of the information;
- try to store a data field in no more than one file. Exceptions to this recommendation are identification and reference fields;
- try to arrange data fields in files in such a way that reports and responses to enquiries require reference to as small a number of files as possible;
- where many constraints concerning input design exist, try to group data fields according to the content of the source documents.

FILE STRUCTURE CHART

system :
subsystem : Manufacturing control
prev. issue:

project no. :
chapter/sect. :
page :
issued :

files	files									
	product	inter prod. rel.	detail order	job	resource	job-tool rel.	tool	routing	tool-routing rel.	prod. order
product		C	C					C		
inter prod. rel.	D									
detail order	D			C						
job	D		D		D	C		C		
resource				C						
job-tool rel.				D			D			
tool						C			C	C
routing	D				D				C	
tool-routing rel.							D	D		
prod. order	D						D			

Example: Details of functional system file design of preceding example for the following files:

- product;
- inter product relation;
- detail order;
- job;
- resource;
- job-tool relation;
- tool;
- tool-routing relation;
- routing;
- production order.

The chart should be read from left to right; for example the job file has a direct pointer to detail orders and recources while a chain is layed for each job over the job-tool relations.
Each direct pointer, as well as each chain can be realized by means of an actual or a symbolic key.

C = Chain D = Direct pointer

Effects on external stores

Make a rough calculation of the net size of each file, using estimated record lengths and quantities. Be careful with the estimates of the file sizes; often it turns out that rough figures which are in wide use within the organization are far from the truth. This is due to the fact that most figures are based on volumes over a given period, and not on total amount available. Besides this complication, there is a difference between "dead" and "live" information concerning the different objects. The decision on what is considered to be "dead", and must not be kept and maintained in external stores, is important for file size determination.

Especially when direct access stores are planned, it is of the utmost importance to pay attention to accurate file size determination. Type and number of external stores is based upon these estimates; when great deviations in size occur, serious problems arise during the implementation, causing changes of equipment configuration and/or file organization and/or processing flow.

Method of splitting up files

When, during the design of the files, it turns out that the size of one or more files is beyond the capacity of the available stores, the file design must be adapted by one of the following means.

Division by class of object

Dividing one master file with dependent relation files into different classes of the object; e.g. a product master file into a file for products belonging to product range *A* and a file for products belonging to product range *B*. A premise is that not much overlap between the two classes exists, because this would result in extra screening, file creation and maintenance.

Function-oriented division

Dividing each logical record of a file into a number of physical parts which are function-oriented. E.g. in a product master file, all data elements required specifically for the preparation of a purchase order are placed together in one part, and all data elements required specifically for the preparation of service documentation are put in another. Next to these parts, which contain information for the execution of one or more functions, there is a general part which holds all the key data elements. The disadvantage of this solution is that duplication of data elements within one logical record might be necessary. Each storage unit contains a part of each logical record of all products; this requires structurally identical physical records in order to be able to access all files with the same central index file or the same key.

This causes a problem of reservation of locations on those units where a physical record is stored which is not yet filled with data elements, while others are already filled in. It also results in a file creation and updating problem which affects the complete file, because the number of storage units for any one file may not exceed the number of units available for this type of store.

Division according to activity rates

Dividing the file into an active file with a high activity rate and an inactive file with a lower activity rate, when there exists a discrepancy between the frequency of file usage and the use of categories of data elements within the file. If on the one hand the run frequency is relatively high, and if on the other the volume of a number of data fields which are rarely used for updating or output processing is relatively large, the cost of file processing in a tape situation or disk occupancy for this number of data fields can become prohibitive. In these special cases a secondary file or inactive file with, in principle, the same identification keys, will have to be designed.

Machine oriented file organization

For each system file the functional file organization as specified should be translated into a machine or external store oriented organization. The description of the different methods available and the advantages and disadvantages of each, are described in the technique data organization (6-4.2).

Documentation

Each file must be documented, giving consideration to the following:

identification
- file number;
- file name.

purpose
- a short description of the reasons why this file is needed.

characteristics
- e.g.:
  - master file;
  - transaction file;
  - table file;
  - inactive file.

contents
- a listing of:
  - the kinds of record appearing in the file, with connecting record identification;
  - average and maximum number of each record for each file item;
  - sequence of the records.

volume
- the average and maximum numbers of records which can occur in a file, the fixed, or average and maximum sizes for each type or record, and the average and maximum number of characters (= number of records × record length).

file organization
- the type of access, e.g.:
  - sequential;
  - indexed sequential;

— direct addressing;
— relative addressing and the sequence of sequential files in terms of major/intermediate/minor.

planned storage media and location
- punched cards;
- magnetic tape;
- disk
  - upper limit;
  - lower limit.

retention
- list the following aspects:

reason	period	media
successive processing		
audit trail		
legal requirements		
company policy		

forms
- the form and file description sheet (3-2.3) and the disk file layout (4-1.3) can be used for documentation; however, in many cases, an appendix will be necessary to cover the different subjects in sufficient detail.

Detailed file layout

The more detailed layout and organization of files including record keys, record counts, blocking factors, compare portions, and a defined sequence of data elements within each record, is deferred to 4-1.3.

Step 3-4.3: Study data processing aspects

At this stage the project is concerned with the data processing aspects of the information flow. As described in 3-4.1, the elements of the information flow are functions to be performed in order to meet the system objectives. On the other hand, a data processing flow is focused on the application of equipment for the execution of these functions. The basic elements of a data processing flow are programs to be executed.
It is the intention of this step to concentrate on the data processing aspects of the system in order to be able to:

- prepare a file design (3-4.2);
- prepare hardware and software requirements (3-4.4);
- assure a well-reasoned division of the system into subsystems from a data processing point of view (3-5).

The detailed layout of the data processing flow is made during the development of the subsystems (4-1.2). However, major decisions concerning the splitting up of functions into programs can be taken during this step. During this step the project team should take into account the general design requirements formulated in 3-3.4.

The output consists of:

- a survey of a major programs which are foreseen;
- a list of functions which are grouped according to data processing aspects, and which will be completely or partially combined in programming;
- a rough sketch of the data processing flow which highlights major programs.

Functions to be performed by computer

Select those functions which can be executed with the assistance of data processing equipment. Some important factors for the presentation of this decision are:

- Do exceptions to the general processing rules of the function exist, and is mechanical identification of these exceptions possible?
- Do excessive peak loads exist which cause delay in a manual procedure, but which can be handled by data processing equipment without extra delay?
- Is the processing to be performed very complex, requiring automatic data processing because manual execution is not possible due to time consuming complex calculations?
- Are volumes of data involved which can be handled most economically by data processing equipment? In most cases, the decision whether or not to use data processing equipment will be clear-cut. It is worthy of note at this stage that a detailed cost comparison for an individual function does not provide a basis for the decision whether or not to use a computer. Cost and benefit calculations must be made for the system as a whole; some functions will be money-makers, others money-losers. However, it may be required that both are performed by computer in order to meet the system objectives.

Functions to be supported by computer

Select those functions which can be supported by information to be processed, retrieved and issued with the assistance of data processing equipment. The functions which will not be executed by data processing equipment due to their nature, (e.g. no defined decision pattern underlies the function) can often be facilitated by specific information required for decision making. This can lead to the identification of functions which have only reporting tasks.

Output presentation method

For the outputs already defined in 3-4.1 for each function, as well as for the additional information to be specified in this step, it is necessary to determine the output presentation method. The output presentation method is a key factor for equipment selection, as well as for the design of the data processing flow. Output presentation methods are:

Listing report
Generally the end result of a computer run is a detailed report of considerable volume. This usually corresponds to requirements for lengthy detailed reports based upon large files, and/or voluminous inputs when response time is not a critical factor.

Tabular report
The computer prints only the subtotals and totals instead of a complete listing.

Exception report
Typically, a by-product output of other processing, such as file updating. Output is usually selective and brief, such as the reporting of items reaching the re-order point in an inventory control system.

Graphical display
Plot or line drawing, usually representing the quantitative asscciation of numerical data; may be either online or offline.

Preprinted form
Detailed item information such as invoices, purchase orders, cheques, etc.

Enquiry response
Usually an online reply to a specific enquiry with direct access to the data requested, resulting in a brief item or summary of information and having a fast response time.

Determine processing mode

After all those functions which will be executed with, or supported by, data processing equipment are identified, and the output presentation methods are determined, the processing approach must be chosen. A brief description of the main characteristics of the different approaches to processing is given.

Sequential batch processing
Under this approach, a master file, or a number of files with identical sequence usually on magnetic tape, is updated or referenced on each machine run. It is most frequently used for large master files. Due to the collection of transactions into batches, and to the necessity of sorting all inputs into the same sequence as the master file, this method usually results in a rather slow system response time. Long-interval batching may be required to justify a computer run against the entire master file, especially if the number of transactions is rather small.

Random batch processing
An input transaction can be processed against many files at the same time without presorting. However, by the user intended processing sequence should be taken into account. This method is capable of rapid response time, since input batches can be reduced to the point of simply awaiting availability, with the length of each run dependent mainly upon input processing time. Since file updating transactions erase prior file data, processing controls and audit trails become more difficult, and more important, than with tape systems. Formerly, this method was most often used with relatively small master files; but with large capacity, direct-access stores presently available, file size is becoming a less important consideration.

Random online processing
Making the computer available on demand in real-time. Files can immediately reflect the occurrence of an event, with continuous current data-response capability. This method provides the most rapid response time, particularly for remote users linked through transmission lines.

Factors influencing the processing mode

For each function, it is necessary to select the most suitable processing modes. Some aspects to be considered in the determination of the processing mode for each function include:

Response time
Elapsed time from enquiry (or condition) to reply, whether in seconds or hours. Quick response time will require brief exception notice output; longer response can utilize any form of output.

Report detail
More detailed reports require listing, unless the number of records is low.

File depth and usage
Whether it is necessary to examine the entire file, or a portion of it, or to gain immediate access to a single item. Large numbers of file records can be accessed

for long-run listings. Although enquiries usually require access to an individual record, the retrieval of a single item may require a relatively long time, due to the fact that a number of chains or indexes must be traversed.

Traffic load
Batched requests or transactions can call for any form of output, since long runs can still be economical. Online requests should result in brief exception notices.

Output frequency and volume of requests
While low volumes of output requests can be handled on an on-call basis between or simultaneous with other jobs, it may prove impossible to handle a high volume, and still to maintain sufficiently low response times. In such cases, it may be necessary to provide additional hardware and software to deal with output requests.

Output trigger, i.e. what causes the output to come into being
Typical triggers include direct enquiry or exception conditions of file items. In the data processing flow of a system, more than one processing mode can be applied. A number of functions can be performed on a batch basis, while other functions will use data collection and enquiry stations for fast response online information handling. This produces a great variety of requirements to be satisfied by the hardware and software (3-4.4).
From a practical point of view, the hardware and software will be limited by budgetary constraints, which may result in changes in the system design. For example if a plotter is required for only one function, and assumes a load of only 5 percent, then for reasons of efficiency it is recommended not to order the plotter, but to prepare the output manually from a listing report.

Identify the major programs

As stated in the introduction to this step, the design of a data processing flow should result in a specification of the required outputs for the different functions with a minimum of costs. This implies that a different point of view must now be taken; that of optimal usage of data processing equipment for the execution of the functions within the system.
The project team will concentrate on the application of data processing equipment for the system as a whole, and not for any one function in particular. In general the team will try to combine as many functions as possible in programming, because a large number of small programs causes inefficiencies, due to:
- reading the same input file many times while performing only a part of the operations of a run;
- a great number of programs handling small input volumes, instead of one program handling a large volume of data. The large program is more efficient; set-up time is less in relation to read time;
- a great number of file updating and creation runs with few transactions, in-

stead of one file updating run with a high activity rate. This is especially true for large sequentially organized files;

- many unrelated and non-integrated processing actions instead of one integrated processing program. In one large program many controls and checks can be built in, which would have to have been handled manually or less efficiently by computer in the case of many small independent programs; also, less retrieval and file handling will be required;
- a great number of retrieval and output preparation operations using the files with relatively low activity rates, instead of efficient file handling with high activity rates. This is also especially true for sequentially organized files.

In spite of the advantages of combining as many functions as possible within one program, there are a number of considerations which limit program size, such as:

- the number of different files which can be connected to the central processing unit simultaneously; because there are only a limited number of external store control units and channels available;
- the size of the internal store. By means of overlay, however, it is possible to bypass this limitation, although possibly with resulting inefficiency;
- the frequency of execution; in general, it is not practicable to combine into one program functions which must be performed with completely different frequencies and processing modes. To do so causes inefficiency in the most frequently used program. This is true in cases of online and batch processing;
- internal control can require separate processing and screening of different inputs.

Apart from the above reasons, the size of the program is less important when non-sequentially organized files must be updated and created, because in such cases activity rate is not a measure of program efficiency.

Approaches to the formation of programs

There are two approaches to the formation of programs, namely:

- combine "horizontally" similar jobs from as many functions as possible into one program, producing e.g. a general input screening program, and a general file update and maintenance program;
- combine "vertically" different kinds of job of one or more functions, into one program, producing a program which executes input screening, file updating, output preparation, or other combinations of this kind.

Combinations of the two approaches described are possible, and will be discussed after the "horizontal" and "vertical" approaches are covered in more detail. Although no general checklist with decision criteria can be given, some advantages and disadvantages of the two approaches will be discussed.

The "horizontal" approach

- The input and output handling is covered in independent programs which use mostly slow I/O units. In a modern computer facility, these programs can be run simultaneously with processing (background) programs, "stealing" but little central processing unit time from the main processing program;

- the language requirements for complex processing and file handling programs are different. A division according to the "horizontal" approach facilitates the use of different languages, and anticipates the use of high level file handling languages;
- it facilitates documentation and maintenance, because different types of operation are completely separated;
- it helps the project team in keeping the design as simple as possible, and facilitates a straightforward system development phase;
- a disadvantage can be the possible inefficiency of the processing as a result of linking many programs together to perform a run from input to output. However, in sequential processing such a string can seldom be prevented, because intermediate sorts are required to establish proper sequences.

The vertical approach

- All processing can be performed in one program, without the use of intermediate files; the transactions can be handled completely in one program facilitating the implementation of control measures;
- overlap between input and output can be handled by third generation computers, although for a second generation computer, overlap between processing and I/O operations is possible when buffer storage is available;
- the maintenance of the program is difficult;
- the testing of the program is difficult, due to its more complex logic.

Combined approach

In modern computer programming, the horizontal and vertical approaches are often combined, because for all programs with high response time the vertical approach is required, in order to satisfy the response-time requirements, whereas, to facilitate maintenance, testing documentation, etc., the different parts of the program are defined as independent "horizontal" routines, linked together with a "vertical" main-line program to take care of the monitoring. Standard application programs can be inserted in this type of flow more easily. This method of programming is often referred to as "modular programming".

Results

Results of the study of data processing aspects are:

- a survey of functions which should preferably be combined into one subsystem from a data processing point of view. This is directly related to the file usage chart of 3-4.2 in which files versus functions are documented;
- a preliminary list of programs based on the above grouping of functions. These programs can be displayed on one or more flows showing the relationships between programs. Use flowcharting technique (6-2.2);
- a brief description of the main programs in terms of outputs, inputs, files and processes. (see for documentation standards 4-5.5).

Step 3-4.4: Prepare hardware and software requirements

Due to the great impact of type and characteristics of the equipment upon system design and development, a selection of hardware and software is required at this stage of system design.
The purpose of this step is to specify a computer configuration which will be suitable for the realization of the new system. It should be understood that not all details required for a performance evaluation of different computer configurations are available at this stage. After the development of the subsystem flow (4-1.2), the runs to be executed are specified, and an evaluation of hardware and software requirements and performance can then take place (4-1.4).

Three different situations can occur with respect to hardware and software selection:

- no hardware is available at present; equipment must be selected;
- hardware is already available, but replacement is under consideration. However, extension of the present equipment should also be considered;
- hardware is available in a configuration which is determined in advance of system design and development. The configuration is specified as a general design constraint (3-3.4). This is an undesirable state of affairs.

In this step, the approach taken is based upon the selection of new hardware. However, the technical considerations can also be applied to the extension of presently available hardware. It is a large topic in itself. A few highlights will be touched on briefly however, by giving a description of the method to be followed, and a checklist of the main criteria involved, rather than by discussing each subject in detail.

Application definition

The suitability and the performance of a configuration can be determined only in the context of a specific application or set of applications in its specific hardware and software environment.
As will be shown in 4-1.2, the application should be expressed in runs to be performed and files to be used. The problem in this substep is that the application is not yet specified in runs, but by means of a system design documented as an information flow, function worksheets, file designs, etc. (see 3-4.1, 3-4.2, 3-4.3). This implies that the definition of the application at this moment does not give enough information for a detailed performance comparison of different configurations. However, the suitability of the different configurations can be determined in terms of the general requirements which the computer configuration should fulfil in order to realize the system.

Bench-mark problems

When for some reason the project team cannot delay the detailed performance evaluation until the application is specified in more detail, it is necessary to start a separate effort, namely the construction or selection of a bench-mark problem as a yardstick, for performance comparison purposes. The project team should be aware of the dangers attendant upon the use of bench-mark problems. The results are only as good as the match of the bench-mark problem to the actual application. In spite of this, and the general recommendation not to spend too much time on the definition of bench-mark problems which might prove to have been useless, some comments concerning bench-mark problem utilization will be given.

A bench-mark performance comparison is best suited to the comparison of two different computer configurations by means of a standard program or bench-mark.

Throughput times and calculations of a specific application are much more difficult to derive from the use of bench-marks. After selection, each program in the application to be assessed must be specified, in terms of realistic estimates for set-up time, compilation time, I/O operation time, printer time, etc.

Example

Thus they relate an application to one or more bench-marks. The result of this process will be to produce data similar to that shown in the following figure, which is an example of an extension timing table.

run name	set-up		compilation		production		printer	
	bench-mark	factor	bench-mark	factor	bench-mark	factor	bench-mark	factor
T-A sort	S1	1.0	S1	0.8	S1	2.0	—	0
L-A update	V1	1.5	V1	2.0	V1	1.0	P1	2.4
etc.								

Example of an extension timing table for computer XYZ.

The second line illustrates the basic method. Thus, the time required for the 'L-A UPDATE' run is estimated at 1.5 times that of the '1' bench-mark. Its compilation time is estimated to be 2.0 times that of the '1', because of its complexity. Its actual running time will be the same as '1' probably because of small volumes. Extension timing tables of this type allow the project team to time the bench-mark problems, and then to produce a detailed estimate for the total application.

Evaluation of results

In order to produce realistic estimates, the bench-mark problems must be programmed by a "typical" programmer in the compiler language to be used. It is desirable that the same person programs for every machine or configuration to be tested; otherwise, the equipment may not be the thing that is being rated, but rather the relative skill of the programmers.

Currently, a number of proposals for standard sets of bench-marks are being studied. These proposals may at some future date make available audited bench-mark times, so that selection can be done without requiring special work on the part of the equipment suppliers.

As will have become clear by the foregoing, critical points in using bench-mark problems are the definition of the actual application, the definition of the bench-mark, and the comparison of the actual application with a bench-mark.

Specification checklist

In what terms should the application be defined in order to be able to determine which computer configurations are suitable for the system realization? The answer to this question should cover four main aspects, namely: files, processes, outputs and inputs.

All relevant facts should be collected from the system specification as prepared so far. As a general rule, it is necessary to take future requirements into account. This can lead to a specification of the application in two stages, e.g. the requirements posed by the application which is operational over one or two years, and requirements to be fulfilled after that period of time.

Files (see 3-4.3)

- Size of files, including rate of growth;
- organization of files. A general decision on tape, disk, or a combination of both has to be made. Although the detailed file organization is often not yet specified, a reliable file size estimate can be made by using a safety factor as described in 3-4.2;
- number of files to be accessible at the same time. This number can easily increase in the coming years, due to the integration of different subsystems and to the shorter response time requirements which will be imposed upon the system in future;
- number of files which should be accessible at the same time, but which cannot be stored on the same external store for reasons of retrieval efficiency;
- activity rate of the different files;
- length of the logical records;
- layout of the logical records.

Processes (see 3-4.1, 3-4.3)

- An estimate of the sizes of the different programs to be designed. Programs are not yet specified, although 3-4.3 should give enough information to serve as a basis for estimating storage requirements;
- the processing mode in which the programs will be executed; is the system

planned to be operated only with random batch processing, or is random online processing also a requirement for the near future? It must be realized that the processing mode determines the software level required;

- the number of programs to be executed;
- the frequency with which the different programs will be executed.

Outputs

- Volume and growth rate;
- frequency, batch or random delivery;
- method of presentation;
- flexibility in presentation and content;
- logical record layout.

Inputs

- Volume and growth rate;
- frequency, batch or random delivery;
- input/output response time;
- method of presentation;
- flexibility in presentation and content;
- logical record layout.

It is important to keep the application definition as general as possible, to avoid highly specialized solutions which can be covered by one manufacturer only. However, "general" does not imply vague. In all cases the definition should be strong enough to serve as a basis of comparison of different types of computer configuration.

Request for proposal

The performance of this substep overlaps that of the next substep which is configuration definition. However, before starting to specify a computer configuration, at least some members of the steering committee and the project team should make themselves familiar with the specific types of equipment currently available, in order to form an opinion on their relative advantages and disadvantages in relation to the system design. Some general aids to this end are a visit to the showrooms of several suppliers, a visit to running installations at government and private enterprises, meetings with manufacturing representatives, attending seminars and lectures on A.D.P., and a review of A.D.P. literature concerning equipment evaluation.

After this general introduction, the steering committee should restrict the request for a proposal to no more than three manufacturers, in whose proposals the steering committee feels that it may place confidence.

The request for a proposal should contain all information concerning the application, as described on the previous pages, and in addition such important information as the scheduled delivery date of the equipment, the price range in which the equipment should fall, and considerations concerning lease, rent or buy of the equipment.

Before the proposals are requested, determine the exact criteria that will be used for selection. Bias will inevitably be present if selection methods are determined after the proposals have been received. Be realistic in defining these criteria, and try to make certain that they will predict reliably the impact of the equipment to be selected on the success of the installation.

The user should make clear to the supplier what he expects from a proposal, and which specific criteria will be considered for the appraisal of the proposals.

The appendix to this step is a checklist which surveys all criteria by which the proposals could be appraised. Two main aspects are:

- the user interfaces A.D.P. equipment through its software. The system actually evaluated must include the compilers, the operating system, and the hardware itself. Criteria such as modularity, efficiency in productive use, etc. must be applied to the total software/hardware configuration;
- organizational requirements for support in training, application software, maintenance, and other services should be stated in writing, and developed to a level which permits the making of realistic plans and commitments.

Configuration definition

The definition of the computer configuration is a task for both the user and the different suppliers. In this substep the user should focus attention in the first place upon the creation of different configurations which could possibly serve his purpose, in order to get a feeling for the variety of solutions which can be expected in the proposals. The project team should not at this stage of equipment requirements definition stick to one or two possible solutions, or spend time on a detailed calculation of performances of these configurations, for two reasons. First, it is desirable to keep the different solutions open until the proposals are received and properly evaluated. Second, a performance calculation based on hardware and software specifications derived from brochures and manuals is hardly possible.

At the end of this substep, the project team should have gained a feeling for the benefits of the different solutions, each of which will meet to a different extent the requirements posed by the application. Although the team members may have strong opinions, they must nevertheless take an objective viewpoint in evaluating the different proposals, any one of which might open possibilities which they had not yet foreseen.
During the detailed reconnaissance of the different solutions, the project team should use the equipment selection checklist which is given at the end of this activity for the evaluation of their own findings, and should moreover concentrate upon the following points.

Language selection
The project team should determine which languages should be selected for the system. See 6-6.2, programming language selection.

Internal store capacity

- Store use of the programs containing the main part of the system logic. Analyze the part which is expected to produce the highest store requirements. Consider reducing these to smaller parts, to minimize equipment costs. Ensure that these reduced costs are in fact reducing overall system operating costs, since breaking jobs into smaller, more numerous runs, increases running time, and may also sacrifice other system benefits, and inhibit growth potential;
- core requirements posed by the monitor, which is of course dependent on the level of monitoring required; and the compilers or assemblers of the languages selected;
- input/output areas required in order to realize efficient use of channels and I/O units; for example, taking blocking factors for sequential use of disk drives into account. When the block length is much smaller than the track length, the efficiency drops;
- is multiprogramming under consideration and, if so, what core requirements are put forward by this approach?

Store units

- Determine the store units possibilities for each file depending on the file organization. The selection of file store units may have been previously decided if existing hardware is to be used, or if requirements of other systems override those of this system. Key factors to be defined, prior to store unit selection, are system file design, 3-4.2 and data organization, 6-4.2;
- file organization. Sequential, indexed sequential, random or relative organized (3-4.2);
- processing mode. Sequential batch, random batch or random online processing (3-4.3);
- capacity. Quantitative data for each record, number of records per file, number of master and work files (3-4.2);
- response times of different files;
- sequence in which the file should be accessed;
- concurrency. Number to be accessible at the same time (3-4.3);
- interchangeability. Fixed or removable store units.

Input/Output units

- Method of input of source data. Punched cards, punched tape, magnetic tape, optical or magnetic reading or online keying;
- method of output. Printer, console typewriter, punched card, punched tape, voice or visual display. Printer features, numeric, alphanumeric, special characters;
- required speed. Speed is a major consideration in selecting I/O units. It is the largest contributory factor to the relatively slow throughput time of many data processing applications in existence today. It is impractical to spend large sums of money for sophisticated central processing units with minimum execution times, only to discover afterwards that the system is input- or output-bound.

In this connection, a summary of average as well as peak loads of input and output volumes has to be made. The general statement that a business application is in most cases I/O-bound is a very dangerous one. Realize that not only the I/O-central processing unit relationship determines throughput time, but also that the simultaneous extension of different I/O units is of major importance. These aspects are both hardware and software dependant.

Data communication
The project team should consider if data communication is required in order to meet information and control requirements.
The use of data communication has a great impact upon size and performance of the hardware and software; the decision whether or not to install data communication equipment is of major importance.

Number and type of channels
Depending on the data-transfer rate required by the information system, a study should be made to determine the number and type of channels required in order to balance processing time requirements with I/O data-transfer time. The study should also include the controllers, to determine if dual controllers or second channel entry switches can improve data-transfer or direct access store utilization.

Software required for the system
Make a list of all standard and special software required in order to operate the system effectively. This includes a study of available application software. Always use standard software and avoid the use of specialities. System generation opens ways for the customizing of standard software.

Special features
Decide if any special features will be required, e.g. floating point arithmetic, a 7-track feature on 9-track tape units etc.

Evaluate proposals and select equipment

Ask the suppliers to give a presentation, in order to get an explanation of the content of the proposals. Sufficient time should be scheduled for a discussion during and after the presentation, in order to get a clear impression of the true value of each proposal. The equipment selection checklist is useful to guide the discussion and to guarantee that all criteria of importance are covered.

After the different suppliers have each had the opportunity of giving an explanation of their proposal, the project team should make an evaluation and a selection. Next to the criteria mentioned in the checklist, there are some considerations which should be brought forward before starting equipment evaluation.

Responsiveness
Is the proposal properly responsive to the request? Does the proposal reflect a proper understanding of the system, and of the problems encountered?

Clarity
Is the proposal clear in all aspects, and are all formulations capable of being interpreted in only one way?

Completeness
Does the proposal cover all the points set forth in the request for proposal and definition of the application?

Accuracy
Are all figures used accurate, and is the source of the figures mentioned? Are deviations given to specify the accuracy?

Proposal evaluation

Several techniques of equipment selection have been developed. They are sometimes referred to as cost-value and weighted-factor selection methods. Although these techniques possess some value because they propose an organized and systematic approach to equipment selection, they have many limitations which make them not generally applicable. For example, a factor which is far beyond the requirements can never get less than zero in the weighted factor analysis, while in practice it might well eliminate the supplier from serious consideration.

In order to perform the evaluation in a systematic manner, it is desirable to make one survey in which the different proposals are compared on each of the decision criteria. Such a survey gives a good overall view of the advantages and disadvantages of the different proposals, and assists in correct decision making.

The project team must constantly bear in mind that a feature which neither increases system performance in the application defined, nor reduces its operating or development cost, does not have any immediate value.
If it becomes clear from the comparisons that the proposed configurations, while meeting the stated requirements, differ too widely to enable valid conclusions to be drawn, it is desirable either to set up a selection board, or to employ experienced consultants, for the final stage of selection.

It is preferable that the steering committee should make their decision at this stage, because the computer configuration should be specified in advance of system development. In 4-1.4, it is possible to make detailed performance comparisons, and to change the configuration if strictly necessary, in order to guarantee that the equipment is adapted to the application in all details.

For this purpose a possibility is to use SCERT, an automated tool for computer performance evaluation, with which it is possible to calculate computer throughput times independently of the manufacturer.

A specification of the input generally required for SCERT is given in 4-1.4.

EQUIPMENT SELECTION CHECKLIST

The checklist is subdivided into hardware and software, general, and economic aspects.

Hardware and software requirements

A general consideration is to study a computer configuration in relation to the next larger configuration within the same series, and to pay special attention to the flexibility and compatibility within the equipment range in terms of hardware and software.

Central unit

Internal store

- What are possible capacities?
- How is the store organized?
- What is the cycle time?
- Is overlay between store access possible?
- How is protection organized?
- Is dynamic relocation of programs possible? This is of the utmost importance for multiprogramming applications.
- Number of bits per access.

Processor

- How is addressing organized?
- Index registers; how many in total, and how many available for each program?
- Floating point available as special feature?
- Representation of instructions?
- How are interrupts effected?
  This aspect influences mainly the principal possible speeds of character handling, binary arithmetic, etc.
- What are instruction execution times?
- Is decimal arithmetic available?
- What types of data representation can be handled?
- Does the processor work in a special mode?
- Is a real time clock available?
- Is code conversion possible?

Channels

- What different types of channel are available?
- What is maximum throughput rate?
- How many memory cycles are required for the storage of one character coming from an I/O unit?
- How independent are channels of the processor?
- What channel commands are available?
- Are interfaces between channels and I/O control units standardized?
- How many channels can be connected to one processor?

- How many control units can be connected to each channel?
- General characteristics of different type of control units, depending upon peripheral units and external stores.
- Applicability of dual control units.
- Are second channel entry switches available?

I/O Control units

Card-reader and card-punch units
- Column or row reader.
- Speed in cards per minute.
- Types of card which can be handled.
- Is selected stacker control available?
- How are hardware checks performed?

Input and output units

Tape punch and punched-tape reader
- Number of characters per second.
- Number of channels on tape.
- Winding equipment.
- Is second read station available?
- Hardware checks.
- Start and stop possibility?

Printer
- Speed in lines per minute.
- Number of characters per line.
- Character set.
- Exchangeability of character set.
- Maximum number of copies.
- Form formats allowed.
- Line spacing and paper skipping times.

Console
- Display
- Keyboard.
- Speed of writing or printing if possible.
- Enquiry possibilities.

Online keyboard
- Alphabetic or numeric.
- Control keys.
- Number of keyboards per control unit.

Terminal
- Alphanumeric or numeric keyboard.
- Card input/output.
- Punched tape input/output.

- Printer.
- Tabulating feature (printer).
- Magnetic tape input/output.
- Home-loop possibility.
- Speed of transmission.
- Switched or leased lines.
- Buffers.
- Error checking and correction.
- Automatic end of block.
- Number of input/output units per terminal.
- Combinations of input/output units.
- Number of terminals per line.
- Number of lines per data communication control unit.

Optical scanners (optical character recognition, O.C.R.)
- Alternative type fonts.
- Size of characters.
- Type and size of documents.
- Numer of lines.
- Speed.
- Tolerance in line and character space.
- Tolerance in void of printed image.
- Tolerance in opacity.
- Method of scanning.
- Alphanumeric or numeric.
- Page reader, document reader.
- Number of O.C.R. units per control unit.
- Possibility of remote use.
- Online possibilities.
- Offline output.
- Stackers e.g. reader/sorter capabilities.

Plotter
- Horizontal and vertical speed.
- Bidirectional movement.
- Size of paper.
- Size of steps.
- Online or offline control.
- Offline control; card, punched tape or magnetic tape.
- Possibility of remote use.

Displays
- Buffered.
- Number of characters per line
- Number of lines.
- Alphanumeric or numeric.
- Speed.

- Input and output features (e.g. keyboard writer).
- Lightpen.
- Possibility of remote use.
- Resolution of image.
- Number of display units per control unit.
- Screen colour.
- Photographic copies.

Magnetic ink character reader. (M.I.C.R.)
- See optical scanners, except for "tolerance in opacity".

External stores

Magnetic tape drives
- Is seven track feature available?
- Density in characters per inch.
- Data transfer rate in characters per second.
- Phase modulation or "non return to zero" data representation method.
- How many tape units can be connected to one control unit?
- Start-stop times.
- Is read backwards feature available?
- Are standard 2400 ft. reels used?
- Compatibility with industry standards.
- Hardware checks.
- Transport: capstan or vacuum?

Direct access stores
- Capacity in octads of one unit.
- Data transfer rate in characters per second.
- Average, maximum and minimum access time.
- What can be done in overlay?
- How many independent access mechanisms are available per unit?
- Is "cylinder concept" available?
- How many units can be connected to one control unit?
- Is data-carrying medium removable?

Software

- Which levels exist in software, and what are the main specifications for the different models?
  — Support package?
  — Basic system?
  — Extended system?
  — Multiprogramming system?
- How is system generation and maintenance executed?
- What are basic elements within the operating systems? (job control, interrupt handler, library, etc.)

- Which support programs are available for what models and software levels?
  — Report and Update program Generator?
  — Autocode?
  — ALGOL?
  — COBOL '65?
  — FORTRAN IV?
- Which utility software, such as
  — Sort?
  — Sort-merge?
  — Data transcription programs, such as
    card-to-tape?
    tape-to-print?
- What hardware requirements are implied by the software for execution, compilation and generation?
- Is software available for all hardware features?
- Which compatibility features are available, and what is the performance of these features in relation to the performance of the imitated configuration? (6-6.5)

General aspects

- How do delivery times fit into the overall system schedule of the system?
- Until what date can changes be forwarded? Define specific dates on which the various hardware requirements must be frozen.
- How is the maintenance of the equipment organized?
  — Is a service organization locally available?
  — Is equipment embodied in the configuration which is not maintained by the supplier?
- Is it possible to use a compatible configuration in case of emergency?
- Will it be possible to share equipment with other users?
- What kind of support can be expected from the supplier?
  — Has the supplier experience in the field of the application concerned?
  — Are application packages available which could be used?
- How much actual support will be given in respect of:
  — Assistance with development, writing and conversion of programs?
  — Training of systems analysts, programmers and operators?
  — Program testing, hours and location?
  — Provision of systems analysts and programmers?
- Expansion potential:
  — Amount of available time free on each unit of the configuration (can only be established by using an automated tool for configuration simulation).
  — Maximum expansion, number of controllers and units which can be connected to a system, upgrading of central processing unit and softwarelevels.
- Size and weight of equipment for each unit to be considered separately.
- Only standard equipment should be selected. Special hardware and software puts the user in an unfavourable position.

Economic aspects

- Cost of the equipment in case of rent, lease or buy.
  On a first assessment, only the overall price setting is of interest. Once the configuration is determined, cost is one of the decision criteria.
  - Computer time available. It is important to know the number of hours during which the machine is at the disposal of the user under different lease or rent conditions.
- How is maintenance arranged?
- What is the cost of a maintenance contract in case of buying?
  - Are the costs of spare parts included?
  - How many hours are required for maintenance per period?
  - What are the maintenance arrangements in the case of a lease contract?
- Is all software included in the equipment price? Is an extra charge for special software made?
- What conversion costs can be expected? Is imitation or evaluation of present programs possible in order to decrease conversion cost?
- What additional costs can be expected in respect of site preparation:
  - Space costs?
  - Special floor construction, walls, ceilings?
  - Airconditioning, cooling, heating and humidity control?
  - Tape/disk/card storage?
  - Power supply, including extra facilities for emergencies when a real time online system is under consideration?
- What are the operating costs of the equipment in terms of:
  - Personnel?
  - Power?
  - Card usage, printed paper and forms?
  - Tape and disk files, etc.?
  - Interest and depreciation in case of buying?
  - Monthly rental and amortization of initial cost?
- What is the price/performance ratio of the equipment for the type of application concerned? For equipment performance evaluation, see the use of SCERT as described in 4-1.4.
- Minimum hire period in the case of lease contract?

Activity 3-5: Divide system into subsystems

Purpose

The purpose of this activity is to identify the different subsystems within the system, and to determine subsystem requirements for each subsystem, so that during the development and implementation phases the different subsystems can proceed concurrently, thus shortening the throughput time of the systems effort.

Considerations

The following considerations are germane to this approach:

- the details which arise during the development of a large system are so numerous that an approach in which all functions of the system are developed simultaneously leads to confusion and chaos. In order to channel and categorize the problems presented by the many details encountered during the system development phase, it is necessary to distinguish subsystems within the system which have as few information-exchange interfaces with other subsystems as possible;
- the task-force required for a system development effort in which all functions are developed concurrently is not available in most organizations. A so-called total system approach performed with relatively few people results in very long delays, because the system can be implemented only after the very last details of each function are considered. This has many disadvantages;
- the teams do not acquire, early in the project, implementation experience which can be applied usefully to subsystems to be developed and implemented at a later date;
- the objectives will be realized earlier, because an overlap exists between the development and the implementation phases, so that project duration will be decreased;
- priority implementation of subsystems which create history files will enable earlier usage of other system functions;
- organizational changes requiring a long implementation period do not necessarily delay the overall system schedule. At the other hand when an organizational change can be triggered by a specific part of the system the subsystem approach is beneficial.

Constraints

In spite of these facts, which indicate that the successful development and implementation of large, complex information systems can in most cases be realized only by applying the subsystem approach, there are nevertheless a number of problems inherent in this approach:

- the subsystem approach carries the danger of the development of a number of independent systems, instead of one integrated system. This danger is most serious when not enough attention is paid to the overall design of the system (3-4) and to the definition of interfaces between subsystems (3-5.3);

- the management and documentation of the systems effort during the system development phase is important, because different subsystem teams are working in parallel on the development of different subsystems. Solid project documentation, including change control, such as is described in 2-4, is necessary;
- a wrong division directly affects the effectiveness of the development effort, and the operational performance of the system.

Summarizing: the division of a system into subsystems is a critical activity, which requires the undivided attention of both the project team and the steering committee.

Subdivision

The steps to be performed in dividing a system into subsystems are:
3-5.1 identify possible divisions into subsystems;
3-5.2 select division into subsystems;
3-5.3 prepare subsystem requirements and constraints.

Step 3-5.1: Identify possible divisions into subsystems

The project team has considerable latitude in splitting up the system into subsystems. The following considerations are of value.

Necessity of subsystems

Determine whether it is necessary to split up the system into subsystems. Can the system be developed and implemented sequentially without overlap or time-phasing? Generally the answer to the first of these questions is obviously yes. However, the following should be taken into consideration:

- number of people available;
- due date of the project;
- specific organizational relationships for parts of the system;
- time required for organizational changes to be executed in advance of the implementation of specific functions;
- computer test time available during development and implementation for error recovery and back-up.

Grouping of functions

Once the decision to subdivide the system into subsystems is made, the first thing to do is to list groups of functions which are directed towards the same organizational task. If the organizational task is that of project planning, then the functions to be listed would include the preparation of plans, the calculation of plans, resource leveling, evaluation, corrective action and reporting. As obvious as this might seem, it nevertheless provides a good starting point for subsystem identification. Give all those groups of functions which fulfil individual tasks in the organization an identification code. (One result of 3-4.1, design new information flow, is a set of function worksheets describing each function separately.)

Implementation sequence

Order these groups of functions, covered in the information flow, from the point of view of implementation sequence. For example, the planning of tools required for production cannot precede the planning of the manufacture of the parts for which the tools are required. When ordering these groups, the project team should take into account also the time required for organizational changes as described in 3-3.2.

In general more than one sequence is possible. For example the development of the project can start with two or more independent groups of functions. These groups can be followed by other groups of functions. The project team should determine the bounds set by the organization and the implementation sequence in order to be able to determine which solutions will best serve the system objectives.

Creation of subsystems

When these groups are numerous, and each contains only a small number of functions, combine several related groups into one subsystem. However, pay due attention to the following.

Files

In step 3-4.2 a file usage chart was prepared. Preferably, all functions within one subsystem should use the same files. When one function requires a file which is used also in another subsystem, consider the possibility of combining the two subsystems into one; or of transferring the function concerned to the other subsystem.

File usage chart for subsystems
To support this task a file usage chart for subsystems can be prepared, see example on page 5.

Data processing

Check if the programs which are investigated for the first time in 3-4.3 use functions which are located within one subsystem. When it appears that a program crosses preliminary subsystem boundaries, consider another division into subsystems, taking the general design requirements into account.

Application software

Study the possible use of standard application software as was done in 3-4.3. When it appears that the use of an application package is spread over more than one subsystem, try to rearrange the division to use the application software most effectively.

Interfaces between subsystems

The information exchange interfaces between subsystems should be as limited as possible. Remember that each subsystem is due to be developed by a subsystem team, which should have sufficient latitude during subsystem design.

Schedules

Overall system schedule
During the feasibility study an overall schedule is prepared, while at the end of the system analysis & design phase a system development and implementation schedule is drawn up in which the development and implementation of the different subsystems are shown in relation to each other. In either case, the planning technique described in 6-1.1 and 2-2.2 should be used.

FILE USAGE CHART FOR SUBSYSTEMS

system :
subsystem :
prev. issue:

project no. :
chapter/sect.:
page :
issued :

files	subsystems									
	cust. order and comm. stockorder formation	product information	main planning	materials control	purchasing	manufacturing control				
customer	x									
order*	x	x	x							
main order activity			x							
inter activity relation			x							
main order prod. relation*			x	x						
main order resource relation			x							
product*	x	x	x	x	x	x				
inter prod. relation*		x		x	x	x				
detail order*				x	x	x				
job						x				
resource *				x		x				
routing						x				
tool						x				
job-tool relation						x				
tool-routing relation						x				
production order*				x		x				
supplier order					x					
supplier					x					
supplier relation					x					

* system files

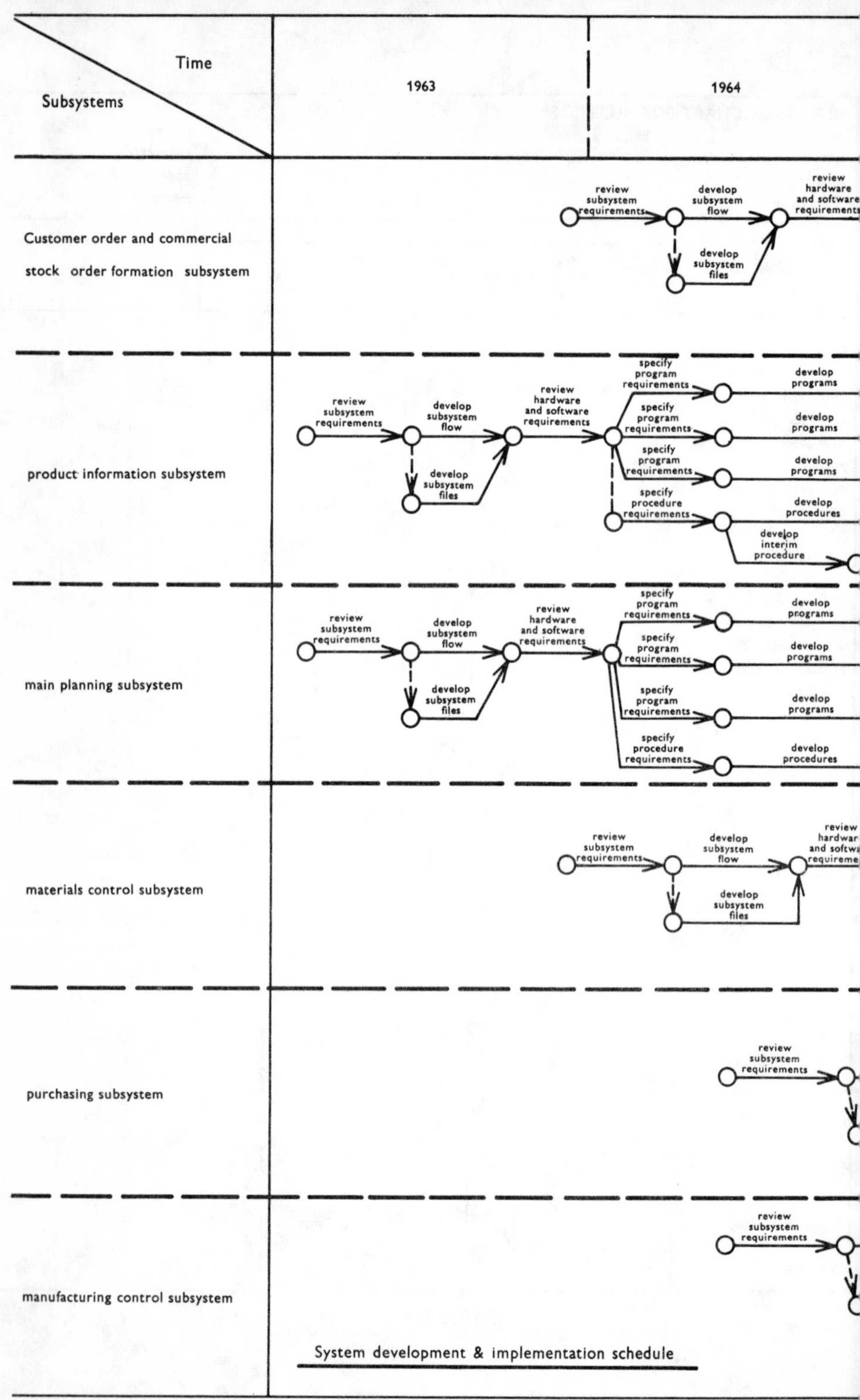

System development & implementation schedule

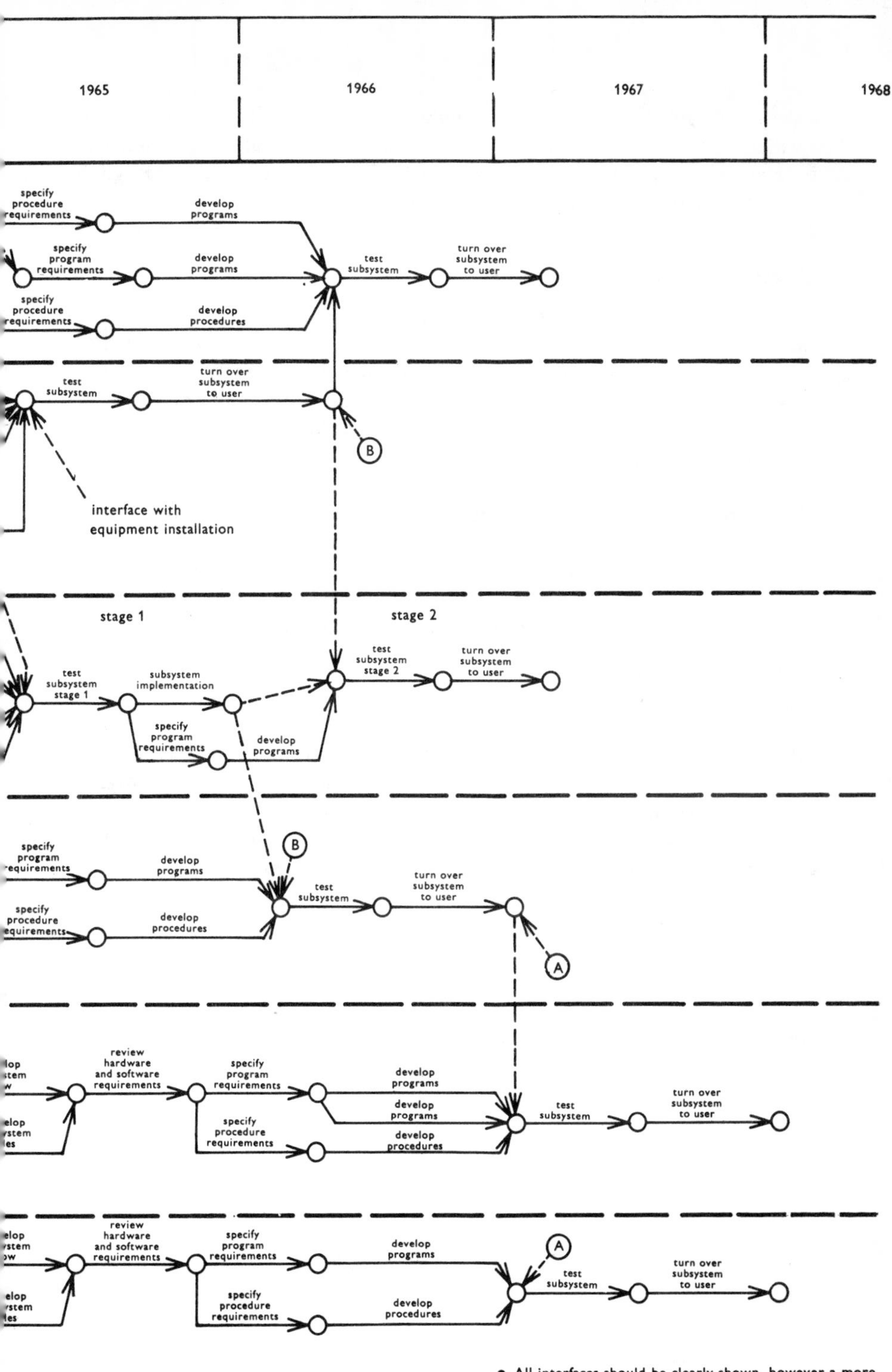

- All interfaces should be clearly shown, however a more detailed schedule for each subsystem will be required.

Example of system development and implementation schedule
To illustrate the result of this effort in the case of system analysis & design, an example of a simplified schedule of a systems effort in relation to its subsystems development and implementation is given on page 6 .

Overlap between subsystems

Consider possible overlaps between subsystems. This is an important consideration for reducing total project duration. For this reason, the project team is obliged to identify events within each subsystem development and implementation schedule which allow a connection with other subsystems. For example, a subsystem which takes care of parts list preparation and maintenance can be linked to a material requirements calculation subsystem as soon as the files are created and being maintained. However, if within the parts list subsystem it is planned to use advanced data collection and enquiry equipment to facilitate the use and maintenance of the files of the different departments, while in the first stage input preparation and updating is performed with punched cards by the computer centre, the parts list subsystem will not be completed at the moment of linking with the material requirements calculation subsystem.

As stated earlier, the division of a system into subsystems is arbitrary; in the above example, the decision could have been made to create another subsystem which would take care of the advanced I/O data transmission of the part lists subsystem. However, this is not recommended for the following reasons:

- both subsystems would have to use exactly the same files; the first subsystem team should anticipate data transmission requirements;
- the contacts with the line personnel in the user organization are similar;
- the documents and information to be used and issued by the different departments should be the same;
- the processing is the same for both situations.

Step 3-5.2: Select division into subsystems

After due consideration of the proposed alternative divisions of the system into subsystems, it must be decided which division best fits the given circumstances.

The decision process can be facilitated by means of the following checklist with decision criteria:

- Is the sequence of system implementation which is implied by the proposed order of putting the different subsystems into operation in accordance with the system objectives?
- Can realization of the results according to the quantified performance ratios (3-3.1) be achieved?
- Does the design permit the realization of a schedule which meets the required due dates, or is the total throughput time too long because of too small an overlap between subsystems?
- Has each subsystem which has a long throughput time been studied, in order to investigate whether one or more events in it can be identified as possible interfaces at which integration of subsystem can be realized? This applies to the development as well as to the implementation.
- Is hardware and software to be available at the proper time?
- Is the sequence of development and implementation in accordance with the realization of organizational requirements? For example, a central inventory control subsystem should not be planned to be implemented over one year if the changeover from decentralized to centralized stocks requires two years because of organizational changes in the distribution system.
- Can resource and personnel requirements called for by the schedule be satisfied within required time limits?
- Is one of the alternative designs preferable because it will be acceptable to the user? (Consider procedures added and deleted by implementation of the system, changes in size, responsibility or composition of the staff, and changes in physical facilities.) The timing of these changes as a result of a division of the system into subsystems can be of utmost importance.
- Are information exchange interfaces between the different subsystems as simple as possible? In this respect consider the following:
  - system files should be used by the smallest possible number of subsystems;
  - all interfaces should be documented in advance in the subsystem requirements in terms of record layout, data field descriptions, data representation, volume (average and peak loads), frequency, time schedule, and processing sequence;
  - when interfaces are seen to be complex or ill-defined, reject the division which produced them;
  - the data storage media should be defined e.g. disk, tape, punched tape, punched cards, written documents.
- Do the sizes of the subsystems allow individual development and implementation of individual subsystems?

- Does the division of the system into subsystems interfere with the data processing aspects?
- Are functions which are likely to be performed in one program combined in one subsystem?
- Is application software under consideration, and are the functions embodied in a package combined in one subsystem?
- Does the scheduled development and implementation of the different subsystems guarantee a smooth conversion from present to new system, with as little reprogramming and file conversion as possible? This applies especially to the phased implementation of parts of subsystems.

Step 3-5.3: Prepare subsystem requirements

The purpose of this step is to lay down and document the subsystem requirements, in order to facilitate smooth development and implementation. The subsystem requirements will be embodied in a set of documents derived from the material developed in previous steps, such as;

- general information flow, derived from the information flow as prepared in 3-4.1 (see chart on page 12);
- list of functions embodied in the subsystem, with function worksheets (see form 3-2.3) and specification of each function prepared in 3-3.3 and 3-4.1;
- system files used in the subsystem (see form and file description sheet in 3-2.3);
- inputs entering subsystem from other subsystems. (see form and file description sheet);
- outputs produced by the subsystem as inputs for other subsystems (see form and file description sheet);
- data processing to be performed by the subsystem. Preferred combination of functions into programs as discussed in 3-4.3;
- subsystem development schedule including due dates for subsystem development and implementation, and due dates for interfacing with other subsystems;
- requirements which are the same for all subsystems, such as hardware requirements, the central project file should be referred to in order to avoid unnecessary duplication of documents. The same applies to system files and interfaces between subsystems;
- list of all interfaces which are not yet defined completely. When too many points are still open, this list will be long. This is a symptom of an incomplete design. In such cases it is necessary to return to the system design activities (3-4 and 3-5.1). Even under pressure from a time schedule, the project team should not start the system development phase until the system design is completed to a sufficient depth. As stated already in the introduction, a premature subsystem division gives rise to many problems, and causes more delay than would be caused by undertaking a more detailed system design effort.

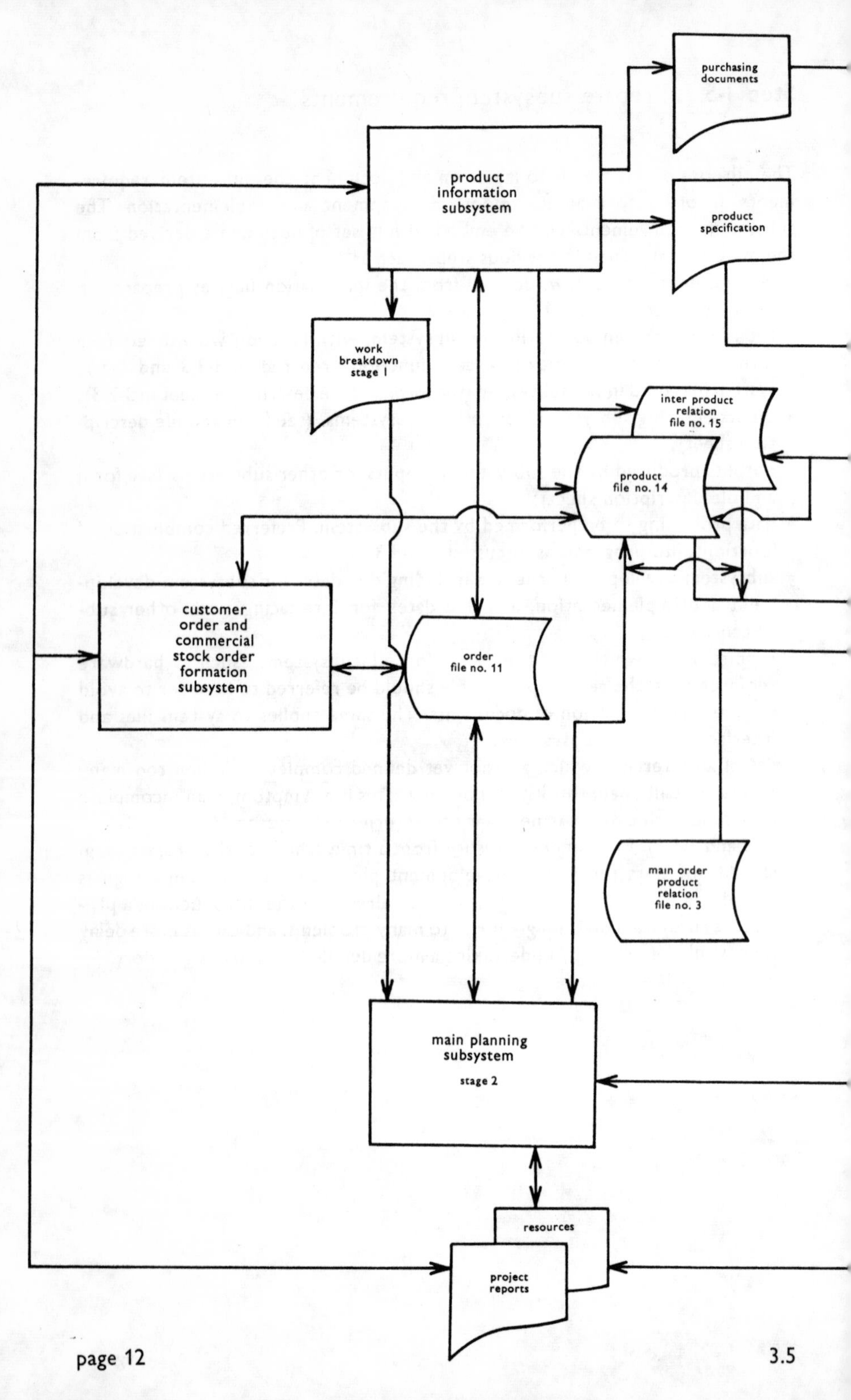
purchasing documents
product information subsystem
product specification
work breakdown stage 1
inter product relation file no. 15
product file no. 14
customer order and commercial stock order formation subsystem
order file no. 11
main order product relation file no. 3
main planning subsystem
stage 2
resources
project reports

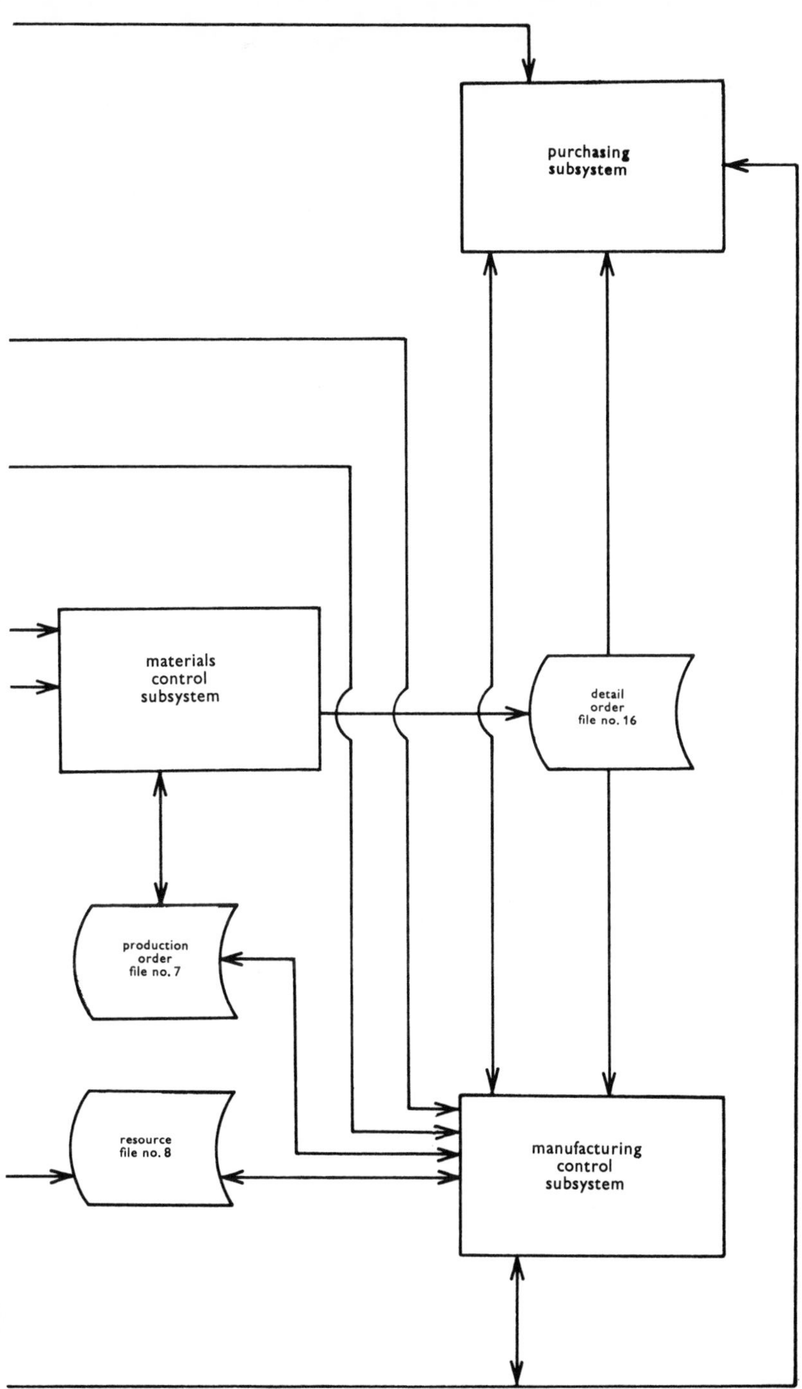

General information flow
Representing subsystems and their interfaces

Activity 3-6: Review system specification and prepare masterplan

During the feasibility study phase, as well as during the system analysis & design phase, all documents collected and/or prepared are filed in the project file, according to the technique described in 2-4.1.

Masterplan

At the end of the feasibility study a masterplan should be prepared in order to inform management and internal auditing department about the results of the study. The main requirement to be satisfied by the masterplan is that the conclusion and recommendations are easy to understand. This implies that the summary, sometimes referred to as "yellow papers", should give all information required for decision making. Details can be covered in a number of appendices, and these can be referred to in the summary where appropriate.
The aim of a feasibility study is a decision from management. A masterplan which does not give a clear statement of the organizational consequences, plans, costs and benefits of a systems effort cannot serve as a basis for the decision whether to start a systems effort or not.
It is highly desirable that in a presentation to management and — internal — auditor all important features are covered in such a way as to guarantee that management as well as auditors are adequately informed.

Contents

The masterplan could for example have the following contents:

- a conclusion in terms of a recommendation to top management whether or not to go on with the systems effort. This recommendation will be supported by a number of facts and consequences which highlight the content of the report and place the reader in perspective;
- a condensed description of the characteristics of the user organization involved (3-2), such as:
  - organization chart;
  - description of business goals;
  - description of product range, markets and production facilities and processes;
- a summary of requirements and constraints (3-4) including:
  - detailed objectives giving as much quantified information as possible about the ultimate influence of the system on the effectiveness of the user organization;
  - consequences for the user organization as a result of the implementation of a system;

— a survey of all problem areas or functions involved which were investigated during the analysis of the present system, and any additional functions for which requirements have been formulated. If required these problem areas or functions can be detailed in terms of outputs, processes and inputs;

- a system design (3-4) which is a rough sketch of one or more possible solutions, to meet the requirements defined, and which must be considered as a prerequisite for the planning of future actions and for a preliminary selection of required hardware and software. The design consists of:
  — one or more information flows which highlight possible solutions, and open ways for detailed systems analysis & design;
  — a file design which shows the system files and gives the relations between files, with estimates of the total sizes;
  — a possible division of the system into subsystems, and function worksheets for the functions involved in each subsystem;
- a hardware and software specification (3-4.4);
- a justification of the recommendation expressed by means of a project calculation (2-3), giving also intangible reasons and benefits, if any;
- an overall schedule for future actions indicating the sequence in which the subsystems will be implemented, and giving the resulting priorities for different actions such as:
  — project team formation;
  — introduction and implementation of changes in the organization;
  — delivery dates of hardware and software (4-1.4 and 5-2);
  — site preparation (5-2.1).

Project file

The results of the system analysis & design phase are the baseline for the system development phase. This means that all details encountered must be solved during the system analysis & design phase in order to get a smooth continuation of the systems effort.

Contents

The contents of the project file, after the system analysis & design phase is finished, include:

- description of present system; 3-2
- system requirements and constraints: 3-3
  — objectives of the system; 3-3.1
  — organizational requirements and constraints; 3-3.2
  — information and control requirements and constraints; 3-3.3
  — general design requirements and constraints; 3-3.4
- system design: 3-4
  — information flow; 3-4.1
  — function worksheets; 3-4.1
  — file usage charts; 3-4.2

— function and file evaluation charts; 3-4.2
— system file definitions; 3-4.2

- hardware and software requirements; 3-4.3
- subsystem requirements including: 3-5.3
  — input definitions;
  — output definitions;
  — file layouts;
- calculation of costs and benefits of the new system; 2-3
- schedule for system development and for system implementation; 2-2
- assignment of subsystem teams; 2-1
- documentation standards for the system development phase. 2-4, 2-1.2

Volume 4: System development

Contents

General

This volume describes the activities of system development. At the end of volume 3, the division of the system into subsystems was decided upon, and the requirements of each subsystem separately specified. This volume details the development of one such subsystem, and provides the additional information necessary to fulfil the development of an integrated system.

Purpose and scope

Purpose

The purpose of the system development phase is to realize in practice the system designed in pursuing the activities of volume 3. During this phase, the subsystems arrived at in volume 3 are developed independently, in terms of programs and procedures; the necessary interfaces are attended to; and the system is prepared for implementation.

Scope

The activities of this volume have much in common with those of volume 3, to which reference should freely be made; this is indicated as appropriate. The difference between this volume and volume 3 is often chiefly one of level. System and subsystem development considerations have a more restricted scope than system design considerations. For example, modifications to a subsystem at the development stage will have comparatively small effect upon the shape of the system as a whole. In particular, it must be appreciated that an incorrect system design cannot be corrected at this level.

Results

The detailed results of the system development phase are manifold. In this phase the physical system components, exemplified by program decks and new forms, are constructed; and four parts of the user documentation are created. These parts are:

- system description (4-7); including a documented account of the structure of the system, the subsystems, and the procedures and programs which belong to or are related to them;
- procedure description (4-6.4); an account of the operations to be performed manually in the organization. This part of the documentation should be so constructed that the individual procedures may be detached for distribution;
- program description (4-5.5); the distinction between system and procedure description on the one hand, and program description and instructions to the computer centre on the other, is made on the basis of responsibility; only together do they describe the system in all its details, but the preparation of the first two will be the responsibility of a systems engineer or analyst, while the third and fourth are the responsibility of a programmer;

• instructions for the computer centre (4-5.6); this part gives in condensed form the documentation necessary to carry out the automatic data processing of the system.

Methodology

The activity network in 2-2.2 gives an example of the relationships between the activities and steps in, inter alia, the system development phase. However, as no two projects will be alike, the actual situation in a project may necessitate adaptions of this network. The team, acting on its evaluation of the situation, may add or delete steps, or change their sequence or relationships as appropriate to the direction and performance of the work.
The chart in page 3 shows the relationships between the activities and steps of this phase and the interfaces with steps in other phases.

New teams

For system development itself, in general one or more subsystem teams will be assigned. These teams will consist of (senior) systems analysts, programmers and user representatives (2-2.1).

The delegation of the systems effort by the project team to a number of subsystem teams is a critical moment in the project. Continuity in understanding of the effort should be assured not only by having one member of the project team participating in each subsystem team, but also in a formal manner by means of documentation in the project file.

Adherence to standards

As the systems effort in this phase will extend to include a large number of new team members, attention must here again be directed to the necessity of adhering to method standards in task performance and development itself. See also 2-1.2. The reader of this volume can make profitable use of chapters 6-4 to 6-6, covering techniques on subjects such as design and development, control and programming.

Change control

The need for changes in all kinds of requirements will become evident in the following steps, no matter how carefully the system design has been done.
Effective change control procedures, as laid down in 2-4.2, must be followed in dealing with them.
These changes may be triggered from outside, i.e. coming from or via the project team to the subsystem team, or triggered by the subsystem team itself. The latter will be the case when, for example, slight changes in the subsystem requirements can greatly facilitate subsystem development and/or improve operating performance.

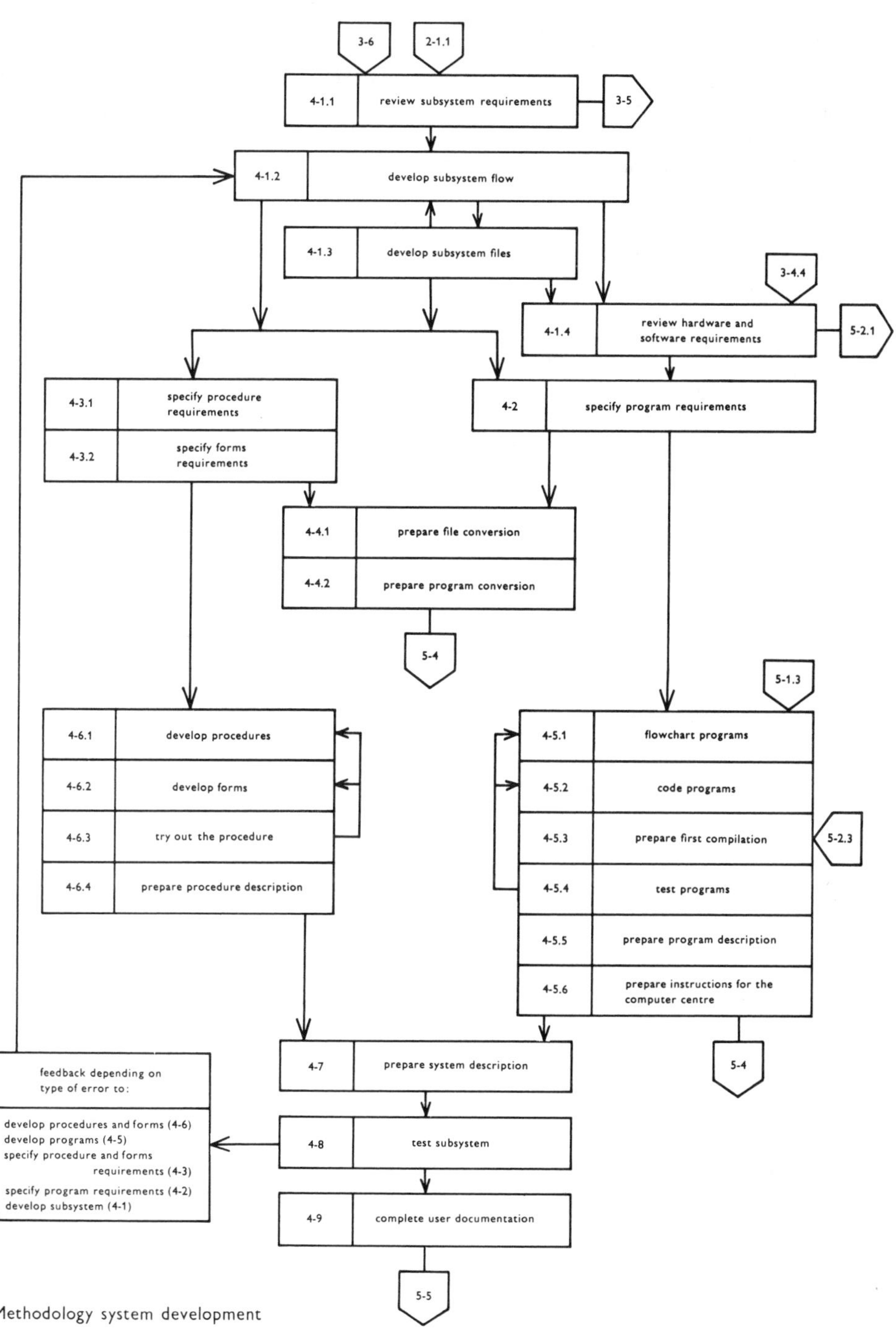

Methodology system development

It cannot be too strongly emphasized that each change request needs careful documentation and study by the project team, in respect of its impact on the requirements of the system itself or on those of other subsystems. After approval it must be ensured that all subsystem teams are informed of the change and duly observe its implementation.
The project team should set target dates for acceptance and review of changes originated by subsystem teams. It may transpire that the design for a new system file itself has to be changed during the system development phase. Such changes must be kept to a minimum, because they delay the progress of the systems effort considerably.

A special kind of change is growth. When considering the development of a subsystem, due care should be taken to incorporate expandibility in the development of the subsystem, in respect of e.g. types of output, transactions and subsystem file records. This is a more farsighted policy than sub-optimization of the subsystem development, which can endanger the operating efficiency and the life-time of the system.

Activity 4-1: Develop subsystem

In activity 3-5 the requirements for, and the outputs of, each subsystem within the system are defined, and system files are specified. In the present activities, detailed flowcharts and/or decision tables are developed for programs and procedures, describing data handling and detailed data processing operations.

This activity is divided into four steps:
4-1.1 review subsystem requirements;
4-1.2 develop subsystem flow;
4-1.3 develop subsystem files;
4-1.4 review hardware and software requirements.

Due to the interrelationships between steps 4-1.2 and 4-1.3, it will be found in practice that these steps have to be performed concurrently.

Techniques applicable to this step are:
- charting technique (6-2.2);
- grid charting (6-2.3);
- decision tables (6-2.4);
- identification of system elements and data objects (6-4.1);
- data organization (6-4.2);
- application packages (6-4.3);
- control techniques (6-5);
- programming language selection (6-6.2).

Step 4-1.1: Review subsystem requirements

The subsystem team must review the subsystem requirements which were prepared in 3-5.3, in order to ensure that all necessary information for subsystem development is available, interrelated and understood. The proposed contents of the project file (2-4) permit the information to be checked for completeness. ARDI standards of documentation, such as standard forms or representation methods, give a more detailed check.
The two examples of parts of the subsystem requirements in page 3 and 4 give respectively a "free" drawing which at first sight shows no incompleteness, and another, drawn according to the rules laid down in technique 6-2.2, which indicates clearly the questions which have arisen.

Interfaces

During this phase, the project team must pay careful attention to the interfaces between subsystems, and to the problems of manpower scheduling in the systems effort, thus complementing the activities performed by the subsystem teams.
It is important, before starting the system development activities, to ascertain whether the interface characteristics are solidly enough specified to establish adequate reliability in the subsystem requirements. If any inconsistencies are detected, they must be reported immediately to the project team, whose responsibility it is to supply satisfactory answers.

Documentation

The documentation package for subsystem requirements will contain, in addition to interface information on the systems level (system files, new information flow and hardware and software, etc.) specific subsystem information. This information is headed by the function worksheet(s), which state in comprehensive terms the processing to be executed by the subsystem in the context of required outputs and available inputs. The description of the required processing can take the form of decision tables, while inputs and outputs are laid down in form and file description sheets.

In addition to the above-mentioned documentation, an assignment in the form of development schedules with due dates will be given to the subsystem team. The subsystem team should evaluate these schedules and either confirm their acceptance or make alternative suggestions.

SUBSYSTEM FLOWCHART "free drawing"

Project	123	System Sales	Prepared by HEB	Date 8/23
Subsystem		Order processing	Approved by DOB	Date 8/24

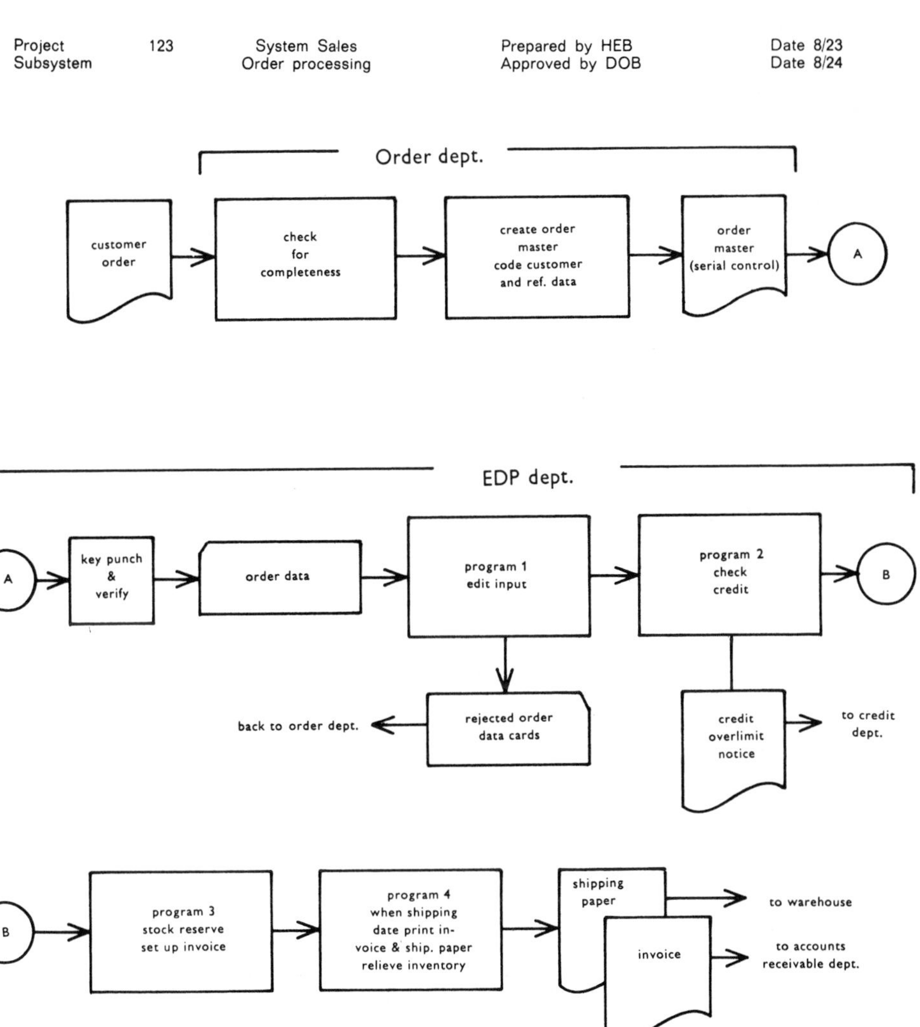

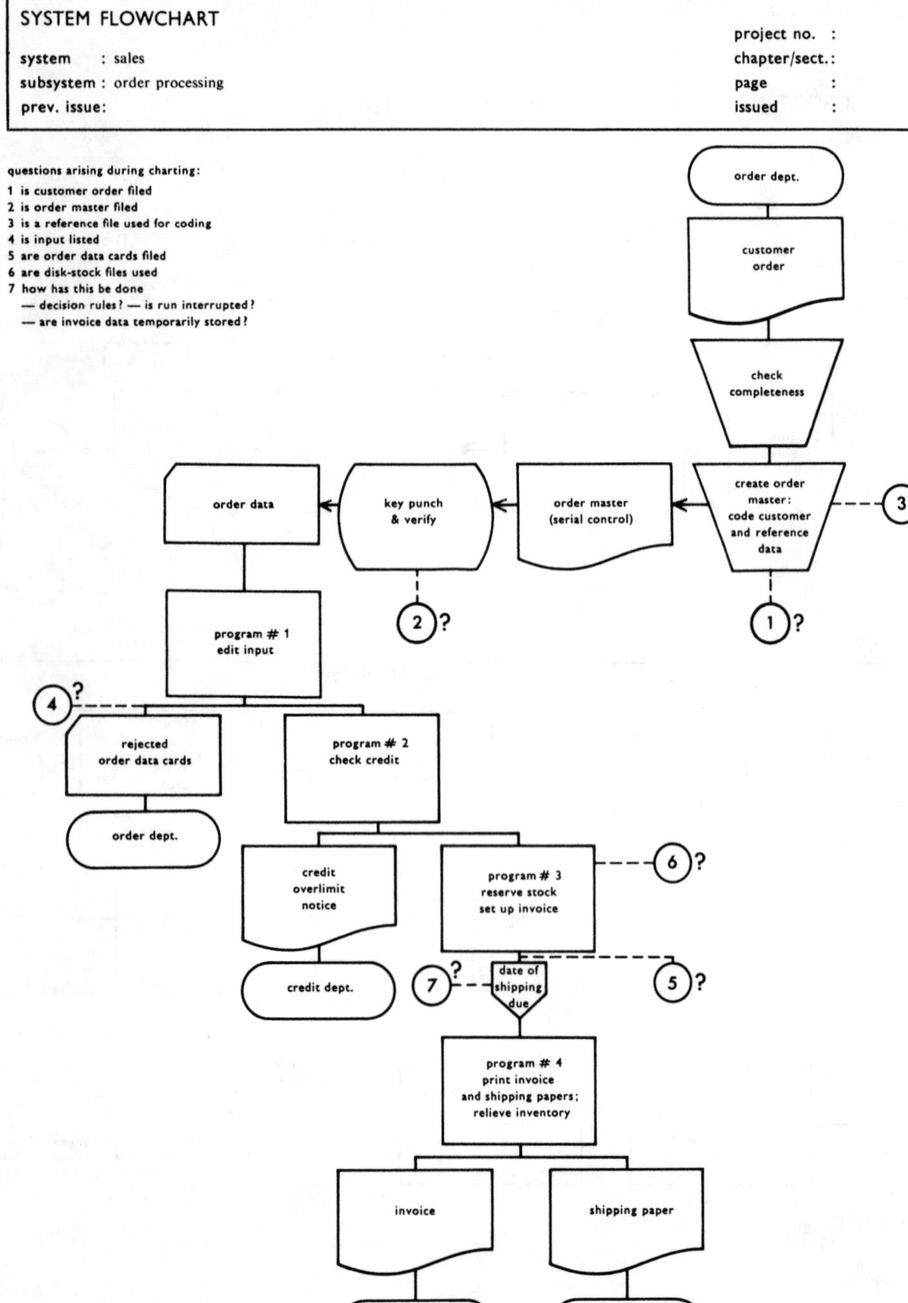

SYSTEM FLOWCHART
system : sales
subsystem : order processing
prev. issue:
project no. :
chapter/sect. :
page :
issued :
questions arising during charting:
1 is customer order filed
2 is order master filed
3 is a reference file used for coding
4 is input listed
5 are order data cards filed
6 are disk-stock files used
7 how has this be done
— decision rules? — is run interrupted?
— are invoice data temporarily stored?
order dept.
customer order
check completeness
create order master: code customer and reference data
order master (serial control)
key punch & verify
order data
program # 1 edit input
rejected order data cards
order dept.
program # 2 check credit
credit overlimit notice
credit dept.
program # 3 reserve stock set up invoice
date of shipping due
program # 4 print invoice and shipping papers; relieve inventory
invoice
shipping paper
accounts receivable dept.
warehouse

Step 4-1.2: Develop subsystem flow

This step is the logical continuation of the steps described in volume 3 as a part of the design activity, and has a similar methodology, i.e.:
3-4.1 design new information flow;
3-4.3 study data processing aspects.

Those problems are now considered which must be solved on the subsystem level, and which need to be specified in one or more detailed subsystem flowcharts. No uncertainty must remain as to what kind of operations are to be performed in one or another program or procedure.

The information flow, from data gathering at the sources to the ultimate use of reports and documents, must be specified and detailed in a number of consecutive and/or parallel running subsystem flowcharts. Within such a specific flowchart, the necessary programs and/or procedures must be identified, taking the following into account:

- as far as possible, avoid interrupting runs by procedures;
- the system interfaces dictate the inputs, the outputs and the usage of system files for each subsystem;
- before deciding on the run and/or procedure structure of the subsystem itself, a decision should be taken as to the (parts of the) standard application packages to be incorporated in the system. (See 3-4.4 and 6-4.4 for further discussion on this subject.)

Outlining the subsystem flow

As an outline for developing a first layout of a subsystem flow, the following procedures are advocated:

- start with prescribed elements of the function worksheet(s);
- represent in a loosely drawn scheme the input constraints, the system file(s), the required processing and the output requirements;
- detect logical relationships and connections;
- try to devise a straightforward, roughly outlined flow concept;
- consider possible sequences of processing for the function(s) involved;
- evaluate pros and cons of the various alternative flow sequences, and select the sequence which seems most suitable;
- concentrate on the possibilities of combining operations;
- detect gaps and problems;
- define these gaps and problems, and consider solutions (by rearranging flow sequence, introducing subsystem files, identifying additional inputs);
- if inconsistencies or impossible situations still remain, enter change request procedure (2-4.2);
- implement controls (6-5) for safeguarding the entire flow, and consequently the quality of its output.

Practical rules

The following rules assist in detailing and finalizing the subsystem flow.

Input

- The data needed to maintain files and to prepare reports must be translated into one or more types of input;
- detailed documentation on all the necessary types of raw data is essential;
- detect the sources of such raw data;
- when the required frequency of submission is known, the appropriate format for each specific input item can be designed. (For details see 3-2.3 with respect to the form and file description sheet);
- incorporate these inputs in their appropriate places in the subsystem flow;
- establish retention schedules for the various types of input developed;
- pay due attention to any organizational constraints which may affect input of different kinds or from different sources;
- eliminate (manual) encoding and decoding as far as possible. Avoid basing the automated information system on codings of data elements other than those of the user organization;
- arrange that data elements are recorded, at a point in the flow as close as possible to the source of information, on data carriers suitable as computer inputs;
- incorporate points of support for internal control in early stages of input procedures;
- be alert for organizational requirements concerning checks on inputs;
- pay due attention to data processing constraints concerning prescribed screening of input;
- avoid composite or summarized data in files and inputs. Use the most elementary data fields which are individually necessary in the system;
- in documenting input details use the following forms:
  - — form and file description sheet (3-2.3);
  - — multiple punched card layout (4-1.3);
  - — dual punched card layout (4-6.1);
  - — record layout (4-1.3).

Processing

Automation will, by its nature, involve the elimination of a number of procedures, but many must remain. Automation creates a change in working conditions and tasks to be performed.
The project team cannot restrict its task of devising new work aids for user personnel merely to the input and output handling aspects of the system.
In ARDI the retained procedures are analyzed, evaluated, and possibly changed, in order to adapt them to the requirements of the new information system.

The following aspects should be considered:

- it is necessary to adapt not only the source data, which constitutes via a number of recording, controlling and conversion stages the input material for the system, but also the material content. For example, consider the implementation of new coding directories for a range of data elements;
- usage of the information gathered during the analysis activity on existing procedures should not be lost sight of, since for a successful development of new or revised procedures a detailed knowledge of manual operating practices is important. Resistance to change will thus be bypassed or overcome more easily;
- minimize the number of runs per period. Perform a run only when its output is necessary to initiate operations in the user organization;
- pay due attention to organizational constraints which may necessitate various operating frequencies;
- try to complete the processing of a given input in one run in order to eliminate "waiting files";
- avoid medium conversion wherever possible;
- avoid the sorting of files, outputs, and inputs, in that order of importance, wherever possible; thus input sorting is valuable if it eliminates output or file sorting;
- the sequence of transactions might be arranged in such a way that a set of transactions would be either "unupdatable" or unacceptable to the system if one transaction of a set were missing or erroneous. A considerable increase in programming effort can be encountered in dealing with such a situation;
- be alert for exception routines for sets of operations which deal with "special policies" concerning specific products, debtors, suppliers or categories of employee. In spite of the basic dictate that exceptions must as far as possible be eliminated, some may remain; where they do, the system must provide means for dealing with them.

The system must serve the user, and should put as few constraints on him as possible.

At this point in subsystem development, main program flowcharts and decision tables depicting the essentials of the accepted problem solutions can be drawn (see 4-5.1, 6-2.2 and 6-2.4). In addition, in appropriate cases it will be necessary to document computations made by means of formulae or other mathematical representations.

Controls

Use technique 6-5 to select and evaluate for embodiment in the system those control techniques which will enable it to satisfy not only the demands of reliability, completeness and accuracy, but also cost effectiveness. This evaluation can bring into focus some second order points, of which three examples are given below:

- the necessity of checking sets of input data in a batch mode, when acceptance cannot take place until the entire set is proven and correct, or until elimination measures are taken. Such special requirements may cause larger programs and internal store usage;

- the checking of characters within each field for validity or for other norms or conditions may call for additional programs, or larger programs and consequently larger internal store;
- intermediate manual checks during processing should be avoided, as they delay the progress of the work, and create overlapping or even duplication of control activity.

The control and checking techniques to be incorporated in the subsystem flow can be documented in a control scheme, which in turn forms part of the overall control network for the new information system.

Equipment

- Pay due attention to data processing constraints such as limitations of:
  - — core capacity;
  - — number of tape units;
  - — disk capacity and number of disk units;
  - — input and outputs units;
- reduce as far as possible the amount and variety of existing tab room equipment; standardize on a central processor and its input, output and storage units. This may seem inconsistent with the outcome of a straight cost comparison, but the resulting simplification of planning jobs for the equipment will in general greatly outweigh the difference in cost.

Output

- Pay due attention to organizational constraints such as:
  - — feedback to users of intermediate results for e.g. checking purposes;
  - — different output timing requirements;
  - — variety of outputs;
  - — output presentation methods;
- keep the amount of physical output (reports, punched cards, etc.) at a minimum. Be aware of the "danger" of high speed printers;
- details must be made available, sometimes in addition to those described in volume 3, to enable the subsystem team to use the required output report as a basis for defining program requirements. A printer spacing chart (see example in 4-6.2) will be necessary for this purpose. This chart may carry information such as:
  - — when it is necessary to skip to a new page (new sort key, or number of lines per page);
  - — spacing requirements;
  - — page numbering;
- use appropriate measures to ensure that reports with different timing requirements can be prepared simultaneously by the same subsystem, using the

same file. A specific example would be a monthly sales report coupled with a bimonthly sales statistics survey, period-to-date figures to be derived with the aid of an additional file. In a magnetic tape situation, this requires two additional tape units to be used by the program every two months, while the print tape will then contain data for one additional report;

- consider the use of a console typewriter or printer. The logsheet produced by this unit could supply messages such as:
  - — number of forms, pages or lines printed;
  - — processing time;
  - — number of records used in respect of each file;
  - — label identifications of tapes used;
  - — date of creation or last update of the files;
  - — total amount of gross and net sales;
  - — total number of transactions;
  - — total number of updated logical records;
  - — total number of back orders;
  - — number and kind of error signals.

  The use of the logsheet for user messages is no longer possible if the computer centre reserves it strictly for housekeeping purposes.

For an example of the outline of the subsystem flow, see page 10.

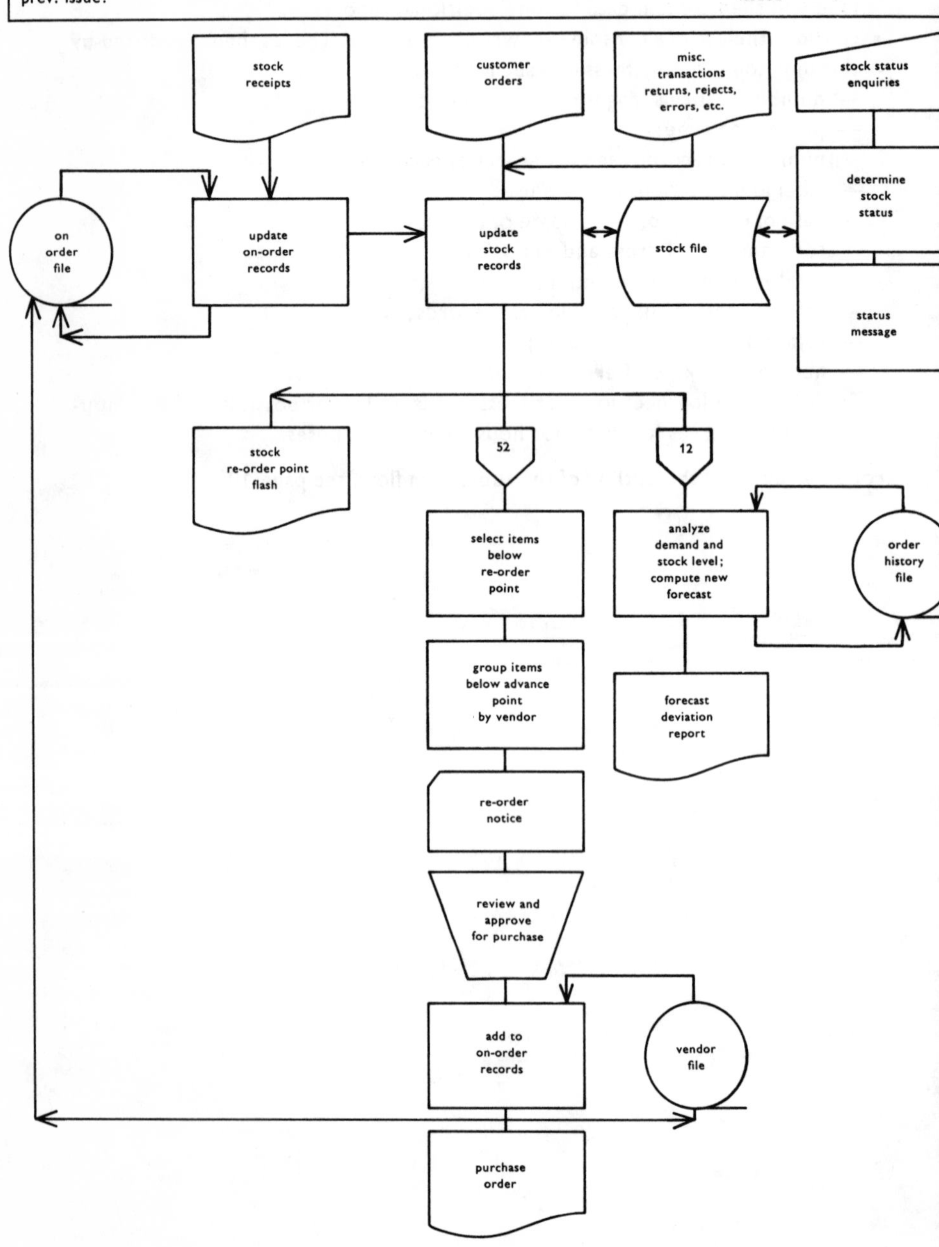
SYSTEM FLOWCHART
system : merchandising
subsystem : inventory control
prev. issue:
project no. :
chapter/sect.:
page :
issued :
stock receipts
customer orders
misc. transactions returns, rejects, errors, etc.
stock status enquiries
on order file
update on-order records
update stock records
stock file
determine stock status
status message
stock re-order point flash
52
12
select items below re-order point
analyze demand and stock level; compute new forecast
order history file
group items below advance point by vendor
forecast deviation report
re-order notice
review and approve for purchase
add to on-order records
vendor file
purchase order

Step 4-1.3: Develop subsystem files

Files

A subsystem may use system files which are used also by other subsystems, and/or its own files. A system file specification will be submitted as a requirement, after its design in the previous phase; subsystems files will be developed in the present step. Since the work involved in developing a subsystem file is virtually the same as that for a system file, reference should be made to 3-4.2, in which the system files were designed; and to technique 6-4.2, which deals with data organization.
An important consideration throughout this step is the enforcement of uniformity in the identification of data objects.

Continued file consolidation

The basis for developing subsystem files is laid during the development of the subsystem flow (4-1.2). At that point, it can become necessary to obtain access to data elements not allocated in system files, or to arrange for the temporary storage of data. The introduction of one or more subsystem files is not just a matter of technical detailing, and must be carefully evaluated. This development has to be controlled from an overall systems point of view. The introduction of new files may place a burden on the resources available for updating and maintenance, and thus endanger the quality of the system. The necessity of new data fields must be investigated, to determine whether they can be derived from other data fields in already defined files, or whether they can be added to one of these files. The addition of new data fields to already defined system files increases the system control task of the project team.
Logical combinations of the material content of the data, of frequency of updating and of source and usage, are the criteria to consider in deciding where each data element can be stored. In this way, file consolidation will greatly contribute to the system performance.

Temporary files

Reference has been made to files which contain data fields which will be updated. The word "file" is used for many other more or less temporary collections of data, such as input file, scratch file, output file, intermediate file.
Such "files", to which the attention of the team will be drawn during the development of the data processing flow, imply only a need for medium conversion and offer no particular problem.

On the other hand error files and suspense files, though of a simple structure, require updating.
Error files [1]) can be used to store rejected transactions. At the time of validation, error messages will have been produced for the benefit of the user; upon receipt of corrective transactions, the erroneous transactions must be cancelled.

[1]) *New light on error detection and control*, EDP Analyzer, Vista, **1** (1963.2) no. 1.

Suspense or waiting files will be used in those cases where certain types of transaction for a file record can be processed only in a specified sequence; for example:

- charge account transactions must be preceded by file item creation;
- jobs must be recorded in the order in which the jobs occur in the production flow.

Transactions which "arrive too early" will be posted to the suspense file; this file must be read frequently to see if the missing input has already entered the system.

Both types of file facilitate control over the completeness of the original input, and provide a means of checking the response time of the user organization.

Tables and indexes

Distinct from files, but closely related to them because they can act as a substitute for or as a controlling instrument of files, are tables and indexes. They should be considered for possible incorporation in the system as seems appropriate. They can be used for validating input data, for monitoring new input data (identifications, keys for further processing), and for translating input data into other representations as necessary for further processing. The tables will be stored either in internal or in rapid access external stores.

Records

Within a file, the subsystem team has to determine the record identification number, and to develop layouts for each of the records. A leading consideration is the grouping of data fields in such a way that fields which are similar in material content, frequency or source of updating, and usage, are placed close together. This will facilitate processing and internal control within the system.

Sequence of fields within a record

Those fields which are used as a record key for identification and sorting purposes are put together in front of the record. The sequence of the fields composing the record keys will follow the pattern major/intermediate/minor with respect to frequency of use.

Especially in case of a consolidated file, it is highly advisable to reserve some amount of blank space in a record, to permit the future addition of new data fields. This will avoid the necessity for the creation of secondary files which would place an additional burden on the resources available for file maintenance. Instead of leaving blank space in a record, the same degree of flexibility can be achieved by an arrangement which makes possible the addition of new types of record to each file item.

Types of record

- Header record, mainly used for identification keys and relations (6-4.1);
- permanent record, which must always be present for each file item before any data can be inserted into the file; this means that such a record can be empty;

- optional record, which will be added to a header record or a permanent record as necessary, e.g. when specific data has to be stored; this kind of record will be deleted as soon as it becomes empty;
- trailer record.

Documentation of files

In development, in addition to the items specified in 3-4.2, details have to be specified for each file to be used by the subsystem:

- method of file organization;
- place of usage:
  - state program number(s);
  - run number(s) or name(s) of procedures;
  - reference to system flowcharts;
- frequency of usage e.g. yearly/monthly/bi-weekly/daily updating, or real time, or upon request of user;
- blocking factor;
- record counts/hash totals;
- compare sections;
- labelling:
  - standard label;
  - non-standard label. If so, it must be described;
  - no label.

Documentation of records

Give a listing of:

- all data fields which are placed in a record;
- the number and kind of characters of each field;
- occurrence of information in the field, and, if occurring, average and maximum size of the information;
- the location of the field in the record.

Documentation of fields

The team has to allocate the data fields within a record or a document. This development work of minor scope is one of definition, and concerns the following aspects:

- field identification code;
- field name and abbreviation;
- deprecated synonyms;
- characteristics of the field;
- average and maximum size;
- type of characters allowed for each field; location or column to permit effective data checking;
- responsibility for input and updating the field;
- input and output picture;
- range of values permitted;
- usage in programs, inputs, outputs and records.

Means of documentation

In addition to the charts discussed in 3-4.2 as tools for file design, page 15 gives an example of the form disk file layout, which is specially suited for documenting the information concerning the structuring of a file into disk records. For non-disk organized files, the more general form and file description sheet (3-2.3) is suitable.

For typical examples of record layout forms, see:

- form and file description sheet (3-2.3);
- multiple punched card layout (see page 16); in the example a.o. the field names are given; in reality also the field identification numbers should be mentioned for reference to the field description sheets;
- record layout for tape or rapid access external store (see page 18).

To facilitate the documentation of data fields, a field description sheet is given in 3-2.3.

Index of data fields

In order to keep track of all the main aspects and different relationships of the data fields, it is worth considering the setting up of an index of all data fields which can, if required, be maintained by mechanical means. If this is done, the composition of the input for the program should include main field characteristics, such as:

- identification code;
- name;
- size or picture;
- and field relationships, such as usage in:
  - — department or function;
  - — files;
  - — programs;
  - — procedures;
  - — reports and other documents.

The relationships can be printed in separate columns, thus creating a representation similar to a gridchart. If this input is available for all fields defined by the system in a coded and machine-readable presentation, it will be possible to sort the fields according to such characteristics as:

- field identification code;
- alphabetic field name;
- abbreviation of field name;
- frequency of usage of fields in e.g. documents or programs;
- documents having fields in common;
- procedures using the same data fields.

When this type of mechanical processing must be done, it is of importance to make provisions in e.g. the field description sheet to facilitate direct key-punching.

DISK FILE LAYOUT

system : PARTSLIST SYSTEM
subsystem : PRINSYS
prev. issue:

project no. : 123456
chapter/sect.: 3/5
page : 1
issued : 9-5-'69

file name: Product Master-File file label: Prodmasfile file identification: PMF

record identification	record key identification	description	length octads	position from	position to	remarks
–	PARTNR.	12 NC-partnumber	7	16	23	

file organisation

☐ sequential ☒ random
☐ indexed sequential ☐ relative

disk areas

ext.	lower			upper		
1	1	0	0	200	0	0
2						
3						
4						

capacity

12 . blocking factor (rec./block) × 3 . blocks/track ×
10 . tracks/cyl. = 360 . rec./cyl.
92 . octads/record × 360 rec./cyl. = 33120 . oct./cyl.

size

average: 36000 records = 100 cyl.
maximum: 71640 records = 199 cyl.

file retention for	period	medium
successive processing	1 week	disk
reconstruction	2 month	tape
audit trail	1 week	disk
legal requirements	1 month	tape

usage in programs

program no.	run no.	input	output	freq.:*
5	A-6	PMF	List	360
10	B-10	PMF	List	52
25	K-2	PMF	List	4

notes:

* R = real time 52 = weekly
720 = twice daily 12 = monthly
360 = daily 4 = quaterly

MULTIPLE PUNCHED CARD LAYOUT

system :
subsystem :
prev. issue:

project no. :
chapter/sect. :
page :
issued :

Product card — identification: . . . .

source	Prepunched					Manual punching				Automatic punching through customer card						
column	1–2	3–8	9–16	17–28	29–31	32–35	36–41	42–44	45–50	51–56	57–59	60–62	63–68	69–73	74–78	79–80
field name and identification	Card code	Storage address	Product number	Product name	Product group	Quantity	Exceptions: Gross price	Exceptions: Discount	Exceptions: Net price	Customer number	Customer group	Sales man number	Document number	Date	Delivery code	Transaction code
remarks			← Interpreted →													

Customer card — identification: . . . .

source	Prepunched						Manual punching				
column	1–2	3–8	9–50	51–56	57–59	60–62	63–68	69–73	74–78	79–80
field name and identification	Card code	Storage address	Customer Name and address	Customer number	Customer group	Sales man number	Document number	Date	Delivery code	Transaction code

identification: . . . .

1 2 3 4 5 6 7 8 9 10 11 12 13 14 15 16 17 18 19 20 21 22 23 24 25 26 27 28 29 30 31 32 33 34 35 36 37 38 39 40 41 42 43 44 45 46 47 48 49 50 51 52 53 54 55 56 57 58 59 60 61 62 63 64 65 66 67 68 69 70 71 72 73 74 75 76 77 78 79 80

card name
source
column
field name and identification
remarks

identification: . . . .

1 2 3 4 5 6 7 8 9 10 11 12 13 14 15 16 17 18 19 20 21 22 23 24 25 26 27 28 29 30 31 32 33 34 35 36 37 38 39 40 41 42 43 44 45 46 47 48 49 50 51 52 53 54 55 56 57 58 59 60 61 62 63 64 65 66 67 68 69 70 71 72 73 74 75 76 77 78 79 80

card name
source
column
field name and identification
remarks

RECORD LAYOUT

system : Merchandizing
subsystem : Stock control — masterfile
prev. issue:

project no. :
chapter/sect.:
page :
issued :

record identification: article record (01–05)

article record

stock item identification				stock levels					control levels			packing	selling
number	description	stock group	discount	free stock	reserved stock	back-ordered	on-order	forecast	maximum	re-order level	minimum order quantity	quantity	price

record identification: article record (01–05)

article record

warehouse	date	vendor			reference	addresses				period
location	of last sale	number	lead time	back-order file	vender chain forward	vender chain back	stock group chain forward	stock group chain back	cumulative sales

record identification: (01–05)

record length 170 characters

record identification: (01–05)

record identification: (01–05)

Scale: 5 10 15 20 25 30 35 40 45 50 55 60 65 70 75 80 85 90 95 100

Step 4-1.4: Review hardware and software requirements

This step is a logical follow-up to step 3-4.4, prepare hardware and software requirements. As the latter step was performed on the basis of the system design as a whole, in practice little or no change can be effected after concluding the design activity.
This review step is necessary, however, to accomodate the possibility that an efficient development of subsystems cannot be made owing to the fact that specific difficulties encountered in this activity were not foreseen. In such a case, it must be decided whether or not the hardware and/or software specification requires alteration, taking into account the impact of the proposed changes on the other related subsystems.
The project team will already have set freezing dates before which any change request must be handed over to prevent delay in hardware and software delivery.

Changes in software present the more difficult problem. This type of change presents difficulties of recognition and description, and subsequently of adaption of the software in order to meet the demand, which are hard to deal with in a tight time schedule. Some compensation can be found in the circumstance that the process of changing software is not an "industrial" one; the work on the change can start at any time, and need not be delayed by production or delivery schedules of hardware.
This step results in a final adjustment of the required hardware and software. For providing a clear picture of the available hardware and software, it is desirable to draw a configuration chart depicting all units and their relationships (see techniques 6-2.2 for an example). To this chart must be added a specification of all software elements.

Evaluating the configuration

In order to be able to specify the configuration which best fits the system design, the use of an automatic tool for performance evaluation, such as SCERT [1]), is recommended. Such a tool permits a simulation of different configurations using the same application for comparison purposes.
The definition of the chosen application should include the following information:

The files used

The file definitions are used to specify the volumes and characteristics of various files involved in the processing. The parameters provided for each defined file can be used for throughput timings and storage requirements.

[1]) • Donald J. Herman, Fred C. Ihrer, *The use of computers to evaluate computers*, Proceedings of the Spring Joint Computer Conference, 1964, pages 383-395.
• Fred C. Ihrer, *Computer performance projected through simulation*, Computers and automation. Newtonville, Mass., **16** (1967,4) no. 4, pages 22-27.

A file should be defined in terms of:
- file number: provides a unique designation for each defined file;
- number of records: describes the number of logical records contained within a file;
- number of characters per record: specifies the number of characters in a logical record;
- number of fields per record, numeric and alphanumeric; describes the number of fields in an average logical record divided into non-quantitative (alphanumeric) and quantitative (numeric);
- category of the file: input (which enters the system for the first time), output (the final output of the system), master file, work file;
- medium: which type of medium the file is going to use;
- file name; a descriptive name of the file. Use the form and file description sheet (3-2.3) or disk file layout forms (4-1.3) to collect these data.

The system definitions

These definitions specify the system design and its processing requirements. All processing requirements are expressed in terms of individual computer runs and/or real-time events. In SCERT, applications are described at the level of runs and operations.

Each computer run is defined in terms of:
- run identity: specifies a run number and frequency of occurrence;
- file identity and throughput parameters; specify the files that are input or output to the run, and other data indicating abnormal or unusual throughput characteristics, such as the percentage of file being used;
- identity and parameters of internal processing; allow for the specification of internal processing requirements by means of the following categories;
  - — general operations: merging operations; synchronization of input files during an update run; sort; internal sequencing of a number of words in store; method of merge for individual sort runs;
  - — data processing operations: update; computer add/subtract; validate; extract; computer multiply/divide; housekeeping;
  - — mathematical operations: square root; logarithm; sine; cosine; arctan; floating add; floating multiply; floating divide; exponentiate;
  - — matrix and table operations: matrix add; matrix multiply; matrix transform; matrix invert; table look-up binary (for a binary search); table look-up serially;
  - — basic computer operations: data move; data multiply/divide; data compare; data edit; data translate; data add/subtract;
  - — report preparation operations: enables the systems analyst to define editing and formatting functions for output print files.

Each run must have a frequency code which:

- defines the time period in which a batch run occurs;
- designates a real-time event or subevent;
- designates compile-and-go run.

Each run must have a number of times per frequency which defines the frequency of occurrence of a batch run, or of real-time events or subevents during a defined period.

Activity 4-2: Specify program requirements

The specification of program requirements consists of laying down in a standard format the relationship of the program with the other parts of the subsystem; the purpose of the program; and development restrictions and processing characteristics. In this way, work packages are prepared which can be handed out for programming.
The program requirements are filed in the project file, and updated if change requests have been accepted; they already provide parts of the final user documentation.

Techniques applicable to this step are:
- application packages (6-4.4);
- programming language selection (6-6.2);
- COBOL programming (6-6.3);
- record key transformation (6-6.4);
- real time testing (6-6.6).

Basic programming information

This first section of program requirements should contain:

Introduction

- purpose of the program;
- place of the program in the run or runs; relationships to other programs, runs, procedures or subsystems, e.g. by means of (sub)system flowcharts;

Development restrictions

- general environment, as information from the project file on hardware (by means of configuration chart), software, and programming language to be used;
- application package or standard programs to be used;

Processing characteristics

- input. By means of form and file description sheets and layouts;
- files. By means of forms and file descriptions sheets, disk file layouts, record layouts and field description sheets;
- output. By means of printer spacing charts (4-6.2) or form and file description sheets;
- processing. Description of decisions and other operations by means of a main program chart, decision tables, formulae, algorithms and tables to be used in the program, a glossary containing identifications of the terms used in the system (3-6 and 4-1.3), and a control scheme;

- test requirements. The test requirements must enable the programmer to test his program, and to discover whether the program meets the requirements, and fits smoothly into a run. The standards applicable to program testing are given in this activity under the heading "requirements for program testing".

General development requirements and constraints

This second section specifies requirements directed at efficiency measures to be considered during programming. These measures can be grouped under the following headings:

Maintainability

Due care must be taken to allow for the introduction of future program changes and modifications by means of modular program construction. This is a standard rule, and not applicable only in situations where a program is designed for adaption and modification by the user. Future modifications might concern:

- logic processing changes in the decision-making pattern, in subroutines, or in the sequence of instructions;
- data alterations, such as changes in record format, record layout, blocking factor, codes, or tables;
- addition, deletion, or replacement of subroutines to reflect new program requirements;

Compatibility

It may be a requirement that a program shall be usable with processors or configurations other than that for which it was compiled. The compatibility called for may be upward (use on larger computers) or downward (use on smaller computers).

When program compatibility is being considered, it is desirable to take into account also data compatibility and overall hardware and software compatibility.

Program compatibility

Program compatibility is dependent upon the language used.

- Source language (COBOL, FORTRAN, ALGOL, etc.):
  - — within one series of computers, upward compatibility usually exists. Downward compatibility may not be available, generally because the internal store of the smaller computer is not large enough. In such a case, compatibility may be achievable by the use of a subset of the language employed;
  - — between computers of different series but of similar capabilities, compatibility can usually be achieved by making small changes in the source program, to accomodate differences in the manufacturers' versions of the language used, and the special features of either computer;

- autocode and machine languages:
  — within computers of one series, upward compatibility usually exists;
  — between computers of different types, compatibility does not exist.

Data compatibility

Data compatibility owes its importance to the fact that the average life-time of consolidated files will normally exceed that of the programs which use them.

- File compatibility
  It is possible to create and maintain a data organization which is suitable for use with two different computers. This type of compatibility is dependent on the characteristics of the data management routines in use. To effect file compatibility calls for a special study of the data organization of each individual case;
- Format compatibility
  Format compatibility is concerned with the organization of stored data, i.e. with record formats, data representations, and file labels. When a collection of data is format-compatible but not file-compatible, conversion can be performed by means of a normal utility program;
- Store unit compatibility
  Store unit compatibility is concerned with the total software-hardware interface of a file stored in an external store. This interface includes the store unit, the control unit, and the channels.
  In the absence of store unit compatibility, files cannot be copied directly. The alternative procedure, which involves dumping the information from one computer on punched cards or magnetic tape and loading the cards or tape on the other computer, is tedious and often impracticable.

Overall hardware and software compatibility

This form of compatibility must be considered from the point of view of the subsystem team and the operators.

- Job-control compatibility
  The job-control language is the interface between runs defined by the subsystem team, and the hardware and software. Theoretically, job-control compatibility can exist only when the computers which are to accept a common run are operating under the same job-control language. Compatibility at the run level in not often called for;
- Operator compatibility
  In general, the support procedures performed by the operator (or other personnel of the computer centre) will have to be changed to accomodate differrent hardware-software configurations. The necessary changes do not normally give rise to serious problems.

Expandability

Expansion needs for program growth should be specified with quantitative references to space, features, or file reservations.

Throughput time

Under this heading should be specified the estimated running times and enquiry response time. (See also evaluation of the configuration by means of SCERT in 4-1.4).

Requirements for program testing

In addition to the test requirements dealt with in the section on basic programming information, two types of preparation must be undertaken before program testing can proceed:

- a testing procedure for the programmer must be drawn up (4-5.4), to indicate:
  - the programs on which hand or machine tests are to be performed;
  - the type of test case to be dealt with;
  - how the test input is to be obtained, with descriptions of special codings or other data needed for specific types of testing;
  - which combinations of routines and subroutines should be tested (degree of completeness of the testing);
  - how the control data, with which the test output is to be compared, must be obtained;
  - a reliable estimate of the manpower required for each test case;
  - a detailed estimate of the assistance required from outside the project;
  - a schedule of dates for intermediate and final test points. These dates should also be incorporated in the schedule for system development.

  A test procedure of this type should be developed by each of the subsystem teams, and checked by the standards group of the information systems department;

- certain testing preparations must be made, independently of the programmer, by the project team:
  - creation or use of test input and test files which include a stated range of conditions likely to be encountered in actual operations, and specifications of any test data generators required;
  - comparison of test results with the results of previous simulations (e.g. desk checking), or with estimates of program operation;
  - further processing of output data by subsequent programs, when such programs have already been fully tested;
  - output review analysis, including comparison of output with results of the present system, with known information requirements, with results of output checking by manual computation, and, if possible, with the comparable outputs of another similar system.

Multiprogramming and multiprocessing

If special requirements for multiprocessing and multiprogramming applications are likely to arise, provisions for debugging measures, such as "introspective control", or use of the so-called analysis mode, must be made [1]).

Introspective control

In a real-time system, many programs may be running concurrently, interrupting each other in a random and unpredictable sequence. To detect errors under such conditions, the system must be self-monitoring and self-correcting; and, if possible, the self-correction should not necessitate stoppage of the operations. Such a system, capable of monitoring and controlling its own actions, and of logging significant data for later analysis, is said to possess "introspective control".

Introspectivity must be planned from the beginning of sybsystem development. Most of the required actions should be built into the monitor program, but it is necessary also that the application programs should be written in such a way that the programmer will be able to determine what is going on.

This method of programming is core-consuming; the aids should be written in such a manner that they can be removed easily, or can be dynamically removed, and brought back into core while the system is running as soon as program errors occur.

Analysis mode

A real-time system can run under a type of "analysis mode". The necessary supervisory or debugging programs are brought into core by means of a monitor, which logs any information required into a core area, (the analysis area), as a log of interrupts, program identifications or macro-trace data.

In multi-thread systems it is possible to use an analysis area for each transaction. This area, which can be chained to the message reference block, is called an analysis block. Both blocks are active simultaneously. The analysis block is dumped when an exit macro is given or when the block is full.

Dumps can be given at any required moment; for example, when transferring from the job control program to an application program, and when control is returned from the application program to the job control program. Times to and from an application program are called respectively entry time and departure time.

[1]) James Martin, *Programming Real-time Computer Systems*, Prentice - Hall, Englewood Cliffs, N.J., 1965.

Activity 4-3: Specify procedure and forms requirements

The development of procedures and forms is closely related to the development of programs, and is performed in parallel with that activity, but by team members experienced in job analysis, work study and forms development.

A formal approach to this activity is advocated, for the following reasons:

- the requirements for quality, content and timing must be more sharply defined for an automated information system than for a manual one;
- changes in the organization render part of the experience of the employees worthless. These situations call for the rapid implementation of new standards of performance. A written procedure will greatly facilitate uniformity of action;
- the effects of personnel turnover are minimized by the preservation of experience in the form of documented procedures; the training of new personnel will be greatly speeded up and good performance will be reached earlier;
- preparation of procedures leads to the establishment of a basis for control over the operations in the organization, and assists in job evaluation and the drawing up of task descriptions;
- maintenance and the implementation of system changes are facilitated when formal documentation is available.

This activity is subdivided into two steps;
4-3.1 specify procedure requirements;
4-3.2 specify forms requirements.

The following techniques are of assistance:

- technical writing (6-2.1);
- charting technique (6-2.2);
- decision tables (6-2.4);
- forms development (6-4.3);
- control techniques (6-5).

Step 4-3.1: Specify procedure requirements

The procedure requirements are the formal specifications of the purpose of the procedure, its place in the (sub)system, and the processing it involves. They must be documented in the project file, and are subject to change control (2-4.2) as are program requirements; they are a part of what will ultimately become the user documentation.

Main procedures

- Independent procedures; those which will be performed wheter a computer based information system exists or not;
- output usage procedures, which are triggered by the occurrence of computer-produced signals, reports, forms or other types of message.

Support procedures

Support procedures are closely related to automatic data processing. Examples are:

- collection of transaction data;
- preparation of file alterations;
- input preparation and control;
- conversion to machine-readable representation;
- data transport or transmission;
- intermediate control of partly finished processing results;
- output dispatching;
- output control;
- correction and exception reporting.

Basic procedural information

This first section of procedure requirements should contain:

Introduction

- Purpose of the procedure;
- place of the procedure in the subsystem; relationships to other procedures, computer runs or subsystems, illustrated by means of subsystem flowcharts.

Development restrictions

Examples of resources which must be specified in procedures are:

- departments and employees involved;
- individuals with specific responsibilities and/or tasks to perform. Design the procedure in such a way as to minimize disturbance resulting from employees going sick, taking holidays or leaving the company;
- equipment to be applied and other specific works aids;
- materials;

- files, directories, tables, etc.;
- information storage and transmission facilities, including telex and other data transmission units;

Processing characteristics

- Input, specified by means of form and file description sheets;
- files, specified by means of form and file description sheets and field description sheets;
- output, specified by means of form and file description sheets;
- operations and management policies, described by means of decision tables, formulae, etc.

General development requirements and contstraints

This second section of procedure requirements specifies requirements directed at efficiency measures to be considered during procedure development. These requirements include:

Maintainability

Directives will be given for maintainability, changes, and the possibility of making incidental deviations from the procedure.
Be alert for the consequences on the workload when splitting up procedures into too many small parallel processed parts.

Throughput timing

Required throughput times can call for the setting up of individual procedures for exception handling; or of groups of simple parallel procedures with short throughput time instead of one complex time-consuming procedure. However, limitations arise:

- when procedures have causal relationships, prohibiting independent parallel running;
- when procedures are consecutive e.g. the output of one procedure is the trigger for another.

Practical rules

The method of preparing procedure requirements comprises the following stages:

- identify tasks and operations which should logically be combined into one procedure (4-1.2);
- determine the data fields in their relation to operations/tasks embodied in the subsystem flowchart;
- identify the departments in the organization which supply the required data, and the data carriers concerned;

- evaluate the dates or frequency of supply of data elements, and the response or throughput times required in order to detect if serial or parallel operations are called for. Parallel procedures tend to increase the number of documents to be converted into machine readable form and the number of types of forms;
- separate the procedures which end with providing data, or data carriers, somewhere in the organization needing another trigger for continuation;
- identify the individual procedures, and determine the desirability of documenting some of the requirements in a causal relationship, by departments or by functions to be performed by the system (e.g. support procedures);
- examine the possibility of using office equipment in the individual procedures in order to improve efficiency and, as far as possible, to detect errors at the point of origin;
- review the requirements posed by the internal control scheme for the subsystem to decide which checks should be built into the programs and, which into the procedures.

Step 4-3.2: Specify forms requirements

Before efficient development of a form or a report can begin, it is necessary to have a clear picture of the need for and usage of the document. These aspects are encountered during the system design activity in 3-4, and in 4-1.2 and 4-1.3 a clear picture is obtained of the place of documents in the organization. For the types of document which can occur in an organization, see 3-2.3. Experience with similar existing documents, and a knowledge of the constraints applicable to the present situation, are also necessary before starting forms development. The requirements are:

- specification of the content of the form; see the form and file description sheet in 3-2.3;
- demands levelled by the method of filling in the form: by hand, by typewriter, or otherwise (see forms development, 6-4.3);
- the need to attract attention to specific data fields;
- demands of appearance and readability. This will differ greatly from one case to another, depending on whether forms are for external or for internal use;
- demands of size. Many situations can occur in use where the size of the form will be subject to limitations, or strictly related to the method of filing;
- demands of rough handling. Where paper is used in difficult environmental conditions, special care must be given to the selection of a suitable grade, or to the substitution of another medium as data carrier;
- demands of machine-readability or keypunching;
- demands for parallel or sequential routing of the form. There are two principal ways in which a form may be used in an organization viz.:

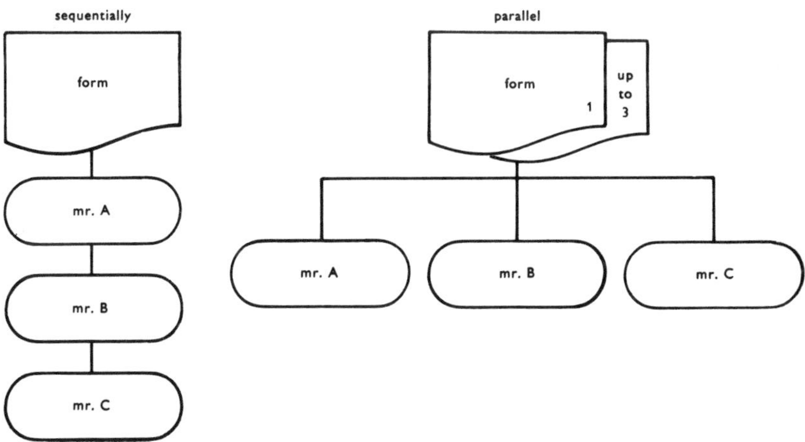

The sequential routing may be required when information has to be added to the form in the successive operations. It will save in costs of forms supply, but may have disadvantages, in that the throughput time can be prolonged

and the employees concerned cannot retain a copy for their own files.
The parallel method eliminates these disadvantages, but may give rise to more complicated and costly preparation of the form if the number of copies exceeds typewriter capabilities, and may initiate unnecessary file-keeping efforts by receiving employees.

Activity 4-4: preparation for conversion

The purpose of this activity is to make an accurate assessment of the content of the conversion task, to plan the task itself, and to perform all the necessary preliminary work. Conversion is a part of the implementation of the new system. During the actual implementation, many simultaneous changes are taking place; it is therefore necessary to plan the whole of the implementation, including conversion, carefully in advance.
Be aware of interfaces e.g. when only the main processing computer is replaced, while other smaller ones remain in operation, to take care of input conversion and screening of output printing.

This activity includes:
- identification of all data representations to be converted (4-4.1);
- identification of all programs to be converted (4-4.2);
- identification of the sequence of actions necessary during conversion;
- identification of additional hardware and storage media to be used during conversion.

The knowledge gained during the preparation for conversion should be utilized in scheduling the actual conversion (5-4), particularly in respect of the allocation of manpower, resources and time.

Step 4-4.1: Prepare file conversion

In this step, standards and guidelines for file conversion are established, the tasks to be executed are identified, programs and procedures are identified, and provisions are made for checking and maintaining the converted files. The documentation produced should be allocated to chapter 6 of the project file (2-4.1), and considered as interface information requiring updating as program or procedure requirements are changed.

Of the many reasons for file conversion, the following are worthy of mention at this stage:

- in their present form, the files do not offer convenient access (outputs of manual procedures, card indexes, sheets of paper in binders etc.);
- the files are on a machine-readable medium, but the new system requires that they be converted to another;
- changed record layouts require rearrangement of the data fields in a file; with or without medium conversion;
- file consolidation is to be undertaken;
- the existence of new system requirements concerning labeling and data representation (fixed length words, octads, packed decimal, character set).

The actual format conversion may be accomplished either by a utility conversion program or by a special program. The development and specification of conversion programs and procedures are essentially the same as those of operational programs and procedures. It must be remembered, however, that in general con-

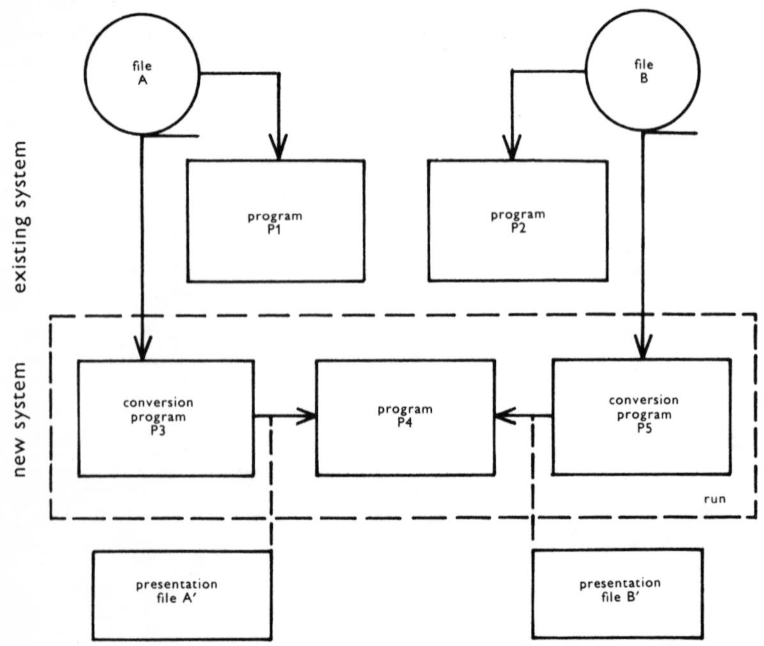

The parallel usage of new system and existing system

version programs and procedures are to be used once only. It is therefore not desirable to spend too much time, when writing them, in ensuring short operating and processing times; it is better to save programming and testing time.

When files are needed by programs of both existing and new systems, files containing the same information may be required in two different formats. Such a conversion is not necessarily a one-time effort, but may be executed repeatedly, as long as the different file representations are required. In this case, the conversion program should be treated as a normal operational program, and may be embodied in runs to provide for online conversion. In the example on page 2 *P1* and *P2* are existing programs, while *P4* is a new program which uses existing files *A* and *B* reformatted by online conversion programs in the same run.

A condition necessary to this approach is that the available hardware configuration is capable of handling both data representations in use for tape, disk, or tape and disk.

Planning file conversion

The planning of the conversion (5-4) depends mainly on the way the new operations will be started (5-5):

- history processing;
- parallel processing;
- straight turnover;
- phased turnover.

The following conversion procedure should be adapted to suit the proposed method of changeover. The activities to be performed should be identified at this stage, in order to prepare a conversion plan. The following checklist gives a summary of individual tasks to be performed in a logical sequence. The description of the tasks is given in the appropriate activities and steps.

Conversion procedure

- Arrange for staffing a conversion team;
- instruct conversion team;
- establish method standards for the file conversion, e.g. for scheduling, usage of forms, codings, checking techniques and accounting of man and machine time. During conversion, files may be available with basically the same information but with different representations; such as for example 7-track, emulation 9-track, and new system 9-track for tapes. External identification by using coloured stickers and/or numbering of reels or disk packs in different series helps the identification;
- establish documentation rules for existing and new files, as well as for the conversion job itself, in order to allow for error correction at any stage;
- make, on the basis of the analysis already performed, a listing of all files currently in existence, whether maintained by hand or in machine-readable format;

- summarize the characteristics of these files, giving particular attention to:
  - — type of data carrier;
  - — size;
  - — complexity;
  - — frequency of updating: which files are most active;
  - — degree of alteration: which files are most variable;
  - — machine readability;
  - — file organization;
- check the existing files for reliability in terms of completeness, accuracy and legibility;
- identify the required files, either to be converted or to be created;
- identify the source of each item and each data field in the new file(s);
- identify the sequence of conversion or creation. It may be possible to use data from the first converted file for the others.

  It is possible to convert a library of files in one sweep, consuming perhaps several hundred hours of computer time. However, to attempt to complete the conversion in too short a time period, when only limited experience in the use of the new equipment is available, is not to be recommended. A more practical approach would be to select those files that are scheduled to be used first after installation of the new computer, and to convert them at the earliest convenient time after their last use;
- identify and specify requirements for necessary file conversion programs, e.g. file records should be printed out in a format similar to that of the original records;
- identify and specify requirements for necessary file conversion or creation forms;
- develop necessary controls on reliability, completeness, accuracy and efficient usage to be employed after conversion;
- provide procedures and measures for updating the converted files until the new system is fully operational;
- gather existing file data (5-4.2);
- create new file data (5-4.3);
- develop and implement a correction procedure for errors;
- check out converted/created files (5-4.4);
- make provisions for documents in the "pipeline" when the conversion has been executed;
- check the use of the new file updating procedure;
- arrange for disposal of the old files.

Step 4-4.2: Prepare program conversion

This step deals with the preparation measures necessary for program conversion. The problem of program conversion exists only in those situations where data processing equipment is to be replaced, and where it is neither strictly necessary nor the intention of the user to replace all existing programs by newly written ones.
Technique 6-6.5 (program conversion) deals with the characteristics and applicability of the various techniques of program conversion. These methods are directed towards making the new installation contribute as quickly as possible to the existing system or to parts of it. A trade-off has to be made between short throughput time and minimization of costs, and the efficiency of a converted program as compared to a newly developed program.
In practice the installation of new equipment is often delayed until the situation occurs that even more shifts do not provide sufficient processing capacity. In such a situation, program conversion techniques provide a ready means of ensuring a continued data processing service to the organization.

Imitation

If the new installation is capable of imitation, there is no inherent reason to limit the use of that feature; in addition a gain in data processing time is obtained. It is advisable to start with some relatively simple programs, and continue with the parallel operation of one or more complete production cycles of the system before complete turnover.

Refabrication

Refabrication of programs should be concentrated on two areas:

- heavily patched programs which require considerable maintenance;
- the small number of programs which give the main load to the installation. Refabrication of these programs gives the maximum gain in data processing time for a given effort.

If refabrication is used, all the advanced features of the new installation should be employed; special attention must be paid to the potential of larger internal storage and external stores permitting the combination of functions or programs.

In the case of refabrication, and to a lesser extent also of imitation, attention must be paid to program interfaces. The smooth operation of partially converted programs, or programs in which different conversion techniques are applied should be tested carefully.
A complication which can not always be avoided arises if an input/output computer remains in operation while the main part of the installation is replaced. If refabrication is applied, it may be desirable to consider also refabrication of re-

lated input and output programs. Schedule the conversion step carefully, taking into consideration time needed for testing and debugging.

Planning program conversion

The action sequence for program conversion is given in the procedure below.

- Introduce method standards of program conversion, including audit procedures to check the quality of the converted programs;
- assign a conversion team to be responsible for the conversion effort, with members familiar with the development of the original information system. This team will be aware of the requirements of their run or program and are in a much better position to evaluate the reliability and performance of the converted programs;
- train programmers for the conversion job: introduction of new hardware, software aids and special conversion utility routines, emulation functions, specific operating system features to be used and software timing data (see 5-1.3);
- review existing program documentation, check correspondence between program documentation, source deck and object program;
- study manufacturers general conversion aids. Consider the efficiency of available emulators and simulators to determine if they are suitable for the conversion effort and the configuration;
- investigate if more economical conversion aids from software companies are on the market;
- consider if additional program conversion programs must be written; if so, identify and specify the requirements for them;
- divide existing application programs into those to be imitated and those to be refabricated;
- select appropriate conversion techniques from 6-6.5;
- the purpose of program conversion is to permit the use of new equipment as soon as possible after installation; therefore applications which require a considerable amount of machine time should be the first to be imitated;
- see if some runs can be processed by replacing only the sort programs, having the application programs to be refabricated later;
- those parts of an application which will make use of advanced features of the new hardware should be reprogrammed first;
- see if less frequently performed runs occur which can be run indefinitely under emulation;
- provide testing material including inputs for online reading units;
- provide tapes, disk packs, and other direct access stores;
- when the majority of the programs are refabricated, it will be more efficient to standardize processing by eliminating imitation, or by replacing at least emulation by a programmed simulator;
- make or adapt new program descriptions; file this documentation in the project file (2-4.1) from which parts will be selected to make the final user documentation before turnover to the user.

Activity 4-5: Develop programs

The purpose of this activity is to develop, to operating status and in accordance with the program requirements, a program whose representation is intelligible both to man and to machine. The program should be accompanied by all documentation necessary for its use and maintenance.

The activity of program development can be subdivided into the following steps:
4-5.1 flowchart programs;
4-5.2 code programs;
4-5.3 prepare first compilation;
4-5.4 test programs;
4-5.5 prepare program description;
4-5.6 prepare instructions for the computer centre.

Techniques to be applied are:
- charting technique 6-2.2;
- identification of system elements and data objects 6-4.1;
- data organization 6-4.2;
- control techniques 6-5;
- methods of computer programming 6-6.1;
- COBOL programming 6-6.3;
- record key transformation 6-6.4;
- real time testing 6-6.6.

Programming aids

Any means of saving programming time, such as automatic coding, programming, debugging, flowcharting and documentation aids, should be considered and applied whenever possible.
In "methods of computer programming", methods are given which will result in the saving of running time. Other possibilities, such as the use of direct access stores and terminals, call for advanced techniques of development and for the use of software on a larger scale.
The interfacing of monitoring programs and application programs must be effected carefully to guarantee the operational reliability of the new system.

Multiprogramming and multiprocessing

Special care called is for in the case of multiprogramming and multiprocessing due to the increased complexity of the programming effort.
Multiprogramming can be defined as the interleaved processing of more than one program, multiprocessing as the simultaneous execution of more than one program by a computer configuration consisting of more than one independently initiable processor, each having access to a common jointly addressable internal store connected to a number of common I/O units.

These types of computer usage give rise to the necessity of taking care of variable types of message, with fluctuating input rates and of different priorities and variable processing requirements; the control of multiple input/output units; the handling of multiple processor interrupts and of queues; the dynamic program allocation and handling of occasional overloads; the switchover of faulty units, including the central processor while operational, fall-back to a limited mode of operation, and recovery from fall-back.
For a discussion of these subjects, in addition to the relevant chapters and techniques in ARDI, see *Programming Real Time Computer Systems* by James Martin, Prentice-Hall Inc., Englewood Cliffs, N.J., 1965.

Step 4-5.1: Flowchart programs

Before actually starting program development it is advisable to check the completeness and clarity of the specification of the program requirements in order to avoid repetitive efforts due to later additions or clarifications. A program flowchart is a graphical representation of a proposed method of solving a programming problem. A program flowchart is useful:

- before coding, during the development of the logic of the new program, it is a representation of a possible solution; it describes how the problem can be processed with a computer according to the solution under study;
- it assists in evaluating the different solutions possible, and in selecting the best;
- after coding and compilation; for instance, during program testing and maintenance it serves as a part of the program description, shows the contents of the programs, and permits easy identification of its structure.

Modularity

Distinction should be made between main and detail program flowcharts. The main flowchart is a part of the program requirements, and is sometimes called the linkage table, since it represents the logical division of the complete program into modular parts. In it, emphasis is laid on causal relationships; details like initializing, processing first record, closing are not necessary. The modular parts consist of routines and subroutines for each of which detail flowcharts are prepared. Each part is constructed in such a way that it maintains its independent character, thus allowing for segmentation. The use of existing standard routines and utility programs reduces the need for flowcharting.
Flowcharting along the lines described in this step results in a set of drawings which, in its composition, is not unlike the engineering drawings for a piece of equipment designed on modular lines. Such a set consists of a general assembly drawing accompanied by drawings of assemblies and subassemblies, and so on down to single parts.

The advantages of this modular arrangement are:

- it allows division of work within one program, which is a necessity for larger programs;
- it furthers the standardization of problem solutions. This holds especially for sub-problems which occur in different programs but do not contain specific parts of any particular program;
- corrections are limited to one chart only, irrespective of the recurrence frequency of the subroutine concerned in a program;
- each modular part of the program is separately accessible, which facilitates changes of the program;
- it facilitates segmentation.

Practical rules for program flowcharting

- As soon as the programmer has a sufficiently good understanding of the program requirements to avoid duplication of work, he can start preparing the detail flowcharts of the program in accordance with the main flowchart. Uniformity of flowcharts in outline and detail, lucidity, readability, and a logical approach are essential for the programs to be readily accessible;
- program flowcharts should not show specific machine-oriented solutions, such-as instruction codes of the computer concerned. The translation of the program flowchart into instructions is done during coding (4-5.2);
- the main program flowchart should depict sequentially the main line of processing the problem (function or functions involved); the detail program flowcharts to be prepared should depict the individual operations concerning subproblems (number of aspects of the functions involved);
- ensure that each routine or subroutine contains only those operations and decisions which are exclusively related to one clearly defined problem or subproblem. Always deal with an identifiable problem in one more or less independent modular parts. This will greatly facilitate maintenance;
- use standard programs, standard subroutines, and utility and supervising routines to the maximum extent;
- use the rules prescribed in the technique: identification of system elements and data objects (6-4.1);
- do not make optimization a major aim in the early stage of programming. Concentrate on obvious processing or store-saving aspects, e.g. streamlining the processing of the most frequently occurring types of transaction. However, try to maintain a balance between the use of storage capacity and the execution time of the machine, so far as this is possible without endangering the simplicity of the program;
- in general, try to save on computer execution time, except for one-time programs (e.g. for file and program conversion), when it is better to save programming time at the expense of more machine hours;
- avoid the necessity of communication with the operator within the program. Develop diagnostic messages which are self-explanatory to the user;
- lay the utmost emphasis on control measures (e.g. block counts, record counts):
  — to ensure maximum accuracy of processing;
  — to benefit correction and recovery when errors are detected;
  — to ensure that no files are read twice;
  — to ensure completeness in reading the input;
  — to guarantee that no transactions are processed twice or mutilated;
  — to prevent the use of active tapes for the writing of new output;
  — to prevent loss of output records.
  For a more elaborated review see control techniques (6-5);
- try to chart in such a way that each specific question occurs as infrequently as possible, while avoiding a complex and nested flow;
- Leave intervals while numbering the connectors in order to insert new areas in a later stage;

- state all conditions. For example, if it is possible for a particular question to have several answers, do not regard all remaining possibilities as belonging to the last correct processing branch. If four codes are allowed, and if the code is not 1, 2, or 3, do not assume that it is 4. Ascertain positively that the code is actually 4;
- be sparing of indicators. Usually an indicator is a question in disguise. If it is necessary to test an indicator instead of repeating a question several times, the meaning of each value should be clearly stated;
- if possible, confine a change in the value of an indicator to one chart. Making changes in more charts only renders the program more complicated. In such cases it would be preferable to consider a revision of the solution of the sub-problem;
- comments (Autocode) or notes (COBOL) can be used to facilitate understanding of the flowchart. If they require too much space, they should be mentioned in the relevant section of the program description. Use comments and annotations to prevent subsequent remarks such as "Why did we do it in this way at the time?"
- exceptional situations should be treated in accordance with their significance. The conditional branches in the main line of a program should in general be sequenced according to the usage rate of the relevant modules.
  This point will be elaborated in technique 6-6.1: methods of computer programming;
- revise existing flowcharts if the program needs extension. Better to re-draft certain charts than to make corrections to them in order to remedy deficiencies;
- apply the conventions in charting technique (6-6.2);
- flowcharts should be drawn on tracing paper. The prints made can be used in the coding stage as well as later on, which means that a considerable part of the final documentation has already been completed;
- for drafting purposes, a large try-out sheet may be employed; a large blackboard is also very useful. Redraw the program flowcharts on a large quarto size such as A4 [1]), to facilitate filing and duplication;
- each (sub)routine should start on a new page of the detail program flowchart.

Flowchart checking

After having made the flowcharts the following checks should be executed before starting program coding.

Significance of checks

The checking of flowcharts is very frequently neglected, lack of time being the usual excuse. Such checking should, however, be regarded as an important part of program flowcharting. Unless it is carried out accurately and comprehensively,

---

[1]) A4 = 210 × 297 mm.

even apparently satisfactory programs which have been used succesfully for some time may become "jammed" due to unforeseen circumstances. The cost saving which occurs because good checking has eliminated such jams does not appear on any financial report; but the losses which arise from the omission of checking become all too obvious.

A detailed check of the method of processing cannot be effected until after coding, and is discussed in step 4-5.2 under the heading desk checking. The advantages of checks include:

- timely discovery of basic errors, reducing unnecessary coding and testing work;
- better understanding of the program, so that errors are found which might have remained undetected even during testing;
- the elimination of unnecessary duplication of operations, which can make for a more efficient program. The checking includes a review of the formal representation and a comparison of the detail flowcharts with the program requirements.

Checking the formal representation

- Is the program structure in accordance with the subroutine technique (modular structure)?
- Have the flowcharts been drawn in accordance with rules of the charting technique given in 6-2.2?
- Are all labels and data objects coded according to the standards? (See identification of system elements and data objects, 6-4.1).
- Have the charts been drawn in prescribed standard format?

Checking against the program requirements

The systems analyst and the programmer should verify, on the basis of the program flowchart, that program requirements are met.

The logic of the flowchart structure

For a check of the logical structure it suffices to test a number of critical points. It is particularly advisable to check:

- initialization; initial setting of index registers, switches and cleaning of work areas;
- processing of the initial input data;
- termination of the programs;
- repetitive operations (are the first and final runs of the loop being processed correctly?);
- break-points to be incorporated in the program;
- entry and exit points of each routine or subroutine;
- values of the indicators at restarting time;
- file relationships and descriptions;

The processing

- if the program does require hardware and software which is not available or which will not be available early enough;
- the theoretical processing possibilities;
- the method of processing these possibilities;
- the layout structure and method of processing of the routines and subroutines indicated at the main flowchart.

Example: Wages control

Program requirements; basic programming information

For clarification purposes an example is given below, based on the specification of program requirements in 4-2. For reasons of simplification many details on wage calculation itself, and on fields which are used for identification and updating are omitted.

Introduction

- purpose of the program: Program 18243 will check the validity of wage cards, update a rates file and print three lists, one for job wage data, one for time wage data and a third for rejected cards;
- place of the program in the run: see subsystem flowchart 182AA;
- relationship to other parts of the system: printtape goes to program 18244.

Development restrictions

- hardware: 64k core; 4 disk units, display unit, punched card reader, high speed printer; 2 magnetic tape units; or: see configuration chart 182BB;
- software: not given;
- programming language: COBOL;
- standard programs to be used: none.

Processing characteristics

- input: input consists of a file of wage cards F0001 (unsorted) which is sorted on a conventional sorter on department code before it enters weekly as F4301 this program 18243:
  - Cardcode 4 contains changed rates for each manufacturing department; each department has a specific code number.
  - Cardcodes 5-7-8-9 contain job wage data.
  - Cardcode 6 contains time wage data. Cards with code 6 account for the largest input volume.

  See multiple punched card layout 182CC for the three types of card (4; 5-7-8-9; and 6).
  See field descriptions 182DD up to 182LL for the data fields in the abovementioned types of card;

- files: see disk file layout 182MM and record layout 182NN for the content of the rates file. See field descriptions 182PP up to 182TT for fields in the rates file other than those already described;
- output: requirements are:
  - — a list for job wage data, report 1;
  - — a list for time wage data, report 2;
  - — a list for rejected cards, report 3.

  See printer spacing charts 182UU to 182WW for format details;
- processing: see main program flowchart 182XX (This is illustrated as R00 in page 13).

  Printing of report 3 (F4303; rejected cards with error indication) is to be done directly, printing of reports 1 and 2 (F4401 and F4402 respectively) is by a separate print program, no. 18244, from printtape F4302.

Rejection takes place in case of:	error indication
— cards with unknown department code	1
— cards with invalid card codes	2
— cards that contain one or more incorrect fields	3
— cards with incorrect ratechange data	4
— time wage cards with unknown rates	5
— time wage cards with incorrect gross wage calculation; above 999 is incorrect	6

  Totals of each type of error are printed on report 3.
  The rates file (F4304) on disk must be updated with the wage rates of each manufacturing department.
  If the input sequence is disturbed, the processing must be terminated;
- test requirements: not given.

General development requirements and constraints

Maintainability

The program must be modular, to permit future addition of new error checks and card codes.

Compatibility

The program must be capable of being run on similar types of hardware of the same manufacturer to guarantee a regular, undisturbed schedule of execution. Special programming solutions are not allowed.

Expandability

Not required.

Throughput time

The results of the first three weeks of history processing should be reported to the project team for evaluation.

Results

The results of the flowcharting step for program 18243 is:

- reports 1 and 2 are written on magnetic tape F4302, to be printed as a next action by program 18244;
- the following detail program flowcharts illustrate the modular arrangement into routines and subroutines:

R01	Initializing	page 10
R02	Process card code 6	page 11
R03	Process card code 5-7-8-9	page 11
R04	Update rates file	page 10
R05	Closing routine	page 10
S01	Print headings of signal report 3	page 12
S02	Error subroutine	page 12
S03	Print line of signal report 3	not given
S04	Screening general data	not given.

Note: F4302 means: file **02** of program 182**43**
18243 means: program **43** of project **182**.
For detailed explanation of the method of identification, see 6-4.1.

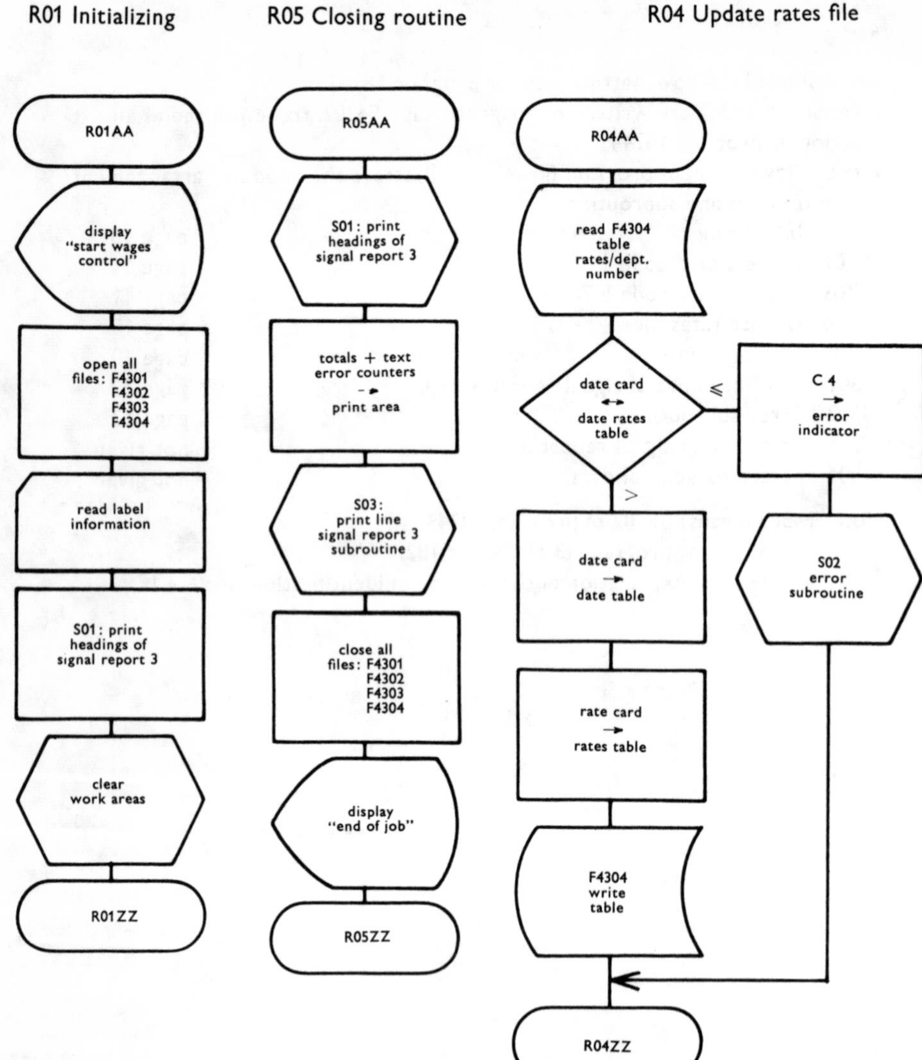
R01 Initializing
R01AA
display "start wages control"
open all files: F4301 F4302 F4303 F4304
read label information
S01: print headings of signal report 3
clear work areas
R01ZZ
R05 Closing routine
R05AA
S01: print headings of signal report 3
totals + text error counters → print area
S03: print line signal report 3 subroutine
close all files: F4301 F4302 F4303 F4304
display "end of job"
R05ZZ
R04 Update rates file
R04AA
read F4304 table rates/dept. number
date card ↔ date rates table
⩽
C 4 → error indicator
S02 error subroutine
>
date card → date table
rate card → rates table
F4304 write table
R04ZZ

R02 Process card code 6

R03 Process card code 5/7/8/9

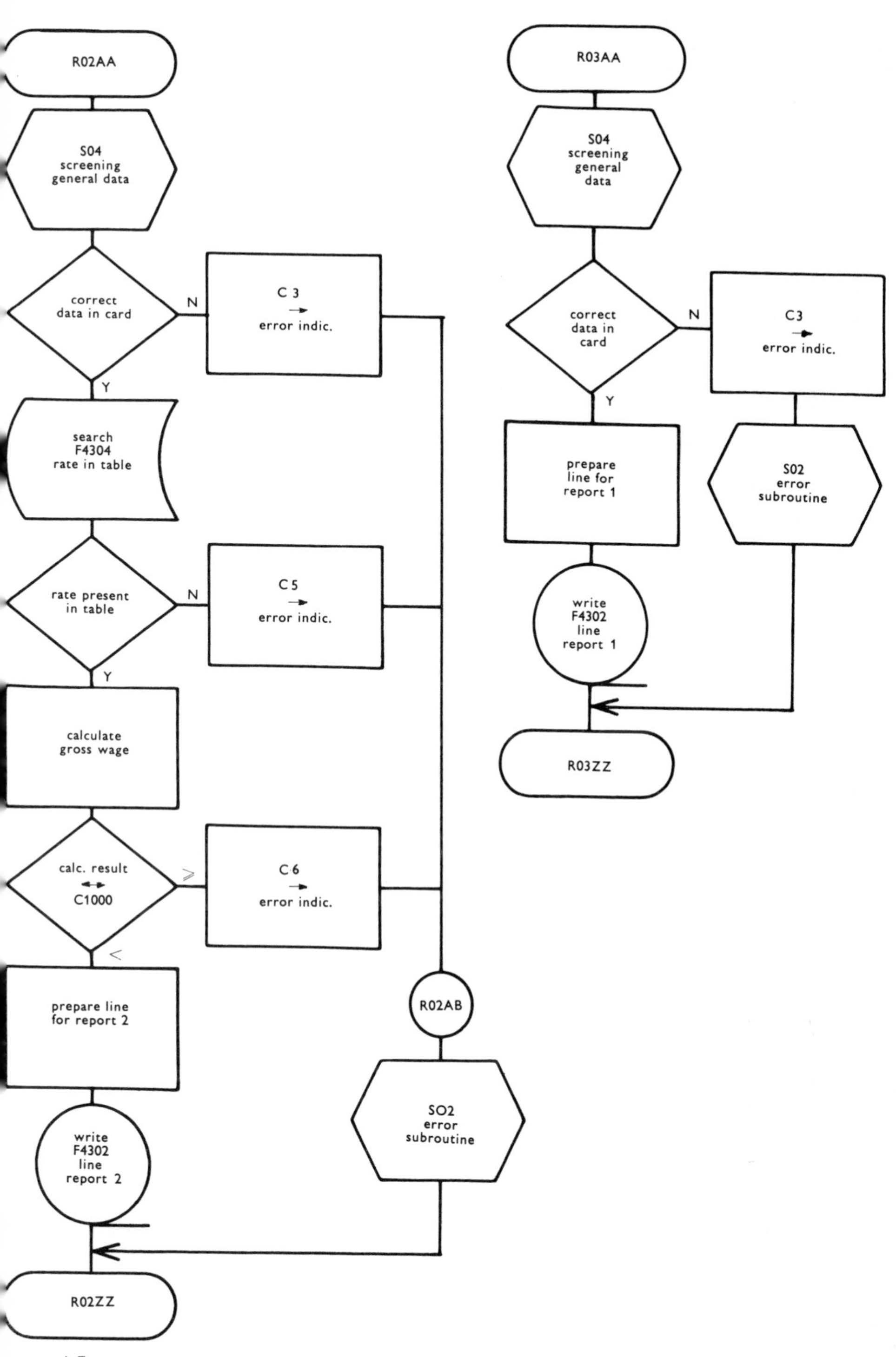

S01 Print headings of F4303 signal report 3

S02 Error subroutine

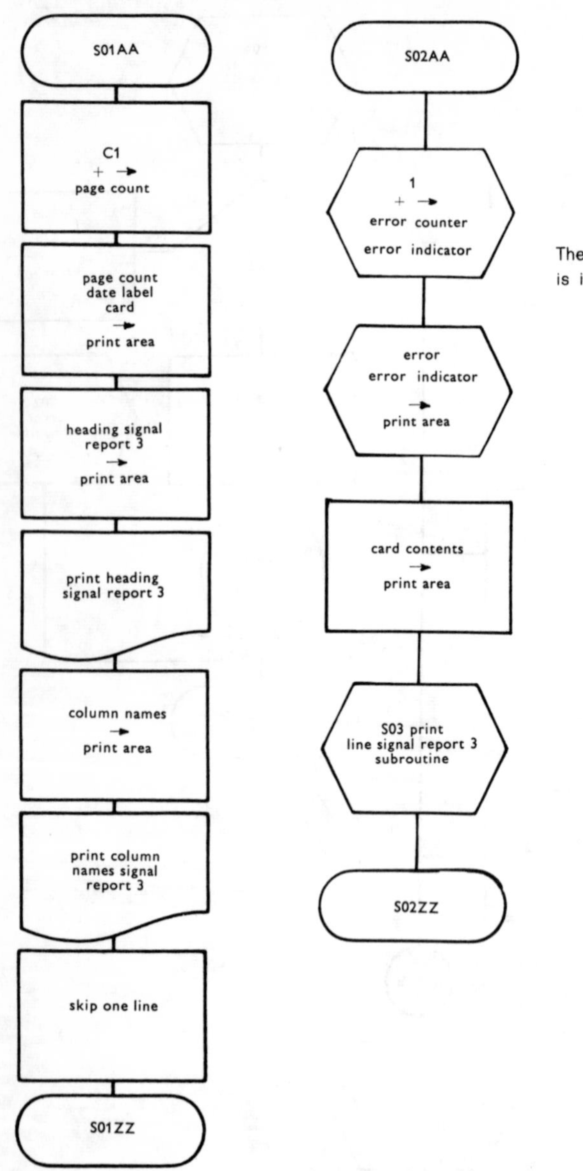

The error indicator information is in an index register

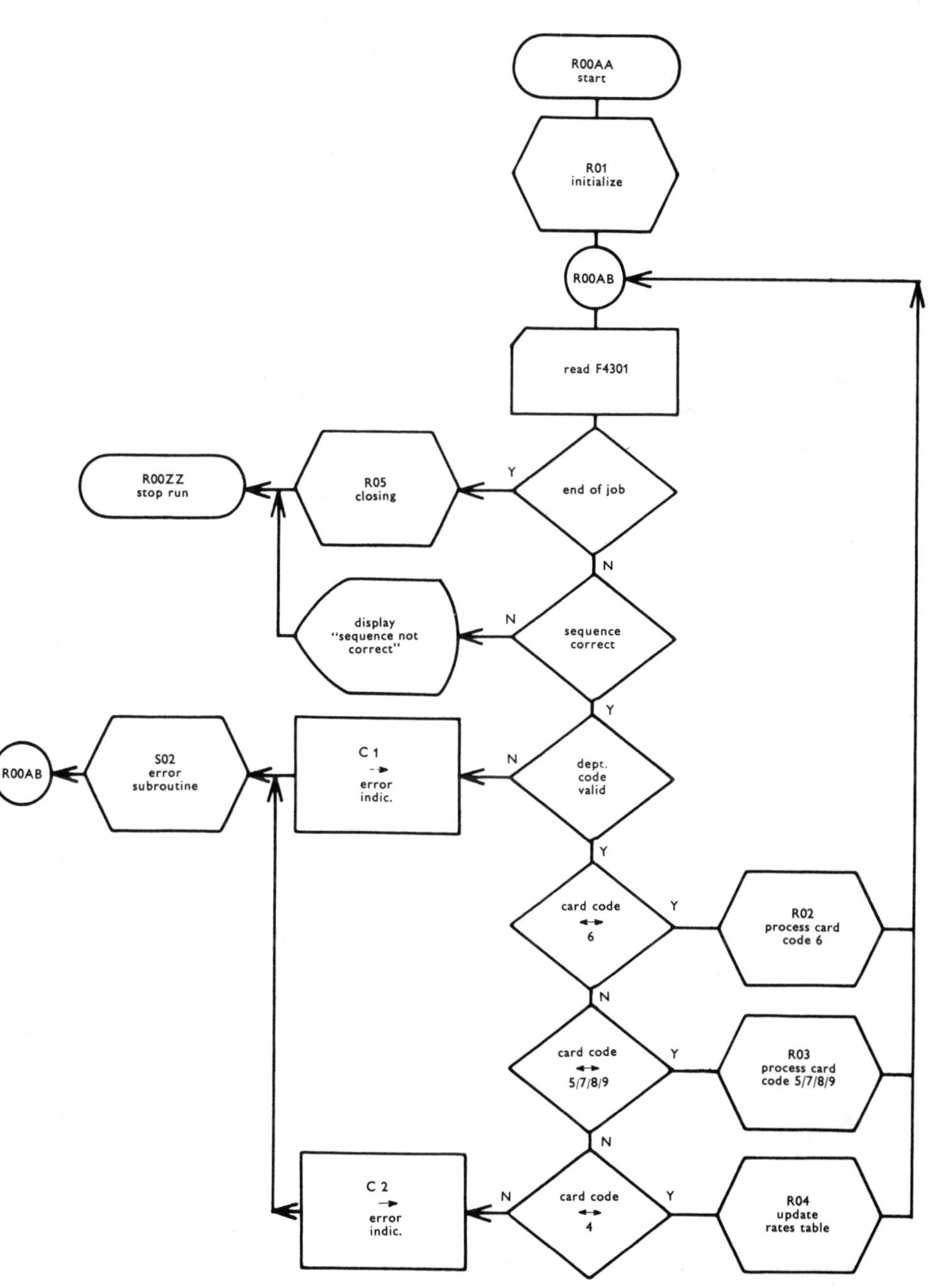

Example Wages control R00 main flowchart of program 18243

Step 4-5.2: Code programs

Coding from flowcharts entails the conversion of flowchart operations to instructions in accordance with the rules of the programming language used. Application of a set of rules is conducive to quick and systematic work. The resulting uniformity in the coding method is of particular advantage for the maintainance of programs.

The work of program coding has been in a state of transition for a number of years. Originally, programs were coded in machine language; nowadays the stage of using symbolic language is being superseded by the use of statement level languages. This facilitates not only the work of coding itself, but also the communication between systems personnel. The next stage will be the use of problem-oriented languages or translators such as DETAB, COGENT and "general file processing" software [1]). This will further reduce the tiresome and tricky job of program coding. It must, however, be noted that some programming problems can only be solved by using assembler language.

Practical rules

- Do not start coding before the detail program flowcharts are finished and checked;
- adhere to the rules for identification of system elements and data objects (6-4.1);
- avoid fancy names or abbreviations for labels and symbolic addresses. They may be a help when coding the program, but in the long run they can be a source of error for maintenance or communication with other programmers;
- identify all labels or paragraph names (COBOL) occurring in instructions, and incorporate them in the program by establishing identity between program names and connectors;
- make name-cards for all routines and subroutines in the form of COMMENTS or NOTE cards, depending on the type of computer;
- Insert one or two blank cards between routines and subroutines to improve readibility of the program print out;
- make certain that the most recent programming manual of the manufacturer is used;
- when the instruction set is powerful or the statements numerous, it can be valuable to specify a subset of the instruction/statement set for internal use only;
- apply consistently the standards for application of the programming language. See e.g. for COBOL 6-6.3;
- use the appropriate coding sheet. For an example of a COBOL coding sheet see 6-6.3;
- leave some lines blank on the program coding sheet — especially between the statements — in order to write additional statements;

---

[1]) *Generalized file processing software*, EDP-Analyzer, Vista **3** (1965.10) no. 10.

- Write in pencil and number the statements, after the program has been written creating intervals for insertion of additional statements;
- apply the following standards for handwriting: In general, when handwritten data must be keypunched, special care must be taken to eliminate any possibility of misinterpreting the characters. This is especially true when filling program coding sheets, because the text is of a purely technical nature and interpretation on the basis of context is difficult. A deviation in punching a single character can cause serious disturbance.

  The most important rules for handwriting on punching documents are:

letter Q	should be written as	Q
letter O	,, ,, ,, ,,	Ø
digit 0	,, ,, ,, ,,	O
letter Z	,, ,, ,, ,,	Ƶ
digit 2	,, ,, ,, ,,	2
letter I	,, ,, ,, ,,	I
digit 1	,, ,, ,, ,,	/
digit 7	,, ,, ,, ,,	7
letter S	,, ,, ,, ,,	S
digit 5	,, ,, ,, ,,	5
letter U	,, ,, ,, ,,	u
letter V	,, ,, ,, ,,	V

- Keep track of creation and usage of work areas;
- adhere to the program structure in routines and subroutines as developed in the previous step. Should it become clear during coding that a change in the program flow is necessary, read just the flowchart immediately;
- remember in general that in the majority of cases the simplest coding solutions yield the best results in the quickest way;
- comments or notes should be used wherever the coded program is not self explanatory. If possible avoid using non-standard solutions or coding tricks, since these require extensive explanation in the program description and can create difficulties in testing, conversion and maintenance.

  This does not mean that the ideas underlying non-standard solutions are necessarily valueless, but they should not be tried out in application programs. They should be passed to the senior programmer or to a programming specialist of the information systems department for evaluation.
- do not assume because many instructions are being used, that immediate optimization is necessary. It is better to optimize after compilation, because the solution is then fully correct and analyzed. The technical aspects can be dealt with separately, and it is possible to judge:
  - — when optimization is really necessary, since internal store is now known;
  - — which routines can most easily be revised.

An exception should, of course, be made for those programs whose first compilation indicates an overflow of storage capacity;

- take care to give the correct OPEN and CLOSE instructions for all files;
- make provision for restarts and breakpoints;
- ensure that no divisor can ever be zero;
- relative addresses (e.g. by means of character adjustments) should be used with discretion. Compilations often fail because an instruction has been inserted between the relative address and the label from which this address was derived. This rule applies only to programs written in Autocode;
- indexing of addresses can be effected in two ways: direct indexing by using hardware index registers for modification of addresses, and indirect indexing by using work areas for this purpose.
  The second method has two variants; the work area contains the modifier, or the work area contains the address of the index register which controls the modification. The latter situation has the advantage that the program instructions themselves are much more permanent.
  In applying indexing methods, the programmer must consider beforehand if they are really necessary; there are many situations in which it will be better to omit them, and so keep the program simpler and (in most cases) faster.

Checking formal representation

This comprises:

- check correct numbering of all used lines per program coding sheet;
- check the formal representation and the content by methods similar to the checks performed after flowcharting;
- check that the practical coding rules of the previous pages have been applied;
- check that the standards of application of the prescribed programming language have been consistently applied;
- check that the hardware requirements of the program (e.g. store capacity, number of I/O units) does not exceed that made available by the computer centre;
- check adherence to directions for the specific computer.

Desk checking

Desk checking should be included in the development of a program. This type of procedure not only checks for mechanical errors, but also checks for likely errors of interpretation (which normally cause more serious problems than logical or clerical errors). The programmer should start by checking his own program carefully. In its simplest form, desk checking can be done by having another programmer review the coding and compare it, instruction by instruction, with the flowcharts. Since debugging on a machine can cost as much as a full working day per bug, it is evident that every error caught with this type of checking will have a beneficial effect on the project's cost and schedule.

In a more general form, desk checking will be carried out by two persons, in the first place because they can check each other's reasoning and secondly because one (the reader) can act as the interpreting part of the "machine" by reading the program, and the other (the writer) represents the memory of the machine. For this type of desk checking test input is required in order to have a realistic simulation. It is desirable that the chosen test inputs should contain both simple and "worst case" examples.

These tests should be carried out with the utmost accuracy; reader and writer must check each other after each step.

The reader starts right from the beginning of the program coding sheets and recites the instructions called for by the chosen type of test input. He must do this "mechanically", without any thought whatever of his original "intentions"; he just reads out the program sequence and checks the notes of the writer.

Special consideration should be given to:

- test cases; are they complete? If not, supplement;
- initialization; are all switches, indicators, working and counting areas in the correct starting positions;
- definition of work areas;
- the condition of files, opened or closed;
- everything entering the storage concerning the program such as position of switches;
- processing of the initial data;
- changes in file data;
- values of modified addresses;
- data in the areas;
- processing of the final data;
- counter position for loops;
- error signalling.

Step 4-5.3: Prepare first compilation

Preparation of the source deck

When the program coding sheets have been made out and checked, they can be keypunched. The card deck, representing the contents of the program coding sheets, is called the source deck or symbolic deck.
The procedure to create a source deck depends on the organization of the computer centre.

Practical rules

- Before starting compiling and/or testing a program, the programmer must take some preparatory steps in order to adhere to computer centre regulations. He will fill in separate run orders for each individual job. An example of a run order is given in 4-5.6;
- the availability of the various facilities must be verified. This covers availability of computer time, standard software programs, keypunching and checking assistance, advice on diagnostics from software specialists, etc.;
- each program should be tagged with an accounting code number, facilitating recording the costs of punching, testing by computer etc.;
- adhere to the rules laid down by the computer centre as regards supply and processing;
- the first and last punched card of the deck must be clearly marked;
- write the number or name of the program on the top card of the source deck (with felt pen);
- supply the cards of the source deck in accordance with the rules of the computer centre for the compilation of a source list.

Checking the source deck

The source deck or symbolic deck will be printed on a source list. This list is used to check whether the punched cards tally with the program coding sheets, and to check if correct statements are used and if all labels are identified where applicable. Such a list is also obtained during compilation. Diagnostics will identify the majority of errors made; the check is facilitated, and the program can be corrected by resolving the diagnostics.
Concentrate attention on:

- sequence;
- completeness: lost cards without labels are not signalled;
- regularity (displacements);
- specialities put forward by the compiler.

The quickest checking method is compilation, but then the program must be acceptable for compilation; if this method is adopted, re-compilation due to deviations as mentioned above may result in longer throughput times and higher costs.

Step 4-5.4: Test programs

Testing the operability of a program can sometimes be a tiresome job even though desk checking has been done thoroughly. The program may not act according to its requirements, and/or some hitherto undetected "bugs" might be present. As a result the amount of time and effort spent in program testing can sometimes be disproportionate to the size of the system.
This step confines itself to the more general aspects of testing. The technique real-time testing (6-6.6) gives additional material for testing of real time, multiprocessing and multiprogramming applications.

Preparation for testing

- Before testing is started, a complete program description should be prepared (4-5.5);
- desk checking based on the concept of "objectivity" must have been performed. Tests should be made at every possible milestone and work should not proceed much further until those tests are successfully completed (see 4-5.2);
- schedule a sequence of tests covering all aspects of the program or set of programs, taking into account different levels of sequential testing: routines and subroutines, the program itself and finally the run. Subsystem testing is dealt with separately in 4-8;
- testing should be performed according to a predetermined scheme, starting with one subroutine or routine and proceeding gradually to more complex combinations. Testing each type of transaction separately may facilitate debugging one (sub)routine or path at a time.
  Independent testing of individual routines or subroutines requires considerable program adaptions in order to run them separately. The most practical manner of doing this is by changing the composition of the program test input. Select input transactions which will test every possible path of the program, logical or not;
- the programmer should make a run order for each test and should specify in advance which parts of core and files should be dumped in the event of an error;
- if the programmer wants to use a special testing aid such as a tracer program, he should familiarize himself with it in advance, or should ask a software specialist to give him advice and assistance;
- employ utility software for core and file dumps and loop check when programs come to an error halt or at end of job. Most utility packages have the capacity of providing "snapshot" memory dumps or of programmer selected areas of memory at predetermined points of program execution. These can be most useful in providing pictures of memory at different stages in the operation of a program, particularly in difficult testing situations when bugs are difficult to locate. Instead of calling for complete file dumps, request that only the first and last ten or so records be dumped and printed;

- always request a dump in the event of any unscheduled termination of the program;
- use simulators when the target computer is not yet available;
- wherever possible, use automated aids for debugging;
- prepare test data containing irregularities and illegal conditions for which the results are already calculated;
- use short input files and restrict the size of output files about the same length. Most types of input data can be represented by test input files of fewer than 100 records;
- during the later stages of testing all input transactions should be combined into one run to provide test conditions similar to those encountered in actual operation;
- test cases which are capable of being used in more than one subsystem should be documented carefully and maintained in a library of test cases. The standards group of the information systems department should select the test cases which are to be included in this file, review and approve the accompanying documentation, and establish and maintain an index of available test cases;
- the test output should be edited in such a way that it is easily readable;
- use short master files specially generated for testing purposes;
- if system files are already available, test files can be created by stripping off selected records which represent the widest possible range of situations in data fields. If system files are not yet available, file generation utility programs can be used to prepare test files;
- record, in a logbook kept specially for this purpose, full details of all tests carried out, the results obtained, the errors that occurred and the measures taken to correct them.

General testing rules

- The program description and especially the detail program flowcharts should be kept up to date during testing. Obsolete flowcharts only cause confusion;
- the programmer should preferably be "accessible" when his program is tested, but the operator should run the computer facility. Usually no computer time will be available for debugging with the machine because this is too expensive;
- in addition to testing program logic, all input, output, initialization, and closing routines must be checked. No special input data is usually required for these routines;
- first test the most probable one from a number of dependent conditions. This may reduce running time;
- skip portions of the program already tested by loading dummy intermediate results into memory and begin program execution at the untested point;
- all output files should be examined closely after running a test in order to check for correct format, data content and labels;
- use all available information at every point of testing. Dumps are useful, not only in determining the error immediately, but also in ensuring that all operations performed, prior to the error where performed correctly;

- when a program gets stuck the programmer should try to identify the point at which it has stopped, or the loop in which it is locked. Then by means of desk checking (4-5.2) the programmer should try to debug that part of the program;
- ask for assistance when progress in error detection or correction halts. A collegue who can look afresh at the problem will in many cases readily detect the error;
- the programmer should always consider a change twice before implementing it. It often occurs that a programmer being focussed upon the aspect of the program that is failing, does not consider the interfaces with other parts of the program;
- any errors detected in the program description should be corrected without delay;
- do not make corrections in the object deck. This guarantees discrepancies between source and object deck and invites serious errors in production and maintenance.

Review

After a program has been demonstrated to be capable of producing satisfactory output, the test results should be reviewed by the systems analyst, assisted by the senior programmer, to ensure that it is accurately debugged and is consistent with the program requirements.

- Review of test inputs and test files to ensure that all elements and situations have been tested;
- review of program termination routine, recorded on logsheets or on outputs, to ensure that all files were closed correctly and the program came to a normal end of job;
- review of output documents and output files for validity in format and data content.

Step 4-5.5: Prepare program description

The purpose of a program description is to facilitate maintenance, system changes and conversions. This documentation will eventually form a part of the user documentation. In the meantime it should be stored in the project file under chapter 5, section 2 (see 2-4.1). The program description should be prepared in parallel with program development, otherwise there will be either great delay owing to new priorities in work for the programmer or the quality of the description can be less by neglecting critical aspects, encountered during the development stage.

Subdivision

The subdivision of the program description is the following:

- list of contents
- chapter 1. first program
  - section .0 program cover
  - .1 program characteristics
  - .2 output (4-2)
  - .3 input (4-2)
  - .4 program changes
  - .5 program flowcharts (4-2, 4-5.1)
  - .6 print of compiled program (4-5.3)
  - .7 console print example (4-5.4)
  - .8 test data (4-2)
  - .9 control scheme (4-1.2)
- chapter 2. second program

  etc.

Detailed contents

Section .0 Program cover

Fixed section names are preprinted on this program cover (see example on page 23).

The check boxes alongside the section names should be crossed if a section is given for a specific program.

Purpose and scope of the program should be mentioned on this cover.

Section .1 Program characteristics

This section contains:

- an indication of the place of this program within the run and the subsystem (see section 2.3 of the system description given in 4-7);
- estimated processing time;
- frequency of use;
- connections with other machines (e.g. punched card equipment);
- runs in which the program is incorporated; refer to run description. (See

PROGRAM COVER

	project no.: :
system :	chapter/sect.:
subsystem :	page :
prev. issue:	issued :

Contents

- ☐ 0 program cover
- ☐ 1 program characteristics
- ☐ 2 output
- ☐ 3 input
- ☐ 4 program changes
- ☐ 5 program flowchart
- ☐ 6 print of compiled program (separately)
- ☐ 7 console print example
- ☐ 8 test data
- ☐ 9 control scheme

Identification

program	— number	:
	— name	:
systems engineer		:
systems analyst		:
programmer	— name	:
	— address	:
	— telephone	:
action number in computer centre		:

Purpose and scope

example in 4-5.6);

- used components of hardware and to what extent;
- used software, standard programs or standard routines.

The last two points may be omitted since they are also given in the instructions for the computer centre.

Section .2 Output

The types of output and output files must be stated.
For details of the output see section 2.6 of the system description (4-7).

Section .3 Input

The types of input and input files must be stated.
For details on input see section 2.6 of the system description (4-7).

Section .4 Program changes

This section is for recording changes, incorporated in the program when it is already in production at the computer centre. (See 2-4.2 change control.)
For some computers it is possible to change the object deck directly, without performing a new compilation. In these cases it is essential that the source deck be corrected at the same time.
A special dual purpose form should be used to write these changes. This form has room for coding lines both for the object language and the source language. When compilation takes place before each production run only the source deck need be changed.

Section .5 Program flowcharts

This section contains the main and the detail flowcharts. Comments should be given for easy maintenance and include:

- an annotation on the main program flowchart;
- a summing up of the more difficult modular parts embodied in the program;
- the usage of indicators, input and output areas, working areas, constants, literals, branches and subroutines;
- the use of tables and the manner in which they are changed.

Section .6 Print of compiled program

It should be on a grade of paper from which copies can be made. On the first page the programmer must note the number of pages the print contains. If the size of the printer-paper is different from that of the program description the print of the compiled program should be bound in a separate cover.

Section .7 Console-print example

Only the programmed messages for the operator are mentioned in this section.

Section .8 Test data

A summary of the test data and the location of the complete test data must be given. The results of the last test should be presented in the form of:

- printer output;
- console print out;
- storage print out (where applicable).

Section .9 Control scheme

The control scheme describes the structure and effect of the internal control measures used, see section 1.4 of the system description (4-7). The control instructions are given in another part of the user documentation, viz. instructions for the computer centre (4-5.6). A summing up of the programmed checks of this program must be given in this section.

Step 4-5.6: Prepare instructions for the computer centre

The purpose of the instructions for the computer centre is to make the data processing of the information system possible without intervention of the project team or other systems people.

The instructions for the computer centre constitute descriptions of each processing run. These instructions will eventually form a part of the user documentation, but in the meantime they should be stored in the project file under chapter 5, section 5 (see 2-4.1).
When devising these instructions it should be assumed that the computer operator knows nothing about the job to be performed and that the only information he receives will be that which is contained in these instructions.
A complete, clear and simple description is therefore absolutely essential for effective system operation.

Subdivision

List of contents:
- chapter 1. flowcharts per run;
- chapter 2. run descriptions;
- chapter 3. files;
  - — file summary;
- chapter 4. run 1;
  - — action numbers, specified by run orders;
- chapter 5. run 2;

  etc.

Detailed contents

Chapter 1: Flowcharts per run
This chapter should contain flowcharts of every run into which the data processing of the (sub)system has been divided (4-2). These flowcharts should be prepared on the basis of the (sub)system flowchart prepared in 4-1.2.
The flowchart for each run must specify:
- input data: type and format, where to obtain;
- output data: type and format, where to deliver;
- specific program numbers, names and sequence;
- when reports must be ready (only in case of fixed target dates);
- how to handle exceptions and errors;
- required hardware including input/output equipment;
- required software;
- required system and/or subsystem files: disks, magnetic tapes, punched cards or punched tape;
- frequency of procession of the run.

Chapter 2: Run descriptions
The run description is a document to be filled in for each run to be performed. See page 28 for an example. It should contain the trigger of the run and a breakdown of the run into actions. It should give details of the input source (either input number or procedure) accompanied by references to responsible user personnel. Processing information (frequency, throughput schedule and operation times per program) should be given. The run description must specify the run processing time agreed between the user and the computer centre. This is essential for planning and control purposes.

Chapter 3: Files
All the files to be used in the run, should be specified in a file summary, see form on page 29.

Chapter 4: Run 1
This chapter should contain the run orders for one of the runs belonging to the system.
As a rule each operation within a run is specified by an action number. These action numbers will serve as a checklist for the operator. For each action number a run order must be devised which can take the format of a preprinted form showing symbols or boxes for the input, output and external storage units. See page 30 for an example.
The run order is a document to be filled in each time a run must be performed. Data which is fixed for a particular type of run should be inserted on the master of the run order for that run. This contributes to efficiency and reduces the risk of error.
To ensure conformity with the operating rules of the computer centre, it is good practice to prepare the master for the run order in co-operation with the production planning or work preparation department of the computer centre.

Fixed data on run order master

The fixed data, to be entered on the master of the run order usually consists of:
- job sequence number;
- action number;
- project code;
- program identification;
- layout of printer carriage control tape(s);
- (fixed) contents of control cards;
- programmer identification;
- compiler to be used;
- list of program halts with required actions;
- procedure in the event of breakdown;
- restart procedure;
- non-standard operating procedures, e.g. regarding tape handling, error handling, etc.;

RUN DESCRIPTION

system : PARTSLIST SYSTEM
subsystem : PRINSYS
prev. issue:

project no. : 123456
chapter/sect.: 4/5
page : 1
issued : 9-5-'69

input: source dept: Construction-department contact person: L. Johnson

action no.	equipment	program	processing			output no.	remarks
			frequency	time	schedule		
input							input no: proc. no:
PP6, A10	2 disks 1 printer	AJC-01	52	0,51	0.75	771	
PP7, C8	1 card reader 1 disk 1 printer	AKL-06	52	0,60	0,75	783	
PP6, PP7 PP8	3 disks 1 printer	AMZ-01	12	0,80	0,70	802	

FILE SUMMARY

system : Production planning & control system
subsystem : Product information subsystem
prev. issue: April 26th. '67

project no. : X 1000
chapter/sect.: 5.5
page : 9
issued : May 31st. '67

file identification	file name	medium	file * type	reference to file description
F 0137	product masterfile	disk	M	system description
F 0138	product structure file	disk	St	system description
F 0241	supplier master file	disk	M	system description
F 0242	supplier structure file	disk	St	system description
F 1220	Update product info. data	tape	Un	subsystem description
F 1224	Changes print file	disk	P	subsystem description
F 2233	Erroneous input data product information	disk	P	subsystem description

* M = master file
Su = subsystem file
St = structure file
Ta = table
H = history file

Un = unsorted transactions file
So = sorted transactions file
P = print file
T = test file
R = relations file

RUN ORDER

programmer name :	job-sequence no.:
address:	date :
phone :	ets. time :
program no.:	project no. :
☐ compile ☐ cobol	machine unit :
☐ test ☐ fortran	action no. :
☐ production ☐	function :
printer 1 printer 2	carriage control tape no.:

	card reader	card punch	papert. reader	papert. punch	printer 1	printer 2	plotter
from							
file no.							
to							
	tape	tape	tape	disk	disk	disk	disk
from							
log. unit							
file no.							
reel no.							
headerlabel							
density							
retention							
to							
2nd. reel no.							
file no.							
log. unit							
to							
3rd. reel no.							
file no.							
log unit							
to							

DATE/CONTROL CARDS

CONSOLE MESSAGES

question	reply

miscellaneous

- specification of types of output:
  - — form numbers;
  - — type of printing paper;
  - — number of copies;
- sources and destinations (in action numbers) of inputs and files used and outputs produced;
  - — delivery addresses;
  - — retention periods;
  - — markings and labeling of output;
- code numbers for physical identification of file storage media should be distinguished from the identification used in the system;
- control instructions: these must be written for those actions, which correspond with section 9 of the referenced programs (see 4-5.5). In many cases there are standard control procedures within the computer centre.

Variable data

The variable data to be entered on a run order usually consists of:
- data/hour of required execution;
- code numbers of file storage media to be mounted;
- run mode for each program e.g. settings of console switches or required control cards;
- contents of date cards, control cards, etc.;
- volumes of inputs and outputs;
  - — number of reels per file;
  - — number of records per tape;
  - — number of punched cards;
  - — number of lines per printed report;
  - — number of printed forms.

Activity 4-6: Develop procedures and forms

The activity "develop procedures and forms" will usually be performed in parallel to the previous one "develop programs" (4-5).
As already stipulated in activity 4-3, procedures and forms are so closely related that it is logical to discuss the development of both in the same activity. This activity is subdivided into the following steps:
4-6.1 develop procedures;
4-6.2 develop forms;
4-6.3 try out the procedure;
4-6.4 prepare procedure description.

When developing procedures or forms, the situation and the attitudes in the user organization must be taken into consideration carefully. The best guarantee for success of this activity will be to work in close co-operation with ultimate participants in the procedures and users of the forms. This enables the subsystem team to detect practical difficulties beforehand instead of at the time of implementation.

The way in which a procedure can be documented, by narrative or by chart, is detailed in 4-6.4. The forms description will form an element of the system description (4-7), while the procedure description forms a part of its own in the complete set of user documentation. In the meantime the procedure descriptions are stored in the project file under chapter 5, section 3 (see 2-4.1).

Techniques to be applied are:
- technical writing (6-2.1);
- charting technique (6-2.2);
- decision tables (6-2.4);
- forms development (6-4.3);
- control techniques (6-5).

Step 4-6.1: Develop procedures

Review the procedure requirements and constraints as developed in 4-3.1 to determine:

- their dependence on implementation of organizational changes, as specified in 3-3.2;
- the interfacing necessary with existing procedures which are to be retained;
- the trigger or stimulus to the procedure;
- the outcome: what must be the result(s) of the complex of operations combined in a procedure;
- the resources needed for execution of the procedure;
- company policies concerning manner and speed of response, e.g. that telephone requests for information must be dealt with within 30 seconds;
- internal control requirements, e.g. in case of invoicing by splitting up the job over a number of employees.

Operations

The following practical rules can be formulated for defining the operations within a procedure:

- select appropriate trigger for the procedure;
- identify the work stations (departments, groups, sections, etc.) in the organization;
- allocate employees to the work stations, prepare task descriptions;
- specify the documents required in the procedure;
- identify the manual files to be used in the procedure;
- calculate execution and throughput times for each operation or coherent set of operations;
- if many situations can arise in a procedure it is good practice to use a block diagram or decision table to ensure that all possible situations have been taken into account;
- describe in clear, plain words the essentials of each operation. Use the technique technical writing (6-2.1);
- description of operations which involve or immediately succeed decisions should start with the word IF;
- end the procedure on a point such as:
  - — transfer to another type of operation e.g. from manual to mechanical;
  - — transfer to another data carrier;
  - — transfer to another geographical location;
  - — different frequency of operation;
  - — separation or combination of operations.

Size of procedure

Although procedures are already specified in 4-1.2, it may turn out that a further breakdown is necessary. It is inevitable, however, that this will create a larger number of relationships between procedures. A procedure must be capable of being handled and supervised by a limited number of individuals.

Step 4-6.2: Develop forms

Documents must be developed on the basis of 4-3.2 in strict relationship to the procedures in which they appear and in such a way that they perform their intended purposes. In development full use should be made of technical possibilities and requirements. To obtain a background picture of the various roles which forms fulfil in an organization, see 3-2.3. Forms development in the general sense is described in technique 6-4.3.

In an information system many kinds of forms will have to be developed:

- forms to be used only in manual procedures, to be filled in either by hand, or by a typewriter or other machine;
- forms with special requirements such as:
  - — suitable for keypunching;
  - — suitable for magnetic or optical reading;
- printer-made outputs; lists, reports or forms;
- punched cards. Although not a form in the strict sense of the word, many applications of punched cards show that this data carrier is used not merely as a carrier of machine-readable information but also in manual operations as a normal readable document. This necessitates consideration of special layout and "make-up" features.

Forms with special computer input requirements

Keypunching forms
It must be stressed that in general the use of special keypunching forms or transmittal forms as intermediate documents between source documents and keypunching must be avoided. It requires the introduction of an extra clerical step, during which errors can occur. Only where source documents are exceptionally complicated should it be necessary to write transmittal forms merely to facilitate keypunching.
To be suitable for keypunching, the arrangement of data fields must conform to the sequence of keypunching. If possible, card columns should be indicated on the form.

Machine readable forms
Forms suitable for optical or magnetic reading must satisfy a number of technical requirements. These include dimensions, material, tear strength and thickness, protection against mutilation and dirt, limitations as to the zones of the form which are legible, the type of ink, the type of character, and the way in which they are written.

Printer-made output

General

- Study the machine to be used for printing. Use the machine reference manual, especially the section devoted to forms design and/or carriage control to learn the specific printer characteristics, including special features such as upper/lower case printing, non-standard characters etc.;

- consider the use of blank paper with computer-printed headings for all internally used forms and reports. The paper known as ZEBRA paper, which has alternate white and shadowed lines, facilitates reading computer-printed reports as it minimizes the tendency of the eye to "jump" a line;
- prepare two copies of the carriage control tape in readiness for use, and arrange for replacement of the one in use before it is worn out.

Contents

- Make an alphabetical legend for the (abbreviated) names in a report or form, or refer to the appropriate chapters in the system description (4-7); section 1.7 of chapter 1 for organizational terms and section 1.8 for system elements and data objects;
- list all data fields to be printed, and the maximum number of characters per field in editing mode: taking into account requirements for printing of such items as amounts in an easily readable format;
- allow adequate space for totals at the foot of any column in which items are added.

Headings

- The heading should contain at least the following information:
  — name and number of form or report;
  — date of issue, and/or run number;
  — page number or document-sequence number;
- specify the headings of the columns. The (abbreviated) field names must not exceed the width of the column;
- a report is more readable if the printing of identical data on successive lines in a column is suppressed. This means that some columns will contain only a few entries. This arrangement necessitates repeating the content of all columns on each new page;
- if data has to be repeated in a report, investigate the possibility of putting it in the heading.
- allocate the headings in a reading sequence corresponding to user retrieving requirements. Before printing the output has to be sorted on these fields. Related fields, although not being important for retrieving purposes, should be allocated in adjacent columns; for example:
  — article group — article code — packing subcode — storage location;
  — document number — date — order number;
  — quantity — unit price — amount.

Layout

- Print the lines left-justified to release space on the right for user notes. (The example on page 6 is an exception to this rule. It is right-justified, to facilitate the study of the text);
- in wide reports print the explanatory notes for totals etc. close to the associated values;

- keep the reports and forms short. Reduce the number of blank lines as much as readability permits. In case of forms, use a fast-feed device from one document to the next; in case of reports, minimize changes in vertical spacing and skips to new pages;
- observe the following general rules for line-spacing:
  - — use single line-spacing wherever possible;
  - — between the heading and the first line of the report itself, skip one line;
  - — if one or more total-lines occur at the end of the data belonging to a sorting key, try to indicate these totals by asterisks:

```
                 123
Total AZZ       1547 *
Total AZ        9376  *
Total A        73897 **
```

  - — if there is no room for asterisks, then skip one line before each total-line;
  - — after the last total line of a sorting key, when the totals have been printed with asterisks, skip one line. If the totals have been printed without astersiks, skip two lines:

```
                 123                              123
Total AZZ       1547 *
Total AZ        9376  *          Total AZZ       1547
Total A        73897 **
                                 Total AZ        9376
BAA               89
                                 Total A        73897


                                 BAA               89
```

  - — skip to a new page after each main sorting key only at the specific request of the principal user of a report. Skip to a new page whenever the next part of the report is used by a different employee;
- keep the lines short; space horizontally only where this is essential to readability. A standard of two blanks between columns will normally be sufficient;
- never use more than one blank at a time for spacing within a column. Blanks are preferable to special characters for editing a column.

  Example:
  product number code — xxxx xxx xxxxx
  quantity — xx xxx
  (Single blanks in prescribed places; no dash, no slash, no period.)
  amount — xx xxx.xx
  (Use of the period for a decimal point);
- consider the discretive use of special characters to be printed in boxes or columns which are left empty to indicate non-appropriateness.

The printer spacing chart in page 6 is part of a computer printed report, the layout of which serves to illustrate the above rules.

PHILIPS DATA SYSTEMS

8 7 6 5 4 3 2 1		0	1	2	3	4	5
		1234567890	0123456789	0123456789	0123456789	0123456789	01234
•	1						
•	2						
•	3						
•	4						
•	5						
•	6						
•	7						
•	8						
•	9						
•	10						
•	11						
•	12						
•	13						
•	14						
•	15						
•	16						
•	17						
•	18						
•	19						
•	20						
•	21						
•	22						
•	23						
•	24						
•	25						
•	26						
•	27						
•	28						
•	29						
•	30						
•	31						
•	32						
•	33						
•	34						
•	35						
•	36						
•	37						
•	38						
•	39						
•	40						
•	41						
•	42						
•	43						
•	44						
•	45						
•	46						
•	47						
•	48						
•	49						
•	50						
•	51						
•	52						
•	53						
•	54						
•	55						
•	56						
•	57						
•	58						
•	59						
•	60						
8 7 6 5 4 3 2 1		1234567890	0123456789	0123456789	0123456789	0123456789	01234
		0	1	2	3	4	

Example of machine printed report

RINTER SPACING CHART Output identification

tem :
system :
v. issue:

project no. :
chapter/sect. :
page :
issued :

```
                                                             RECEIPTS DRUMS STORE WEEK 508
                                                                                  PAGE  12
LOC     DEPT     PRGR     PROD      DOCUM      QUANT
                                                          single
112     2213     0114     44315     16912        1 000
                                    21034        2 000
                                    08345          400
                                    00987          200
                                    98645       10 000
                                    12376        1 500
                                    56382        2 000
                                    23486        1 000*
TOTAL   PROD                                    18 100
                                                          single
                          44316     61756        1 500
                                    30267        2 000
                                    05643          300
                                    00898          200
                                    12367          300
                                    12671          200
                                    18999          500
TOTAL   PROD                                     5 000*
        PROD     GROUP                          23 100  *
                                                          single
                 0115     20352     57112          200
                                    44577        1 000
                                    00112          300
                                    09142          700
                                    11244          300
                                    19876          400
                                    02020          600
TOTAL   PROD                                     3 500*
        PROD     GROUP                           3 500  *
        DEPT                                    26 600**
                                                          single
        2214     9983     15540     76544       13 300
                                    87343       12 400
                                    44221        5 000
                                    77223        4 000
                                    00887          800
                                    88335        8 200
                                    44331        3 000
                                    02567        1 000
TOTAL   PROD                                    47 700*
```

Pre-printed forms

When considering the use of pre-printed forms for use with mechanical output units, apply the general rules for forms development (technique 6-4.3). The following should also be considered:

- use as small a number of form sizes as possible;
- to reduce processing costs use wide forms so that both the length of the form and the number of lines to be printed are minimized. Consider printing two or more forms next to each other;
- consider prenumbering the forms;
- place filing information near the top right-hand corner;
- avoid horizontal rulings: they make it difficult to adjust the form in the machine;
- calculate the character width and line spacing;
- where appropriate, pre-print a suitable type of check protection for specific items, e.g. by filling the field for an amount with zeros or asterisks to the left of the expected position of the most significant digit;
- print alignment guides on the form to facilitate printer set-up operations.

Punched card development

Keypunching can be a major bottleneck in systems operation, because of its throughput time and cost, and because it is a manual procedure which can cause error and personnel problems (e.g. high labour turnover). It is necessary therefore to design the layout of the punched cards in such a way as to simplify the work of the keypunch operator as much as possible. The following considerations are of assistance:

- the machine manual must be studied before an efficient card design can be made;
- full advantage should be taken of the features of the keypunching equipment used, in particular the program card device;
- the fields to be punched should be arranged next to each other;
- the source document need be read in normal reading sequence;
- as a rule, use a card as a unit record. Try to incorporate a transaction into a single card;
- it is not always possible to make fields large enough to accomodate the maximum number of characters, especially if the total number of columns needed in such a case could exceed 80. The use of header and trailer, or master and detail cards, should not be encouraged, as this would complicate source data preparation, keypunching, error checking and correction and initial data processing operations;
- in attempting to pack all necessary information into a single card, consider the following:
  — suitable coding can greatly reduce the size of many data fields;
  — standard abbreviations can prevent excessive lengths of name and address fields;

- fields for sequence numbers can be reduced by repeating the numbering series more frequently. E.g. stock issue numbers could start at each quarter, instead of each year;
- use single columns for more than one type of coding, e.g. income tax category and sex. Sex can be indicated by zone punching as 11- or 12- punching. The same holds true in statistical applications when information of the yes-no type has to be collected;
- combination of fields in the layout if the fields do not appear simultaneously in the same type of transaction;

- if the method fails consult the subsystem team (or the project team when subsystem interfaces are involved) to find ways of changing the design of the input. The sort of questions to be investigated are:
  - Can some data fields be eliminated?
  - Can data fields be incorporated in one or another field instead of becoming a part of each input?
  - Can an input medium other than punched cards be used more easily?
- if it still proves impossible to allocate all necessary data fields to one card, the master and detail card method will have to be adopted.

Master and detail cards

Where the amount of data necessary to describe a transaction is greater than can be accomodated on a single punched card, then obviously a group of two or more cards must be used. This creates a problem of allocating the various data elements to the fields on the different cards in the most economical and convenient manner.
For example to minimize the number of fields that must be skipped place the fields for the most-frequently used data elements on the first card and the least-frequently used data elements on the last card. The identification fields must be duplicated in each detail card; in addition all cards require a field for identification of their sequence within a set.
This method results in an economical usage of cards, in that the number required to describe a transaction is kept to a minimum. It does, however, make checking more difficult, and therefore makes additional input controls necessary. Where the number of detail cards is variable, a field on the master card should be reserved for indicating this number.
In designing the layout of master and detail cards, the data elements must first be classified to determine which fields should be assigned to the master card and which to the detail cards. Factors which influence this classification are:

- the occurrence of more than one source document involved in the transaction, data fields which occur on one document only should preferably be allocated to one card;
- master and detail cards must contain an indication as to their internal sequence, either by transaction code or by means of a special field;
- the frequency of occurrence of data fields: less frequent ones should be assigned to the (last) detail card;

- processing constraints, such as the need for updating separate files;
- printing constraints, such as the occurrence of distinguishable parts on the form or report;
- the invariability of the content of the data itself, which permits the use of card pulling files for fixed data.

Multiple punched card layout

Profitable use can be made of the multiple punched card layout form on which space for the layout for a number of punched cards is given. This guarantees that the location of identical fields is to a maximum extent in the same columns. This will greatly facilitate sorting and screening operations as well as the programming effort to this respect e.g. owing to the fact that a number of separate operations can be combined.
For an example of a multiple layout form see 4-1.3.

Dual or turn-around cards

A dual or turn-around card is a card which is both an output and input document and which is used in between in the user organization. The cards contain identification information concerning a transaction which generally is also — or even more extensively — maintained by the computer. In addition to the identification the card can also contain information for the execution of an operation, which after performance, should be returned for processing an update. The text on the card is either printed by interpreting the punched card or printed simultaneously during punching.
If variable data should be put in into the computer this can be done either by means of in plant point of origin devices which have both a capability for reading punched cards and for input of variable data, or by filling in boxes preprinted for this purpose on the card. Then the completed card should be punched. Turn-around cards can be very useful in reducing the amount of transcription from source documents, eliminating duplication of file data, etc.

Practical rules
When designing a turn-around card for use in one or more procedures, the following practical rules should be borne in mind:
- pre-print on each type of card a name, code name and/or number to permit easy identification in the procedures;
- pre-print approved standard names to all fields just above the zero punching positions;
- reserve adequate space for the boxes for the handwritten data;
- identify each box by printing in it the approved standard name for the desired content. These names should be printed between the punching rows so that they cannot be mutilated by punchings;
- reserve sufficient space (normally about 6 columns) between the right-hand edge of the handwritten data and the first field to be punched from it, so that

handwritten data will not be obscured by the card pressure lever of the keypunch machine;

- do not use space within about 4 mm of the top and bottom of the card for handwritten data. These areas are obscured when the card is in the keypunch machine;
- print periods (full stops) or dotted lines between columns to indicate the position of a decimal point, or the comma after a "millions" or thousands digit, where necessary as an aid to punching and verification;
- when considering the use of pre-printed or coloured cards, or cards with coloured stripes or with corner cuts, remember that these are aids to visual identification only, and do not permit identification by machine. The use of such cards can cause difficulties in automatic punching, because the operator must change the complete stack of unpunched cards when a new type of card must be used;
- handwritten or punched fields which are to be checked visually should be placed at the extreme left- or right-hand side of the card to facilitate reading;
- if non-numeric characters are used in a field, the punched card layout can be adapted by replacing the normally pre-printed digits by the appropriate characters.
- depending on the kind of equipment used, different kinds of printing can be done on the punched card:
  - — end printing, in general on the left side and/or the right side of the card, of e.g. 8 characters;
  - — interpreting anywhere on one or two top rows of the card. As a rule, interpreting requires more space than the corresponding punchings, and therefore the names of those fields which are to be interpreted should be pre-printed in two places; above the punching columns and in the interpretation box;
  - — writing by the keypunch machine. In this case, the top row of the card is written as each column is punched. The written content requires the same space as the punching.

An example of a dual card layout appears in page 12.

DUAL CARD LAYOUT

system :
subsystem :
prev. issue :

project no. :
chapt/sect. :
page :
issued :

order card

article no.				quantity	delivery time asked	external order no.					internal order no.		interpreted
article group	capacity group	internal order no.	run no.	article no.	country code	quantity	external order no.	delivery time asked for	delivery time confirmed	trans-action code	stock no.	card code	card fields

1 2 3 4 5 6 7 8 9 10 11 12 13 14 15 16 17 18 19

delivery time confirmed col. 62-67

transaction code col. 68-72

stock no. col. 73-77

date | signature

remarks

1 2 3 4 5 6 7 8 9 10 11 12 13 14 15 16 17 18 19

0 0 0 0 0 0 0 0 0 0 0 0 0 0 0 0 0 0 0 0 0 0 0 0 0 0 0 0 0 0 0 0 0 0 0 0 0 0 0 0 0 0 0 0 0 0 0 0 0 0 0 0 0 0 0 0 0 0 0 0 0
20 21 22 23 24 25 26 27 28 29 30 31 32 33 34 35 36 37 38 39 40 41 42 43 44 45 46 47 48 49 50 51 52 53 54 55 56 57 58 59 60 61 62 63 64 65 66 67 68 69 70 71 72 73 74 75 76 77 78 79 80
1 1 1 1 1 1 1 1 1 1 1 1 1 1 1 1 1 1 1 1 1 1 1 1 1 1 1 1 1 1 1 1 1 1 1 1 1 1 1 1 1 1 1 1 1 1 1 1 1 1 1 1 1 1 1 1 1 1 1 1 1
2 2 2 2 2 2 2 2 2 2 2 2 2 2 2 2 2 2 2 2 2 2 2 2 2 2 2 2 2 2 2 2 2 2 2 2 2 2 2 2 2 2 2 2 2 2 2 2 2 2 2 2 2 2 2 2 2 2 2 2 2
3 3 3 3 3 3 3 3 3 3 3 3 3 3 3 3 3 3 3 3 3 3 3 3 3 3 3 3 3 3 3 3 3 3 3 3 3 3 3 3 3 3 3 3 3 3 3 3 3 3 3 3 3 3 3 3 3 3 3 3 3
4 4 4 4 4 4 4 4 4 4 4 4 4 4 4 4 4 4 4 4 4 4 4 4 4 4 4 4 4 4 4 4 4 4 4 4 4 4 4 4 4 4 4 4 4 4 4 4 4 4 4 4 4 4 4 4 4 4 4 4 4
5 5 5 5 5 5 5 5 5 5 5 5 5 5 5 5 5 5 5 5 5 5 5 5 5 5 5 5 5 5 5 5 5 5 5 5 5 5 5 5 5 5 5 5 5 5 5 5 5 5 5 5 5 5 5 5 5 5 5 5 5
6 6 6 6 6 6 6 6 6 6 6 6 6 6 6 6 6 6 6 6 6 6 6 6 6 6 6 6 6 6 6 6 6 6 6 6 6 6 6 6 6 6 6 6 6 6 6 6 6 6 6 6 6 6 6 6 6 6 6 6 6
7 7 7 7 7 7 7 7 7 7 7 7 7 7 7 7 7 7 7 7 7 7 7 7 7 7 7 7 7 7 7 7 7 7 7 7 7 7 7 7 7 7 7 7 7 7 7 7 7 7 7 7 7 7 7 7 7 7 7 7 7
8 8 8 8 8 8 8 8 8 8 8 8 8 8 8 8 8 8 8 8 8 8 8 8 8 8 8 8 8 8 8 8 8 8 8 8 8 8 8 8 8 8 8 8 8 8 8 8 8 8 8 8 8 8 8 8 8 8 8 8 8
9 9 9 9 9 9 9 9 9 9 9 9 9 9 9 9 9 9 9 9 9 9 9 9 9 9 9 9 9 9 9 9 9 9 9 9 9 9 9 9 9 9 9 9 9 9 9 9 9 9 9 9 9 9 9 9 9 9 9 9 9
20 21 22 23 24 25 26 27 28 29 30 31 32 33 34 35 36 37 38 39 40 41 42 43 44 45 46 47 48 49 50 51 52 53 54 55 56 57 58 59 60 61 62 63 64 65 66 67 68 69 70 71 72 73 74 75 76 77 78 79 80

card columns

file number: program no.: run no.:
procedure name:

corners to be cut	interpretation	card colour	colour bar	. . . mm from top	ink colour
☐ L ☐ R upper	☐ none	☐ manilla	☐ none	☐ red	☐ black
☐ L ☐ R lower	☐ 45 char. p/c	☐ yellow	☐ yellow	☐ purple	☐ green
☐ none	☐ 60 char. p/c	☐ green	☐ green	☐ brown	☐ blue
	☐ numerical	☐ orange	☐ orange		☐ red
	☐ alphanummerical	☐ rose	☐ rose		☐ brown
	☐ end printing	☐ blue	☐ blue		
		☐ american white	☐ chamois		

Step 4-6.3: Try out the procedure

The newly developed procedure, together with forms to be used in it, should have a field try-out to establish whether or not it operates according to expectations. The try-out is also a check of the adaptiveness of the organization, and permits an assessment of the amount of training in the use of the new procedure which will be needed (5-1.2).

In close co-operation with the heads of the departments involved in the new procedure, a time schedule and the test areas must be selected. New procedures are tried out in parallel with existing ones. Peak moments of business activity should be avoided, because personnel are then usually too busy to perform additional duties. A new procedure may initially take longer than the existing one, because its unfamiliarity can give rise to mistakes and misunderstandings.

Practical rules

- An introduction, and an explanation of the purpose of the change in procedures, should be given by management before the try-out starts;
- in addition to the introduction, a training course should be given by the subsystem team or project team for the benefit of everyone involved (5-1.2);
- plan the try-out procedure in consultation with the user personnel;
- hold a review meeting afterwards, and give everyone a chance to comment. Take time, and be patient;
- confirm after a successful try-out that the new procedure will come into operation on a specific date. Make sure that the procedure is acceptable to all personnel concerned.

Step 4-6.4: Prepare procedure description

It is recommended that a procedure be documented either by narrative description, by flowchart or by decision table. Each method possesses particular advantages. In general, where the flow of the operations in a procedure is relatively straightforward, it is better to use narrative description only; for more complicated procedures the flowcharting or decision table method is preferable.
Either type of documentation must be accompanied by filled-in examples of the forms or reports used in the procedure. The developed procedures must ultimately be incorporated in a separate part of the user documentation. This part may be arranged according to the subdivision indicated in 4-3.1. In the meantime, they should be stored in the project file under chapter 3, section 3 (see 2-4.1).

Narrative method

Practical rules for procedure writing are:

- use technique "technical writing" (6-2.1);
- describe the operations in a strict time sequence;
- give each operation a number;
- use for each operation the structure "who-does-what", except when a condition has to be inserted between "who" and "does";
- do not repeat the name of the acting employee, (the "who"), in a sequence of operations;
- good layout of the procedure sheet requires sufficient empty space. Avoid underlining;
- if an operation has several courses of action, give each one a sub-number and start on a new line;
- use a large quarto size, paper e.g. A4 and specify standard margin settings, column widths etc. to ensure an easily readable layout;
- an example of a narrative procedure concerning an order confirmation is given in pages 15 and 16.

Flowcharting methods

Apart from the flowchart representation in a standard format many other formats using similar or different symbols are possible. Out of these alternative formats two have been selected for implementation in ARDI, the task-oriented flowchart and the forms flowchart.

Standard flowchart

In the flowchart representation of a standard format, standard rules such as those given in 6-2.2 must be used throughout. The diagram in page 17 presents a flowchart for the procedure described in the previous section.
The advantages of using the standard format for procedure flowcharting are that it is more easily usable by people who are already familiar with system flowcharts

PROCEDURE 999PO3		
system : Sales		project no.: 999
subsystem : Receipt of customer orders		chapt/sect.:
prev. issue:		page : 1
		issued :

ORDER CONFIRMATION PROCEDURE

This procedure specifies the operations to be performed upon receipt of customer orders. The outputs of the procedure are an order confirmation for the customer and au order tape for input to the finished goods information system.

mail clerk	1	Upon receipt of a customer order, logs in order register, then dates and numbers the customer order;
	2	sends customer order to pulling clerk;
pulling clerk	3	pulls customer tapecard;
	4	pulls article tapecard for each article ordered;
	5	sends customer order and pulled tapecards to typist;
typist	6	prepares with paper tape typewriter order confirmation in duplicate and order tape;
	7	sends order tape daily to computer centre as input for the order registration subsystem of the finished goods system system;
	8	sends customer order and the original and copy of the order confirmation to order clerk;
	9	sends customer and article tapecards to pulling clerk;

PROCEDURE 999PO3

system : Sales
subsystem : Receipt of customers orders
prev. issue:

project no.: 999
chapt/sect. :
page : 2
issued :

order clerk	10	verifies order confirmation against customer order;
	11	sends the original and copy of order confirmation together with customer order to mail clerk;
mail clerk	12	logs in order register the preparation of the order confirmation;
	13	sends original of order confirmation to customer;
	14	sends copy of order confirmation and customer order to filing clerk;
filing clerk	15	files both the copy of order confirmation and the customer order on customer name sequence in customer order file;
pulling clerk	16	sorts the article tapecards twice daily in article name sequence;
	17	refiles the article tapecards in article pulling file;
	18	refiles daily the customer tapecards in customer pulling file.

Explanation: Standard margin settings and columns:
Paper setting at 30
Margin ruler at 50: start of WHO; 2nd line of "WHO's" name 2 spaces to the right.
at 70: sequence number of operation on 70-71.
at 74: description of operation until position 109

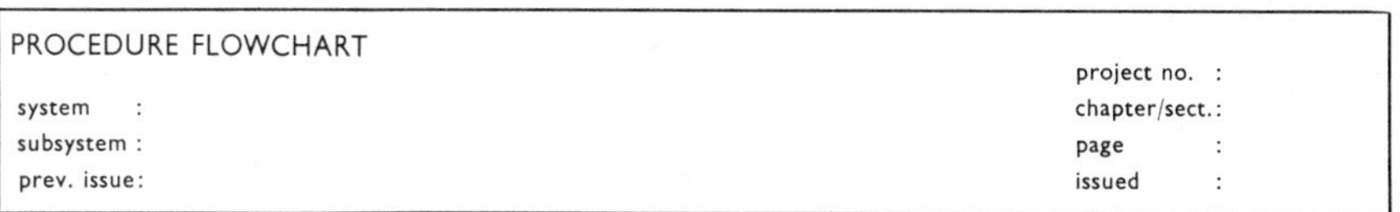
PROCEDURE FLOWCHART

system :
subsystem :
prev. issue:

project no. :
chapter/sect.:
page :
issued :

customer order
mail clerk
logs, dates and numbers
order register
pulling clerk
pulls customer/ article tapecards
customer pulling file
article pulling file
typist
prepare order confirmation

order tape
360
computer centre
order registration stock control/ invoicing/ debtors acct. system

order confirmation 1 2
customer order
order clerk
verifies order confirmation
mail clerk
logs confirmation
sends order confirmation 1
customer
filing clerk
files order conf. 2 & cust. order on cust. name
customer order file

customer tapecards
360
pulling clerk
refiles customer tapecards

article tapecards
720
pulling clerk
sorts on article name
refiles article tapecards

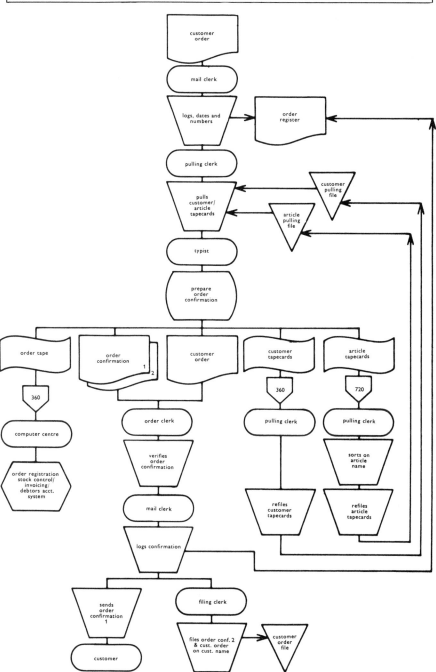

Example order confirmation procedure

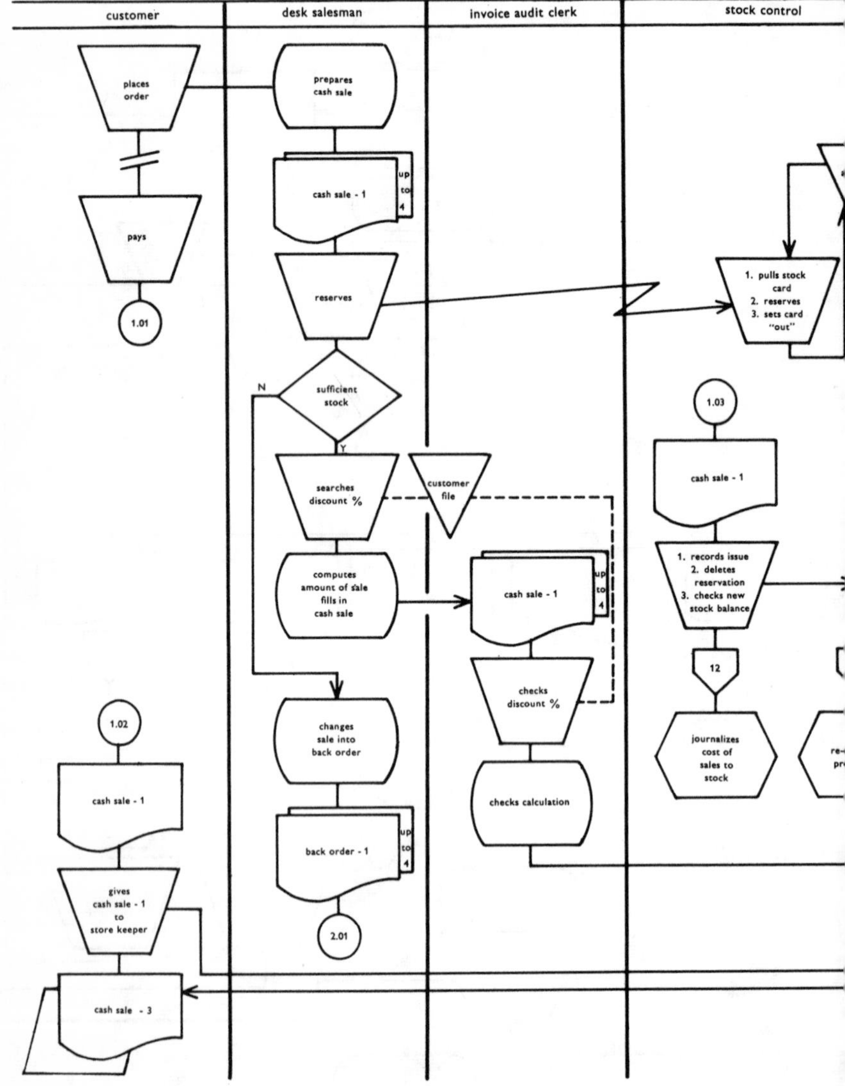

customer
desk salesman
invoice audit clerk
stock control
places order
prepares cash sale
cash sale - 1
up to 4
pays
reserves
1. pulls stock card
2. reserves
3. sets card "out"
1.01
N
sufficient stock
Y
1.03
searches discount %
customer file
cash sale - 1
computes amount of sale fills in cash sale
cash sale - 1
up to 4
1. records issue
2. deletes reservation
3. checks new stock balance
12
checks discount %
1.02
changes sale into back order
journalizes cost of sales to stock
cash sale - 1
checks calculation
back order - 1
up to 4
gives cash sale - 1 to store keeper
2.01
cash sale - 3

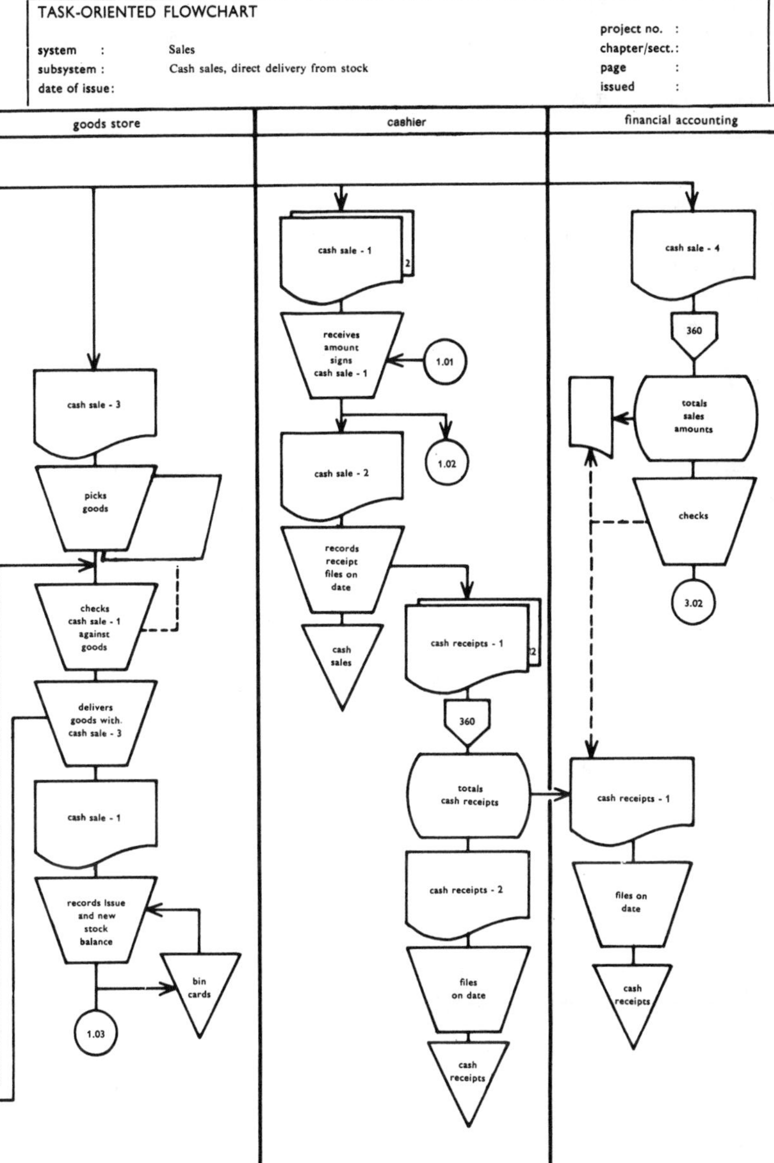
TASK-ORIENTED FLOWCHART
system : Sales
subsystem : Cash sales, direct delivery from stock
date of issue:
project no. :
chapter/sect.:
page :
issued :
goods store
cashier
financial accounting
cash sale - 1
2
receives amount signs cash sale - 1
1.01
cash sale - 4
360
totals sales amounts
checks
3.02
cash sale - 3
picks goods
checks cash sale - 1 against goods
delivers goods with cash sale - 3
cash sale - 1
records issue and new stock balance
bin cards
1.03
1.02
cash sale - 2
records receipt files on date
cash sales
cash receipts - 1
2
360
totals cash receipts
cash receipts - 2
files on date
cash receipts
cash receipts - 1
files on date
cash receipts

and program flowcharts; further it lays the emphasis in depicting the sequential performance of operations and the splitting up of them at decision points.
On the other hand, there are some disadvantages: the standard format does not show directly what a specific employee or department is doing nor in which operations a specific document is involved.

Task-oriented flowchart

For this method the symbols of the standard charting technique are used, but the operations are arranged in such a way that they can be fitted into columns which illustrate the various employees or departments which are involved in the procedure. An example of this type of representation, showing a cash sales procedure with immediate delivery of the goods, is given in page 18.

Forms flowchart

This method of flowcharting uses only the characters and symbols to be found on a standard typewriter. This chart has a similar function to a gridchart that it establishes relationships between the personnel who carry out the operations and the objects on which these operations are carried out. It also gives the route taken by all copies of the documents or other objects used in or produced by the procedure.

Alphabetic characters are used to indicate operations as follows:

X	**the object is subject to an operation, specified in the left-hand column;**
O	**the object initiates the creation of a new document;**
=	**the object is used for checking purposes;**
V	**the object is checked;**
X-O	**the object is merged into another object;**
X-O	**the object is created from another object;**
H	**the object is temporarily halted;**
F	**the object is filed;**
D	**the object is destroyed;**
X ┘┌ V	**the object is sent to a department or employee already listed on a higher line.**

This method, with slight adaptations, is derived from R. W. Starreveld, "Leer van de Administratieve Organisatie". An example of a procedure based on this method is given in page 22. The subject is the same as that for the task-oriented flowchart.

The forms flowchart is arranged according to the employees involved in the procedure. Thus all the operations that each employee performs are grouped together. Some backtracking occurs, particularly in the case of cash-sale 1. The numbers given to the actions indicate the sequence in which they are performed. A simpler method of this same chart would have been in straightforward chronological sequence which would have caused the insertion of the same employee at different places in the chart.

Decision table method

A procedure or parts of it can be represented by decision tables, especially if the emphasis is laid on decisions or choices, which must be taken or conclusions which must be drawn before a specific sequence of operations can be executed. See 6-2.4 for a discussion of decision tables.

FORMS FLOWCHART

system : sales
subsystem : cash sales, direct delivery from stock
prev. issue :

project no.: 123
chapt/sect.:
page :
issued :

dept.	operation	seq. no.	cash sale original A1	cash sale copy A2	cash sale copy A3	cash sale copy A4	stock file B	"cards out" C	customer file D	cash receipts original E1	cash receipts copy E2	goods F	backorder original G1	backorder copy G2	backorder copy G3	backorder copy G4
	customer places order	0														
desk salesman	prepares	1	X	X	X	X										
	contacts stock control	2	O	O	O	O	X									
	if insufficient stock: change cash sale	3	O	O	O	O							X	X	X	X
	file backorder; go to procedure 123 P24	4											H	H	H	H
	if sufficient stock: searches discount	5	X	X	X	X			O							
	computes amount of sale	6	X	X	X	X										
	fills in	7	X	X	X	X										
invoice audit clerk	checks discount	11	V	V	V	V			=							
	checks calculation	12	X	X	X	X										
	files	13							F							
stock controller	pulls stock card	8					X									
	reserves	9					X									
	sets "card out"	10					O	X								

	checks new stock balance	22
	do reordering procedure 123 P44	23
	sets back	24
	files	25
	go to journalizing procedure 123 P52	26
store keeper	picks goods	14
	checks	18
	delivers	19
cashier	customer pays	15
	receives amount	16
	signs	17
	records receipts	27
	files on date	28
	totals	29
	files on date	30
financial accountant	counts total of sales	31
	checks	32
	files on date	33
	go to procedure 123 P31	34

Activity 4-7: Prepare system description

Purpose

The system description is a user-oriented description of the new information system by means of which the system becomes independent of its designers and manageable for its users from the moment it is brought into operation. The system description forms a part of the user documentation. A reliable, up-to-date system description will greatly facilitate maintenance, introduction of changes, conversion from existing to new situations or new types of hardware, and research for similar applications. The achievement of the purpose can be facilitated by applying a uniform method not only for system description, but also for procedure description, program description and for computer centre instructions which form the other parts of the user documentation and which were produced in the earlier activities of this volume.

As long as the user documentation has not been distributed, the items prepared for it form part of the project file; they are stored according to the rules laid down in 2-4.1 or concentrated in chapter 5, section 6 of the project file.

Advantages

A system description has the following important advantages over verbal introduction and instruction.

- All relevant information is assembled in one location and not just known to exist "somewhere" in the organization;
- it serves as a training guide for newcomers, and as a reference guide for those who are already in the user organization. It also establishes for implementation the decisions on policies and procedures taken during the course of the systems effort;
- it saves time, settles arguments, and gives all personnel involved the sense of confidence necessary when changing over to a new system;
- it improves morale by demonstrating to the departments and employees involved how their tasks fit into the whole information system;
- it facilitates efficient delegation of authority; the head of the department knows how his subordinates will handle a situation, while the employees themselves are more willing to accept responsibility since they can rely on written procedures. Thus, it relieves management from the many repetitive routine decisions which are now laid down;
- it facilitates work measurement and performance audits.

Checklist for a system description

In contrast to the project file, which is to be used only by team members who are intimate with the systems effort, the user documentation will be employed by all personnel involved in the new system. It is primarily intended for those who have not been directly connected with the project. Because of this, the following rules should be borne in mind when writing user documentation, in particular the system description.

- Write only what the user needs to know;
- as far as possible, make use of material already collected in the project file;
- concentrate on producing documentation which is easy to read, easy to refer to and easy to revise;
- give clear directions for using each element of the system;
- keep the subject index up to date;
- divide into chapters, sections and subsections, according to the structure of the system, and ensure that subjects of equal importance are dealt with at the same level (see the next section of this activity for a suggested subdivision);
- use simple, logical numbering for chapters, sections, subsections, pages and, if necessary individual paragraphs;
- select clear, distinctive titles for the description itself, and for the chapters sections and subsections;
- use easily recognizable pre-printed forms with a quiet layout for the descriptions, avoiding non-essential text;
- use generous spacing and margins, short sentences, and short paragraphs; use emphasis (capitals, underlining, etc.) only when absolutely necessary;
- distinguish clearly between policy or decision matters on the one hand and procedural statements on the other;
- refer to standards whenever applicable;
- insert illustrations where needed; in the case of forms, those with sample entries and explanatory captions are preferable to blank ones;
- see that the binder is strong enough to withstand intensive use, and that it permits easy insertion of new or revised pages;
- see that the quality of printing or duplication permits easy reading;
- state plainly whether a rule is:
  - — mandatory: "must" or "shall";
  - — advisory: "should";
  - — permissive: "may";
- use the technique "technical writing" (6-2.1);
- keep the description up to date.

Subdivision

In the following suggested subdivision, chapter 1 is at system level, and is followed by a chapter for each of the subsystems.

Chapter 1: General

Section 1.1. Purpose and scope.

Purpose and scope of the system, including quantified system objectives specified on the system objectives form, and relationships with other information systems. This will be a short section, written in simple language, and avoiding professional jargon.

Section 1.2. Organization.

- Description of the organizational environment in which the system will operate (3-3.2);
- newly defined departmental responsibilities;
- predetermined rules which impose a constraint on the operation of the new system, such as coding systems and control methods;
- description of the technical constraints which have been taken into account in the realization of the new information system, such as predetermined equipment or use of machines outside the company with or without own personnel.

Section 1.3. System structure.

General description of the system design showing the relationships between the functions incorporated in the subsystems and the interfaces and contents of the different subsystems.
This section should be supported by the new information flow as prepared in 3-4.1, giving a summary of the individual functions and subsystems.

Section 1.4. Control network.

This section explains the principles on which the reliability of the system is based.

- The controls during processing are explained in detail in the subsystem chapters;
- for control instructions per program, see the program description;
- controls on input and on output are given in the procedure descriptions (4-1:2). It is recommended that this section is submitted to the auditing department for approval.

Section 1.5. System files.

Description of system files, explaining the aims and organization of the multiple used data bases, supported by a general file design as prepared in 3-4.2 showing the functional relationships between files.
This section contains only information on the system files themselves and not in connection with the subsystem usage involved. In this way the information about a file needs to be documented only once. See the form and file description sheet in 3-2.3. For description of subsystem files see the subsystem chapters.

This section contains also specifications of the tables used, the responsible persons, the time of validity, etc. When these tables form a separate file, a detailed description of the contents can be given in the same way as for a file.

Section 1.6. Hardware and software.

This specification can be given by a configuration chart accompanied by a list of all additional items such as special hardware items and software packages used. See 3-4.4. and 4-1.4.

Section 1.7. Glossary of terms and abbreviations used in the organization.
Together with the glossary on data elements occurring more specially in the system itself, this section should provide adequate information in all terms used in an easily accessable way. See 2-4.1.

Section 1.8. Identification of system elements and data objects.
The standards used for the identification of system elements and data objects should be explained and a complete summary given.

- General fields. These are fields whose names are standardized within the company and used in all her information systems.
- Specific fields. These are fields whose names are used in one system only. Denotion of the meaning of fields and their contents must be done in this section by means of field description sheets (see example in 3-2.3).

It is necessary that there is a responsibility assigned for this, especially where fields can be used — in future — in more than one information system or subsystem.

- codes. Examples are codes for:
  - — file alterations;
  - — transactions;
  - — time indications;
  - — articles;
  - — debtors;
  - — employees;
  - — costs;
  - — production units;
  - — signals and standard remarks (e.g. for indicating the type of error) on printed reports;
  - — programs.

The responsibilities for updating of coding systems should be clearly defined.

Section 1.9. Maintenance.
A description of the procedures in case of errors or proposed changes should be given. Completed specimens of an error report and a change request form as given in 5-5.4 and 2-4.2 should be included.

Section 1.10. Addresses.
This section contains all addresses that are important for the operation of the information system:

- manager or systems engineer of information systems department;
- computer centre: production planning, computer room, control room;
- users;
- auditing department;
- input groups;
- despatching groups;
- maintenance employee or team.

Chapter 2. Description subsystem AA

Section 2.1. Purpose and scope.
Purpose and scope of the subsystem. This should be derived from the appropriate function worksheets and the subsystem requirements.

Section 2.2. Organization.
Description at subsystem level of the organizational environment, responsibilities and predetermined rules as described at system level in section 1.2.

Section 2.3. Subsystem structure.
Description of the subsystem flow supported by:

- subsystem flowchart, showing all interfaces between programs and procedures (see 4-1.2);
- references to: run descriptions, prepared for the instructions for the computer centre (4-5.5);
  - — programs embodied in the subsystem (see program descriptions 4-5.4);
  - — procedures embodied in the subsystem (see procedure descriptions 4-6.4);
- annotations on the processing, such as:
  - — use of inputs, system and subsystem files, tables, formulae and other processing rules, console instructions, carriage control tape, plug board layout;
  - — identification of outputs, channel numbers, tape unit numbers, disk drive numbers, stacker numbers.

Section 2.4. Control network.
Control network for the subsystem, containing control schemes for the user departments as well as for the computer centre. The description of the manner in which these checks are performed is specified in the various procedures for input creation and for dealing with data errors, signals or other exception reportings.

Section 2.5. Subsystem files.
Description of subsystem files explaining the aims and the organization of the subsystem files, by means of a disk file layout form (4.1.3) or a form and file description sheet (3-2.3). See also the section 1.5. for system files.

Section 2.6. Documents.
Each document appearing in the subsystem should be described with reference to the programs and procedures to which it is an input or an output by means of form and file description sheets. (see 4-1.2).
For specific documents such as punched cards or printer outputs special forms can be used for the description of layout and content, such as:

- multiple punched card layout (4-1.2);
- dual card layout (4-6.2);
- printer spacing chart (4-6.2);
- record layout (4-1.3).

Legends of comments and (error) signals which may appear on outputs must given.

Section 2.7. Maintenance.
For the procedure to be followed is referred to section 1.9 of this activity.

Section 2.8. Subsystem operating schedule.
According to the procedures and run descriptions prepared for the computer center (see 4-5.5), a time table for the operation of the subsystem should be given. (See 5-3).

Section 2.9. Appendices.
Layouts, filled-in examples of all forms and diagrams such as flowcharts and descriptive and layout charts should be given in this chapter, unless they have already be incorporated in the previous sections of the (sub)system description. Items that can be changed by the user departments involved in the normal procedure without influence on the programs (e.g. exchange rate tables) should bear the annotation: "specimen, will not be updated".

Chapter 3. Description subsystem BB

Section 3.1. Purpose and scope.
Purpose and scope of the subsystem. This should be derived from the appropriate function worksheets and the subsystem requirements.

Section 3.2. Organization.
etc.

Activity 4-8: Test subsystem

As stated in 4-5 and 4-6 each program and procedure is tested separately. In system and subsystem testing, the project team has to create and execute a test procedure to ensure that the completed (sub)system can operate without disturbance, that its performance is up to standard, and that it meets the requirements originally set. This involves testing the interfaces already in use, as well as the interfaces which are built in for future extensions. Interfaces already in use are those between programs, and between programs and procedures. The practical rules for program testing and procedure try-out apply to subsystem testing also.

Testing

First stage
The first stage of subsystem testing should be run as if it were an actual operation, but using test input and test files. People who will actually be involved in the information system should prepare test data which will be processed by the programs.
If possible, programmers should be on hand when these tests are being run, to provide assistance in accurate run preparation and in locating rapidly the causes of errors. A number of different error transactions should be deliberately included in the test input, in order to check the validation routines. The output of the data processing should be used to test the relevant procedures. Determine in advance the results that should be obtained from the test. Inconsistencies in system operation should be corrected, and the tests repeated until the entire subsystem functions correctly.

Second stage
The second stage of subsystem testing involves using live data to check that all possible kinds of data have been foreseen. Select live data from actual transactions in the existing system. Begin testing with a low volume of data, gradually increasing the volume as the system is debugged. Check out the conversion effort while the rest of the system is being tested. Accumulate enough data to approximate an average run, which may be a daily, weekly, or monthly batch size, depending upon the processing cycle.
In addition, augment live data with some artificial transactions which will test the extreme high or low limits of quantities or sizes. Process all data errors flagged by validation programs, through the clerical review and correction procedures, then back again through the system. This provides a check on the interfacing of runs and procedures within the system.

Results
Test results are compared to pre-computed answers, including the following:

- console log sheet. This should indicate the correct program initialization and termination;

- error listing. This should indicate input items which were deliberately inserted as checks on validation routines;
- printouts of subsystem files. These can be compared with input data and file format specifications to check the validity of the updating;
- printouts of intermediate files. These can be checked to provide assurance of accurate interfacing between programs;
- control totals on amounts, number of transactions, number of errors, number of file records updated or interrogated, etc.;
- line-by-line checking of output reports.

After subsystem testing has been completed, a timing run can be made using input volumes similar to those which will be encountered in actual operating conditions.

Review meeting

Complementary to the technical aspects of testing the subsystem, a review meeting should be convened by the project team. The following procedure is suggested:

- the chairman of the project team should schedule a development review meeting within one or two weeks after receipt of the subsystem documentation;
- he should devise a meeting plan, and minimize the discussion of non-pertinent points and arguments about earlier decisions;
- upon receipt of their copy of the documentation, the project team members must examine it to assess the degree of success achieved in respect of fulfilment of the subsystem requirements, and completeness, consistency and implementability of the solution, the file design and interfaces with other subsystems;
- the team members must send notice of all errors, problems, and criticisms and proposed solutions direct to the chairman of the subsystem team, with copies to the chairman of the project team. If major problems occur a meeting with the project team should be called immediately;
- the secretary of the project team must document any problems and/or disagreements that arise during the meeting, and follow up on these to make sure they are resolved and that the method of resolution is documented;
- new review meetings must be called if major problems arise during the first meeting, or if any changes in the subsystem requirements did occur.

Activity 4-9: Complete user documentation

It is impossible to overemphasize the importance of the user documentation. Neither during nor after the systems effort should attempts be made to degrade any of the documentation standards.

During the activities of volume 4, the following documentation will have been created:

- program descriptions (4-5.5);
- instructions for the computer centre (4-5.6);
- procedure descriptions (4-6.4);
- system description including subsystem descriptions (4-7).

Other documentation (in addition to that concerned with project management) created during the execution of this phase should be added to the project file and/or the history file. Examples are:

- conversion documentation;
- change requests.

Distribution

Though it will be difficult to realize in practice owing to the stress of the actual situation, the project team should strive for completion and distribution of the user documentation prior to implementation.

On the basis of the diagram in 2-4.1, separate distribution lists can be drawn up for each part of the user documentation. Either a master of these distribution lists or separate mailing lists should be used to forward the first issues of the documentation to all parties concerned. Updating instructions should be specified on the mailing lists (see also 2-4.1). It is recommended that the last sequentially numbered copy of the mailing list be kept in the user documentation to illustrate the accuracy of its updating.

Volume 5: System implementation & evaluation

Contents

General

This volume describes the implementation and evaluation of either a completely new system or of an existing system executed with the support of different equipment.
The ARDI approach to system implementation & evaluation includes a range of activities whose execution can be spread out over a considerable period of time according to the activity network (2-2.1).

Purpose and scope

Implementation consists of bringing a developed system or subsystem into operational use and turning it over to the user. It includes the training of personnel, the conversion of programs and files, and the installation and check-out of equipment. Since in practice few systems are perfectly designed and developed, implementation includes also the correction of system shortcomings, which results in partial repetition of previous activities.

Conversion deals with the problems related to program, file and library conversion of existing computer programs resulting from a change in data processing equipment or a change in data carriers used in the organization.

The purpose of evaluation is to determine the performance of each part of the new or converted information system, in terms of achievement of the objectives defined during the requirements determination (3-3). The post implementation evaluation can be either indirect, in terms of performance ratios, or direct in terms of costs & benefits and fulfilment of requirements such as outputs, duration of processing runs, response times, etc.

Results

The result of this phase should be a smoothly running system which meets the goals expressed in the objectives and requirements stated in (3-3).

Methodology

The methods of determining the manpower requirements and schedules for carrying out the activities of this phase are described in volume 2.

The teams and the time schedules necessary are as follows:

- teams:
  - installation team, for supervising the preparation of the computer centre and installing and checking out the equipment. This team must be headed by the data processing manager;
  - conversion teams, for carrying out file and program conversion;
  - implementation team, for putting the information system into operation. This team must be headed by user management (systems analysts and

programmers should be phased out gradually as the system nears operational status);
  - maintenance team, to handle improvements, changes and error corrections after turnover of the system to the user. This team is mainly composed of personnel from the information systems department;
- schedules:
  - equipment delivery schedule for the stage of installing hardware;
  - conversion schedule, especially for file conversion which can be a long and tedious job requiring a high degree of accuracy;
  - implementation schedule, which allows adequate time for making changes in computer programs and specifies the latest dates by which procedures and forms must be available.

The activities involved in this phase are as follows:

5-1 conduct training programme;
5-2 install equipment;
5-3 prepare operating schedules;
5-4 convert programs and files;
5-5 begin new operations;
5-6 evaluate implemented system.

The chart in page 3 shows the relationships between the activities and steps of this phase and those of the previous phases.

Techniques to be used are:

- human engineering (6-1.2);
- presentation techniques (6-1.3).

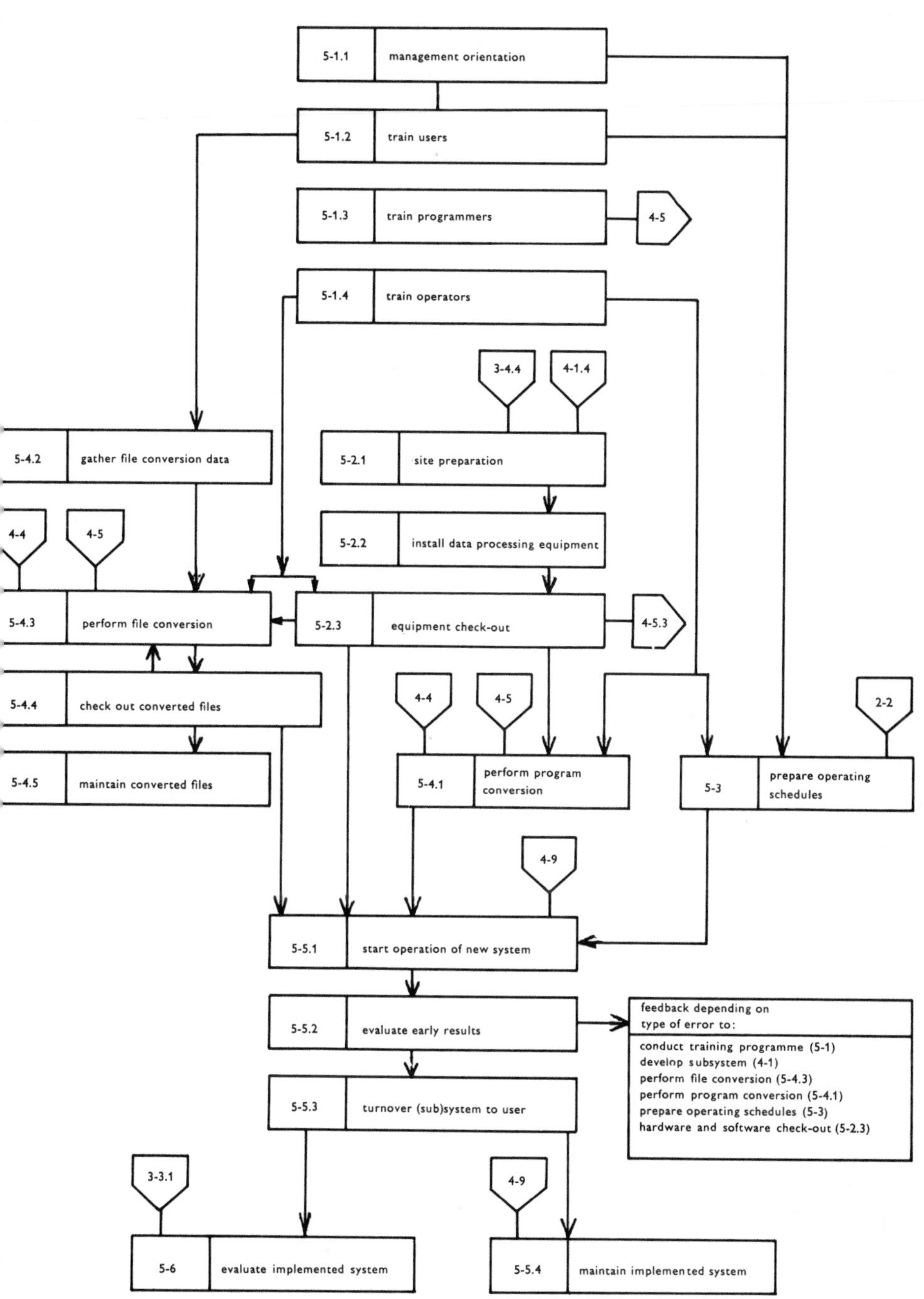

ethodology system implementation & evaluation

Activity 5-1: Conduct training programme

This activity is concerned with the indoctrination and training of the management and personnel of the user organization, and of the application programmers and operators.
The purpose of this training is to ensure that all personnel concerned possess all the knowledge and skills required for implementation of the new system.

The bulk of this training relates directly to system implementation and should be completed just before implementation is started. The training of programmers, however, must be completed before commencement of the system development phase, while the training and orientation of the various levels of user management is a continuing process which starts early in, or even before the start of, the systems effort. However, all the various types of training are brought together and described in this activity for the sake of completeness and convenience.

The training programmes consist of:

- presentations to management as a general introduction to the systems effort to initiate an adequate understanding for the necessity of the tasks, described in volume 2, project management;
- presentations to management to introduce the need for the involvement of user management or user representatives in many activities of the systems effort, of which especially must be mentioned:
  — analyze present system (3-2);
  — identify system requirements and constraints (3-3);
  — divide system into subsystems (3-5);
  — preparation for conversion (4-4);
  — test subsystem (4-8);
  — prepare operating schedules (5-3);
  — convert program and files (5-4);
  — begin new operations (5-5).
  This also serves to introduce the system to those members of management who have had no responsibility for approving the system, and who might therefore have missed earlier presentations;
- a user training programme for those directly concerned with the preparation or use of system inputs and outputs, or otherwise involved in procedures which are contained in or related to the new system. This programme includes intensive training not only on the use of the new information system, but also on the preparatory work, notably file conversion, that must be carried out before the new system can be put into operation;
- programmer training;
- operator training.

The last two types of training are necessary only if a new type of hardware is to be installed, or new software is to be used. To supplement the types of training discussed in this activity, full advantage should be taken of any courses in systems engineering and related disciplines given by professional institutes and equipment manufacturers.

Step 5-1.1: Management orientation

The orientation of user management should start at the very beginning of the systems effort (2-1.1), to inform all levels of management and to secure their cooperation.

Orientation method

Those members of management who have been involved in the systems effort will already be familiar with some aspects of the new system, but it is nevertheless desirable that they be given a comprehensive introduction to the new system by means of a formal meeting. Such a session should be attended by top management and organized by the steering committee.

The project team should present the major portions of these orientations. The steering committee members should stress management views and sponsorship.

Subjects

The orientation should include:

- an explanation of the system objectives;
- a survey of changes in the organization and in the procedures which are planned and should be introduced before, or at the time of, implementation. The role of management in this respect must be specified; for example that the implementation and conversion teams have been authorized to take all measures required for system implementation;
- the responsibilities of the departments involved in the implementation and operation of the new system should be identified;
- the conversion and implementation schedules (2-2.2) should be explained, and any interim procedures to be followed during the transition period should be agreed upon;
- an explanation of information exchange interfaces between subsystems must be given, with particular reference to the sequential introduction of the different subsystems;
- an explanation should be given of the costs and benefits of the new system as derived by means of the project calculation (2-3).

Step 5-1.2: Train users

"User personnel" in this context implies not only the personnel who will actually prepare the inputs, operate the procedures and use the outputs of the new system but also those who will be in any way affected by it.

Conditions

Before an appropriate training programme can be put into effect, a number of conditions must be fulfilled:

- if any changes to the user organization are planned to coincide with system implementation, all details, including job descriptions giving a precise definition of each task to be performed (3-3.2), must have been fully worked out; and all personnel involved must have been forewarned;
- full details of the work to be performed in the new system must be available and properly documented (4-9). All relevant documentation, including all types of forms, should be available in sufficient quantities;
- personnel must be available to undergo training. If new personnel are required, they should be engaged sufficiently early to have received a general introduction to the user organization before detailed training is commenced.

Sessions

Schedule training sessions for user personnel sufficiently early. Since these sessions will entail training the largest number of people, and will be more exhaustive in scope, the major emphasis on preparation should be in this area. Sessions should have a limited audience, preferably of fewer than 20 people. They should be conducted by user management and organized by user representatives who have participated in the systems effort. Systems analysts should lecture on professional subjects.

For the user personnel, an initial general presentation should be followed by more detailed training sessions to show consequences of the integrated system. Ensure that everyone involved can understand why the new system is to be introduced, and stress the importance of their cooperation in ensuring a successful implementation of the system.

The sessions for user personnel should stress the advantages of the new system for their daily work, and should teach them how to use the system reports in the correct way.

Direct each training session towards the task of the group being trained. Individual classes should be held for each major user group; mail room clerks, credit clerks, keypunch operators, etc.

Include case work for each class member to work out by applying the rules given in the user documentation.

The project team should evaluate the result of the training sessions before turnover of the system. Personnel who are not prepared to give their full cooperation, or who misunderstand the procedures, can seriously disrupt the implementation and can easily cause a well-designed system to fail.

Sessions for the direct users should be timed to finish before system implementation. Personnel more remotely concerned with system operation may receive instruction after implementation.

Step 5-1.3: Train programmers

Programmers must be properly trained before they can be effectively employed in the systems effort. This training should be completed by the start of the system development phase, and should cover:

- introduction to objectives of the user organization;
- introduction to existing systems in the user organization;
- organization of the systems effort; teams, schedules, responsibilities;
- briefing on the requirements, constraints and design of the new system;
- computer knowledge; principles of operation, configurator possibilities;
- general introduction to software and standard programs for auxiliary operations;
- programming, comprehensive course;
- method standards, such as:
  - — writing program descriptions (4-5.5 and 6-2.1);
  - — writing instructions for the computer centre (4-5.6);
  - — charting technique (4-5.1 and 6-2.2);
  - — identification of system elements and data objects (6-4.1);
  - — methods of computer programming (6-6.1);
  - — cobol programming (6-6.3);
- data organization (6-4.2 and 6-6.4);
- data communication (6-4.6);
- program testing, including real-time testing (4-5.4 and 6-6.6);
- program conversion (4-4.2 and 6-6.5).

The hardware manufacturer will be able to provide training facilities for the majority of these subjects.

Step 5-1.4: Train operators

The training of operators for the computer centre should be completed prior to equipment installation, in order that enough qualified personnel will be available at the time of equipment checkout.

To ensure that the operators can be effectively employed in data processing, the training should include:

- introduction to objectives of the user organization and the systems effort;
- introduction to the main aspects of the information system;
- computer knowledge; principles of operation, configurator possibilities;
- software knowledge and standard auxiliary programs; introduction and operating rules;
- computer operating; comprehensive course;
- instructions for the computer centre; how to write, evaluate and use them (4-5.6).

The equipment manufacturer will be able to provide training facilities for the majority of these subjects.

Activity 5-2: Install equipment

The result of this activity is on-site tested equipment, ready for system testing, conversion, training, and all other activities in this system implementation & evaluation phase.

This activity should start early in the systems effort, usually at the end of the feasibility study, to allow for delivery conditions of the supplier or the need to erect a new computer centre. Some installations may require only electrical work or the installation of data communication equipment and lines.

As a preliminary to this activity, the application programs might be tested on a computer similar to that to be installed; any necessary tape/disk conversion should be attended to; and the magnetic tapes to be employed should be retested for physical reliability.

This activity consists of the following steps:
5-2.1 site preparation;
5-2.2 install data processing equipment;
5-2.3 hardware and software check-out.

Step 5-2.1: Site preparation

The hardware manufacturer(s) will provide all specifications for equipment installation, and these should be consulted before site preparation begins. The provision of adequate site preparation, storage cabinets, magnetic tapes, cards and other supplies, is the responsibility of the information systems department.

The project team must provide the information necessary for obtaining the required equipment and supplies. This specification includes the hardware configuration as specified in 3-4.4 and detailed in 4-1.4 as well as storage facilities for cards, disk packs, tapes and paper. It also includes details of the retention periods for tapes and disk packs. The information provided by the project team should take into account possible future expansion.

A checklist for computer centre preparation follows.

Space

The location of the offices of the computer centre should be such as to permit quick and easy access to and from user departments.
Ensure that the size and capacity of the access routes (doors, elevators, stairways, etc.) are adequate to accommodate the equipment to be received.

Calculate space requirements for all staff and services:

- the offices for the manager of the computer centre, for the operators, computer planners, work preparation department, technical computer service staff, etc.;
- the library rooms for magnetic tapes, disk packs and cards:
  - the magnetic tape and disk pack storage should preferably be located in a conditioned area, but for security reasons it should be completely partitioned off from the computer room;
  - an estimate should be made of the total number of tape reels and disk packs to be stored;
  - other storage space will be needed for cards, punched tapes, printing paper and forms;
- the output despatch room, with paper bursters, decollators, and binding machines. The output despatch room should not be in the conditioned area. Paper decollators should be available in order to prepare individual copies of printed outputs;
- the computer room: space occupied by central processor, controllers and I/O units, taking into account:
  - engineering service;
  - cooling requirements of equipment;
  - operating space;
  - good overall view from operator's seat at console typewriter;
  - movement of trolleys;
  - air circulation in relation to location of I/O units which cause dust, e.g. printers, card punches, card readers, etc.

Power

The requirements vary according to the type and size of the equipment. The equipment manufacturers will specify mains supply:

- voltage and tolerance in volts and volts/second;
- frequency and tolerance in Hz and Hz/second;
- number of phases;
- power consumption, maximum and average.

Where the existing power supplies do not comply with the specification, special measures must be taken. These might include:

- the installation of a transformer;
- the installation of a voltage regulator;
- the provision of stand-by power supplies;
- the provision of a motor-alternator with heavy flywheel to ensure break-free supplies.

Light

The computer room should be evenly illuminated in accordance with office standards. The lighting should be diffused to prevent deep shadows inside the equipment during machine maintenance.

Floor

The following should be taken into consideration:

- the floor must be capable of withstanding both the distributed loads and point loads imposed by the weight of the equipment;
- sections of the floor should preferably be removable to provide access to all cables;
- the floor covering should be of a material which does not retain dust or dirt.

Ceiling

The ceiling should be constructed of sound-absorbent materials which do not accumulate dust. A false ceiling can facilitate light diffusion and accommodate air conditioning ducts and power supply cables.

Air conditioning

Air conditioning is concerned with the control of temperature, humidity and dust content.

Temperature

Temperature control equipment should be applied; the manufacturer will specify the temperature range and the rate of change of temperature that the equipment can tolerate. The temperature will be influenced by:

- heat dissipated by equipment and lighting;
- heat dissipated by personnel (about 100 W per person);
- heat transfered through floors and building walls.

The design of most air conditioning systems usually imposes an upper limit on the number of persons that can be present in the controlled environment. Any event which causes this maximum to be exceded, e.g. the admission of a group of visitors, should be of as short a duration as is reasonably possible.

Humidity

The range of relative humidity permitted will be specified by the manufacturer; these requirements should be taken into account when calculating air conditioning capacities.
It is recommended that temperature and humidity recorders or indicators, preferably fitted with high-limit and low-limit warning devices be installed in the computer room.

Dust

The degree of air cleanliness will be specified by the equipment manufacturer, and will usually be expressed as a filtering efficiency e.g. 95% at 5 micron. For some equipment, e.g. hyper-tape, very clean room conditions will be required; this might imply a filtering efficiency of 95% at 1 micron.

Safety

It is advisable to fit smoke detection equipment in the main extractor duct of the air conditioning system. This equipment should be arranged so that the presence of smoke triggers an alarm and, after a short delay (e.g. 20 sec.) shuts down all equipment in the controlled area.

Office and special equipment

Sufficient and suitable aids to communication, e.g. telephones, lifts, internal postal service, pneumatic message carriers etc. should be provided. The internal layout of offices and machine rooms must be such that the flow of work is facilitated by minimizing distances between work points and eliminating backtracking.
Determine requirements for:
- desks, chairs, storage cabinets for removable disks, tapes, cards, paper, forms etc.;
- test equipment, trolleys, telephones and other communications equipment.

Step 5-2.2: Install data processing equipment

When the preparation of the computer centre is complete and the different facilities within the computer room have been tested, the data processing equipment can be installed.

It is essential that the computer room be thoroughly cleaned before the data processing equipment is installed. The floor should be swept and scrubbed to remove all dust, dirt, construction debris, etc., and the air conditioning system should be run for at least a day to remove dust etc. from the ducting.

Usually the equipment will be installed by manufacturer's personnel with the assistance of electricians, carpenters, etc. provided by the user organization. The personnel of the computer centre should be available to advise and assist during installation, and to ensure that equipment is sited correctly. Their participation can be of considerable value, since it enables them to work with the manufacturer's representatives and thus become familiar with the equipment as early as possible.

Step 5-2.3: Hardware and software check-out

Manufacturer's engineers will test equipment and operating systems. The project team and the computer centre personnel should co-operate in this activity to ensure that the tests are accurate and complete. Usually the check-out will include the running of special test programs provided by the manufacturer.

All software, including monitoring systems, assemblers and compilers, should be thoroughly tested for correct operation on the new equipment. This is particularly true if prior tests were run on simulators or on a different machine configuration.

Data communication equipment can be tested by transmitting data similar to that used in actual operation. The testing of data communication equipment to be used online may require co-operation between installation engineers from various manufacturers. These tests should be monitored closely by the project team to ensure that they are accurate and complete.

The project team, in co-operation with computer centre personnel, should also conduct their own testing of the computer, its peripheral equipment, and the accompanying software, to ensure that they have become sufficiently familiar with the use of the new equipment to be able to operate it without assistance from the manufacturer's representatives. For this purpose, solidly debugged usermade programs should be used.

Activity 5-3: Prepare operating schedules

The purpose of this step is to devise operating schedules which ensure that all system outputs are produced at the correct times, and that the best possible use is made of the available resources such as computer time, personnel etc.

Operating schedules are documents which specify the dates and times by which:
- each output of the system must be produced;
- the processing necessary to produce each output must be carried out;
- the inputs required for each processing operation must be available.

The information necessary for preparing the operating schedules should be obtained from the run descriptions prepared in 4-5.6.

Scheduling factors

The scheduling of computer processing entails balancing the processing requirements of the system against available computer time. This includes such factors as:
- operating requirements, including processing frequencies, response times and volumes of input and output;
- program and run timings developed during testing;
- sequence of programs within runs;
- computer set-up times for each program or run;
- intermediate manual procedures (e.g. checking the validation listing before an updating run can proceed);
- further processing of output prior to delivery (forms bursting, decollating, binding, etc.);
- in some subsystems the runs can be scheduled separately, in other cases the entire subsystem must be processed without interruption.

Types of schedule

Two types of operating schedules are necessary:
- a schedule for each of the groups of programs that must be processed without interruption. This schedule can be prepared by the subsystem team on the basis of the run descriptions;
- a schedule for the daily processing, giving the sequence of the above-mentioned groups of programs. This may enable the daily processing to be arranged so that it meets the time requiremens for all operational jobs. The preparation of this type of schedule is one of the planning activities of the computer centre.

Input timing

Data to be processed must be available at the proper time, as specified in the procedure descriptions.
Time schedules for input delivery must allow efficient computer scheduling.
All input transactions should be scheduled to the run to which they belong.
The input scheduling is the first action line of a run description.

Activity 5-4: Convert programs and files

This activity deals with the performance of the actual conversion of programs and files.

The preparations for program conversion are dealt with in 4-4. Program conversion is necessary whenever existing programs are to be run on a new configuration.

File conversion is necessary in those situations when a new information system will incorporate files which were previously kept on a different medium, or when changes in file layout or data representation have to be implemented.

This activity consists of the following steps:

5-4.1 perform program conversion;
5-4.2 gather file conversion data;
5-4.3 perform file conversion;
5-4.4 check out converted files;
5-4.5 maintain converted files.

Step 5-4.1: Perform program conversion

This step must be performed according to the requirements and procedural rules given in 4-4.2.

Although dealt with for formal reasons in the implementation phase, program conversion has much in common with program development.

Program conversion results in programs which are tested and ready for implementation in the same way as newly developed ones.

Depending on the technique used — imitation or refabrication — the amount of testing required will vary from very little to very significant. See also program testing (4-5.4).

Step 5-4.2: Gather file conversion data

In many file conversion situations, it is necessary to collect all or some of the information for the new files from a variety of non-machine-readable sources such as documents, cardex files, ledgers, etc.

Conditions

All files concerned must be ready for entry into the new system. This means that no backlog in updating these files must occur, and that the filed data must be consistent and in current mode of representation.
In some cases it is necessary to collect new data to supplement information already available in the files. For example, it may be necessary to add unit prices and lead times to a file used to maintain stock inventory balances.

Procedure

Procedures must be written and forms designed to facilitate this step of data collection. The conversion team must be trained in the techniques to be used, especially if they are not already familiar with the files.
This step often involves transferring data from existing files to intermediate files for manipulation before creating the new files. For example, existing, manually-accessible data might be converted into punched cards, and then, after sorting and screening the cards, the data might be transferred to disk.

Step 5-4.3: Perform file conversion

The conversion team is responsible for supervising the running of the conversion programs which were developed and tested in earlier activities. File input data produced by the conversion team and/or mechanical files is sorted, validated, and updated into the new file format.

Methods

File creation can be carried out in three ways:

- straight machine processing which entails gathering the data mechanically from cards, tapes, or disks;
- collecting the data required on punching documents and then converting them into a representation acceptable to the machine;
- collecting data from the moment the new system becomes operational and gradually building up files using information relating to current transactions. It might, for example, be impractical or impossible to accumulate a sales history for each item in a stock inventory system using manual methods. It is possible, however, to begin the new system operations without sales history data and to allow the system to accumulate sales for each stock item starting from "Day no. 1". After the new system has been in operation for some time (possibly up to one year with some types of stock), adequate sales history will have been accumulated.

  This history can be employed for stock and sales forecasting, for simulation, or for other functions or subsystems which require historical information. This method has the advantage of eliminating conversion costs for the data collected, but the disadvantage of delaying implementation of those programs which require historical data. It is therefore most frequently used for low-priority programs, or in cases where historical data does not exist.

Combinations of the three above mentioned methods are also possible.

Sequence

To minimize the amount of updating required, history-files should be converted first and active files last.

Step 5-4.4: Check converted files

After each file conversion run, all the file records which have been processed should be printed in a format similar to that of the records from which the data was originally collected. Essential relationships between specific data fields and the validity of codes can be checked and indicated in the list. The conversion team should check the list for transcriptions and other conversion errors.

Error handling

Any errors remaining in the original files should be corrected, both in the new files and in the original. The corrections should be introduced by filling in file correction forms, to be processed in the next conversion run or in the first file updating run.

In a case where several conversion runs must take place, special care must be exercised to safeguard intermediate parts of converted files and to control the consolidation into one new system or subsystem file.

Step 5-4.5: Maintain converted files

Time phasing in the maintenance of converted files is extremely critical, since new transactions must be used to update both the existing and the newly converted files in order to continue present operations and provide up-to-date files for use by the new subsystems.
Unless the file conversion process itself is short enough to be run during a weekend or a vacation shutdown of the organization, provision must be made to maintain both sets of files until the conversion activity has been completed. The conversion team must work in close co-operation with all personnel engaged in updating the existing files.

Practical rules

Practical rules for this step include:

- mark or tag each record of an old (manual) file when it has been entered on the conversion input form. This indicates to other personnel that any further transactions affecting this record must be updated in both the old and the new file;
- use new subsystem input forms and procedures for entering file transactions into the new system. In addition to the maintenance of files on a current basis, this will provide a test of input procedure forms and programs in advance of the formal commencement of new system operations;
- if the existing system uses and updates machine-readable files, it may be possible to modify the existing file-updating run to enable it to produce information suitable for updating the files of the new system. As in the manual situation it would be necessary to append a marker or tag to each record of the existing file that has a counterpart in the new files, and to use this tag to trigger the routine that updates the new file.

Activity 5-5: Begin new operations

As an introduction to the steps of this activity it is useful to discuss four possible methods for actually starting to process live data from the organization by means of the new information system.
These methods are history processing, straight turnover, parallel processing, and phased turnover.

History processing

The method of history processing can be employed in the first stage of turnover. In it, the newly developed subsystem is subjected to inputs which actually occurred in the recent past. The old system continues to process all new data, while the new system processes data from one or more previous periods. The advantages of this method are that it permits a selection both of a subsystem and of the data to be used, and enables the results to be analyzed in a quiet and calm offline atmosphere conductive to the implementation of rigorous control measures.
Furthermore, since the results are already available in the form of outputs of the existing system, and since the input data used has already been validated by the existing system, all the information necessary for comparison and evaluation is readily available.
The results of history processing should be evaluated to check if the method planned for the next stage of turnover is still appropriate.
The two methods available for this next stage are straight turnover and parallel processing.

Straight turnover

This method entails ending operations under the old system and then as soon as possible beginning operations under the new system.
It has the severe disadvantage that live testing of the new system becomes impossible, thus increasing the risk of disturbance or malfunction of the system at the very beginning of its existence.
Furthermore, it imposes a severe strain on operators and user personnel, who will have had no opportunity of gaining operational experience, when no history processing has preceded the straight turnover. Situations do exist, however, in which straight turnover without history processing is feasible. If only a small volume of data or a small sized system is involved, or if a fully-experienced conversion team is available, straight turnover is justified.

Another situation which favours straight turnover is the availability of escape programs and/or emergency procedures. This guarantees recovery should the new system malfunction.

Straight turnover must be used in those cases where the other methods given later are, owing to volume of work, shortage of personnel, insufficient computer capacity or interdependences between subsystems too costly or impossible to apply. Even when a larger system, or a system containing high-volume rapidly-changing files is concerned, it might be necessary to undertake a straight turnover because of the impracticability of handling transactions in parallel updating both old and new files.

To minimize the risks of straight turnover, it should be arranged to take place during an off-peak period, at a time when none of the personnel involved in system operations is on holiday.

Parallel processing

Parallel processing entails processing current data by the existing system as well as by the new information system. If the new system turns out to be effective, two complete sets of outputs will become available. If the outputs of the old system only are distributed along their usual channels, there remains the task of checking the outputs of the new system to ascertain if they are meeting their requirements.
An alternative which saves time but is accompanied by a certain degree of risk, is to begin immediately to make use of the new system by distributing its outputs as working papers. The outputs of the old system are kept for reference, or, in case of need, for checking purposes. This method is particularly valuable where new types of output are concerned.

Parallel processing can be advocated as a safe method, because it minimizes the risks of disrupting the user organization. In many cases, however, costs and/or the volume of work prohibit parallel processing.

In those cases where the new system differs greatly from the old system, the advantages of parallel processing are more obvious, because there would be little duplication of work in the input, processing and output procedures.

It sometimes occurs that the users of the new system are not ready to accept it, or are suspicious of the accuracy or usefulness of the calculations or outputs. In a situation such as this, there is justification for instituting parallel processing for a limited period as a logical step towards user indoctrination. Parallel processing introduced for this reason alone should be continued only for as long as is necessary to demonstrate the usefulness of the new system (e.g. for one reporting period). The old system should then be terminated as soon as possible.

Phased turnover

Phased turnover is to some extent a combination of, and to some extent a comprise between parallel processing and history processing. It involves processing a part of the current work by the new system, and the remainder by the old system.

Much depends on the way these parts are selected, either by department, by kind of transaction, by taking a segment out of the systems file or by taking a stage in the processing itself. Phased turnover generally means bringing only a few of the functions of the new system into operation at a time.

If phased turnover is introduced, it is essential that the sequence and timing for introducing additional parts of the new system and terminating the corresponding parts of the old system should be properly scheduled. Only in this way can the main disadvantages of the parallel processing method (cost and work load) be avoided, while preserving most of its advantages. An important characteristic of this method is that its outputs are used from the very beginning.

The steps into which this activity is subdivided are:
5-5.1 start operation of new system;
5-5.2 evaluate early results;
5-5.3 turnover (sub)system to user;
5-5.4 maintain implemented system.

Step 5-5.1: Start operation of new system

Selection of method of implementation

Whichever of the four implementation methods described in 5-5 is chosen, the aim is to introduce a maximally reliable system as smoothly as possible. The selection of the implementation method is influenced by the following criteria:

- strong demands for short-term introduction from the side of the user organization will necessitate straight turnover;
- complexity and vulnerability of the system, great dissimilarity with the existing system, or high demands for reliability will favour history processing or phased turnover;
- uncertainty about meeting the requirements or the expectations of the user will tend to parallel processing, as this offers a physically convincing proof of what the system can perform in an actual operating situation and at the same time gives a solid basis for comparison;
- great volumes of transactions and files might require too much additional processing time if run in parallel. In this case costs would be a determining factor in making a choice between straight turnover and phased turnover;
- availability of escape possibilities in case of emergency can make straight turnover feasible.

Acceptance procedure

It is recommended that the user organization should arrange and conduct its own system test by means of an acceptance procedure. This test should take place after the (sub)system tests of 4-8 which were performed by individual subsystem- or implementation teams.

The project team must develop an acceptance procedure. This procedure should be designed to test not only the final system, but also all documentation delivered during the development and implementation of the system. This acceptance procedure must be approved by the user management.

If the authorized representative of the user organization feels that the system test completed earlier has been sufficiently rigorous, then the acceptance test could take the form of running a collection of actual user programs in various sequences. In a more advanced information system the tests could include also the performance of online and remote batch processing simultaneously with various responsive types of processing. The acceptance tests could thus simulate an actual user environment.
For very advanced systems, "scenarios" should be produced for responsive tests, in which two or more people exercise different system capabilities in different combinations and in different ways at the same time. Someone could also be assigned to a remote console to try to find ways of "blowing up" the system as it is running.

The successful completion of the acceptance tests is usually regarded as the main criterion of readiness for final turnover of the system to the user. The acceptance tests should therefore be thorough and complete. No part of the system should be turned over to the user before these tests are completed. The time and money spent in conducting properly organized and comprehensive acceptance tests is well invested, because it lessens the possibility of trouble occurring after system turnover. Such troubles can be very expensive and time-consuming to rectify.

Practical rules

If either the parallel processing or pilot processing methods of implementation are to be used, the following should be taken into account:

- maintain records and files in both the old and the new systems. This may require double processing of inputs. In some cases, it may be possible to utilize conversion programs in order to convert old-system inputs into formats acceptable to the new system. Establish adequate controls, however, to ensure detection of all conversion errors;
- compare all outputs produced. Although results may differ in format and data content, it should always be possible to check outputs for validity and correctness. Apply as much random checking as possible, using manual computation or simulation methods, e.g. checking customer orders against invoices to verify the presence of all order items, or manual proving of computed results (re-order points, invoice amounts, etc.);
- process all errors flagged by the subsystem through the correction process to provide assurance of validity;
- check console logsheet for proper initialization and termination of each program;
- check error listings to ensure that they are approximate and trace their source;
- check printouts of files for valid updating (compare with input transactions and output results);
- keep a logbook of all errors and problems; record actions taken and document the solutions achieved. See also the error report in 5-5.4;
- ensure that the period during which the system will be paralleled or phased is carefully planned. Do not expect that any problem not solved in advance of parallel processing will easily be solved in this period. The number of problems has a tendency to increase, not to decrease;
- user personnel should ensure that the actual inputs and outputs are in accordance with the originally stated and agreed requirements.

Step 5-5.2: Evaluate early results

After each program or run has been executed during several production cycles, all observations and comments should be gathered and evaluated. Some subsystem shortcomings may be immediately apparent, and some of these may be troublesome enough to warrant quick corrective action.

Problem reporting

These problems should be solved as soon as possible to keep the implementation of the new subsystem proceeding in a smooth manner. Details of all problems and the actions taken to overcome them should be recorded, either in a project logbook or in error reports (5-5.4).

Problem solving

If operating problems which seriously affect company operations cannot be rectified quickly, it may be better to suspend operation of the new (sub)system until a solution can be found, even though this may delay completion of implementation.

If early results prove to be unsatisfactory on major points, the project team should seek the co-operation of the user in deciding what immediate corrective measures are necessary.
Refinements and/or alterations must be postponed until after turnover. The agreed amendments should be co-ordinated to produce a properly organized plan of action which is then put into effect. This process should be repeated as often as necessary to achieve continuously satisfactory system operation.

It is emphasized that close co-operation and efficient communication between the project team and the user during this "running in" period are essential.

Step 5-5.3: Turn over (sub)system to user

When evaluation of the early results indicates that the new (sub)system is running smoothly the (sub)system can be turned over to the user. It then becomes the responsibility of the user to maintain the system in operational status. A part of this responsibility — usually that for program execution, file storage and protection — should be delegated to the computer centre.

Turnover requirements

A (sub)system can be considered to be ready for turnover to the user when:

- it is running smoothly and giving satisfactory results. All error reports should have been dealt with, and any major deviations between performance and requirements should have been corrected before turnover;
- complete and up-to-date user documentation is available in the necessary quantities;
- the appropriate personnel in all line departments involved have received sufficient training;
- all new procedures are fully understood and accepted.

Actions after turnover

Immediately after system turnover, the steering committee should initiate the following actions:

- relieve the project team and subsystem teams of their responsibility for the systems effort;
- assign the maintenance of the system to an employee or team reporting to the manager of the information systems department;
- assign responsibility for system operation to the appropriate user departments and to the computer centre.

Step 5-5.4: Maintain implemented system

The concern of the information systems department for the information system does not end at the date of turnover. Like a business organization, a system is a dynamic entity; one can be sure, even if the developed system is near-perfect, that within a short time after turnover the first questions will arise. An error may be detected, some output signals may appear to be without value of sense, the user organization may demand modification of the system logic or processing flow, a (sub)system requirement may be changed.

Maintenance team

The task of dealing with these matters is assigned to a maintenance team, the size and composition of which will depend on the size and complexity of the system and on the amount of changes expected.

In addition, the maintenance team should act on its own initiative to detect errors and inefficiencies in the system (development bugs) as well as in the operating (handling errors in the computer centre, deviations from operating schedule, non-delivery of inputs or outputs). Furthermore, the team must seek to prevent any deviations from the system as laid down in the user documentation, whether intentional or unintentional.

Deviations may occur when temporary measures instituted to overcome peak loads or program difficulties, are allowed to become the rule rather than the exception. Under these circumstances the possibility that modifications in procedures and programs may be required should be investigated. In addition, measures taken by programmers to deal with exceptional circumstances or to correct production errors may not have been deleted, so that they become sources of deviation in subsequent runs.

After system turnover the maintenance team should deal with all recommendations from user departments. These recommendations should be carefully handled so as not to discourage the submission of suggestions. If any suggestions are found to be disruptive or nonfeasible, this should be thoroughly explained to the originator.

Error reports and change requests

After the system has been turned over to the user a well planned, properly documented and adequately controlled procedure for making modifications to the system should be instituted. The stimulus for this procedure will be an error report originated by a user department. An example of an error report is given on page 9.

ERROR REPORT

system :
subsystem :
prev. issue:

project no. :
chapter/sect.:
page :
issued :

user :

program no.:

run no.:

computer :

description of error or problem

enclosures:
(e.g. computer output which illustrates the malfunction)

☐ printer ☐ plotter ☐ program listing ☐ tape dump

☐ teletype ☐ typewriter ☐ core dump ☐ disk dump

☐ other:

date received: assigned to: reference change request no.:

analysis of error:

resolution of error:

date of disposition:

An error report should be made out if a deviation is detected between the actual operation of the system and what is written in the requirements at subsystem, program or procedure level. If these errors can be corrected without affecting the requirements, the error report can be used as a work statement, and no personnel other than the maintenance team need to be involved in the correction. If errors are detected which necessitate changes in the requirements for the system and in the documentation, the error report should be evaluated, and one or more change requests prepared by the maintenance team. In 2-4.2 a change request procedure is described for these situations. By absence of a project team, the changes should be evaluated by the manager of the information systems department and appropriate user personnel.

Evaluation of error reports

When analyzing an error report and — if appropriate — preparing a change request, the maintenance team should take the following into account:

- Is the correction necessary or merely a recommendation?
- Will any benefits be derived from the change? If so, what are they and can they be measured in money, resources etc?
- What will be the cost of implementing the change?
- Will the change affect the system operating cost? If so, in which direction and by how much?
- Will the change affect other system elements or interfaces with other subsystems? If so, will other changes be necessary? If so, are these changes feasible? If so, what will they cost?
- Do the benefits to be expected from the change outweigh the costs incurred in implementing it?
- Are resources (manpower, money, equipment) available to carry out the change?

A recommended procedure for dealing with error reports is given below.

Error report procedure

This procedure defines the course to be followed when a competent person discovers an error in, or encounters a difficulty in connection with, the information system.

Originator of error report	1 Fills in upper part of error report (ER) form number 121D08 in duplicate.
	2 Sends ER to maintenance team.
Maintenance team	3 Logs ER on error report summary.
	4 Compares content of ER with contents of requirements (subsystem-, program and procedure level).

5 Informs originator of acceptance or reasons for rejection or postponement by returning annotated copy of ER.
6 IF rejected, logs on error report summary, files ER, end of procedure.
7 IF accepted, initiates corrective action; allocates work statement number.
8 Sends ER to appropriate systems analyst.
9 IF impact on requirements is detected evaluates interfaces; prepares one or more change requests.
10 Sends change requests to manager of information systems department.

Systems analyst or programmer

11 Prepares correction.
12 Prepares appropriate documentation.
13 Tests corrections.
14 IF results satisfactory goes to 16.
15 IF results unsatisfactory goes back to 11.
16 Sends completed ER and documentation to maintenance team.

Maintenance team

17 Evaluates modified documentation
18 Authorizes correction for incorporation into the system.
19 IF appropriate, provides input to computer centre for correction to system tape or disk.

Computer centre

20 Modifies system tape or disk.

Maintenance team

21 Tests correction under actual operating conditions.
22 IF test unsatisfactory postpones correction and returns to 11.
23 IF test satisfactory, goes to 24.
24 Adjusts user documentation.
25 Updates error report summary.
26 Distributes user documentation.
27 At monthly intervals submits error report summary to manager of information systems department.
28 At 2-monthly intervals reviews all outstanding ER's and notifies the originators of those on which action is not imminent.

For an example of an error report summary refer to the change request summary in 2-4.2.

Activity 5-6: Evaluate information system

Between three and six months after turnover to the user, and at regular intervals thereafter, the information system should be subjected to a post implementation evaluation to determine to what extent the system is satisfactory.

The post implementation evaluation should be carried out by the steering committee for two reasons:
- to establish whether or not the benefits derived from the new system justify the costs of instituting and running it;
- to ascertain whether or not the new system adequately satisfies its requirements.

Practical rules

The following rules assist in performing the evaluation:
- consult the user documentation for system requirements, constraints and quantified objectives (3-3.1);
- for more detailed or background information, consult the project file (2-4.1);
- study the latest version of project budgets and cost and benefit reports;
- collect actual initial costs of the systems effort and relate them to the budgets;
- collect all data relating to operational costs. This includes equipment rental, staff of computer centre, user personnel involved in system operations, sundries, housing and other overheads;
- relate these actual operational costs to the precalculated ones in the last version of the project budget;
- inspect actual system operations to verify that personnel and equipment to be phased out as parts of the previous system have in fact been eliminated;
- investigate the actual benefits of the new system in relation to precalculated benefits. For this purpose measure the performance ratios defined in 3-3.1 and the project calculation made in 2-3;
- determine the extent to which non-measurable benefits, which were planned, have been achieved. These other benefits are not necessarily related to the physical performance of the system, but rather to the way in which the user takes advantage of it. It should be noted that this analysis is usually no "desk" evaluation, since accounting records are not structured for this purpose. It may very well require special analysis and field collection of data in order to determine the extent to which these other benefits have been achieved;
- if the new system realized benefits other than those anticipated make a point of stating them;
- investigate the degree of conformity with the system requirements as described in the user documentation regarding:
  - — flexibility, expandability and maintainability;
  - — inputs, outputs, files, processing, logical structure of operations, procedures and forms;

— equipment configuration, software specification, tasks, areas of responsibility, frequency of operation;

- discuss realization of requirements with user management and user personnel;
- check if stipulated organizational changes are complete and that everybody is accomplishing tasks and procedures according to expectations;
- explain all deviations detected and specify their significance.
  For example, if the inventory reduction was estimated to be between $400,000 and $500,000, but the actual reduction is virtually nil, the explanation might be that the improvement has been expected too soon after system turnover and the system has not yet been able to re-balance the inventory. Another possible explanation could be that the system was poorly-designed in that insufficient emphasis was placed on eliminating obsolete items from the inventory.

Reporting

Report the results of the post implementation evaluation under the following headings:

- initial cost (actual and planned);
- operating cost (actual and planned);
- benefits, measurable (actual and planned);
- benefits, non-measurable;
- realization of organizational changes;
- realization of information and control requirements;
- realization of general design requirements;
- summary of deviations;
- explanation of the important deviations;
- measures suggested to correct deviations.

Volume 6: Techniques & standards

Contents

Activity 6-1: Management techniques

Technique 6-1.1: Network planning[1])

Purpose

To provide an effective method of planning, coordinating and monitoring the progress of complex systems efforts.

Definition

Network planning is a scheduling and progress-monitoring technique employing specialized graphic and often computer-processing techniques to organize, sequence, assign priorities to, and monitor coordinated progress of, the various interrelated activities required in a large-scale project. Network planning is particularly suitable for developmental activities which are difficult to define, quantify, or coordinate in advance.

Description

The network planning technique consists of a set of principles, methods and techniques for effectively planning project-oriented work, thereby establishing a sound basis for effective scheduling, costing, controlling and replanning that work.
The most suitable technique for planning a project is activity-oriented network planning.
If it is to be dealt with by means of network planning, a project must satisfy the following conditions:

- the project should have clearly defined beginning and end points;
- the project should be sufficiently complex; that is to say, it should consist of chains of activities which run in parallel between the starting points and the end points, and which can be related to one another at intermediate points.

Network planning requires thorough project analysis, and encourages a systematic approach to the project. It enables a watchful eye to be kept on the interfaces between activities, and clearly shows the organizational relationships between them, a necessary consideration from the technical point of view for effective and rapid progress control of a project.
Similarly, it highlights the extent to which the various activities are critical in their effect on the overall situation, and enables the consequences of breakdowns

1) This technique is based on an internal paper written by P.G.M. Gielisse, Philips — Electrologica, Apeldoorn. In this paper some minor parts are adapted from the publication: PERT Coordinating Group, *PERT-GUIDE: for Managements Use*, U.S. Government Printing Office (0-698-452), 1963, 56 pp.

to be assessed. By means of network planning the amount of float (slack) associated with the various activities of the project can be determined.
The planning and control of project costs can be carried out more efficiently with this technique than by conventional methods.

Project planning techniques are known by several names, e.g. PERT (Project Evaluation and Review Technique), and CPM (Critical Path Methods). A special version of PERT, called PERT/Cost, utilizes the network structure and the work or product breakdown structure reference for estimating and controlling the schedule, as well as the cost of the effort. This feature permits more complete measurement of progress, and enables managers to appraise more realistically the consequence of alternative courses of action.

Network planning can easily be processed by computer, and possible solutions can therefore be quickly simulated. Thus network planning makes it possible, through its efficient, economical simulation capability, to evaluate and forecast the outcome of alternative plans before implementation; simulating and measuring the effect of proposed changes in scheduled plans permits of early identification of the most efficient plan, when parallel approaches are utilized on "crash" efforts.
The network planning technique is based on the network of a project. This network is essentially an extension of the bar chart, which usually shows the

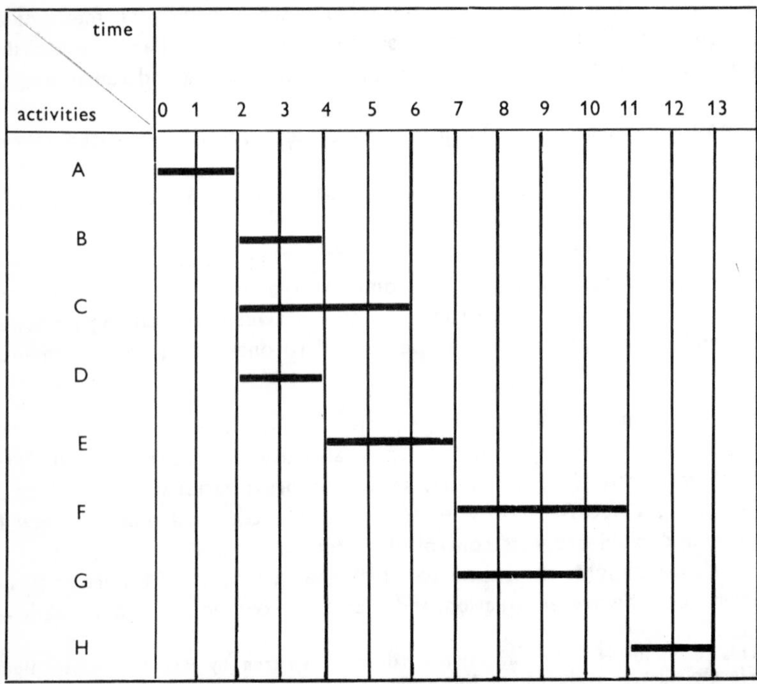

Bar chart

most important activities of a project with their planned starting and finishing dates.
In a network the activity-dependence can be shown explicitly, and it is often possible to have a more detailed description of the activities, whereas in bar charts activity-dependence cannot always be observed even if the activities are few in number.

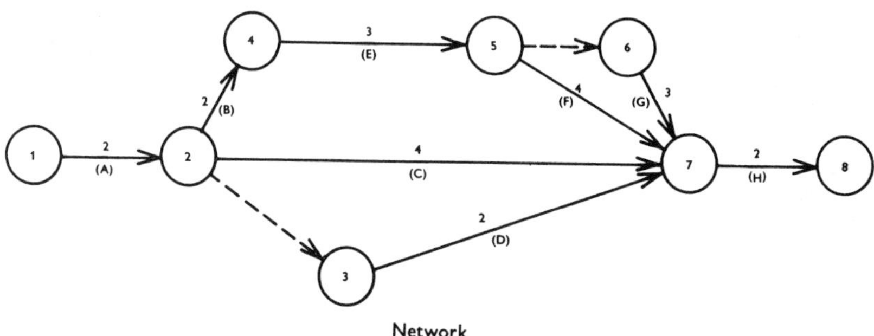

Network

The lines in a network indicate activities, usually requiring time and means for their realization. The length of a line is of no consequence (the expected duration of the activity is stated above it).
In a network the beginning and the end of each activity is an event. Each event is indicated by a circle; time is taken as moving from the tail to the head of an arrow on each activity-line. An event indicates an instant of time (for definitions see the next section).

The network can also be drawn on a time scale, but this is not usual because a change in the planning of any activity might necessitate shifting all subsequent activities. The use of time-scale networks to indicate the results of already accomplished network analysis however, can often be very valuable.

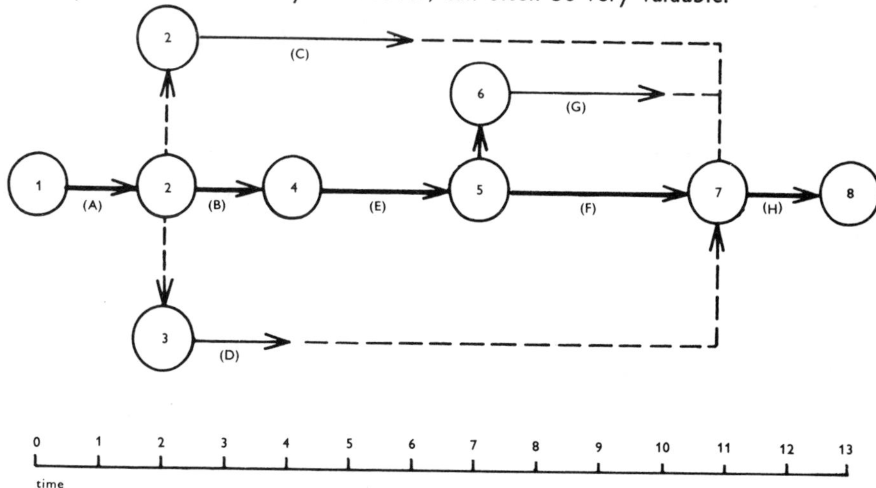

Time scaled network

Subdivision

The technical aspects of network planning are dealt with under the following sections:

- structural stage;
- estimating stage;
- time calculating stage.

Structural stage

In this stage each activity is identified and the relationships between activities are defined.

Definitions

Note that the definition of the terms project and activity given here have more general meaning than those used in the other parts of ARDI.

project	Two or more activities with a given aim in view.
network	A graphical representation of a project plan, which shows activities and the relationships between them, thus defining the structure of the project.
activity	A part of a project, which has a defined beginning and end, and which requires time and means. Activities are indicated in a network by means of arrows.
events (milestones)	The beginnings and ends of activities are called events. Theoretically an event is an instant of time. Events are indicated in a network by circles, each of which is numbered. Activities are identified by means of the numbers of the events with which they begin and end.

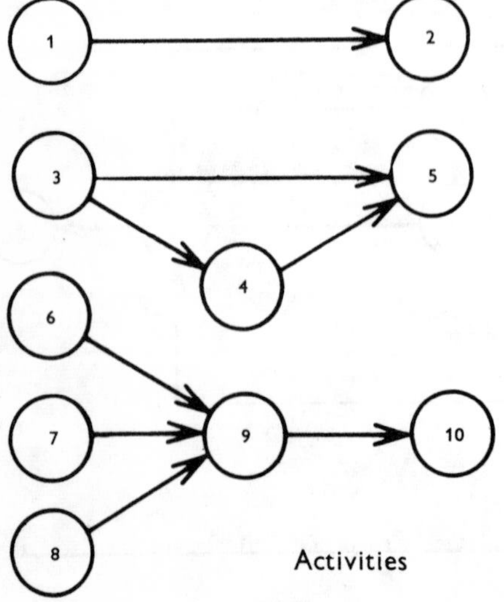

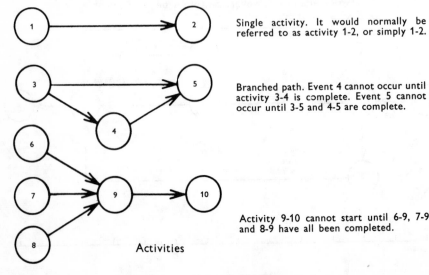

Single activity. It would normally be referred to as activity 1-2, or simply 1-2.

Branched path. Event 4 cannot occur until activity 3-4 is complete. Event 5 cannot occur until 3-5 and 4-5 are complete.

Activity 9-10 cannot start until 6-9, 7-9 and 8-9 have all been completed.

Activities

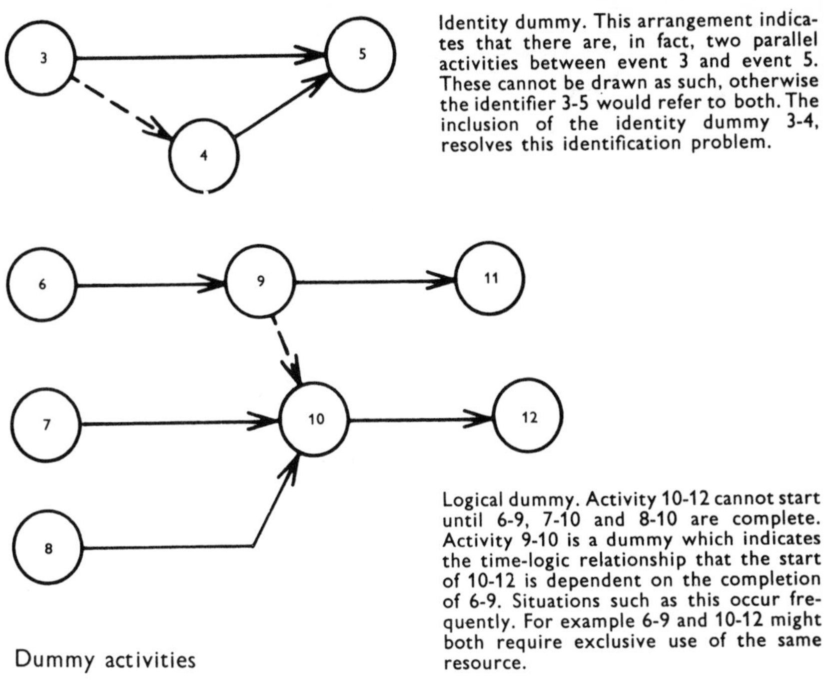

Identity dummy. This arrangement indicates that there are, in fact, two parallel activities between event 3 and event 5. These cannot be drawn as such, otherwise the identifier 3-5 would refer to both. The inclusion of the identity dummy 3-4, resolves this identification problem.

Logical dummy. Activity 10-12 cannot start until 6-9, 7-10 and 8-10 are complete. Activity 9-10 is a dummy which indicates the time-logic relationship that the start of 10-12 is dependent on the completion of 6-9. Situations such as this occur frequently. For example 6-9 and 10-12 might both require exclusive use of the same resource.

Dummy activities

dummy — An arrow which indicates only the dependence of one event or activity on another is called a "dummy" activity. A dummy requires neither time nor means. Dummies are usually indicated in a network by means of dotted lines.

Constructing the network

The most obvious way of constructing a network is to start at the initial event and to work forwards towards the end event by drawing-in the activities. Experience has shown however that there are advantages in constructing a network by starting with the end event of the project and proceeding backwards to the initial event. Since the end event is constantly and clearly in view, a plan may be developed in direct relation to it.

When constructing a network, the following points should be borne in mind:

- an activity must be indicated by an arrow connecting two and only two events. Should more than one activity have to be realized between two events dummies must be used;
- each event must be uniquely numbered, so that each activity is uniquely identified by naming its initial and final events;
- events must be connected to one another (if necessary, by means of dummies)

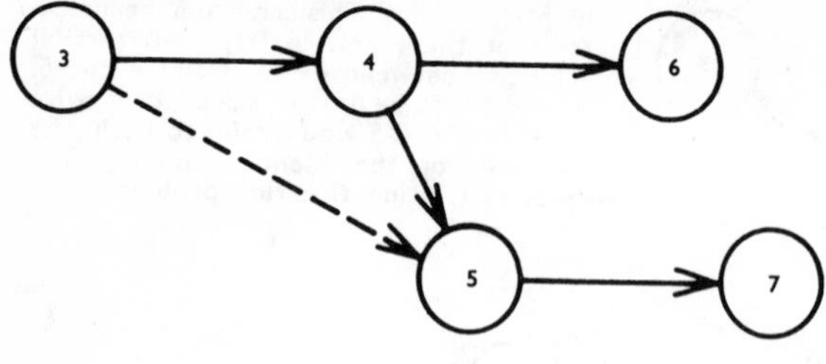

Redundant dummy. Event 3 must occur before 3-4 can start and 3-4 must be completed before 4-5 can start, so that event 3 will always occur before event 5.

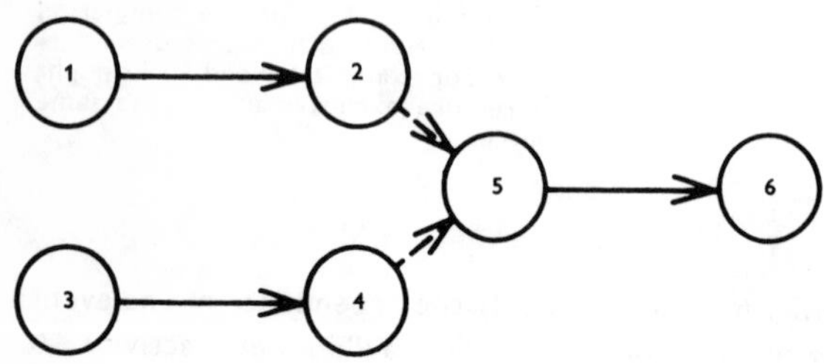

Incorrect dummies

Both dummies are redundant. Events are effectively time-logic elements having an AND function. Output cannot occur (succeeding activities cannot start) until all inputs are present (all preceding activities are complete).

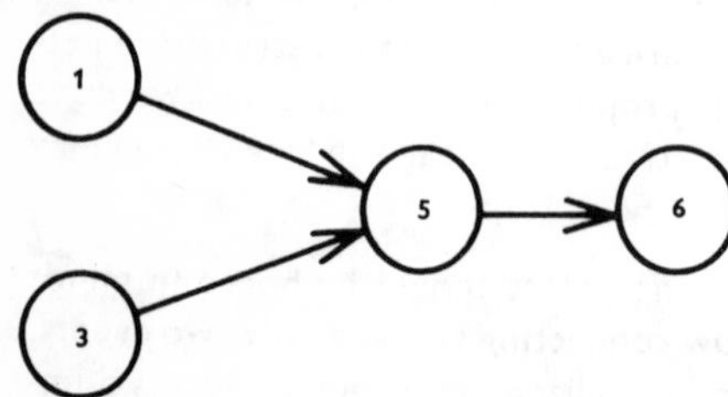

This is the logical equivalent of the previous diagram.

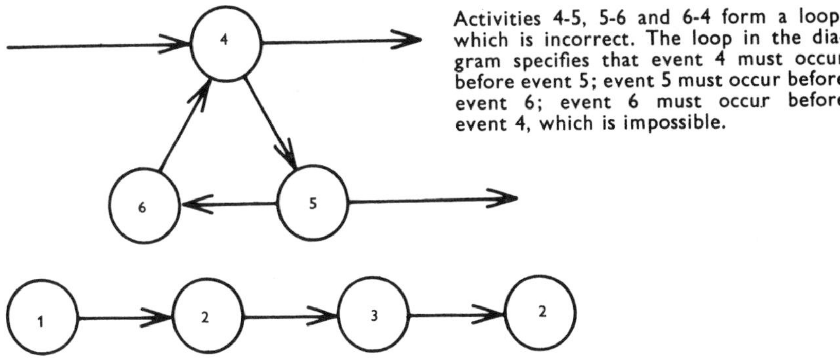

Activities 4-5, 5-6 and 6-4 form a loop, which is incorrect. The loop in the diagram specifies that event 4 must occur before event 5; event 5 must occur before event 6; event 6 must occur before event 4, which is impossible.
4
5
6
1
2
3
2

This is also a loop, and therefore wrong, because event 2 appears twice.

Loops

so that the activity-dependence can be indicated. An activity cannot begin before its initial event has occurred, i.e. before all the activities which precede (terminate in) that event have been accomplished;

- arrows usually point from left to right, but in order to save space on paper they can also be made to point in other directions. They may cross one another. The length of an arrow usually has no significance;
- arrows must point in such a direction that a path of activities can not be made into a loop: one event can not be reached several times;
- in most large projects it will be desirable to prepare a number of separate networks describing individual segments and delineating the detailed plan of work in these areas. Interface events and activities must be identified before the networks are completed. An interface event is one which is common to more than one network; an interface activity lies between two networks;
- the description of an activity is usually written along the arrow; the description must be unambiguous, clear, and as short as possible;
- the network must be sufficiently detailed to allow it to be used efficiently. The degree of detail must be based on the purpose of the network planning (time and/or capacity and/or personnel planning); on the requirements of those who will use the network (the level required inside or outside the factory); and on the nature of the project to be planned.

Estimating stage

After the network has been set up, the next step is to assess the duration of each activity. The duration of an activity is the time required for its completion. In assessing duration, either a single time estimate or a range of estimates may be made. If a range is considered necessary, "optimistic", "most likely", and "pessimistic" estimates are obtained, to indicate the spread of uncertainty. The probable duration of each activity is then derived statistically from these three estimates. The usual formula is:

$$\frac{OPT + 4 \times ML + PESS}{6}$$

However in practice a single estimate by the man who is responsible for carrying out the activity sufficiently serves the purpose.

Time estimates must be as accurate as possible, since all other calculations depend upon them. The estimated duration of each activity in the network is based on:

- planned manpower or other resources;
- average resource application rates or work schedules (the 40-hour week, the number of shifts, etc.).

This duration should be considered initially in terms of elapsed time. Do not attempt to specify calendar dates for events at this stage because this will nullify one of the major advantages (flexibility) of this method of project planning.

Time estimates should be made by the project team or by the personnel most familiar with the individual activities. The quality of an estimate will depend on the background of the estimator, and on his understanding of the work concerned.

Time estimates may be expressed in any convenient units, weeks and tenths of a week being the most usual.

The duration of an activity must be estimated entirely independently of the activities immediately preceding and following it.

Each estimate should take into account all factors known to affect completion of the activity under normal conditions.

When estimating activity durations it is not generally advisable to allow any tolerances or safety factors. A major advantage of the network planning technique is that it permits calculation of the tolerances that are inherent in activities as a result of the structure of the network. It also provides a method of calculating the smallest increase in overall project duration which will confer any desired tolerance or safety factor on any activity.

Time calculation stage

The result of the structural and estimating stages is a diagram showing all the activities contained in the network together with the relationships between them and their individual durations.

It is now necessary to calculate the earliest and latest times at which each event can occur in order to be able to establish the overall duration of the project, the earliest and latest starting and completion times of each activity, and the effects of variations in the duration of each activity.

These calculations, which entail no more than simple addition and subtraction, can be carried out by hand, but with large or complex networks, e.g. those in which there are more than about a hundred events or activities, it is usually advantageous to use a computer. If the network is to be used as the basis for capacity planning, workload or cost calculations, however, it is almost always necessary to use a computer.

The calculation stage can be broken down into three steps:

- calculate the earliest time at which each event can occur. This establishes the minimum overall project duration;
- calculate the latest time at which each event can occur. This establishes which of the chains of activities determine the minimum overall project duration;
- calculate the amount by which the start of each activity may be delayed, or its duration extended, without increasing the overall project duration.

Definitions

The meanings and definitions of the various parameters to be derived during the calculation phase are as follows:

earliest event time (EET)	The earliest time at which an event can possibly occur.
latest event time (LET)	The latest time at which an event can occur without delaying the completion of the project.
earliest start time (EST)	The earliest time at which an activity can start. This is the same as the EET of the initial event of that activity.
latest completion time (LCT)	The latest time by which an activity can be completed without delaying the completion of the project. This is the same as the LET of the terminal event of that activity.
latest start time (LST)	The latest time at which an activity can start without delaying the completion of the project. This is equal to the LCT of the activity minus the duration of that activity.
earliest completion time (ECT)	The earliest time by which an activity can be completed. It is equal to the EST of the activity plus the duration of that activity.
duration (of an activity)	The amount of the time necessary to accomplish it. This is denoted by the letter "d".

It is important to note that EET and LET refer to events whilst EST, LST, ECT and LCT refer to activities.

Example

Throughout the remainder of this technique chapter the network depicted in the diagram overleaf will be used as an example. In the text, parameters relating to particular activities and events are identified by means of subscripts e.g.:

- EET_3 is the earliest event time of event no. 3;
- $d_{3\text{-}5}$ is the duration of activity 3-5.

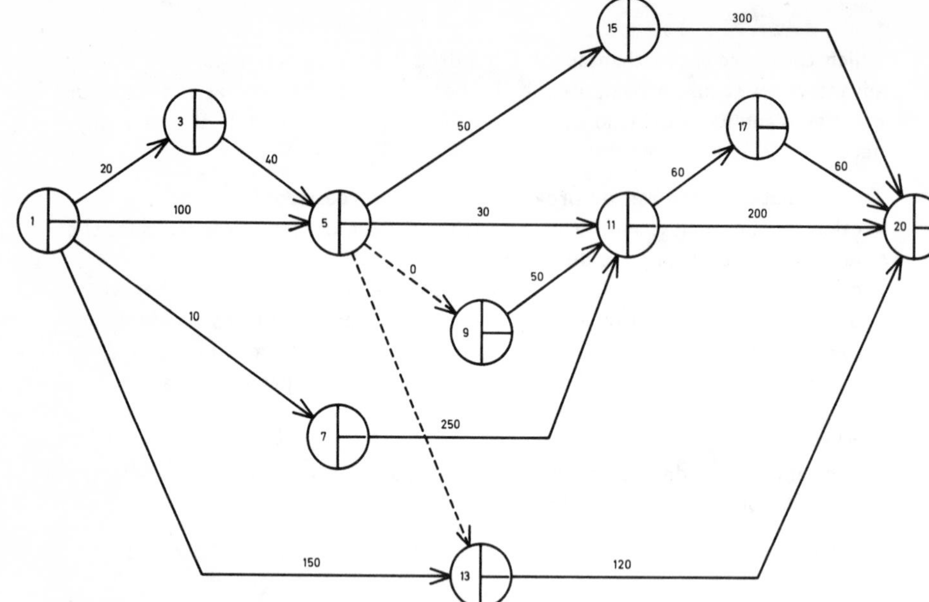

This network contains:

- sixteen activities, of which two are dummies;
- ten events, which interrelate the activities;
- eleven activity-paths between the initial event and the terminal event of the project.

Although there are only ten events, they have been allocated numbers from the range 1 to 20. This leaves gaps in the numbering system so that if it is found desirable later to introduce additional activities, the associated events can be numbered without affecting the original numbering system. Also the events have been numbered in such a way that for every activity the initial event has a lower reference number than its terminal event. The number placed alongside an activity arrow represents the duration of the activity in arbitrary units of time. The two dummy activities 5-9 and 5-13 are of different types. Activity 5-9 is an identity dummy: if it were not present the identifier 5-9 would represent two activities. Activity 5-13 is a logical dummy: its presence indicates that activity 13-20 can not start until not only activity 1-13, but also activities 3-5 and 1-5 have been completed.

Calculate the earliest event times

The purpose of this step is to calculate the earliest time at which each event can occur, in order to establish the minimum duration of the whole project. This involves starting from the initial event of the project and working through to the terminal event of the project, calculating the EET of each intermediate event.

The earliest event time of the initial event is conventionally taken as zero.

The following rules must be used in the calculation:

- if an event is the terminal event for one activity only, the EET of this event is equal to the sum of the EET of its initial event and its duration;
- if the event terminates more than one activity then the EET of this event is found by determining, for each activity, the sum of the EET of its initial event and its duration, and selecting the greatest of the times thus obtained.

Example

In the example given previously, therefore, having defined the EET of event 1 as zero, the EET's of events 3 and 7 are:

$EET_3 = 0 + 20 = 20$
$EET_7 = 0 + 10 = 10$

The EET for event 5 (EET_5) is whichever is the greater, the sum of EET_1 and d_{1-5} or the sum of EET_3 and d_{3-5}.

$EET_1 + d_{1-5} = 0 + 100 = 100$
$EET_3 + d_{3-5} = 20 + 40 = 60$

So EET_5 is the greater of 100 and 60, which is 100. Using the same method for determining EET_{13} results in a value of 150.

As each EET is calculated it should be entered on the network diagram, the usual practice being to enclose it in a square close to, and preferably above, the appropriate event.

Continuing the calculation process the EET's for events 9 and 15, which are each preceded by only one activity, can be seen to be 100 and 150 respectively. In calculating the EET's of events which are preceded by many activities, e.g. event 11 (three predecessors) and event 20 (four predecessors) it is advisable to use a rigorous method which ensures that nothing is overlooked. The following method is suggested:

- make a list of all activities which immediately precede the event;
- alongside each activity write the EET of its initial event and its duration;
- add each EET and duration to determine the ECT;
- select the greatest of these ECT's as the EET of the terminal event.

To find the EET of event 11 of the example therefore:

preceding activity	previous EET	activity duration	ECT	EET
5-11	100	30	130	—
9-11	100	50	150	—
7-11	10	250	260	×

From this table it can be seen that EET_{11} is 260.

The EET of event 17 can now be calculated as follows:

$EET_{17} = EET_{11} + d_{11-17} = 260 + 60 = 320$

A table can be used to determine the EET of event 20 as follows:

preceding activity	previous EET	activity duration	ECT	EET
15-20	150	300	450	—
17-20	320	60	380	—
11-20	260	200	460	×
13-20	150	120	270	—

From this table it can be seen that EET_{20} is 460, and since event 20 is the terminal event of the project, it follows that the minimum duration of the project is 460 time-units.

By the end of "calculate EET's" step the EET's of all activities will have been added to the network diagram so that it will now appear as shown below.

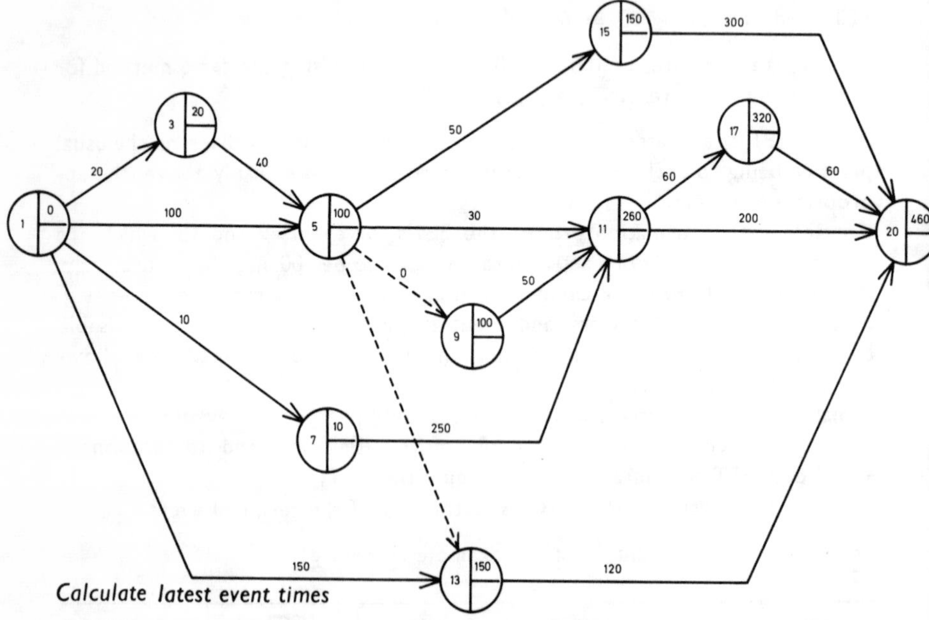

Calculate latest event times

The purpose of this step is to calculate the latest time at which each event can occur, in order to establish which of the chains of activities determine the minimum project duration. This entails starting at the terminal event of the project and working back towards the initial event, calculating the LET of each event.

The LET of the terminal event is usually taken as being the same as its EET, calculated in the previous step, which in the case of the example being used is time 460. The following rules must be used in the calculation:

- if an event is the initial event of one activity only, the LET of this event is found by subtracting its duration from the LET of its terminal event;
- if an event is the initial event of more than one activity, then the LET of this event is found by determining for each activity, the difference between the LET of its terminal event and its duration, and selecting the smallest of the times thus obtained.

Example

In our example, therefore, having established the LET of event 20 as time 460, the LET's for events 13, 15 and 17, each of which is the initial event of only one activity can be calculated as follows:

$LET_{13} = LET_{20} - d_{13-20} = 460 - 120 = 340$

$LET_{15} = LET_{20} - d_{15-20} = 460 - 300 = 160$

$LET_{17} = LET_{20} - d_{17-20} = 460 - \ \ 60 = 400$

Event 11 is the initial event of activities 11-17 and 11-20 and therefore its LET is the smaller of the differences between LET_{11} and d_{11-17} and between LET_{20} and d_{11-20}.

$LET_{17} - d_{11-17} = 400 - \ \ 60 = 340$

$LET_{20} - d_{11-20} = 460 - 200 = 260$

So LET_{11} is the smaller of these, which is 260.

As each LET is calculated it should be entered on the network diagram, the usual practice being to enclose it in a circle close to, and preferably underneath, the corresponding event.

The LET's of events which initiate many activities should be calculated using a tabular method to ensure that all activities are taken into account. The table given below was used to calculate LET_5.

subsequent activity	subsequent LET	activity duration	LST	LET
5-9	210	0	210	—
5-11	260	30	230	—
5-13	340	0	340	—
5-15	160	50	110	×

From this table it can be seen that LET_5 is 110.

When the LET's of all events have been calculated and added to the network diagram, it will appear as shown on page 14.

From this diagram the following observations can be made:

- critical activities and the critical path. For four events, numbers 1, 7, 11 and 20 the EET is the same as the LET. Also the sum of the duration of the activities comprising path 1-7-11-20 (shown by a heavy line on the diagram) is the same as the minimum overall project duration of 460 time-units. It follows that if the duration of any activity on this path exceeds its estimated duration then

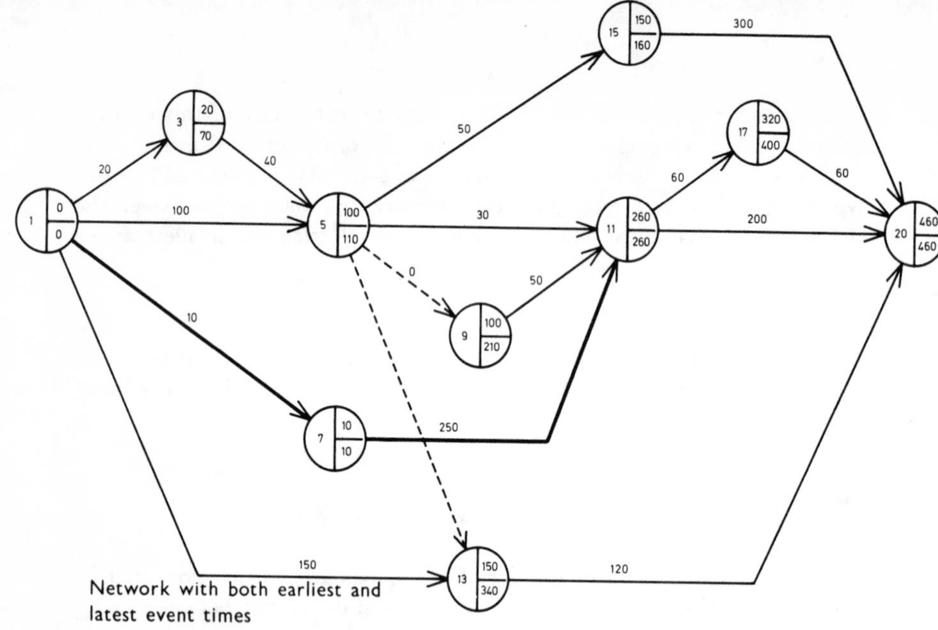

Network with both earliest and latest event times

the overall duration of the project will increase beyond the minimum. For this reason these activities are called critical activities and the path on which they lie is called the critical path of the network. It is possible for a network to contain more than one critical path;

- non-critical activities. For the activities that are not on the critical path the EET is always earlier than the LET. This implies that the activities preceding and/or succeeding them can exceed their estimated durations without necessary affecting the overall project duration. This property is called float, and it is dealt with in detail in the next step of this calculation phase.

Calculate float

As mentioned previously any difference that exists between the EET and the LET of an event confers the property of float on the activities that immediately precede or succeed it. It is the purpose of this step to define the various types of float, explain their significance and describe how to measure them.
There are four types of float:

- total float;
- free float;
- interfering float;
- independent float.

Definitions

total float (TF) (of an activity) — The time surplus which can be allowed it, assuming that its initial event occurs as early as possible and its terminal event occurs as late as possible. The TF of an activity is defined as the LET of its terminal event, minus the EET of its initial

event, minus its duration. I.e.:
$TF = LET_j - EET_i - d_{i\text{-}j}$
where the letters i and j represent the event-numbers of the initial and terminal events of the activity concerned.

free float (FF) (of an activity) The time surplus that can be allowed it, assuming that its initial event occurs as early as possible and that its terminal event must occur as early as possible. The FF of an activity is defined as:
$FF = EET_j - EET_i - d$

interfering float (IF) (of an activity) The difference between its total float and its free float. I.e.:
$IF = TF - FF$

independent float (Ind. F) (of an activity) The time surplus that can be allowed it, assuming that its initial event occurs as late as possible and that its terminal event must occur as early as possible, i.e.:
$Ind.\ F = EET_j - LET_i - d$

The relationships between the various types of float are illustrated in the diagram below.

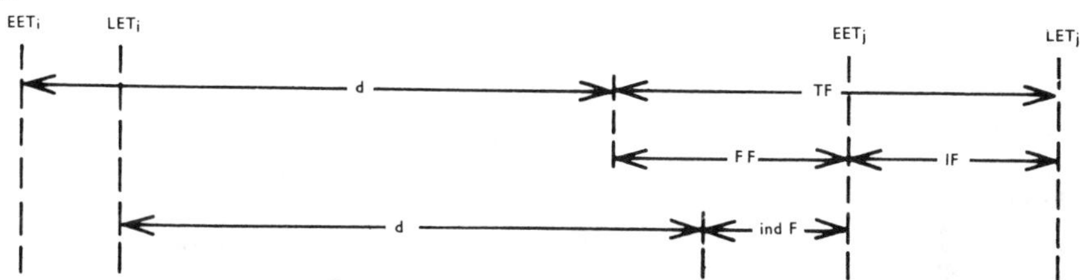

Note that although the diagram shows the float as appearing at the end of an activity, the float can be used at any part of it, e.g. to prolong its duration, delay its start, or a combination of the two.
All critical activities, by definition, have no float whatsoever. However, if in a practical situation it is the path(s) with the least float that is called the critical path.

Significance of the types of float

First of all, it must be emphasized that float is an attribute of an activity, not of an event. Events are the interfaces between activities and serve only to define the time-logic which interrelates them. Event-times are used solely as landmarks from which to derive the earliest and latest starting and completion times of activities and to determine the floats available.

General
Fundamentally, float occurs when the time necessary to complete a chain of activities is less than the time necessary to complete a parallel chain. In our

example, activity 1-5 requires 100 time-units but the parallel chain consisting of activities 1-3 and 3-5 requires a total of only 60 time-units, so that 1-3 and 3-5, between them, could take an extra 40 time-units without delaying the EET of event 5. Under ideal conditions, however, event 5 need not occur until time 110, so that activity 1-5 could over-run by 10 time-units and events 1-3 and 3-5 between them could over-run by 50 time-units.

Total float

This "ideal" situation is the basis of the concept of total float. Assuming that event 5 does not need to occur until its LET of 110 the total floats of 1-3 and 3-5 are both 50 and TF_{1-5} is 10. Even if activity 1-5 were to over-run by up to ten time-units, therefore, it would not delay project completion. If 1-5 over-ran by more than 10 time-units, however, it would delay project completion because increasing LET_5 beyond 110 would increase LET_{15} beyond 160 and this, in turn, would increase LET_{20} (project completion) beyond 460.

If activity 1-5 were to over-run by even a small amount, however, it would make it impossible for event 5 to occur at its earliest possible moment. It would therefore affect the total float of the immediately succeeding activities (because total float assumes an initial event to occur at its EET) and may possibly affect other activities as well.

Free float and interfering float

The interaction between total floats forms the basis for the concepts of free float and interfering float.

Free float is that part of the total float of an activity which can be taken up without affecting the total float of any succeeding activity, and interfering float represents the remainder of the total float which, if taken up, will affect the total float of the immediately succeeding activities (and possibly others).

In our example the total float of activity 3-5 is given by:

$TF_{3-5} = LET_5 - EET_3 - d_{3-5} = 110 - 20 - 40 = 50$

and its free float is given by

$FF_{3-5} = EET_5 - EET_3 - d_{3-5} = 100 - 20 - 40 = 40$

from which the interfering float can be derived:

$IF_{3-5} = TF_{3-5} - FF_{3-5} = 50 - 40 = 10$

These three values signify that activity 3-5 can over-run:

- by up to 50 time-units without increasing the project duration;
- by up to 40 time-units without affecting the total float of any succeeding activity;
- by between 40 and 50 time-units, but this will affect the total float of all immediately-succeeding activities.

It is important to note that the values obtained for all types of float apply equally to all the activities in an unbranched chain. The method of calculating total float does, in fact, give the same value for each activity in such a chain, but the standard methods of calculating free float and interfering float attribute them to the last activity in a chain. It is obvious, however, that the explanation of the meaning of the floats calculated for activity 3-5 applies equally to the activity-chain 1-3-5.

Independent float

The concept of the independent float refers to "worse case" conditions and is, in a sense, the opposite of total float, which refers to "best case" conditions. "Worst case" conditions occur when the initial event of an activity occurs as late as possible and its terminal event occurs as early as possible. If the duration of the activity is less than the interval between these event-times, then the activity can over-run to the extent of the difference without affecting any other activity in the network in any way whatsoever. Hence this float is truly independent. Of course an activity that has independent float must also have total float, and will usually have free float and interfering float as well.

Example

The amount of each of the four types of float possessed by each activity in the project should now be calculated. In order to reduce the possibility of error it is advisable to use a tabular method for the calculations.

First of all prepare a table having columns for the activities, their durations, the earliest and latest event-times of the initial and terminal events, the earliest and latest starting and finishing times of the activities, the four types of float and a "remarks" column.

The completed table for our example project is given on page 18. The first six columns were filled-in using the information from the completed network diagram of the project.

Column 7 (earliest start time) is a repeat of column 6 (earliest initial event time) and column 8 (earliest completion time) is obtained by adding column 2 (activity duration) to column 7.

Column 10 (latest completion time) is a repeat of column 3 (latest terminal event time) and column 9 (latest start time) is obtained by subtracting column 2 (activity duration) from column 10.

Column 11 (total float) is obtained either by subtracting column 4 from column 6, subtracting column 7 from column 9, or subtracting column 8 from column 10, whichever is the most convenient.

Column 12 (free float) can be calculated by subtracting the sum of column 2 (duration) and column 6 (EET_i) from column 4 (EET_j) in accordance with the definition of free float i.e.:

$$FF = EET_j - EET_i - d$$

Free float can also be calculated by subtracting column 8 (ECT) from column 4 (EET_j), because:

$$ECT = EET_i + d$$

activity		event				activity times earliest		latest		float				remarks
reference	duration	LET_j	EET_j	LET_i	EET_i	start	compl.	start	compl.	total	free	interf.	indep.	
1- 3	20	70	20	0	0	0	20	50	70	50	0	50	0	
1- 5	100	110	100	0	0	0	100	10	110	10	0	10	0	S
1- 7	10	10	10	0	0	0	10	0	10	0	0	0	0	★
1-13	150	340	150	0	0	0	150	190	340	190	0	190	0	
3- 5	40	110	100	70	20	20	60	70	110	50	40	10	0	
5- 9	0	210	100	110	100	100	100	210	210	110	0	110	0	
5-11	30	260	260	110	100	100	130	230	260	130	130	0	120	
5-13	0	340	150	110	100	100	100	340	340	240	50	190	40	
5-15	50	160	150	110	100	100	150	110	160	10	0	10	0	S
7-11	250	260	260	10	10	10	260	10	260	0	0	0	0	★
9-11	50	260	260	210	100	100	150	210	260	110	110	0	0	
11-17	60	400	320	260	260	260	320	340	400	80	0	80	0	
11-20	200	460	460	260	260	260	460	260	460	0	0	0	0	★
13-20	120	460	460	340	150	150	270	340	460	190	190	0	0	
15-20	300	460	460	160	150	150	450	160	460	10	10	0	0	S
17-20	60	460	460	400	320	320	380	400	460	80	80	0	0	

Legend S = no free float
★ = critical path

This method is usually easier than the previous one and is less liable to error because it involves fewer arithmetic operations.

Column 13 (interfering float) is calculated by subtracting column 12 (free float) from column 11 (total float) in accordance with the definition of interfering float.

Column 14 (independent float) can be calculated by subtracting the sum of column 5 (LET_i) and column 2 (duration) from column 4 (EET_j) in accordance with the definition of independent float i.e.:

Ind. F = $EET_j - LET_i - d$

Where the calculations produce negative values (as in the case with activities 3-5, 5-9, and 5-15) these values should be discarded and zeroes should be inserted at the appropriate places in column 14.

The "remarks" column, column 15, can, of course, be used for any convenient purpose but it is usual to use it to indicate the degree of criticallity of the activities.

It is recommended that the critical activities (those with zero total float) be marked with an asterisk; and the sub-critical activities (those with the next lowest total float) be marked with the letter S.

Interpreting the table on page 18

The table clearly shows which activities are critical, or nearly critical, and which activities are not. Activities 1-7-11-20 are critical because they have zero total float and activities 1-5-15-20 are sub-critical because they have a total float of only ten time-units.

This indicates that if one attempted to reduce the overall project duration by reducing the duration of any activity on the critical path, one could only effect a reduction of ten time-units before path 1-5-15-20 became critical. After this point it would be necessary to reduce the duration of paths 1-7-11-20 and 1-5-15-20 simultaneously but after a further reduction of 40 time-units, path 1-3-5-15-20 would become critical.

Thus the table indicates the sequence in which the various activity paths must be shortened if it is required to reduce the overall project duration.

Practical applications of network planning

The purpose of this section is to indicate some of the ways in which the theory and the techniques of network planning can be put to practical use. It must be emphasized that although network planning can be a very powerful management tool, it is nevertheless only a tool, and as with any other tool, the skill of knowing when to use it, and the skill with which it is used can contribute as much to the final product as the tool itself.

The fundamental difference between the theoretical and the practical aspects of network planning lies in the additional requirements and constraints imposed by the need to work in real time, generally expressed in calendar dates. Usually the latest completion date for the project is specified as a result of external requirements e.g. to comply with a delivery data confirmed to a customer. Also the earliest start times for some particular activities or even the complete project are usually specified as a result of internal constraints e.g. certain resources are already committed to other projects and will not become available for use in this project until specific dates.

Calculation using previously defined event times

To calculate the network using previously defined event times, the following procedure is recommended:

- draw a diagram of the network putting in only the events, the event numbers, the activities and the activity durations;
- for each event for which a required earliest event time (RET) has been specified, enter this time on the diagram as the EET for that event;
- for each event for which a required latest event time (RLT) has been specified, enter this time into the diagram as the LET for that event;
- starting with the initial event of the network, calculate the EET of all subsequent events, using the basic method described in the paragraph calculate earliest event times but with the following modifications in respect of the calculation of the EET's for events which already have specified RET's:
  - — if the calculation shows the EET to be earlier than the RET, discard the calculated result and use the RET of the event for all subsequent calculations;
  - — if the calculation shows the EET to be later than the RET, discard the RET and use the calculated EET for all subsequent calculations;
- starting with the terminal event of the network, work backwards calculating the LET's of all preceding events using the basic method described in the paragraph calculate latest event times .but with the following modifications in respect of the calculation of the LET's of those events which already have specified RLT's:
  - — if the calculation shows the LET to be later than the RLT, discard the calculated result and use the RLT for all subsequent calculations;
  - — if the calculation shows the LET to be earlier than the RLT, discard the RLT and use the calculated LET for all subsequent calculations;
- having entered the earliest and latest times of each event on the network diagram, calculate the floats available, using the tabular method advocated in the paragraph calculate float.

The critical path of the network can be determined by inspection of the completed table. In contrast to the theoretical situations discussed previously it is possible to have a critical path (or paths) that do, in fact, possess total float, and this can be positive or negative. In such a case the critical path is then

formed by the chain of activities which has the smallest positive or the largest negative float.
The total float on the critical path is positive if the RCT of the end event of a project is later than the EET of the terminal event. It is always true, however, that the difference between the EET end LET of every event on the critical path is less than the difference between the EET and LET of every event not on the critical path.

Scheduling the activities

In the previous parts calculating rules have been applied to give a quantitative insight into the time related constraints valid for the execution of activities.
Scheduling is the location of the activities into a time scale taking into account:

- the availability of capacity in the resources and the resource requirements for each activity;
- the time limits for the activity concerned, which may be either the result of a calculation or previously defined.

For the scheduling and planning of usage of manpower the manpower usage chart in 2-2.2 can be applied.

Extensions of the network planning technique

One of the most important things about network planning is that the basic principles described can be extended in a number of ways:

- capacity planning (determining the capacity required in terms of personnel, machines, etc.);
- employment planning (employment and capacity to be balanced as efficiently as possible);
- cost estimating and cost-calculation.

For example, it is possible to couple an activity with the resource it uses, the number of man hours expended and the costs incurred in accomplishing it.

The activities can be phased in time such that, taking into account the results of the calculation of the network, i.e. the earliest and latest starting and completion times of activities and the floats available, the employment state and available capacity can be adjusted to one another to the best advantage.
It is also possible to use the network planning technique to facilitate project cost planning and cost-calculation during the running time of the project.

Progress control

Progress information must be available early enough to permit effective replanning and control. An indication of an approaching problem today is more valuable than a detailed report tomorrow.

Network planning allows very effective control to be exercised on the progress of a project. This is done as follows:

- the completion dates of important activities particularly those which deviate from planning are reported. The durations of activities are revised as more accurate estimates become available. Any alteration to the logic of the network that becomes necessary can easily be worked in; in this way the latest network planning is always available;
- the basic calculations are then made again, beginning with the latest reported completion dates of each activity or chain of activities in a network so as to obtain the new start and completion dates for every still unfinished activity;
- the new critical path(s) is (are) laid down and floats of activities are recalculated;
- the earliest completion date of the whole project is determined again.

Updating

This continuous updating of the project data enables effective progress control to be carried out. By classifying the new information in surveys in various ways, the management of the project can determine the progress made by the project, where delays or accelerations have occurred, at what places extra care is necessary to avoid delays, what the project completion date will be, etc. It is now possible to make better decisions as to required changes in planning and therefore re-planning is made easier.

Simulations of corrective actions

Generally, as a result of the recycling process, management decisions result in a change of the schedule, the network plan, costs, or some combination. Although recycling is not completely accomplished by PERT, decision-making, and the evaluation and implementation of changes, are facilitated.

As a rule, management considers a number of possible solutions to project problems, but only one can normally be chosen as realistic. Simulation offers a method for testing and evaluating each of these alternatives. Simulated time changes in activities, or the addition or deletion of activities may be fed into the computer in the same manner as up-dating information. Analysis of the outputs of the simulation will indicate the new situations which would be expected to occur.

Simulation can frequently be accomplished manually if small networks are involved. This technique is particularly useful when unexpected troubles necessitate rapid corrective action.

Using a computer in network planning

It is possible to calculate the various times, floats and the critical path of a network using manual methods but they are very time-consuming and liable to error.

The following factors should be considered when contemplating whether manual or computer assisted calculation is to be used:

- availability and costs of a computer;
- size and complexity of the network;
- frequency with which the calculations must be made;
- way in which the calculated results must be presented.

If it is decided to go over to capacity planning, employment planning and budgetting and post-calculation of costs per activity, the use of a computer is usually essential.

The most important advantages of using a computer are as follows:

- speed (this includes the facility of rapid simulation to evaluate alternative solutions);
- updating capability to dynamically maintain the network;
- possibility of preparing different surveys containing different grouping of data for the same network; or a department at little extra cost at the same response time;
- accuracy;
- finding errors, such as loops, and double activities, including identifying the type and location of the errors discovered;
- calculating networks whose events are randomly numbered. This random numeration is, in fact, easy in large networks and increases flexibility when altering the logic of the network;
- calculating networks with previously-defined RET's and RLT's.

Technique 6-1.2: Human engineering

Purpose

To make full use of, and realistic allowance for, human, physical and social characteristics in the systems effort, this technique discusses for the systems engineer some of the terms and concepts peculiar to human engineering.
Familiarity with these concepts — especially those derived from the fields of industrial and social psychology — should aid the communication process within the human engineering team [1]), and assist the implementation of changes in the existing system and organization with as little friction as possible with existing employees.

Areas of application

The human element in information systems should be considered carefully during all phases of the systems effort. However, special attention is required during problem definition, system analysis, requirements definition and implementation.

General considerations

Human engineering is the application of psychology to the efficient integration of the human element into the information system.
In most conventional computer applications, the only interfaces with the human element are at the initial input and final output stages. The computer specialist has, as a rule, ignored these interfaces, and allowed the industrial engineer, the systems engineer, or the user manager to handle the incorporation of the human being into the information system. This approach is proving increasingly unsatisfactory as more integrated systems are developed. It is becoming necessary to regard humans as integral components of the information system. The human factors surveyed in this section are those which affect the interaction between human capabilities and limitations, and the specific requirements of information systems. No attempt will be made to describe how each factor or element is actually to be incorporated into a system; instead, the scope and content of each major factor will be surveyed, and references given to suitable sources for further reading.

Human engineering team

The scope of the background and experience needed for a complete human engineering job is so extensive that a team approach has of necessity evolved. A team of this sort usually includes at least three people — an experimental psychologist or a social psychologist; the systems engineer; and a representative

---

[1]) For an introduction to the field read: A. Chapanis, *Man-machine engineering*, Wadsworth and Tavistock, 1965.

of the user. These three individuals join in the evaluation of the human elements during the systems effort.

Levels of investigation

Human engineering operates on two distinct but inseparable levels. The basic level encompasses the skills of the experimental psychologist or industrial engineer, who investigates man simply as a productive unit. He evaluates the perceptive, discriminative, decision-making, and manipulative requirements of a given function, and attempts to match them to the abilities of the personnel available. This is the essentially mechanistic level of human engineering, and assures the team that the humans selected will, with a high degree of probability, be inherently capable of doing the job required, if properly motivated and supported.

The second level is encompassed by the social psychologist's skills; he investigates man and his environment as a complexly interrelated unit, analyzing motivation, attitudes, communication techniques, and group structures, both formal and informal. This is the ethological level of human engineering which assures the team that the tasks have been grouped into a job hierarchy which maximizes the probability that the necessary levels of individual support will be established and maintained, as a basic characteristic of the information system.

Can the job be done?

There are many behaviourial variables (some very poorly understood, as yet) that determine whether a properly motivated human can perform a given job well. That this is an important problem is attested to by the fact that in most man-machine systems (such as airplanes, boats, information systems, etc.) an average of well over half of the errors (or system malfunctions) are caused by the human element.

The science of experimental psychology identifies many reasons for these high human-error rates; these reasons can be summarized by the statement that humans appear to be probabilistic systems, and despite extensive training, virtually any possible reaction to any stimulus will occur, sometime.

Perception and discrimination

The human must perceive if he is to react. Man's senses are his means of perception, and serve to direct his conscious attention to the phenomenon perceived. The generalization usually used to define levels and thresholds of perception states: "in comparing magnitudes, it is not the arithmetical difference, but the ratio of magnitudes, which we perceive"; not only the identification of a difference i.e., something which exists obtrusively enough to be perceived, but also the speed of human reaction follows this general rule.

Decision making

The human element in an information system is able to reason and profit from experience, and to modify his behaviour on the basis of past experience, by diagnosing general conditions from specific occurrences. This flexible behaviour is facilitated by trial-and-error sequences of action — which, incidentally, are one of the many causes of the high degree of variation in human reactions to given stimuli.

Manipulation

Manipulation refers to the factors which determine whether a person is physically capable of performing the act his brain commands his body to do. The human body is an enormously complex "servo" system, and many actions cause unexpected side effects and unwanted learning patterns.

Reaction times to original and correction stimuli are also appreciable, and vary substantially from person to person. Individual differences, such as delays measured in tenths of seconds, make the analysis and definition of manipulation requirements an important part of human engineering.

From the above, it can be seen that the role of the experimental or social psychologist is to assist in determining what operations should be performed by the human element. The human engineering team then allocates the required operations between the man and the machine. Many psychologists have stated that this man-machine allocation of operations is the weakest link in information system design.

Will the job be done?

The social psychologist specializes in analyzing and defining human-motivation factors; his task is to identify the organizational and technical elements that will effect and affect proper motivation. Experiments have shown that the complex of group and individual attitudes, interrelationships, and communications affect productivity quickly and drastically.

Motivations differ

Individual motivations and performance depend on the total environment of the job, and on the individual's reaction to that environment. It is important to note that persons of different types and classes have different patterns of needs, attitudes, and potential responses. "What motivates the boss will not usually motivate the worker" is the rule, not the exception. The failure to understand these differences can cause the incorrect allocation of tasks and rewards to jobs, and jobs to organizational units, and can easily result in ineradicable, crippling malfunction of the information system.

The whole man

The product flow and the information flow are not the sole basis for the assignment of functions to personnel, and personnel to organizational units. Most people want jobs that are interesting and varied, but well within their capabilities. The social psychologist studies the attitudes, organization, and motivation of each group of people involved, and should assist in designing an information chart that meets the requirements for good control and productive system operation, and fosters organizational stability and harmony as well.

Working conditions

The humans in the information system must be supported by such commodities as equipment, tools, technical data, intra-system communications, satisfactory physical environment (lighting and noise levels, working space) and training. Responsive and responsible supervision should be included in the provisions of the organization and information system designed. Basically, the human element of the information system should not be left to chance.

Applied psychology [1])

One of the greatest challenges to the systems engineer is the avoidance or efficient resolution of the potential conflict between the organization's need for change and its employees' resistance to change. As an organization tries to adapt to changing conditions, its employees are required to accept new patterns of thought, new procedures, and new social relationships. Frequently, the psychological discomforts created by the new conditions cause good employees, regardless of position, to resist necessary changes.

One of the major tasks of a system engineer is to reduce this resistance by bringing order and understanding to the process of change. To do this successfully, a systems engineer must have not only a grasp of the technical needs and resources of the organization but also a sound understanding of the basic principles of psychology. He must understand what motivates people's behaviour and use that understanding to develop good human relations.

Motivation

It is a principle of human motivation that every experience involves cause and effect; every motive produces some effect, and every response or effect is preceded by a motive. Motivation affects every area of human behaviour. Its field of influence ranges from the directing of a simple act where the motive is obvious, to a complex formal activity pattern such as career behaviour, which represents the effects of numerous detailed aspects of motivation.

---

[1]) This section is largely adapted from Bower, Zlatkovitch and Schlosser's chapter in *Accounting systems theory and practice*, Allyn & Bacon. Inc., 1965.

One list [1]) of essential motivating forces includes the following:

- the urges arising from bodily needs;
- the urge to succeed and to achieve;
- the urge to avoid failure and disappointment;
- the urge for recognition and approval;
- the urge for sympathy, affection, and security;
- the urge to experience the new and the different.

The systems engineer should be aware of these motivating forces and use this knowledge in carrying out his assignments. Each of the forces cited can play a part in carrying a systems effort through to a successful — or unsuccessful — conclusion. An organizational change aimed at improving production efficiency might fail if basic motivating forces were either overlooked or given insufficient weight.

Injury to self-respect

In redesigning any information system, in whole or in part, the systems engineer must be aware of the strength of the urge to succeed or to avoid failure. His efforts may be seriously jeopardized if suggested changes seem to reflect adversely on the competance of the employees who are expected to carry out the revised operations.

It is frequently possible to avoid such frustations of basic motivations if the analyst is sensitive to their existence and adjusts his approach accordingly.

Need for recognition

One of the principal motivating forces with which a systems engineer must deal is the urge for recognition and approval. Almost invariably, when personnel are consulted and their opinions are given thoughtful consideration and fair-minded evaluation, the changes to be effected become joint projects. An approach which evokes both the urge for approval and the urge to experience the new and the different is likely to be very effective.

Most organizational changes involve more than one person and more than one department.

In making such changes, management should enlist the help of representatives from the departments affected. This is the team approach as advocated in volume 2. Results from a team effort will be workable compromises, and the fact that departmental representatives helped to develop the solution will assist the acceptance of changes by all user departments involved.

Indeed, this approach can assist in offsetting deleterious effects from any of the motivating forces. By using this approach, project management is permitting various human urges to be expressed, and solutions found, rather than ignoring the psychological reactions of the people concerned, which in many instances would doom the efforts to inefficiency or failure.

---

[1]) Lester D. and Alice Crow, *Understanding our behaviour*, Alfred Knopf Publishing Co., 1956, pp. 53, 54.

Employee goals

Goals can either be proximate or remote. A proximate goal to an employee may be the finishing of a particular work assignment. A remote goal may be self-advancement.

If the project team is to initiate and maintain effective employee attitudes toward the changes it proposes, it must be able to create attainable goals for the employees involved in the information system.

Personal characteristics

Personal characteristics include "all the abilities and all the typical responses that the person brings to the situation" [1]). This element of behaviour specifically involves the frame of mind of the individual and what he has already learned from previous experience.

The element of personal characteristics in human behaviour may need special attention by the project team in situations where increased mechanization or automation of an information system is being recommended. Employees who have not been properly introduced to the information system often resist the proposed innovations because they are not personally ready to embrace the new concepts and the new approach made possible by the computer. An important part of the work in the systems effort is to get employees ready to accept the information system so that they can learn to operate it properly. Many information systems have been set back or could not be effected because the project team did not recognize personal characteristics as an element of human behaviour and failed to give sufficient weight to the human factor in a systems effort.

Organizational attitudes

"The situation consists of all the persons, objects, and symbols in the individual's environment. Experience in one situation prepares a person to respond to similar situations in the future." [1])

A systems engineer who realizes that the situation in which certain employees have found themselves during their normal working hours will affect both their current behaviour patterns and those toward which he would like to see them move, is in a better position to judge what effect a new information system will have on these employees. Employees who understand that the proposed changes in the organization are good, and contribute to long-term stability, can therefore feel secure enough to realize that there is pleasure in experiencing a new and more efficient information system procedures, and will welcome the new and different situations when they are confronted with them. However, it must be remembered that employees who have been actually or implicitly encouraged by their employer to resist change usually do so without listening to the merits of the proposal. The systems engineer must recognize or discover the organization-wide attitude toward change.

---

[1]) Lee J, Crombach, *Educational psychology*, 2d ed., in consultation with Ernest R. Hilgard and Willard R. Spalding; Harcourt, Brace & World, Inc., 1963.

Interpretation of proposed changes

In any systems effort, changes will be proposed to certain employees. Depending on how the employees interpret these changes, they will either be convinced that the changes are worthwhile or will be opposed to them. If the project team has sufficient depth of understanding of human behaviour, its presentation of proposed changes will be such as to permit favourable interpretation of the proposals.

User representatives co-operating in the systems effort should receive much of the credit of the new design. The project team should be skilful enough in presenting the situation properly to ensure that the desired interpretation is drawn from it. The effective goal of the team is not to impose its will upon the personnel involved, but to see that the system is understood and accepted.

Response to change

To some extent, the element of response to change in employee behaviour is dependent on other elements of motivation. If enough is known about the effect of those other elements, the action that an individual will take in response to change can often be predicted accurately.

In recommending a proposed systems innovation, the systems engineer can be reasonably sure that it will be received favourable if he has suitably prepared the individuals affected by the innovation. If acceptable goals have been outlined for them, if they are in a proper state of personal readiness to accept the change, and if the situation has been so presented that the desired interpretations will be made, the systems engineer can expect a favourable response.

Employees who have had favourable experience of working with a systems engineer are far more willing to work with him again. Those who have not tend to be hesitant and stand-offish until they are motivated and willing to accept this new experience as part of their learning process.

Management support

It is essential for success that the project team should see that the consequences of its proposals are salutary. To be assured of this, the project team must have the support of the steering committee. Employees must know that it has this support, and, from past experience, that cooperation is more beneficial to them in terms of their own long- and short-run goals than opposition to or rejection of new proposals.

Response to thwarting

Up to this point in the discussion of the elements of human behaviour little doubt has been expressed that the project team can, in every instance, create proper goals, induce a proper state of personal characteristics, and present the situation so that the proper interpretation will be made and desired action taken. Unfortunately, this is not always the case. Systems engineers and other members of the project team are as imperfect as anyone else in properly utilizing the various elements of human behaviour. Furthermore, not all actions result in favourable consequences for the employees who must accept new procedures and must be taught how to use them, nor are the consequences always favourable for the teammembers themselves.

Usually, when an individual's first response is thwarted, one of two reactions occurs. He may re-assess the situation and try another action, or he may give up and refuse to respond at all. A successful systems engineer should never be guilty of the latter reaction to thwarting. He should believe "that the mountain can be moved" and should act accordingly.

Another problem presents itself, however, when the team or the systems engineer encounters a nonadaptive reaction from the individuals who will be responsible for effecting the changes that are being recommended. How should this be handled? The ultimate solution, if the changes have been approved by management, is to reassign the nonadaptive employees or to separate them from the organization. Such a solution should be resorted to only if the individual's reaction to thwarting is definitely and firmly nonadaptive.

Summary

Human engineering, as an organized discipline, has not yet had a substantial impact on information systems; however, now that man-machine systems are being developed for business and scientific applications, human engineering will become a part of the systems effort.

People are an essential part of any information system. No matter how highly automated information systems become, people will be part of these systems, and will present a series of problems to the project team, and to systems engineers that are very different — although no less susceptible to logical analysis — from those posed by the communication media and machines that are essential physical elements of a data processing system.

Anyone engaged in the systems effort must understand that every individual strives for goals. His previous experience has prepared him in certain ways to be personally ready for new experiences. When a new situation is presented to him, he will interpret this new situation in terms of previous experience, and respond in a way he thinks will meet his goals. If consequences in previous similar situations have brought him closer to his goals, this will have increased his personal readiness to accept the new situation. However, favourable consequences do not always result, and then the individual is said to be thwarted.

The project team must concentrate on teaching employees to accept and operate new procedures in such a way that none of them feel that they have been thwarted.

It must also be realistic enough to know that this ideal cannot always been attained, and should work out ways to deal with nonadaptive behaviour. Special advice and assistance can be supplied by the human engineering team.

Technique 6-1.3: Presentation techniques

Purpose

The purpose of management presentations is to obtain management approval at review points during the course of a system effort. The purpose of this techniques chapter is to show how to plan, prepare and deliver such presentation.

Areas of application

Management presentations are necessary throughout the whole of the systems effort, certainly prior to each major step. At every level of project management there exists a responsibility for communicating formally and for informing those members of management who will be concerned with the systems effort in a part time capacity only.

Planning of the presentation

Perhaps the most critical point in any phase of the systems effort occurs when the work is completely planned, but management approval has yet to be obtained. At that point, the number and type of recommendations that must be developed, has to be decided and the approval strategy developed.

The approval strategy should include a phased sequence of approvals, starting with a general top management approval based on e.g. the results of a feasibility study, and then after a positive decision, moving from the lower management levels of the organization upward; a translation of the design description into the language and format best understood by the various reviewers; and effective presentation methods.

Working from the bottom upward is the key concept leading to understanding and acceptance of most new systems. Most managers depend on their subordinates for advice and detailed evaluation of matters on which they must make a decision. Executives seldom turn down proposals on which their line managers are sold; therefore, the analyst should start at the lowest level of management that will have supervisory responsibilities under the new system, and make certain that such managers understand and approve of the portion of the system design that will affect them. The presentation should then move up the line. Repeated presentation of the system description will help improve the critical final presentation to top management, and will resolve any questions that give rise to major objections.

In planning a presentation the following aspects have to be taken into account:
- organization of the presentation;
- use of visual aids;
- lecture and discussion.

Organization of the presentation

To ensure that his audience is permanently interested, the systems analyst will have to take care that his presentations are efficiently organized and will be appreciated. Not everybody has a talent for delivering an absorbing lecture. Even of the good speakers only very few have it. Most of them have taken great pains to become a good speaker. Here too, the saying, practice makes perfect, is true. By following the undermentioned hints, also those people, who, at first, shrink from delivering a presentation, can develop themselves into good speakers. A continuous self-analysis moving between the extremes: "what must and do I want to reach" and "what did I reach" will permanently activate him, as a result of which improvements cannot fail to come.

Division of the presentation

The succes of a presentation depends on a good preparation. When preparing his lecture the speaker has to keep in mind the level, knowledge and experience of his audience.

A preparation normally comprises a number of parts, and therefore, acting on previous experience, the speaker reserves a number of minutes for each part, for example:

• introduction		3 minutes
• lecture on the project		35 minutes
• summary		3 minutes
• discussion		15 minutes
• conclusion		4 minutes
	total	60 minutes

Introduction
In order to obtain the attention of the audience, it is essential that, before beginning the lecture, to indicate the stage of the project and, after that, the purpose and division of the lecture.

Lecture
It is the job of the systems engineer to translate the system objectives into an operable system, meeting these objectives, and to present the results in the language of the organizations management.

In general, presentations to management should emphasize only the major points, with substantial back-up available in understandable form.
The phrase "management language" must not be misinterpreted as meaning superficial explanations, sweeping pronouncements, or unsupported claims. The language of management is one of objectives, measurement, and variance, and demands an emphasis on effect and cost, rather than on how specific, detailed operations will be carried out.

The lecture will be best understood if it is built up of a number of chapters.

In this case the speaker has to make sure that the chapters are in the right order.

It is recommended, when for the first time a speech is made, to write it down entirely. However, a speaker should get accustomed to only writing down the divisions and some major points. The major points could be displayed on a flap-over sheet to serve both the speaker and the audience. It is desirable to arrange the material in such a way that, what is absolutely necessary, is said first. The advantage is that major subjects are not omitted because of lack of time.

The speaker should be aware which parts of the presentation should be dropped if a discrepancy occurs between time available and subjects to be covered. Quality is more important than quantity and it should be noticed that mentioning too many subjects will result in a decrease of attention.

Summary

At the end of the lecture a summary should be given. This will assist the audience in reflecting on the lecture.

Discussion

In most cases it is necessary that the audience is activated into a discussion. This can be done by asking questions. It is preferred to compose these questions during the preparation and to write them down. Moreover, it is recommended to make notes on the experiences gained with this particular audience, after the lecture is over. These notes can be used for composing questions for the next lecture.

A discussion can easily go on for a long time, as a result of which the time limit will be exceeded. Therefore only questions on major topics should be asked.

Conclusion

The conclusion serves to state action points, so that everybody knows which activities are expected from him in the next period. Weighing alternative possibilities beforehand will contribute to fastly making decisions.

Conference room

Before the lecture takes place, ensure that the conference room is ready for use. Ensure that the blackboard is clean and that chalk, and rubber or sponge are available.

Ensure that the visual aids have been put in their correct places and that the name cards of all persons present are put on the tables.

The room must present a tidy impression.

Use of visual aids

Man observes with the organs of sense and in order to achieve the best results of a presentation appropriate aids have to be used.

Investigations have shown that in acquiring knowledge by means of the organs of sense the following percentages can be attributed to:

- eye 60%;
- ear 30%;
- touch, smell, taste 10%.

These percentages are averages and may differ considerably per individual. However, it may be concluded that, during a presentation an appeal has to be made to the eye and to the ear, but especially to the eye by means of visual aids.

The following demands may be imposed on visual means:

- large enough;
- natural and plain;
- simple and complete;
- different colours;
- explaining and complementary.

Presentation aids

Use can be made e.g. of the undermentioned aids.

Blackboard

- Know beforehand what you are going to draw.
- drawings should be kept simple.
- do not talk when you are writing, because:
  - it may be difficult to hear you;
  - the attention of the audience is divided between what you are saying and what you are writing;
- use colours to accentuate essential points;
- wipe off what is no longer needed (unnecessary drawings divert the attention).

Flap-over sheets

Flap-over sheets should be prepared beforehand. They can be used at different times and offer the advantage that all information which is not necessary at a certain moment, is hidden from view.

Flannel board

An aid, not to be underestimated:

- it saves time;
- it can be used again;
- it can easily be read;
- it makes it impossible to forget important points.

Overhead projector

- Easier in use than a blackboard;
- group control better possible;
- preparation can be used again.

Films and slides

Experience learns, that it is wise to discuss the contents of a film just before it is shown, and to explain it. Such an explanation is especially important when language difficulties may arise. After the film some time should be reserved for asking questions.
If it is necessary to check to what extent the contents are understood, the speaker himself should compose questions too. These questions must be formulated in such way, that the answers show whether the contents of the film have been understood or not. Of course, the speaker himself should know exactly what the right answers are.

Striptease

In order to save time during a presentation the points to be covered can be written on the blackboard before the presentation. If this is done, however, there arises the disadvantage that this may distract the audience, i.e. they may be thinking about one point when the speaker wants them to concentrate on another.

This disadvantage can be overcome by the use of a striptease technique, in which all the points to be covered are separately hidden from view by means of e.g. strips of paper.

Whenever the lecturer starts to discuss a new point, the cover is removed from that point.

Diagrams

Diagrams, especially previously prepared ones, can save much time and may explain more than minutes of talking.

Lecture and discussion

Lecture

The result of the preparation will be that the speaker will deliver his lecture with self-confidence. However, he should be prepared to meet a slight resistance of the audience. Some self-consciousness on the part of the speaker is quite normal and even desirable, because without psychological strain he cannot hold his audience. He must be aware that he has to transfer his subject to the listeners and that this is possible only if he speaks with enthusiasm and assurance. Only then will contact in both directions be possible.

To reach this degree of assurance a thorough knowledge of the subject is essential, but this, by itself is not enough; voice, posture and gestures are important too.

A monotonous voice can have a bad influence on a lecture but much can be done about it. Some training in reading the text aloud, and underlining stressed words, will bring improvement soon: if a tape recorder is available, recording of and listening to the text, if necessary a number of times, will be helpful. To overcome monotony, the speaker should change his rate of speaking, the pitch and volume of his voice and he should introduce short pauses now and then.

By constant practice a speaker can learn to hold this audience. He will come to know when people are still concentrating and when they are not. If it appears that someone is not listening, he should make a brief interruption to establish whether or not this particular person has understood everything. It is important to be able to detect this sort of inattention, because otherwise parts of the lecture may be misunderstood, which will present difficulties later.

Whenever a question is asked, ensure that everyone has understood it. If not, either repeat the question or formulate it in a different way. The answer given should not be addressed solely to the questioner; it should be directed to the entire audience.

Make the person addressed feel that you are presenting your material not as final recommendations but as ideas for discussions. Even on points that are well-settled in your own mind, it is often wise to convey the idea that you have not yet reached definite conclusions.

Do not miss any opportunity of convincing any person, even the least-important, that what you are doing is sound and beneficial to the company and therefore to himself. Acquaint him with the anticipated benefits of the new system, so that he will see the changes affecting him as being part of a broader picture.

Finally, try to make each member of your audience feel some responsibility for success of the system. Ask for their help and advice in putting it across. Get their suggestions as to how to slant the presentation to the higher levels of user management. Ask for their ideas on tackling the installation of equipment or of coordinating the new procedures smoothly with related routines. Tell them that you would like to make the final presentation a product of your joint thinking.

Discussion

It is essential that after the lecture is finished time be set aside for a discussion of the topics covered. This is necessary to check whether what has been said has been understood or not.

Approach the discussion with an open mind. Think of it more as an opportunity to test your ideas and less as a challenge to put them across. Be ready to modify them as weaknesses or better ways become evident.

The speaker can stimulate his audience by asking questions himself. First he should address himself to all listeners and afterwards, if necessary, he can direct himself to a particular person.

Good question should:

- be brief, simple and clear;
- relate to one point at a time;
- be in logical order;
- be asked at the right moment;
- be divided over the entire audience;
- be asked in the right intonation.

If he speaker is drawn off the subject of the lecture he should return it as soon as possible.

The following points are important too:

- with the possible exception of higher-level policies or organizational relationships, discuss all the proposed changes openly. Don't be mysterious about them.

  Tell the listeners quite frankly what you are trying to do. By disclosing your own thinking, you will encourage them to exchange ideas with you;
- when objections arise, as they surely will, be sure to hear the arguments fully to find out exactly why the objector thinks that a given approach will not work. Where necessary set the point aside for further analysis or research. If however, you are absolutely certain that the original approach should be adopted, proceed as follows:
  - try to show him clearly why it will work, and persuade him that it is at least worth a trial;
  - if he still does not agree, concede the point, provided that it is a minor one that will not seriously interfere with the overall plan. Compromises on small points will often help you win the larger ones. If you are reluctant, as a matter of principle, to make such compromises, you need only remember how frequently operating management must adjust its ways to your ideas;
  - if agreement cannot be reached on a major point, explain as tactfully as possible exactly how the point in question has an important bearing on the whole system and stress that you do not believe it should be abandoned without reference to a higher authority. At the same time, assure the objector that you will present all the pros and cons of the case clearly and impartially. Write out, e.g. on the blackboard, the reasons for non-concurrence and review them to ensure that they are a fair and complete statement of the position. It is important to note that no matter how carefully this kind of a "showdown" is handled, a certain loss of good-will inevitably results. For this reason the method should be resorted to only when important gains are at stake.

Activity 6-2: Documentation

Technique 6-2.1: Technical writing

Purpose

The purpose of technical writing is to record useful technical information in a form which allows the reader to understand it as rapidly and efficiently as possible.

Areas of application

Technical writing is necessary during the phases of systems analysis & design, and development, to define objectives, describe planning, record action, and explain procedures.

Preparation for writing

Technical writing is a production job. It has a maker and a user; and the maker must give proper consideration to the requirements of the user. It has an input, upon which manhours are expended in order to produce an output; and the maker must pay due attention to the quality and quantity of the input, as well as to the quality of his workmanship, if he is to produce an acceptable output. Adequate preparation is therefore as necessary to the creation of good technical writing as to any other form of manufacture.

Evaluation of the task

The first stage of a preparation is evaluation. Before starting work on any writing job, the author must reach a clear understanding of the nature and scope of the task he is about to undertake.
Lack of such understanding will not only lead to confused work; it will prevent the proper fulfilment of the steps of the preparation.

Evaluation of the intended readership

It is possible to write clearly and accurately, and yet to fail totally in the job of communication, if the needs of the intended readership have been insufficiently consulted.
This would occur, for example, if an otherwise well-written text employed a terminology unknown to its intended readers, or mathematical methods beyond their understanding. Therefore, before he starts working, the technical writer should determine who the reader will be, so that he can write at an appropriate level, and use an appropriate vocabulary.

Detail level

It is not sufficient for the author merely to ensure that he is writing at a level which the reader will understand. The level must be determined by the reader's "need-to-know". This is dependent upon the needs of the system; the function of each document is to ensure that the reader is placed in possession of information which he will need in order to fulfil his responsibilities to the systems effort. Thus, the effective determination of the detail level appropriate to each document calls for careful coordination of the communication requirements of the systems effort with the systems documentation breakdown.

There are two cases to be considered. In the first, the detail level derived from system considerations is not beyond that arrived at in evaluating the readership. This presents no problem. In the second — likely to be encountered, for example, when writing instructional material for user personnel — it becomes evident that the detail level called for by the system exceeds the probable present capacity of the intended reader. In this case, suitable additional instruction will have to be given. This may take the form of a lead-in section of the document under consideration, or of a separate document, or a training course may be called for.
The technical author, when he considers that he has encountered an example of the second case, should not, of course, attempt to make the decision-on-action himself. The matter should be referred, clearly explained in a brief report, to the project team.

Evaluation of the available information

The input for a technical writing task is information. In order that the task may be successfully carried out, the information input must be adequate both in kind and in quantity. Having made an assessment of the natura and scope of the task, and of the intended readership, the writer should compare the results of these assessments with the information available to him. If there is a good match, he may proceed with the writing. If there is insufficient information, he must obtain more.

Collection of information

The initial input to a technical author can range from copious written material requiring only editing or reorganization, through copious written material requiring total rewrite, to nothing more than a verbal instruction to "write a piece about so-and-so". Much more often than not, the writer will find that some essential pieces of information are missing. It is his duty to repair these omissions.

In attempting to achieve completeness of his information input, an author should observe the following points:

- he should decide precisely what he wants to know before he starts to ask questions. If the previous parts of the preparation for writing have been done thoroughly, the omissions will be clearly pinpointed;
- he should ascertain the appropriate source for the information he requires. To be directed from person to person through a long chain of "wrong addresses" annoys many people, and wastes much time. Moreover, somewhere along the chain, some person not properly qualified may take it upon himself to give incorrect or garbled information, which the author will accept as correct;
- whenever possible, he should make an appointment with any person from whom he seeks information, and should give advance notice of the questions he proposes to ask.

Outlining

Before he begins the writing job itself, the author should prepare a detailed outline of what is to be written. A simple practical method of outlining is as follows:

- start with a piece of heavy-grade paper. Divide it into columns about four inches (10 cm) wide;
- from the information available at the end of the preparation stage, derive a set of main headings under which the subject will be dealt with. Write these in capital letters at suitable intervals — perhaps one at the head of each column and one halfway down;
- consider each main heading in turn. Underneath it write any topics which will be discussed when dealing with it.
  When ideas are temporarily exhausted in respect of one heading, go on to another. Continue in this manner, putting down any ideas as they occur under an appropriate heading, until no more topics suggest themselves. Do not, at this stage, spend any great amount of time in considering the relative importance of the topics, or even whether or not they are in the best place;
- cut out each heading, sub-heading and topic, so that each occupies a narrow strip of paper of column width. Permute these strips on a table, rearranging, upgrading, downgrading, adding and discarding as seems desirable;
- when a satisfactory arrangement is reached, stick all the strips in order on another sheet of paper, or copy down the arrangement;
- now add a beginning and an end. The two headings "Introduction" and "Conclusion" will suffice. Any necessary background information should be outlined under Introduction, and a summary of general principles will appear as part of the conclusion;
- when this outline is complete, offer it to qualified technical people for criticism and comment.

Figure 1 shows the outline from which this paper was written. The fact that "Introduction" does not appear is due to the fact that the paper is one of a set of techniques, rather than an independent document.

Preparation

General
Evaluation of readers
Level of detail
Evaluation of job
—"— information
Collection of information
Outlining

Starting

Rough draft
Inertia

Organizing

Orderliness
Paragraphs
Headings.

Style

General
Clarity
Simplicity

Style (cont)
Jargon
Brevity
Padding
Punctuation
Sentence length
Telegraphese
Sense
Voice
Terminology
Meaningless phrases
Imprecise phrases
Humour
Description

Illustrations

General
Content
Purpose
Quantity
Cartoons

Technical review

Reports

Procedures
Quality
Conclusion

Fig. 1.

Starting to write

When the outline has been approved, a rough or first draft of the text should be prepared. The word rough, often used in this context, should not be taken too literally. To produce poor or careless work at this stage is to waste time; 90% of the material of a first draft from a competent author will probably figure in the final text.

The purposes of the rough draft are as follows:

- any minor residual deficiencies in the information input are revealed. When such deficiencies are encountered during the preparation of a rough draft, they must not be allowed to hold up the work. A note should be made, and, if necessary, a gap left in the draft;
- the validity of the proposed organization of text is tested. As a result of writing a rough draft, reasons for making small changes in the outline may emerge;
- a rough draft, with notes of any deficiencies in information input and any proposed changes in organization, is presented for technical approval. This procedure avoids wasting editorial and "polishing" time or an unvetted draft.

Difficulty in starting

The most difficult sentence is the first. Words will flow, once the initial inertia is overcome; but it is useless to sit staring at a blank writing pad. After the first few minutes, an author in this attitude usually has a mind as blank as his paper. Before reaching this condition, he should ask himself three questions:

- Do I fully understand the nature of the writing task I am about to attempt?
- Have I sufficient technical information for the purpose?
- Do I understand the technical information?

If the answer to one or more of these questions is no, then the writer has two courses open to him. He can repair the deficiency (by asking pertinent questions of appropriate people, reading up source material, and so on), or if this is for any reason impossible at the time, he can turn to a different task. He should not, in these circumstances attempt to proceed with the present task; still less should he continue to stare at blank paper.

If the answer to all these questions is yes, then there is no good reason why the task should not be performed. To overcome inertia, it is often a good idea to write down anything at all on the paper, relevant or not, and, once started, to keep going. Once the pen is firing well, the mind can be directed to the subject in hand. Finally, the rubbish which was produced in the first few minutes can be discarded, and a new beginning written. This method possesses the advantage that the beginning, which will give the reader his first impression of the work, is written last, when the writer is warmed up and running well.
When words are flowing, the critical faculty is partially suspended. It is difficult

to achieve spontaneity and precision simultaneously; so, write spontaneously, and edit for precision. So:

- write freely, and cover the subject as fully as the detail level warrants;
- go over the text, ruthlessly scoring out every word not essential to sense or structure, and replacing involved phrases by simple ones.

  Sometimes a slight rearrangement of word order will permit simplification.

Organization

Orderliness

Orderliness increases the efficiency with which information can be conveyed from document to reader. It is secured by clear thinking and a good understanding of his subject on the part of the author, and is first expressed in the preparation of the outline. It is maintained by careful adherence to the outline. Changes must not be made to a well-worked and approved outline without giving full consideration to the possible repercussions of such changes throughout the structure of the work.

Paragraphing

Start a new paragraph for each new idea presented. Over-paragraph rather than under-paragraph. Paragraphs longer than ten or twelve lines may lose the reader's eye. Shorter paragraphs, of varying lengths, will pattern the page, and the reader will be less likely to skip a line, or to read the same line twice.

The formal itemization of a series of related subtopics of approximately equal importance, or of sequential steps in a process, can increase visual interest, emphasis, and memorability.

While the division of text into basic and subordinate topics, leading to paragraphs, sub-paragraphs, sub-sub-paragraphs, and so on, makes the text easy to scan and conveys an indication of the relative importance of the various parts of the subject matter, it can be overdone. Not more than four levels of importance should normally be used. If a greater number is apparently called for, some rearrangement of the hierarchy of headings will be necessary. It will usually be found that at some point there is a heading which can be logically upgraded. If this is not the case, a more radical rearrangement of the text is indicated.

Headings

Headings should be short and informative; they should indicate the topics discussed in the paragraphs they subtend, and not summarize the discussion. This approach enables the reader to skim the headings in order to locate a specific topic, but prevents him from skimming to avoid reading the text, and gaining only a superficial and inadequate understanding of the material.

Style

A widely-read person can identify an author with whose work he is familiar from a reading of an isolated paragraph. He recognizes the style of the author. In referring to style in relation to technical writing, this kind of personalized style is not what is meant. Indeed, a highly personal style is objectionable in good technical writing, since it focuses the attention of the reader upon itself, and distracts him from the material being presented, thus impeding communication. Moreover, it is often desirable to be able to combine the work of several authors into one document, without the joins showing. A technical author must therefore cultivate a style, using the word in this sense, which is neutral.

In technical writing, the word style is used to refer to the manner in which the author selects and organizes his verbal material. Whereas style in the literary sense is an imponderable, in the sense in which it is used in relation to technical writing it has a diminished but more precise meaning, In this sense, it can be broken down into components, and described in detail.

It is to be expected that a professional technical writer will be competent in the mechanics of his language. The fact that he is producing technical material does not excuse him from formal and grammatical accuracy. Language which is academically sound is better able to achieve precision and avoid ambiguity than is slipshod usage.

Clarity

The objective of technical writing is communication; therefore, the quality most to be sought is clarity. If a passage is clear to the reader, it has achieved its goal.

Simplicity

The factor of style which has the greatest effect on clarity is simplicity. Technical writing can be made almost as precise as mathematics if it is kept simple. The use of "literary" devices destroys simplicity.

Jargon

It is a tendency of specialist groups to develop a jargon, usually consisting of coined words and subtly misused phrases which cannot be relied upon to mean the same thing to all readers.

The use of jargon should be avoided in technical literature; the writer must not be seduced into the employment of shop- or bench-talk. It is a fallacy to believe that communication with technicians is so enhanced; the requirements of speech and of writing are very different.

Brevity

The briefest of technical notes can communicate effectively to well-qualified individuals; but in fields growing as rapidly as system engineering and data processing, most people are very well-informed in certain areas and unpredictably ignorant in others. Consequently, the technical writer should often assume, in his reader, even at the expense of brevity, a level of understanding lower than the ideal. Brief explanatory digressions can be helpful in relating concepts.

Redundancy and "padding"

The three chief reasons for redundancy and "padding" in technical literature are unclear thinking; the desire to produce an apparently large volume of work; and unwillingness to score out and rewrite.

Less frequent, but still important, are the desire to exercise a "fine" style of writing; and self-doubt as to whether a point has been made sufficiently clearly.

Unclear thinking
If a writer does not fully understand the subject he is discussing, he is unable to think about it properly. Such a state of affairs produces "woolly" writing, in which the author skirts around the points he does not understand, putting up a barrage of largely meaningless verbiage. An honest writer pulls up short at this stage, and looks for technical help.

Production of volume
This cause arises where an author feels that his ability is judged solely or largely by his output-per-day. It is, of course, essential in any documentation-producing group, to have a yardstick; so many pages per manmonth average. It is important for an author to remember that it is a longterm average. It is worse than useless, when engaged on a slow and difficult job, to pad out the text with meaningless generalities in a mistaken attempt to keep up a page rate.

Unwillingness to rewrite
When an author has written a paragraph which, on re-reading, seems inadequately to describe the point he was trying to make, there is a temptation to add another, in an attempt to repair the deficiency. Thus he has two bad paragraphs, one inherently poor and another to patch it up, where one good one should be. If a piece of writing does not do what it was intended to do, it must be rewritten, not shored up.

"Fine" style
The style appropriate to technical writing is clear and unadorned; there is no place in it for "fine" writing. This does not mean that technical writing may not possess a good style; it may even become genuine literature, as for example in Darwin's "Origin of Species", an acknowledged masterpiece in the genre. A good writer in any field is sensitive to the style appropriate to his subject.

Self-doubt

This cause differs from that dealt with under "unwillingness to rewrite" in that the author has written a perfectly good paragraph, and is suddenly seized by the need to elaborate it. The commonest symptom is the scattering of "e.g." and "i.e." and "in other words" about the work. To write "i.e." or "in other words" is to admit that the same thing is being said twice. It should be said once, and said well. The employment of examples in technical literature is occasionally necessary; but not nearly so often as an unconfident author believes. In most cases, explicitness and clarity in the text obviate the need for examples. While one example may sometimes be desirable, there are practically no cases in which more than one is called for. Proliferation of examples clutters up the text, and impedes the flow of thought.

Punctuation

The rules of written English have grown out of the need for clarity. Punctuation, for example, developed as an indication of the inflections and rhythms of the spoken word. Without punctuation of this sort, a passage that is intrinsically clear can become ineffective. The mandatory punctuation marks (! ? " ' .) must be correctly placed by the exercise of ordinary technical knowledge; only expercience, and careful reading to his "inner ear", will enable a writer to determine the best positioning and use of the dash, comma, semicolon, colon and parenthesis.

Sentence length

Technical writing must not consist entirely of short, dry statements of fact. On the other hand, the habit of writing one clause after another in a seemingly endless chain is equally irritating. Avoiding both extremes, a natural variation in sentence length will hold the reader's interest, and increase the clarity of the writing.

"Telegraphese"

In the "telegraphese" style, the principle of omitting superfluous words is carried to extremes. Any word not contributing directly to the meaning is omitted, even at the expense of grammar and sentence structure; for example "first locate the character required in approximately the correct position; next, find the true position by aligning the stencil-guide with the paper-guide; now draw the character" would be rendered as "Locate character approximately; align guides; draw character". The style is totally unsuitable for the majority of applications, but has its place in summaries and checklists.

Verb tense

Style is enhanced by the consistent use of the proper verb tense. Most documents should be written in the present tense; even in proposals, what is proposed should be described as if it already existed. The use of the past tense is sometimes appropriate in communicating background information, as is the use of the future tense in discussing the expected results of particular actions. In writing specific instructions, use the imperative mood. When in doubt, use the present.

The passive voice

The passive voice — "The START button is then pressed", instead of "Then press the START button" — is often adopted by those who wish to lend an air of solid calmness and professionalism to an otherwise lightweight document. In fact, the passive voice is cumbersome and slow-moving; it impedes communication and degrades clarity.

Terminology

The terminology throughout a technical document should be consistent. In explaining complicated processes, the repetition of terms is unavoidable. The replacement of a term by one of its synonyms may make the reader think that some difference in meaning is intended, and will divert his attention from the thread of reasoning or description he is trying to follow.
Technical writing serves to describe and to explain, but not to praise. Laudatory terms are appropriate in advertising and proposals, and are sometimes used in preliminary system design concepts which seek to obtain management approval in addition to transmitting technical information; but precision, not persuasion, is the goal of technical writing proper.

Meaningless phrases

Each language is rich in meaningless words and phrases e.g. in English; actually, in fact, as a general rule, really, just, absolutely, definitely, incidentally, substantially, considerably, virtually . . . . .

Each of these examples has, of course, a proper application; but they, and many others like them, have become so degraded by misuse that an author who finds himself about to write one of them should first consider whether or not his usage is meaningful. Even if he decides that it is, he should examine the possibility of employing an alternative. Such expressions are commonly ignored by the reader, even when used correctly.

Imprecise phrases

Imprecise words and phrases should be avoided in technical writing. To write "the throughput time will be substantially shortened" is lazy and misleading. If the text concerned is of a general and descriptive nature, write "will be shortened by . . . .%". If measurement or calculations will be undertaken by the reader in connection with the text, find out the limits, and put them in. Similarly avoid such expression as "within a short time", "as soon as possible", "near the maximum", and so on. They frustrate the reader and indicate that the writer is not in full possession of the facts.

Verbal humour

Verbal humour has no place in technical writing. The purpose of a technical document is communication, not entertainment. Moreover, sense of humour varies radically and unpredictably from individual to individual, and what may appear innocuously amusing to one reader may prove incomprehensible to a second and offensive to a third.

Description

In describing a complex process or system, it is often difficult to decide whether to describe "each brick, then the walls, and finally the house", or "the house, then the walls, and then each brick". A workable method is to start with a brief description of the entire system or process; to continue with logically ordered descriptions of the major components; to follow with a detailed treatment of each element; and to close with a summary. In some cases, it will be more appropriate to divide the description according to the functional, rather than the physical, breakdown of the system.

Description of environment

In describing certain system functions, it is often helpful to include a brief description of the environment in which they are exercised, in order to show how it has affected the system design in relation to these functions.

Overall system description

The user documentation of systems, subsystems, programs and procedures requires the inclusion of at least a short description of the system as a whole. Since the project team members who initially man a project understand its purposes and products from the beginning, they may find little use for this description; but as time passes and these people depart, it will prove its value in the training of newcomers and user personnel.

Illustration

The illustrations of a technical document should be planned conjointly with the text, and their planning should receive the same care.

There must be a close integration of text and illustrations. As the author proceeds with his work, he must remain alert to perceive those points where illustrations are necessary, or desirable, or where a well-designed illustration might shorten and simplify the text. The planning of the illustration content is the responsibility of the author, although he should welcome suggestions from illustrators and technical reviewers. An author should be able to produce, no matter how crudely, some sort of representation of each illustration he calls for. If this is not so, much time is wasted in having an illustrator prepare drawings which are subsequently discarded or greatly modified. In the act of preparing the "sugar-bag" versions, the author may be brought to realize unexpected facts about his proposed illustrations. This may save duplication of work for the illustrator, and will frequently enable the author to make timely small modifications to his text as he goes along, when otherwise serious retrospective changes might have been necessitated. The sugar-bag drawings should be no more than explanatory sketches. Little time should be spent on them. Clarity, not artistry, is the aim.

Illustration content

The number and type of illustration must be related to the needs of the intended readership, and to the nature of the subject under discussion. In order to determine the appropriate illustration content, it is necessary to appreciate the purposes which can be served by illustrations.

They can be summarized as follows. Illustrations can:

- give the reader an idea of the appearance of objects which he may not be able to see for himself (photographs and drawings);
- display physical aspects and relationships not readily seen otherwise (interior views, sections, cutaways, exploded views, detail drawings, enlargements);
- show system and hardware configurations in a logical, rather than a physical, arrangement (block diagrams, configuration charts, system flowcharts);
- show logical relationships with a clarity not possible in words (program and system flowcharts, logic diagrams, circuit diagrams, block diagrams, configuration charts);
- simplify, by showing idealized representations of complex realities (simplified drawings, simplified logic diagrams, main program flowcharts, simplified circuit diagrams);
- emphasize, by suitable operations on the artwork ("ghosted" and "boosted" drawings and photographs).

The level of an illustration should parallel the level of the corresponding text. A text passage presenting an overall system description should be accompanied by an illustration identifying only the major functions and subsystems, while a detailed discussion of program logic calls for a comprehensive flowchart.

Redundancy of illustrations

Too many illustrations is as bad a fault as too few. The author should question the necessity of every illustration he proposes to use. Equally bad is the attempt to cram too much into any one illustration. An overfilled drawing fails in its main purpose, which is to clarify, because it is difficult to read.

Cartoons

Cartoons have no place in technical literature. If they are good, they distract the reader's attention from the technical content; if they are poor, they are intrinsically useless. Cartoons raise the publishing budget without raising document quality. The common justification of cartoons — that they size the reader's attention and inveigle him into reading the text — is fatuous. Nobody reads technical literature unless he has a "need to know". No impediments to efficient communication should be built into a technical document.

Document review by technical personnel

Most technical writers are not as well-qualified in the discipline they support as the personnel responsible for vetting the technical accuracy of their output. Consequently, the writer must be prepared to edit or re-write as often as necessary to meet the technical requirements of the reviewer. The relatively ignorant writer, however, may be a good judge of clarity and informativeness, because he corresponds more closely to the intended reader. The writer's judgement concerning specific needs for additional explanation should therefore be trusted within reasonable limits.

Report writing

All the considerations of this chapter can be applied to report writing. It is probable that the preparation stage will be shorter and more direct in the case of a report than in that of an instructional or descriptive text; the necessary information should be to hand, and the outlining stage may be greatly simplified.

A report is the most evanescent form of technical writing. Although it will pass into a historic file as a record, its purpose is to give information about a certain state of affairs at a certain point in time. Its most important features are therefore accuracy and speed of preparation. If it fulfils these aims, the lack of other niceties may be forgiven. Technical reviewers and editors should equally bear this fact in mind. The practise of tidying up a report after it has served its primary function, but before it is filed, is to be deprecated; it should be undertaken only if deficiencies in clarity and accuracy have been discovered while the report is still "live", and then only with the consent of all parties concerned.

Procedure writing

A procedure is here taken to mean an instruction for the performance of a specific task or set of tasks. The main requirements are completeness, accuracy, and simplicity. Verbs should be imperative and active; not "the card is now withdrawn", but "Withdraw the card". It is not impolite to use imperatives in such a document; rather, in increasing the clarity, it is a politeness to the reader. The exercise of completeness, accuracy, and simplicity will not produce a short document for a long procedure. A procedure may not be short, but it should be as short as possible compatibly with these essential characteristics. It is very desirable that the author of a procedure should be given the opportunity of himself performing the task it describes. Ideally, he should go through the task twice — once before writing, and once after — on the second occasion attempting to follow his own documents. If he will be able to go through the task once only, the second performance, which is a test run for the document, is the more important.

There is no place for outlining in procedure writing. The sequence of the document must follow rigorously the sequence of steps in the task. Equally, the author has no choice in paragraphing; each distinct step must be given a separate paragraph, and if a clearly defined logical step has a number of subdivisions, they must appear as sub-paragraphs within the paragraph describing that step. There is thus less scope for any form of literary expression in the procedure than in any other form of technical writing, and no such expression should be attempted.

Quality

Technical writing is generated to satisfy specific communications needs, fashioned to communicate with specific readers, and limited in quality by time and budgetary restrictions. This does not mean that high quality is not expected, but it does imply that polishing should be stopped when a state of effective clarity, completeness, and orderliness is achieved.

Each editorial "pass" through a given manuscript will raise both the quality and the cost of the document. The point of diminishing returns is often reached at the end of the first pass. Once an effective organization and treatment of the required material has been achieved, the document should be regarded as complete.

Conclusion

The goal of technical writing is to communicate technical information as clearly and completely as possible, in an orderly manner, within the allotted budget. Technical writing must be as carefully planned as any other industrial activity.

Writing is a lonely business, and the technical writer must be a "self-starter"; however, the qualities of initiative and persistence that make a self-starter are often accompanied by a strong sense of identity and self-respect. These should never tempt the writer into foolish pride of authorship, haggling over minor points of style, organization or phraseology.

There are no fixed rules which will automatically ensure good technical writing. The best technical authors write by ear, not by rule. If something sounds right, then it probably is right — but the ear that can recognize good writing is developed only by years of good reading.
For this reason, it may be easier and cheaper to make a technical writer out of a non-technical writer than to teach a technician to write.

Bibliography

Erlich and Murphy, *The Art of Technical Writing*, Bantam Books, 1964.
A good general text.

Follet, et al., *Modern American Usage*, Hill and Wong, 1966.
A guide similar to the classic Fowler, with stress on American usage, and on simplicity and straight-forwardness of expression.

Fowler and Gowers, *Modern English Usage*, Oxford Univ. Press, 1965.
A well-organized guide to the writing of good English; a pleasure to browse through, and an invaluable reference work.

Technique 6-2.2: Charting technique

Purpose

The purpose of charting technique is to give visual expression to a complex of relationships, so that they may be more clearly understood and manipulated.

Areas of application

Charting techniques are applicable at all stages of the systems effort, from the feasibility study to system maintenance.

Definition

A flow- or configuration-chart is a conventional drawing of a system, program, or hardware configuration, in which elements or concepts are represented by standardized symbols, and relationships by connecting lines.

General

Types of chart

In automatic data processing, these types of chart are used:

System flowchart
A system flowchart describes the flow — machine or manual — of data carriers within a system. The data carriers may be documents, tapes, punched cards, etc. The character of a system flowchart may be either organizational (problem oriented) or operational (machine-oriented).

Program flowchart
A program flowchart describes the method and sequence of the data processing in a computer. Program flowcharts can be drawn at any required level of detail. A main program flowchart shows a whole program at a relatively low detail level; its content can be presented in greater detail in one or more detail flowcharts.

Configuration chart
A configuration chart employs symbols to represent the physical units which comprise the data processing equipment, and directed lines to indicate the sense of the data-flow. Configuration charts are machine-oriented.

Template and symbol conventions

When drawing flow- and configuration-charts, use should be made of a template in accordance with American Standards Association (ASA) approved flowcharting technique.

system flowchart

1

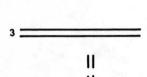

CONNECTING LINE

Indicating transport of data carriers or transmission of data.

NOTE:

Normal directions are from top to bottom and from left to right. When combining directions, right angles must be drawn, avoiding sloping lines.

2

BROKEN LINE

Represent the relation between data or their derivation from data carriers, e.g. checking or copying an amount.
See also above note.

3

—

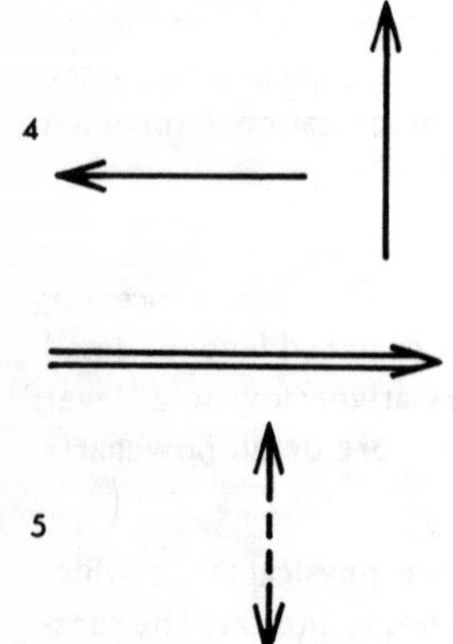

4

POINTERS

Must be used:

. for directions other than normal;
. if necessary for clear interpretation.

NOTE:

Use *open* arrows.

5

—

program flowchart	configuration chart
CONNECTING LINE Indicating the sequence of operations.	INFORMATION LINE Representing data transmission between units.
As for system flowchart.	As for system flowchart.
As for system flowchart.	CONTROL LINE Denoting the transmission of control signals or the delegation of instructions between units.
——	BUS LINE Transmission as per 1) and 2) may take place to more than one unit, (not necessarily simultaneously).
As for system flowchart.	POINTERS May be used at the end of the lines to indicate the direction of the transmission, as the unit may have transmitting and/or receiving capacity.
——	HALF DUPLEX Communication for alternate two-way transmission, represented by *one* line with *two* pointers.

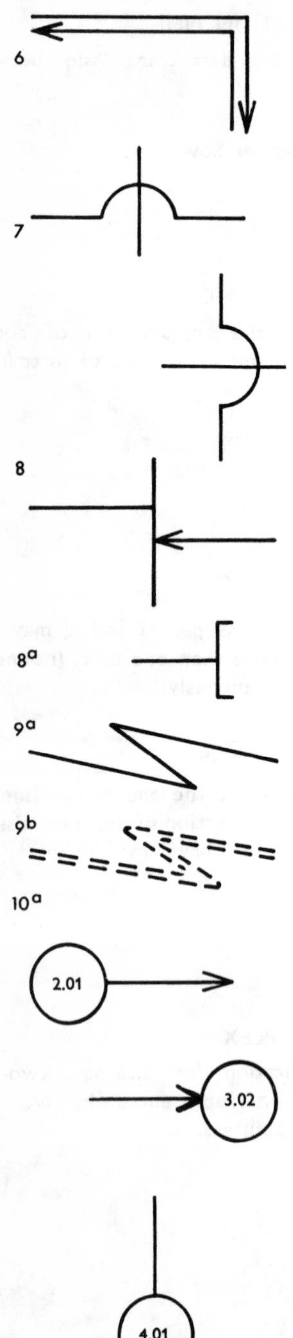

—

BRIDGE

For crossing of unconnected lines.

NOTES:

- Half of small connector is used.
- Whenever possible, avoid crossing lines by rearranging the chart.

JUNCTION OF LINES:

Form two three-way instead of one four-way connection by drawing at different levels.

—

COMMUNICATION LINK

For data transmission between different locations.

PAGE CONNECTOR

For transfer in the flowchart:

- to a location on the same page, to avoid intersecting lines or lines which are too long;
- to a location on another page: exit connector;
- from a location on another page: entry connector.

Coding for this kind of connector:

9.99 = format, consisting of:

* page number of entry connector;

** sequence number of connector on entry page.

NOTE:

To permit back-references in the flowchart, the entry connector, if on another

program flowchart	configuration chart
—	FULL DUPLEX Communication for simultaneous two-way transmission.
As for system flowchart.	As for system flowchart.
As for system flowchart.	As for system flowchart.
—	FORK Indicating connection possibilities between controllers, channels and I/0 units.
As for system flowchart.	TELECOMMUNICATION LINK Indicating automatic teletransmission of data (9a) and signals (9b).
As for system flowchart.	—

page, must carry an annotation indicating the page number of the corresponding exit connector.

10b

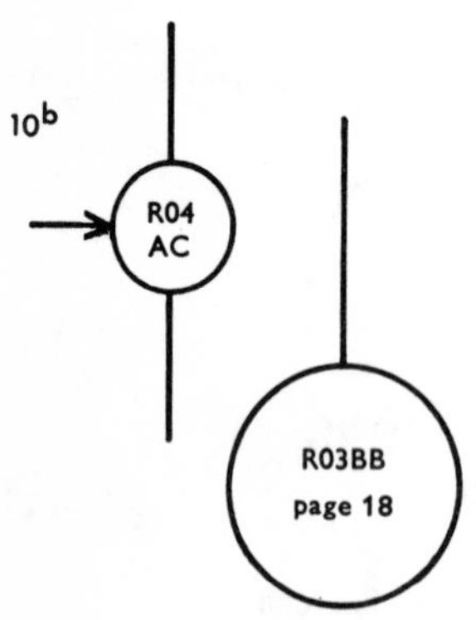

10c

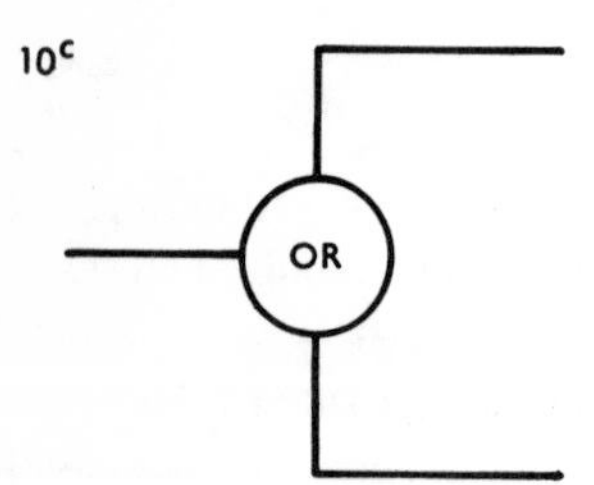

11

11a

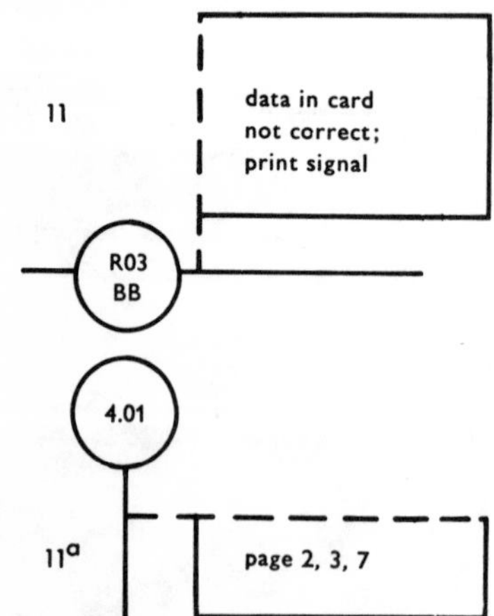

ANNOTATION

May be added:

- in general, for explanatory comments on procedure or processing;
- in particular, to refer to an entry connector, in order to indicate the page or pages on which exits to this connector will be found.

NOTE:

This is the only symbol not to be incorporated in the flowline.

CONNECTOR

For the transfer to an instruction in the same or another routine. It gives the label-code of the instruction and, if necessary, the page number of the program flowchart. A connector can be used for each label in the program, except for those used in modification instructions.

—

OPTION

Optional choice of units to be applied.

—

As for system flowchart.

—

12a

52

FREQUENCY SYMBOL

Indicating the number of times an operation is carried out in a year, e.g.

360 = daily
52 = weekly
12 = monthly
1 = yearly

12b

AND

—

13a

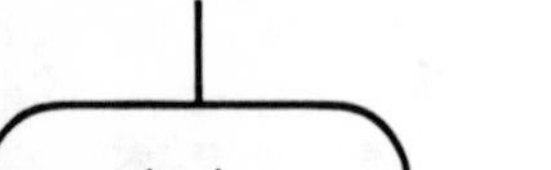

TERMINAL

Department, work station.

13b

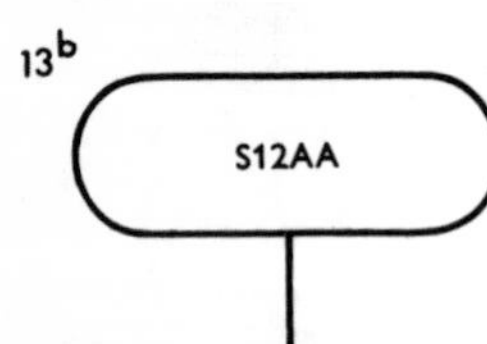

—

13c

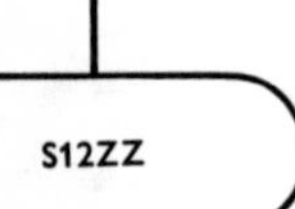

—

13d

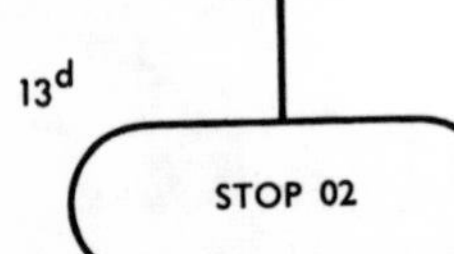

—

COMBINATION

Several units may be applied simultaneously.

TERMINAL

Online unit in remote location for data input and/or output.

START or ENTRY

of program or module.
It is not necessary to use "*from*" references to page numbers, as a module may be mentioned in many places in the program.
A subroutine can have several entries.

STOP, END or EXIT

of program or module.
In case of a subroutine, this is a "jump" instruction, which usually has a modifiable address supplied by the subroutine itself. A return will then be made to the main program flow.
One subroutine may have several exits.

BREAKPOINT INSTRUCTION

The number mentioned after each interruption indicates where the process will be resumed.
Cobol: STOP 02.

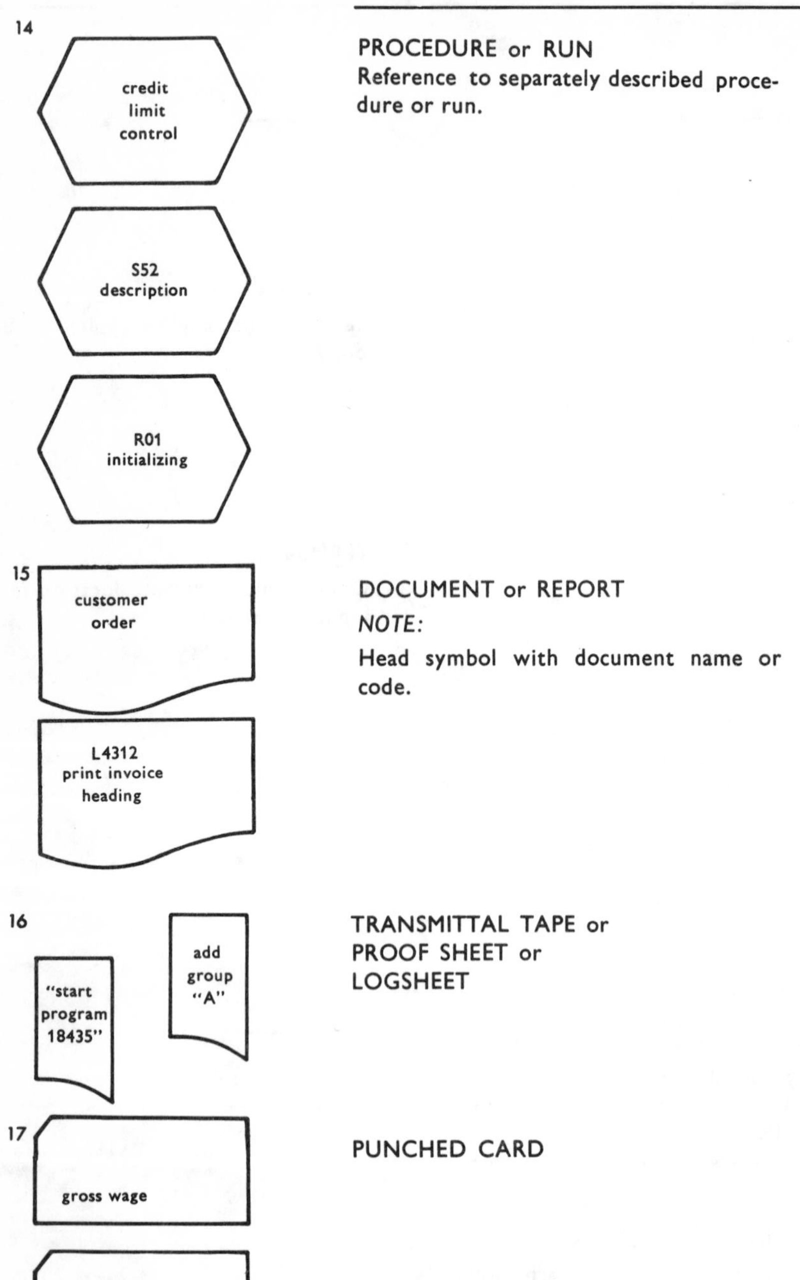

14 PROCEDURE or RUN
Reference to separately described procedure or run.

15 DOCUMENT or REPORT
NOTE:
Head symbol with document name or code.

16 TRANSMITTAL TAPE or
PROOF SHEET or
LOGSHEET

17 PUNCHED CARD

MODULE

Stating the label and the description of the routine, subroutine or macro.
After completion, a jump is made to the instruction following this symbol.

CONTROL UNIT

Whether or not physically independent, coupling directly or via transmission units, special input/output units to processors.

PRINTER or MACHINE READABLE DOCUMENT

Print one or more lines or read document (magnetic ink, optical reading) e.g.
Cobol: WRITE L4312.

PRINTER, X-Y-RECORDER, PLOTTER OR DOCUMENT READER

LOGSHEET

Printing or input of messages by console typewriter or console printer.

ONLINE CONSOLE PRINTER or TYPE-WRITER

For initializing, messaging, restarting and terminating the processing.

PUNCHED CARD

Reading or punching.
Cobol: READ F2101.

CARD PUNCH and/or CARD READER

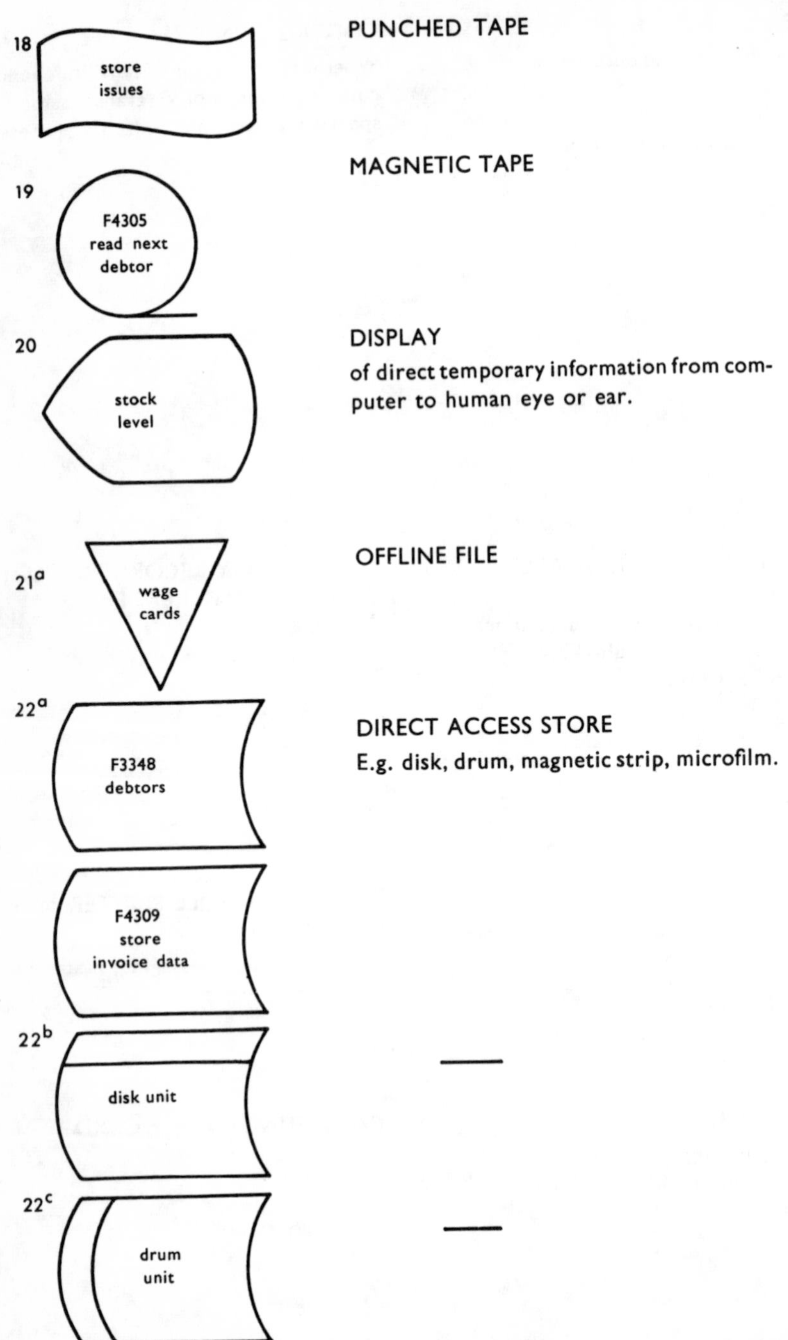

PUNCHED TAPE

MAGNETIC TAPE

DISPLAY

of direct temporary information from computer to human eye or ear.

OFFLINE FILE

DIRECT ACCESS STORE

E.g. disk, drum, magnetic strip, microfilm.

—

—

program flowchart	configuration chart
PUNCHED TAPE Reading or punching.	PUNCHED TAPE READER and/or PUNCHED TAPE PUNCH
MAGNETIC TAPE Reading or writing.	MAGNETIC TAPE UNIT
DISPLAY operation.	DISPLAY UNIT With video or audio devices.
—	BUFFER UNIT Independent or built in, synchronizing data or signals by means of temporary storage.
DIRECT ACCESS STORE operation.	DIRECT ACCESS STORE • *fixed disk unit*
—	• *interchangeable disk unit,* • *magnetic strips* • *magnetic cards*
—	. *fixed drum unit*

23

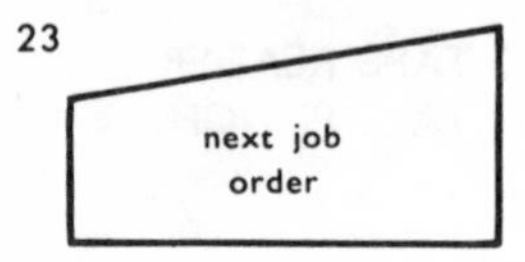

ENQUIRY STATION or
ONLINE KEYBOARD
Direct communication between man and machine.

24

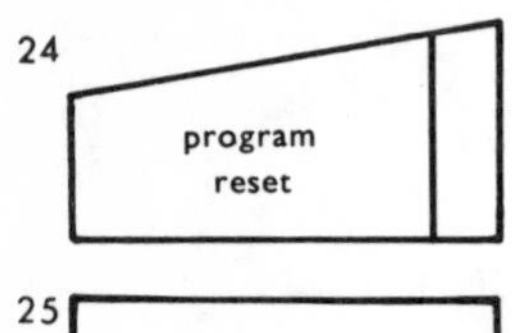

CONSOLE
Console operation without using console typewriter or console printer.
See TRANSMITTAL TAPE, no. 16.

25

sort

PROCESSING BY COMPUTER

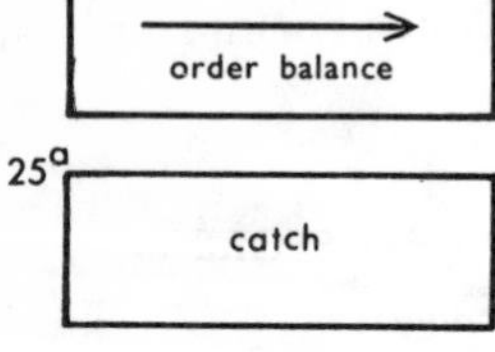

25a

catch

—

26

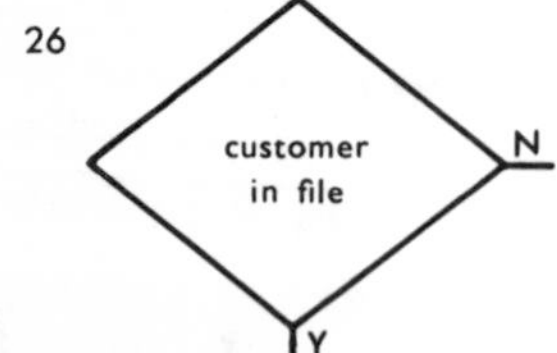

CHOISE or DECISION
Selection of the flow path to be followed.

26a

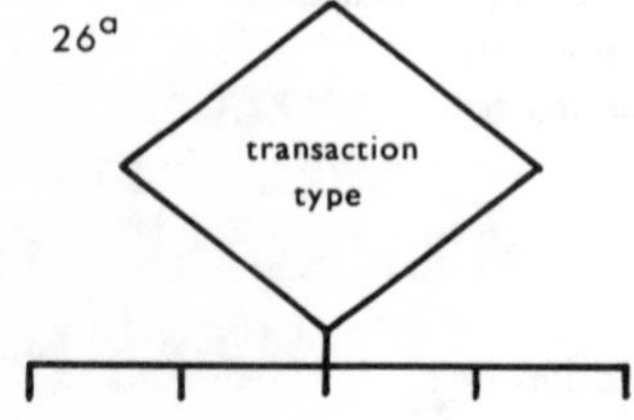

· Branching into more than three exits.

program flowchart	configuration chart
ENQUIRY STATION Input of data. *NOTE:* Output can take place via remote typewriter, printer or display.	ENQUIRY STATION
As for system flowchart	CONSOLE UNIT Whether or not physically independent
COMPUTER OPERATION Excluding enquiry, comparison, switch, indicator, modification, input or output.	PROCESSOR
COMPUTER OPERATION Alternative symbol to be used when space must be saved.	CHANNEL Identifying the type of channel.
ENQUIRY, COMPARISON, SWITCH or INDICATOR	ADAPTER, Usually not physically independent, coupling two units. *NOTE:* To be drawn between units concerned.
As for system flowchart.	

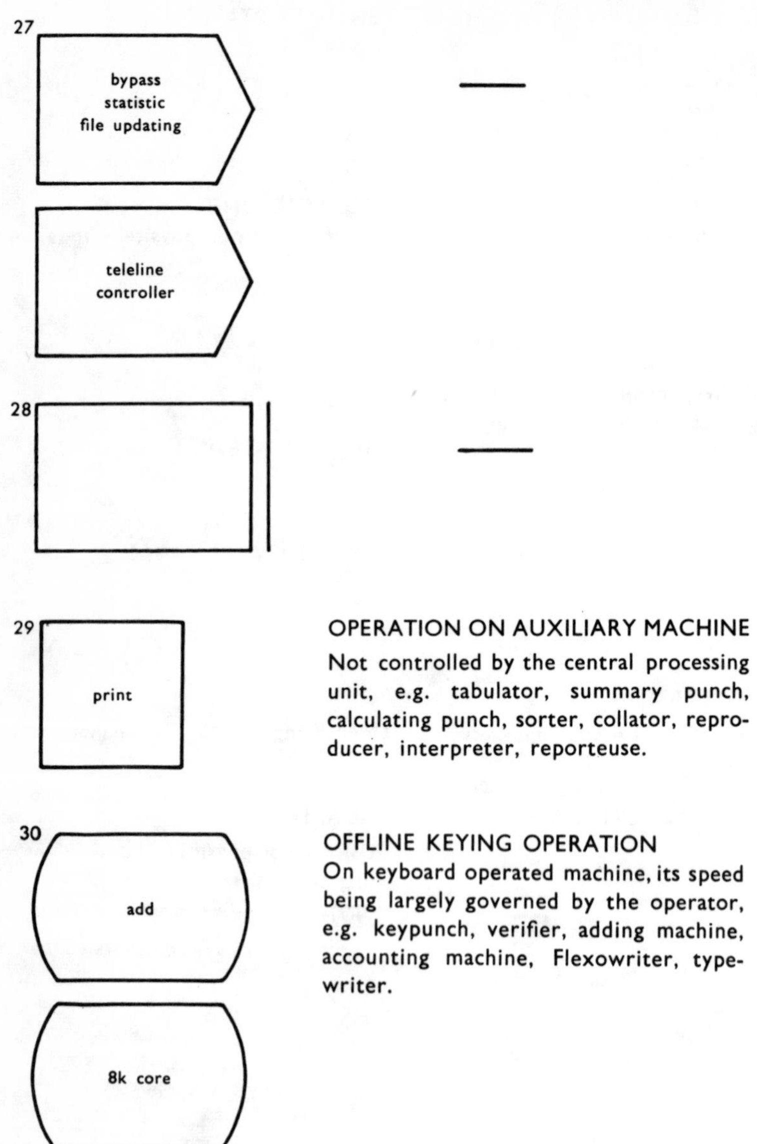

—

—

OPERATION ON AUXILIARY MACHINE
Not controlled by the central processing unit, e.g. tabulator, summary punch, calculating punch, sorter, collator, reproducer, interpreter, reporteuse.

OFFLINE KEYING OPERATION
On keyboard operated machine, its speed being largely governed by the operator, e.g. keypunch, verifier, adding machine, accounting machine, Flexowriter, typewriter.

MODIFICATION

The changing of instructions.
Cobol: ALTER R03W1
TO PROCEED TO R03AD.

TELECOMMUNICATION UNIT

Controlling the automatic teletransmission of data or signals.

MODIFIABLE INSTRUCTION

If one or more operands of an instruction are modified (see MODIFICATION, no. 27), a shadow line should be drawn on the right side of the symbol.

INTERNAL STORE

Autonomous or non-autonomous physically independent unit for temporary storage of data, providing direct access for processing. Storage may be static (in cores) or dynamic (delay lines).

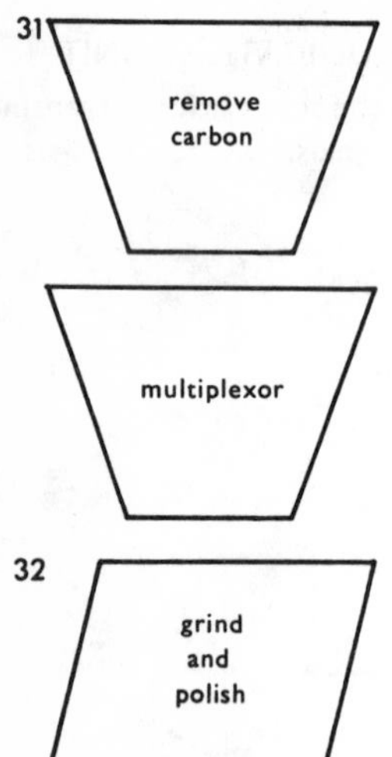

MANUAL OPERATION

(With or without machine)
No keyboards are used in this type of operation, the speed of which is mainly governed by the operator, e.g. Fanfold guillotine.

OTHER OPERATION

Other than specified operations, e.g. in charts representing a product flow.

TRANSMISSION UNIT

Carries out control instructions independently and provides a shared boundary for the connected input and output units ("standard interface"), permitting simultaneous operation.

The symbols of the template represent:

- in system flowcharts: entities, locations, functions;
- in program flowcharts: operations, functions;
- in configuration charts: equipment units, concepts.

Pages 2 to 19 give an example of a standard for the charting symbols for each type of chart.
When a symbol is employed in more than one type of chart, it assumes in each chart a meaning closely related to those which it bears in the others.
The size of a symbol does not affect its meaning.
The symbol annotations should be filled in by hand; this avoids the necessity of adjusting a completed chart in a typewriter.

As far as possible, charting techniques should be standardized throughout an organization.

Type and format of paper

Translucent tracing paper of the format A4 (297 × 210 mm) should be used for drawing charts. This will greatly facilitate filling in, correcting, duplicating and inserting in reports and project documentation.

System flowcharting

Purpose

The purpose of system flowcharting is to clarify the order of work in an information system, or in a logically self-contained part of a system such as a procedure or a run.

General recommendations

A system flowchart comprises a heading, a chart section, and, optionally, a narrative section.

Heading
The heading of a system flowchart should contain all necessary identifying information, including the project number, (sub)system name, name of process being charted, date, and initials of draughtsman.

Chart section
This section is built up from the standard symbols already described. As required, annotations are inserted in these symbols. Such annotations should be brief and unambiguous; in general, it is best to start each annotation with a short, clear verb.
The charting should be done in such a way, that as much as possible within the limits of the size of the paper, the symbols for different data objects (forms,

files) occuring in the flow are drawn on separate, imaginary vertical lines. Imaginary, as the printing of these lines would clutter up the chart.
This method of presentation will facilitate the study of the flow of single documents.

Narrative section

A column at the right of a flowchart may be reserved for information which cannot conveniently be placed in the symbols. Entries in this column should be at a level appropriate to the operations to which they refer. Items suitable for treatment in this manner include:

- quantitative data;
- throughput time: time elapsed from arrival of first input to an operation until related output is produced;
- detailed explanation;
- exceptions not charted in detail;
- authority when the process has to be halted for written approvals or confirmations;
- alternatives.

Example

Page 22 gives an example of a system flowchart.

Program flowcharting

Purpose

A program flowchart displays a proposed method for processing a problem on a computer by means of a program, routine, or subroutine.

General recommendations

The programmer should first concentrate on the fundamental logical relationships involved in the problem. Having drawn a chart adequately representing these relationships, he should then proceed by logical steps to simplify it as much as possible. He should not attempt to make the chart correspond in detail to the actual performance of the program.

A program flowchart is useful not only when designing programs, but also later, during debugging and maintenance. To enhance its value in these applications, steps must be taken to ensure that it can be understood by persons other than the original draughtsman, and by the draughtsman himself after a lapse of time. Such steps include:

- the use of a narrative description, e.g. by adding a page of notes to each page of the program flowchart. Experience has indicated that the programmer easily tends to forget why he has solved a problem in a particular way. For this reason it is better to clarify the method of solution right on the moment;

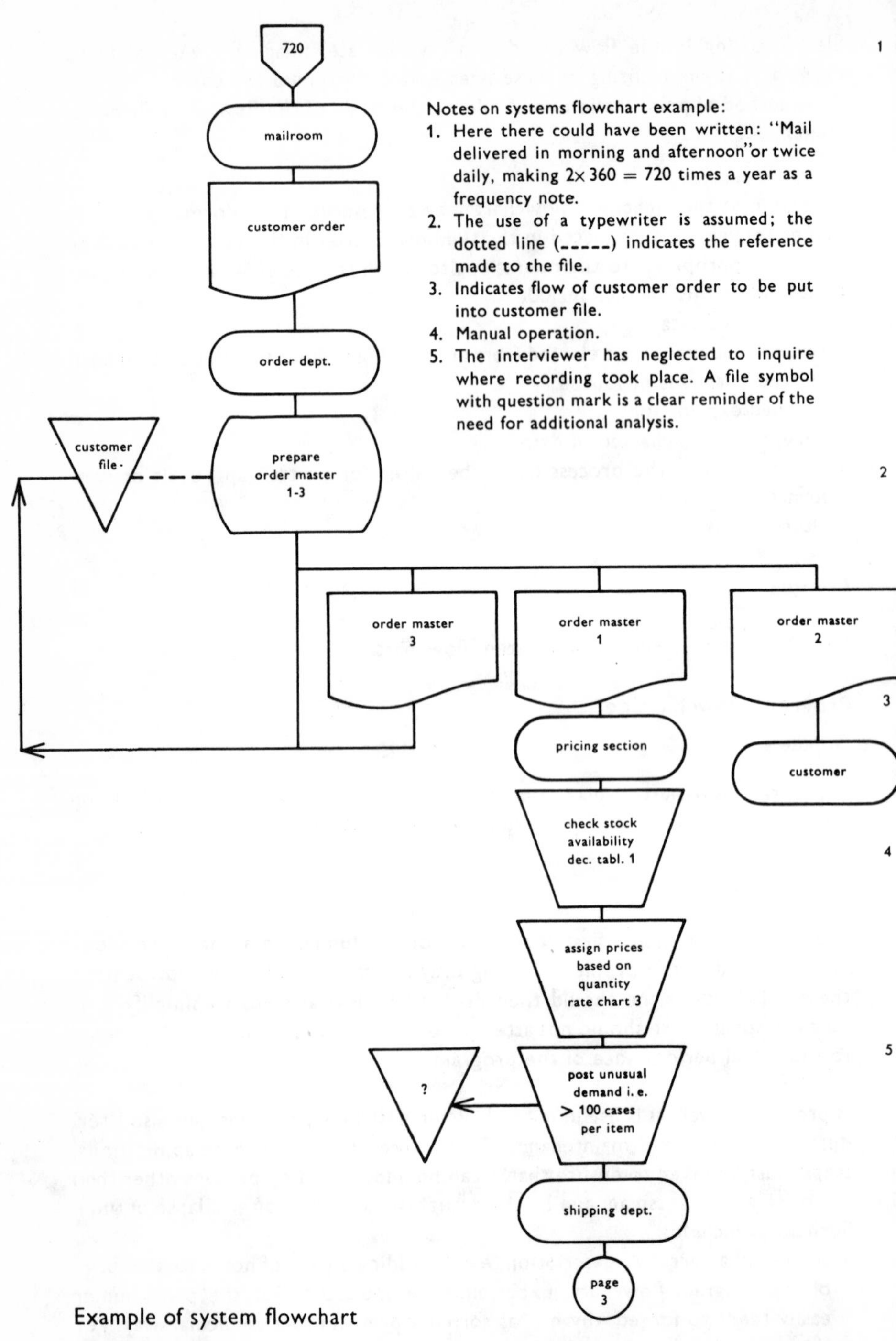

Notes on systems flowchart example:

1. Here there could have been written: "Mail delivered in morning and afternoon" or twice daily, making 2× 360 = 720 times a year as a frequency note.
2. The use of a typewriter is assumed; the dotted line (-----) indicates the reference made to the file.
3. Indicates flow of customer order to be put into customer file.
4. Manual operation.
5. The interviewer has neglected to inquire where recording took place. A file symbol with question mark is a clear reminder of the need for additional analysis.

Example of system flowchart

- the use of modular methods. Each logically separable subdivision of the problem should be treated in a separate chart, on a separate sheet of paper;
- the use of a consistent set of principles:
  — keep the main flow in the middle of the paper, and less frequently traversed branches to the side of the main flow;
  — make a balanced design; for example, put like processing operations at the same level;
  — avoid long connecting lines and complex crossings;
  — use prescribed names for system elements and data objects.

Notation in program flowcharts

In the interests of clarity, a standard notation must be employed in program flowcharting.
This notation should conform to labels (paragraph names or symbolic addresses) and/or program instructions.
The following notation is recommended:

- Move
  - In general →
  - With zero suppression at left side 0̸→
  - With standard punctuation (editing) E→
- Add
  - In general +→
  - With preceding resetting of receiving field 0+→
- Subtract
  - In general −→
  - With preceding resetting of receiving field 0−→
- Absolute value
  Place the element between two vertical lines, e.g. |GI 12|
- Compare
  Use the symbol ↔
  For two exits use the symbols = ≠ > < ⩾ ⩽
  Where three exits are required, the comparison should be repeated to allow an entry between the two remaining exits.
- Multiply
  Use the symbol ×
  E.g. transaction quantity × price → transaction amount.
- Divide
  Use the symbol :
  E.g. total turnover: number of orders → average order quantity.

- Constants
  Place a constant in quotation marks, e.g. "23b̸JUNEb̸1968"

- Roundoff
  Standard rounding: 0,5 and up becomes 1, other values become 0; note the number of digits to be rounded off with a slash through the figure:
  e.g. 1562350000 to become 15624 5̸
  156249 to become 1562 2̸
  Rounding by truncation,
  e.g. 15620 to become 15 — 3p
  Addition of noughts,
  e.g. 15620 to become 1562000 + 2n

- Operation to be modified
  Use the symbol ?
  In addition mention the conditions governing the modification.

- Modification
  This is a transfer, represented by a hexagonal symbol.
  Use round brackets for transfer of an address, e.g. (GC04)

Examples

Page 26 gives an example of a page layout for a program flowchart while page 27 shows an incorrect layout of the same problem.
Page 28 illustrates the location of connectors as much as possible at the top or bottom of a page.
Page 29 gives an example of a main program flowchart, whereas pages 30 and 31 illustrate in detail program flowcharts two routines of this main flowchart.

Configuration charting

Purpose

A configuration chart displays the interrelationships by virtue of which a group of units of data processing equipment becomes an operative configuration. It demonstrates the usage capability of the configuration, and facilitates the specification of the hardware order.
An extension of the configuration chart, the "configurator", is used by manufacturers to present in one chart as many as possible of the configurations in which a given group of units can exist.

General recommendations

- Configuration charts are used to depict specific combinations of equipment. The preparation of alternative charts greatly assists in judging the relative effectiveness of different contemplated configurations. Where future trends in usage or application are sufficiently known, these should be indicated as optional extensions;

- general considerations of uniformity, layout, annotation etc. as described in relation to system and program flowcharts are applicable also to configuration charts.
- built-in units may be drawn with their appropriate symbol, either separately or within another configuration symbol. If necessary the latter one can be given a larger size;
- to represent a standard unit of a configuration, the symbol should be drawn in solid lines; optional units should be drawn in broken lines;
- according to the specific purpose of the configuration chart, the following information can be inserted in each symbol:
  - — unit name;
  - — unit identification number;
  - — speed/capacity;
  - — rental/purchase cost.

Example An example of a configuration chart is given on page 32.

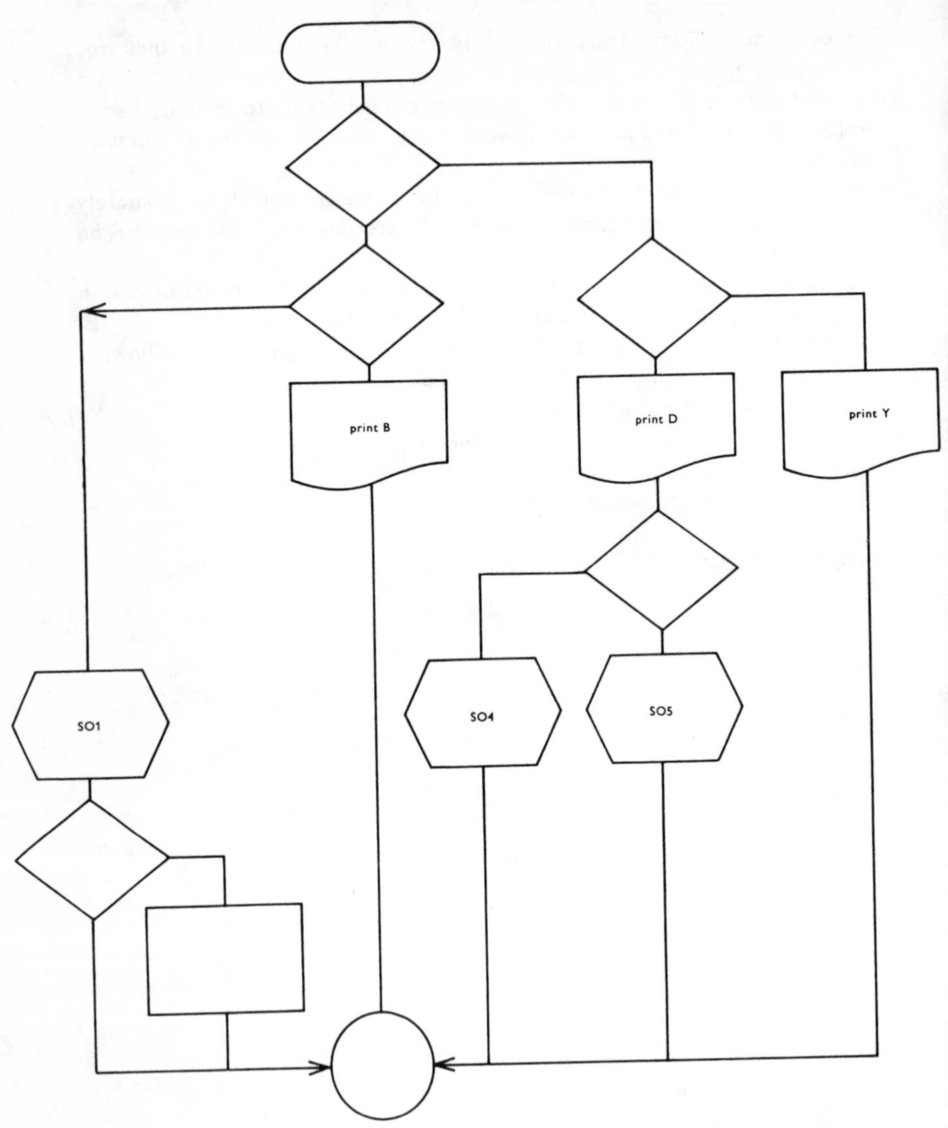

In flowcharting, it is strongly advisable to draw instructions of the same nature at an equal horizontal level.

Page layout of a flowchart: how it should be done

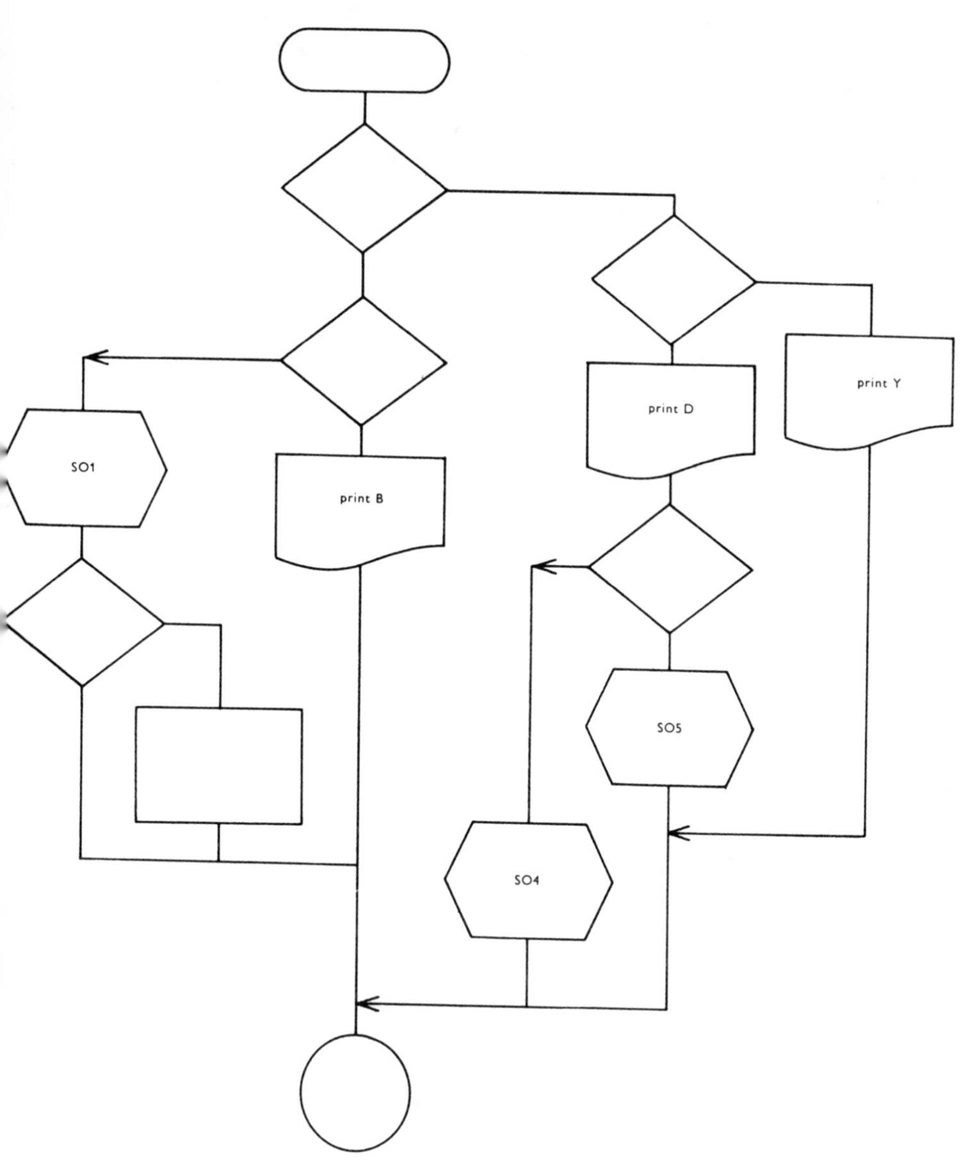

ge layout of a flowchart: how it should not be done

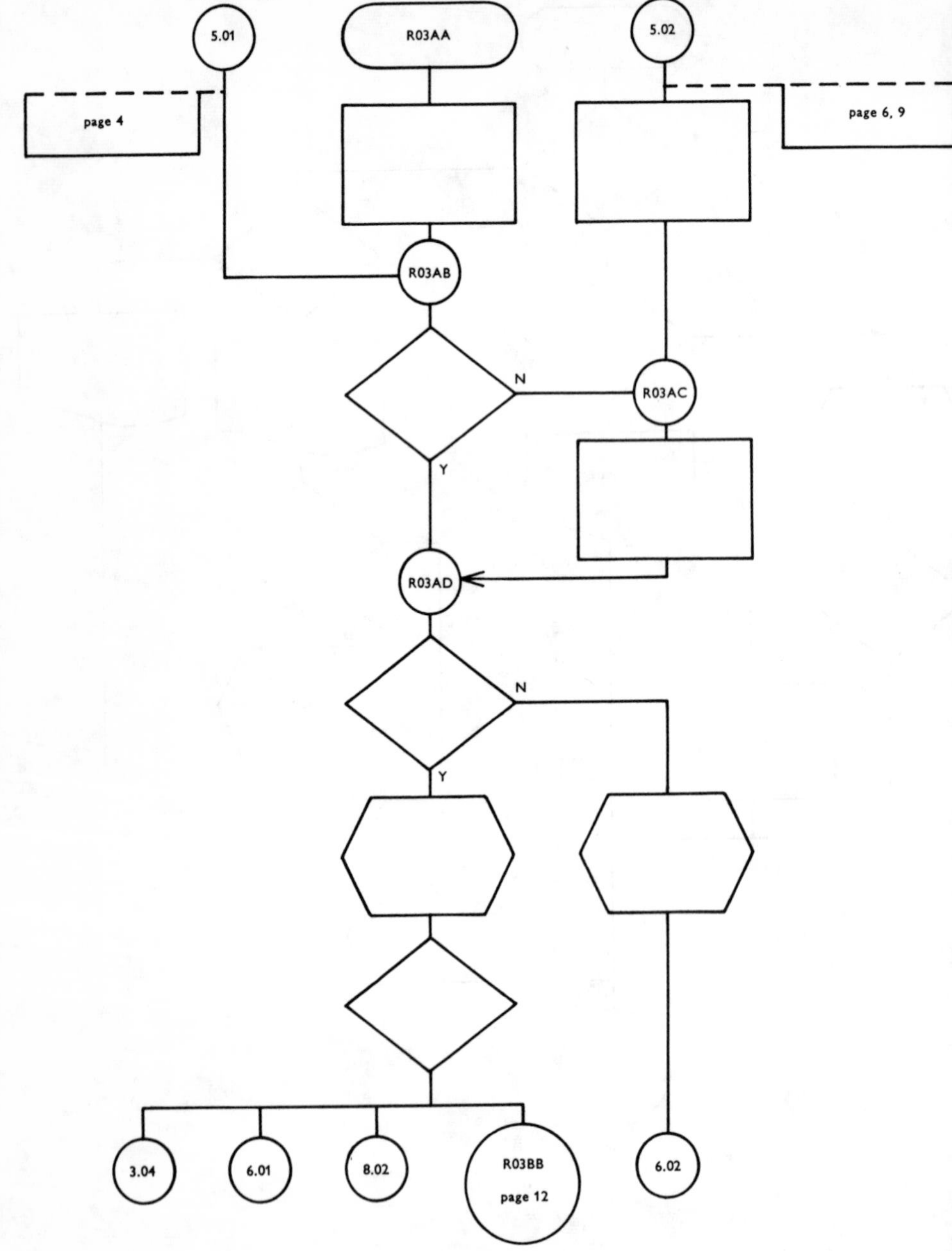

Page layout of a flowchart: as a rule, place the page connectors at the top or bottom of the page

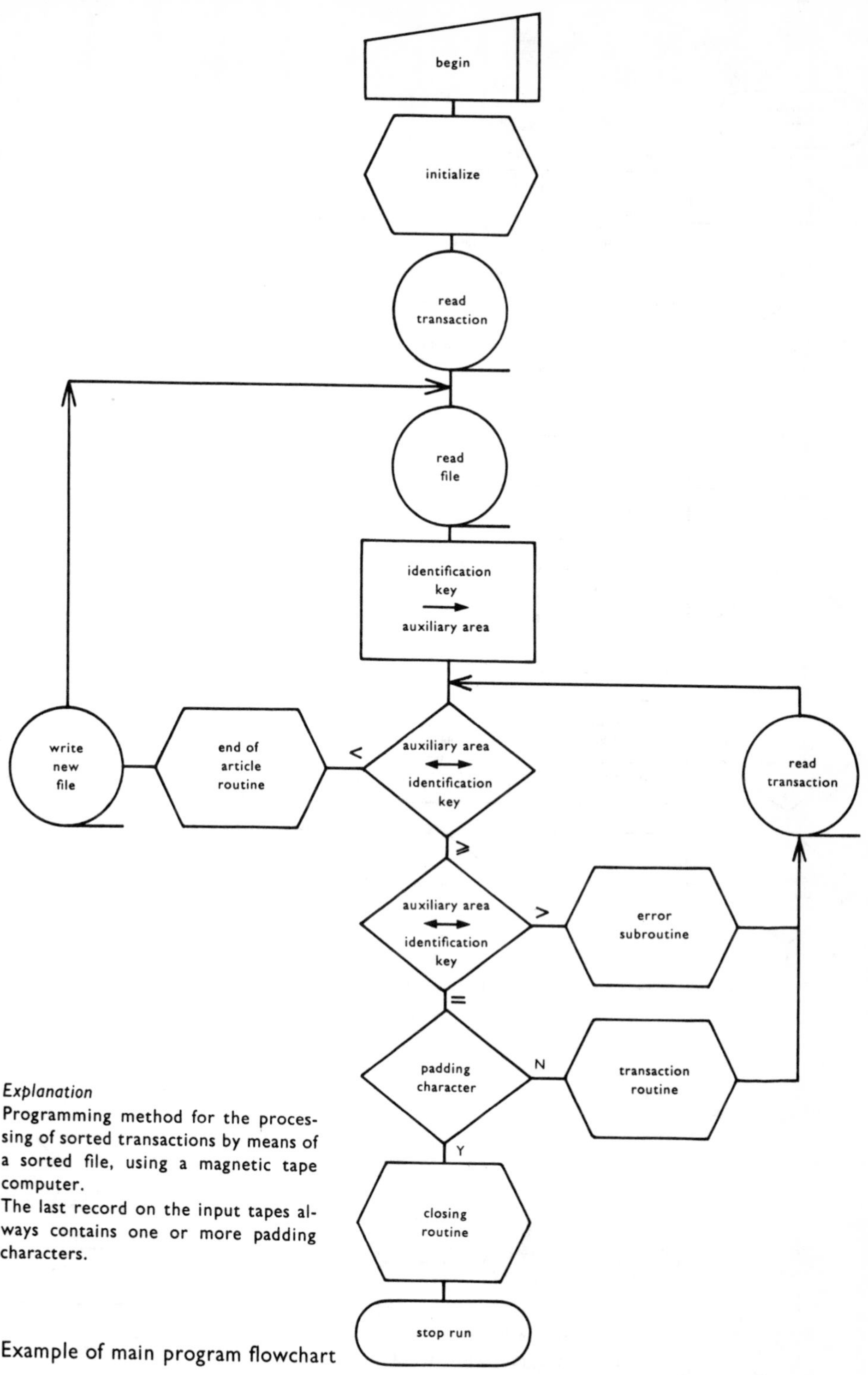

Explanation
Programming method for the processing of sorted transactions by means of a sorted file, using a magnetic tape computer.
The last record on the input tapes always contains one or more padding characters.

Example of main program flowchart

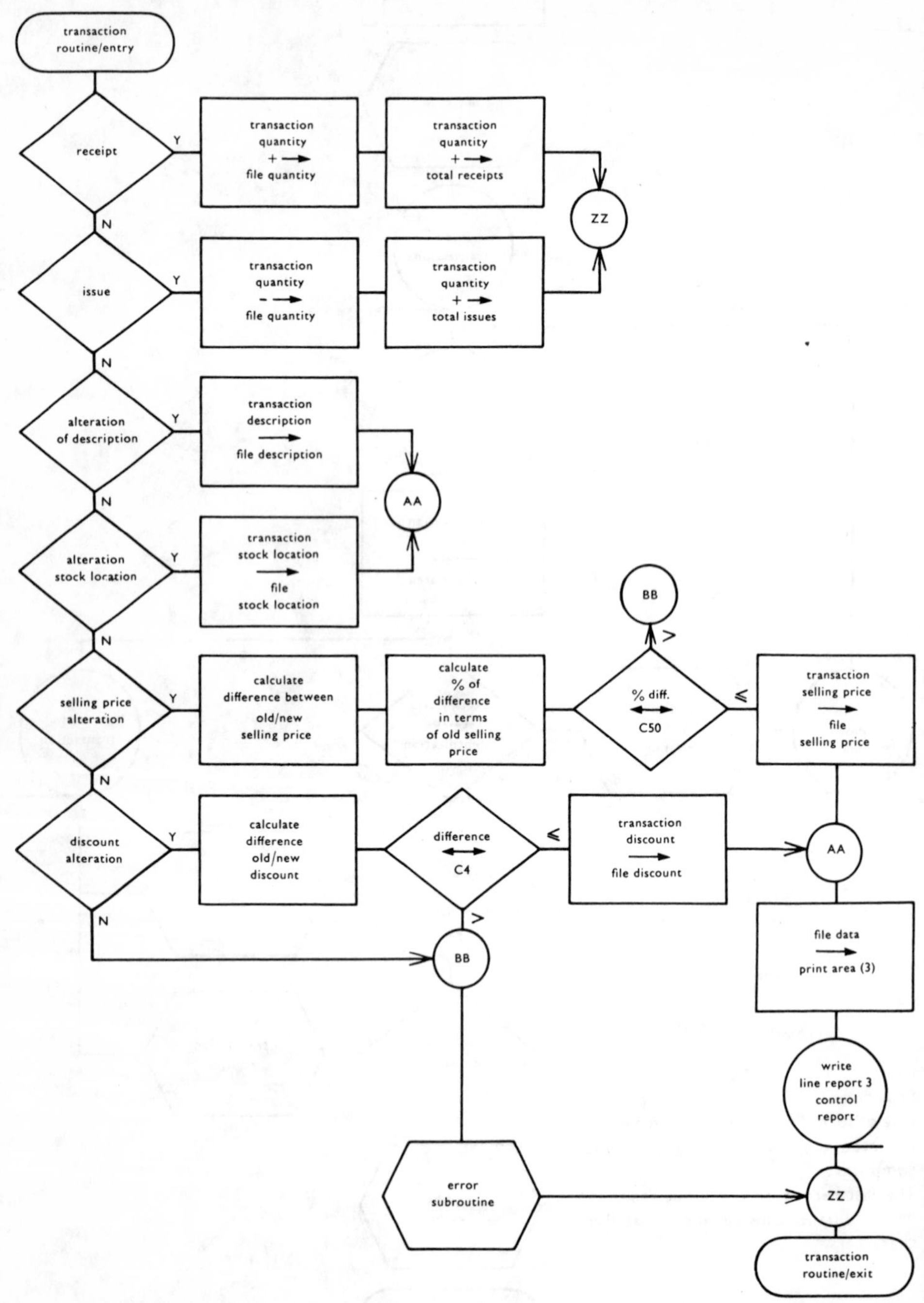

Detail program flowchart; transaction routine as a detail of the main program flowchart of previous page

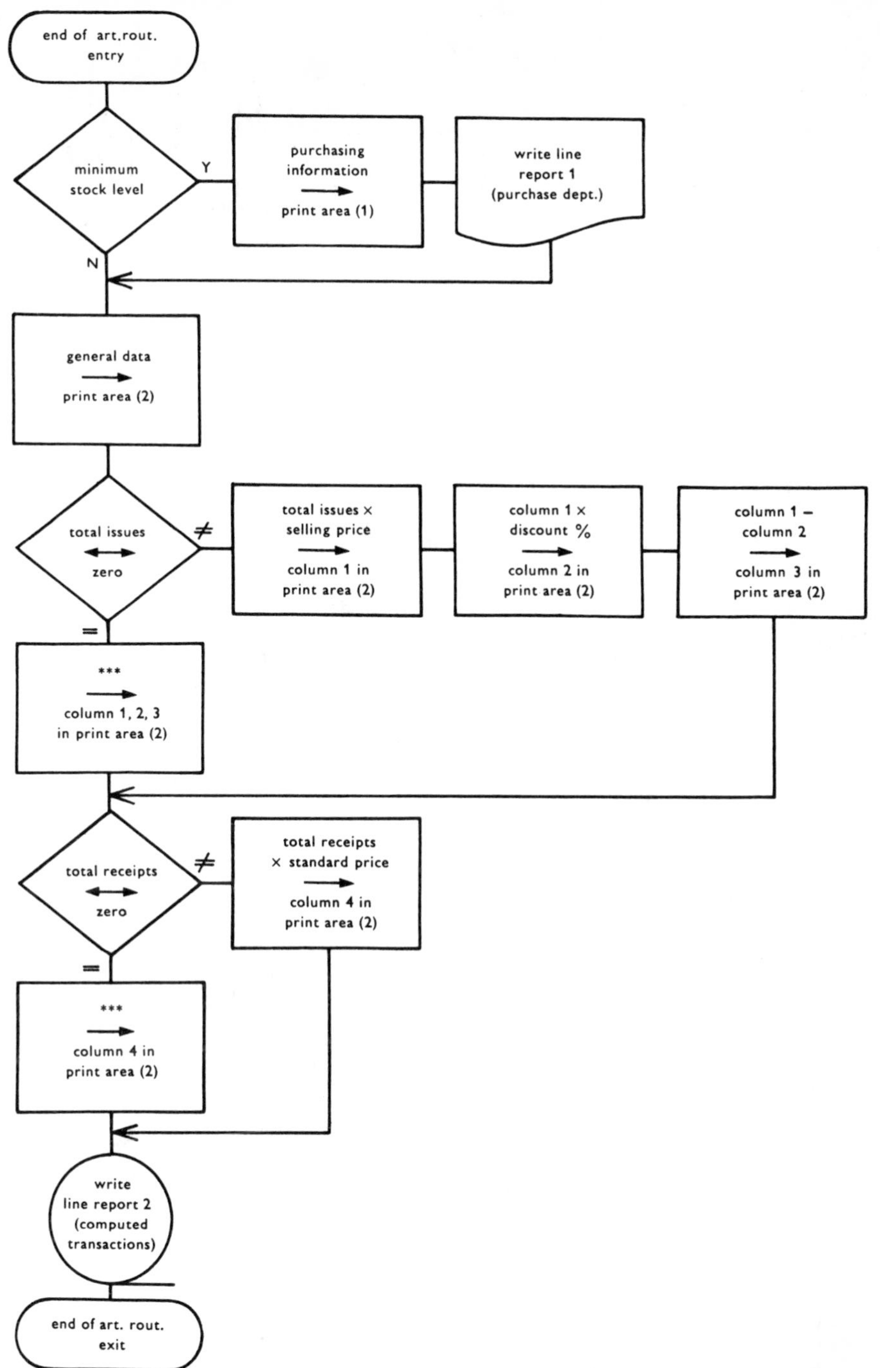

Detail program flowchart; end of article routine as a detail of the main program flowchart on page 29

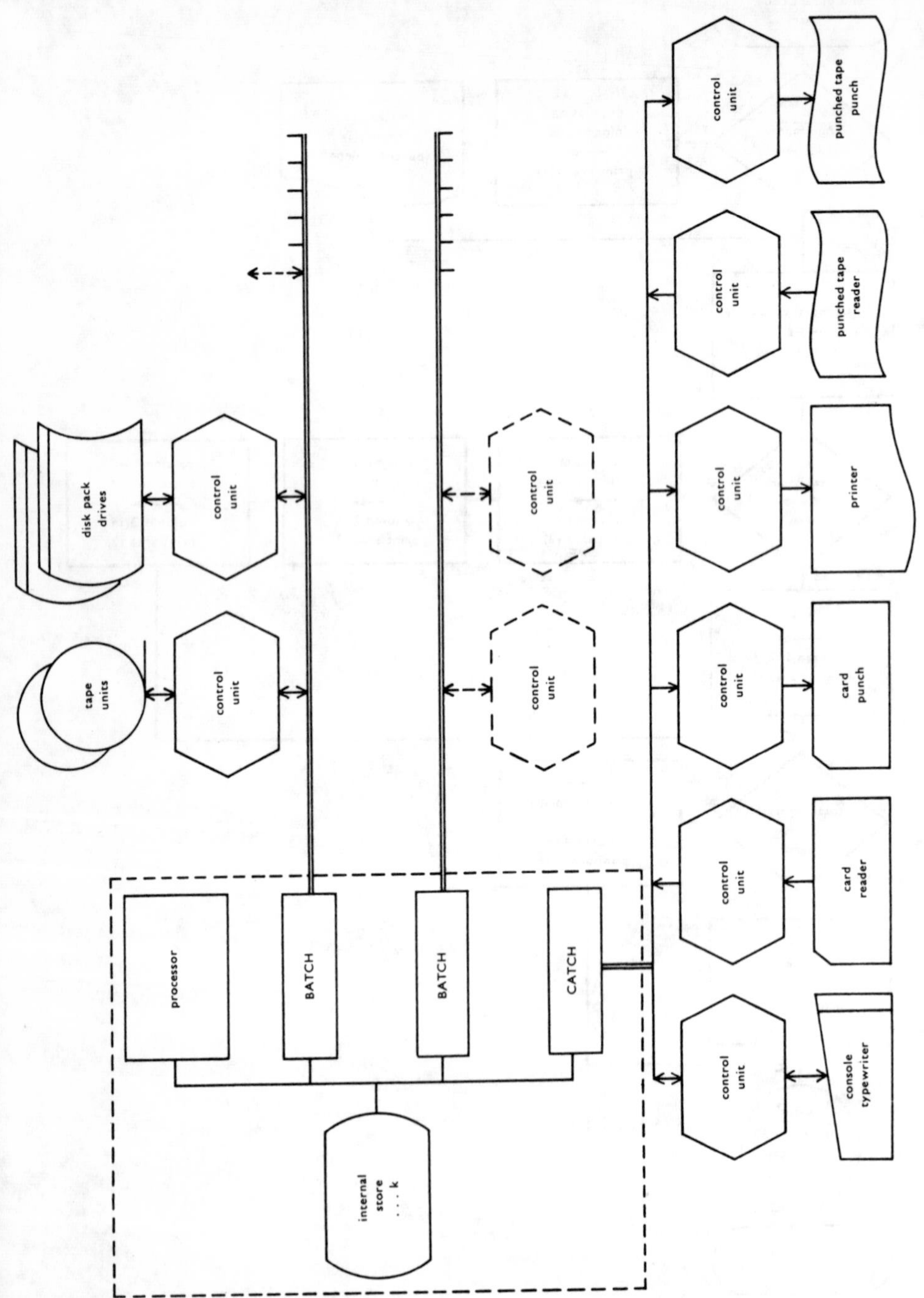

Legend: CATCH- Character Allocated Transport CHannel,
BATCH- Block Allocated Transport CHannel.

Example of a configuration chart

Technique 6-2.3: Gridcharting

Purpose

A gridchart is a formalized representation of the relationships between two groups of system elements. In this context, the term "system element" means any defined operation or physical object which is part of the system.
Even when the number of system elements involved is high, representation by means of a gridchart remains clear. In addition it is amenable to analysis and manipulation. It is thus a valuable tool for use in circumstances where it is necessary to consider rearrangement, or reduction in the number of system elements. In many instances, gridcharting can serve as a useful design check.

Areas of application

Gridcharting finds application at all phases of a project.

General

The following list, giving data-element pairs whose gridcharts might be useful, is intended to be suggestive rather than exhaustive:

- departments — functions
- departments (personnel) — reports (forms)
- departments — data elements (fields)
- reports — data elements
- input forms — output forms
- input forms — data elements
- reports (forms) — files
- functions — data elements
- functions — files
- programs — files
- data elements — files
- programs (procedures) — data elements
- programs (procedures) — reports

The first example of the use of gridcharts is not drawn directly from the field of systems engineering; in order to achieve simplicity, we shall deal with an imaginary manufacturing situation in which assemblies 1 and 2 are constructed from sub-assemblies A, B and C, which in turn contain components M, N and P.

comp \ sa	A	B	C
M	4	2	—
N	—	10	5
P	3	2	4

Chart 1

ass \ sa	A	B	C
1	1	1	3
2	—	2	3

Chart 2

Chart 1 shows the number of components M, N and P required for the manufacture of each of the sub-assemblies A, B and C, while chart 2 gives the composition of assemblies 1 and 2 in terms of these sub-assemblies.

It is obviously possible from these two charts to discover how many of each component is present in each assembly. Assembly 1 contains one "A", contributing four "M's", one "B", contributing two "M's", and three "C's", with no "M's" — a total of six "M's". Similarly the entire component content of each assembly can be derived, leading to the following gridchart.

comp. \ ass	1	2
M	6	4
N	25	35
P	17	16

Chart 3

To permit a simple and systematic procedure for this sort of manipulation, the following type of layout is suggested:

		sub-assemblies			assemblies	
		A	B	C	1	2
components	M	4	2	—	6	4
	N	—	10	5	25	35
	P	3	2	4	17	16
assemblies	1	1	1	3		
	2	—	2	3		

The procedure is now as follows:
For the number of "M's" in assembly 1, take corresponding boxes in the "M" and "1" rows, multiply and add as shown
$1 \times 4 + 1 \times 2 + 3 \times 0 = 6.$
and enter the result in the appropriate box on the right, in the 1 column.
Similarly, for the number of "P's" in assembly 2,
$0 \times 3 + 2 \times 2 + 3 \times 4 = 16.$

Whilst no special mathematical knowledge is necessary in order to be able to combine gridcharts in this manner, it will be noted by those familiar with matrix methods that the operation is equivalent to the multiplication of two matrices.

Manipulation and interpretation

Hierarchical relationship

The manipulation of gridcharts as shown above is useful for obtaining an explicit set of relationships which was implicit but not obvious from the original two gridcharts. It is applicable only when the two sets of system elements related by the first chart, say X and Y, and those related by the second chart say Y and Z, are in a continuing relationship of the "hierarchical" or "continuous inclusion" type. This is true of the relationship between components — subassemblies — assemblies, as in the above example; and also for such groupings as data elements — files — functions, because functions access data elements via files. In groupings with this type of relationship, a gridchart relating the first two sets of system elements can be combined with one relating the last two, to eliminate the middle set of system elements, thus providing a grid chart relating the first and last sets.

Example

The next example shows a chart of data elements against files combined with a chart of files against functions to produce a chart of data elements against functions.

It would be physically possible to combine by multiplication the chart of data elements against functions with that of functions against files; but since in this case the ordering of the sets of system elements would not be correct the resulting chart would not represent the relationship between files and data elements. Indeed, the result would in the context of systems analysis be meaningless.

The hypothetical system dealt with in this set of charts comprises the material requirements calculation, the production planning, the external order planning and the goods inward inspection in respect of the manufacture of assembly "A", which is constructed from components "P" and "Q". Component "P" is bought out, and component "Q" is manufactured in plant from material "R".

It will be noted, that the set of files dealt with is oriented more to a "paper" system than to an automated one; this has been done in order to keep the example clear and simple.

Interpretation

Where a figure 1 appears in the chart of functions against data elements, this implies that the data element in the row concerned is accessible to the function in the associated column via the proposed file design. If a 0 appears where access

		files					functions			
		stock	article	capacity	customer Order	external Order	mat. reg. calculation	production planning	extonal order planning	goods inward inspection
data elements	code number of assembly "A"	1	1	1	1	0	3	4	1	0
	number of "A's" in stock	1	0	0	0	0	1	1	1	0
	number of "A's" on order	0	0	0	1	0	1	1	0	0
	code number of component "P"	1	1	0	0	0	2	2	1	0
	number of "P's" in stock	1	0	0	0	0	1	1	1	0
	number of "P's" per "A"	0	1	0	0	0	1	1	0	0
	code number of component "Q"	1	1	0	0	1	3	3	2	1
	number of "Q's" in stock	1	0	0	0	0	1	1	1	0
	number of "Q's" on order	0	0	0	0	1	1	1	1	1
	number of "Q's" per "A"	0	1	0	0	0	1	1	0	0
	code number of material "R"	1	0	0	0	1	2	2	2	1
	quantity of "R" in stock	1	0	0	0	0	1	1	1	0
	quantity of "R" on order	0	0	0	0	1	1	1	1	1
	quantity of "R" per "P"	0	1	0	0	0	1	1	0	0
	reorder level for "Q"	0	0	0	0	1	1	1	1	1
	reorder level for "R"	0	0	0	0	1	1	1	1	1
	machine group (MG) code	0	0	1	0	0	0	1	0	0
	total capacity per MG	0	0	1	0	0	0	1	0	0
	committed capacity per MG	0	0	1	0	0	0	1	0	0
	capacity required per "A"	0	0	1	0	0	0	1	0	0
functions	material requirements calculation	1	1	0	1	1				
	production planning	1	1	1	1	1				
	external order planning	1	0	0	0	1				
	goods inward inspection	0	0	0	0	1				

to a data element is required, the file design must be modified accordingly; inspection, particularly in a case where more than one element is missing, will often reveal the most economical modification.

If a figure greater than 1 appears, redundancy may be indicated. In the example given, the figures greater than 1 do not indicate redundancy so long as the number of files and their named purposes remain as shown; they appear only in the rows of those data elements which are identifiers, and thus necessary at least once in each of the files which contain data referring to the system elements which they identify.

Value in design

The restriction of gridchart "multiplication" to those cases which involve the elimination of the middle set of a group of three ordered sets of system elements means that the technique is in general more applicable to design checking than to design itself. To "divide" one gridchart by another is not normally possible.

However, first approximations to design requirements are often possible by means of a critical examination of the appropriate gridcharts; an examination of the functions against data elements and functions against files charts of the above example, entry by entry, will not permit reconstruction of the files against data elements chart; but it will give a valid, although not necessarily the most economical version of it. In complex cases, however, the version thus found may be of considerable value in that it offers a workable starting point.

Standard form

A standard blank for the construction of gridcharts is reproduced on page 6.

GRIDCHART

system :
subsystem :
prev. issue:

project no. :
chapter/sect.:
page :
issued :

aspect 2	aspect 1									

Technique 6-2.4: Decision tables

Purpose

The purpose of a decision table or logic structure table is to display in a clear and concise form the way in which each relevant factor contributes to the structure of a problem, and how each of the possible combinations of these factors leads to an appropriate solution. The technique is applicable in all phases of the system effort.

General

The decision table technique provides a tool for the analysis and documentation of individual problems, and hence of entire systems, by tabulating the logical relationship between conditions and actions in such a way that the related data manipulations are clarified.
Although decision tables in one form or another have been in use for a long time — e.g. insurance rate tables and certain accounting procedures — their application in information systems is of recent origin.
They were not used to any extent in this field until 1960, since which time continuing attention has been given to their development. Their use is still (1968) confined to a relatively small number of organizations.

Description

Decision tables are of value in situations where we must consider simultaneously a number of factors, each of which may vary independently of the others, in kind or in quantity, over a finite range of "values". In these circumstances, a decision table is used to show all possible combinations of the factors for every value in each range. This eliminates the possibility of overlooking an unlikely combination, whose omission might cause an otherwise wellplanned system to fail.
Each combination is called a "rule". The theoretical total number of rules is equal to the product of the numbers of values which each variable factor may take.

- If there are n variable factors under consideration; f_1, f_2, ... f_n; and if f_1 has m_1 values; f_2, m_2 values ... and f_n, m_n values; then the total number of

rules is $m_1 \times m_2 \times \ldots \times m_n$, or in abbreviated form $\prod_{i=1}^{i=n} m_i$

Consider the case where there are two independent variables, one having four possible values, and the other five.

	condition entries																			
	rules																			
	1	2	3	4	5	6	7	8	9	10	11	12	13	14	15	16	17	18	19	20
condition stub																				
demand	S	S	S	S	C	C	C	C	S/C	S/C	S/C	S/C	C/S	C/S	C/S	C/S	B	B	B	B
availability	B	S	C	N	B	S	C	N	B	S	C	N	B	S	C	N	B	S	C	N
action stub	action entries																			
action 1	S	S	N	N	C	N	C	N	S	S	C	N	C	S	C	N	S	S	C	N
action 2	T	T	V	V	U	V	U	V	T	T	U	V	U	T	U	V	T	T	U	V

Seat booking table

Legend

	demand	availability	action
S	stalls only wanted	stalls only available	issue stalls tickets
C	circle only wanted	circle only available	issue circle tickets
S/C	stalls preferred, circle acceptable	—	—
C/S	circle preferred, stalls acceptable	—	—
B	both acceptable	both available	—
N	—	no seats available	inform customer on non-availability
T	—	—	subtract number issued from stalls availability
U	—	—	subtract number issued from circle availability
V	—	—	contact customer realternative dates

Note to rule 17: It is assumed that stalls is a better seat then circle, giving also a higher return to the theatre.

Example of seat booking table

First representation of the seat booking table
There will be $4 \times 5 = 20$ rules, covering between them every possible combination of one value of one variable with one value of the other. If the 5-value variable is a demand for the theatre seats and has the values — stalls only, circle only, stalls preferred, circle preferred, no preference; and if the 4-value variable is the availability of seats and has the values — both, circle only, stalls only,

	code	condition stub	1	2	3	4	5	6	7	8	9	10	11	12	13	14	15	16	17	18	19	20
demand	Sp	stalls preferred	×	×	×	⊗	⊙	⊙	⊙	⊙	×	×	⊗	⊗	⊙	⊙	⊙	⊙	⊙	⊙	⊙	⊙
	Cp	circle preferred	⊙	⊙	⊙	⊙	×	×	×	⊗	⊙	⊙	⊙	⊙	×	⊗	×	⊗	•	⊙	⊙	⊙
	B	both acceptable	⊙	⊙	•	⊙	⊙	•	⊙	⊙	⊗	⊗	×	⊗	⊗	×	⊗	⊗	×	×	×	⊗
availability	Sa	stalls available	×	×	•	•	⊗	⊗	⊙	•	×	×	•	•	⊗	×	⊙	•	×	×	•	•
	Ca	circle available	⊗	⊙	⊗	•	×	•	×	•	⊗	⊙	×	•	×	•	×	•	⊗	•	×	•
action stub		usage %																				
	S	issue stalls tickets	×	×	•	•	•	•	•	•	×	×	•	•	•	×	•	•	×	×	•	•
	C	issue circle tickets	•	•	•	•	×	•	×	•	•	•	×	•	×	•	×	•	•	•	×	•
	T	subtract number issued from stalls availability	×	×	•	•	•	•	•	•	×	×	•	•	•	×	•	•	×	×	•	•
	U	subtract number issued from circle availability	•	•	•	•	×	•	×	•	•	•	×	•	×	•	×	•	•	•	×	•
	N	inform customer on non-availability	•	•	×	×	•	×	•	×	•	•	•	×	•	•	•	×	•	•	•	×
	V	contact customer re alternative dates	•	•	×	×	•	×	•	×	•	•	•	×	•	•	•	×	•	•	•	×
equivalent to rules ≡				1					5	4	1	1		4	5		5	4		14	11	4

Seat booking table

Legend

symbol	conditions	actions
×	yes	yes
•	no	no
⊗	yes, but irrelevant	—
⊙	no, but irrelevant	—

none; then the full 20-rule decision table is as shown in page 2. The third row, entitled "action", gives the appropriate response for the booking clerk in every possible set of circumstances.

The first section of the table is the identifying heading. The four quadrants are referred to as the condition stub, the action stub, the condition entries and the action entries, as indicated. "Condition" is an inclusive term, covering both "factor" and "aspect". Although the situation dealt with in the figure in page 2 is not a very complex one, it is manifestly simplified by the application of decision table technique. Where Πm_i does not exceed, say 50, this type of table is of real practical use, and is much the simplest to construct. It possesses most of the advantages of the more sophisticated tables described later, and in addition:

- the condition entries section is drawn up by a simple, logically obvious method, which calls for no analytic thought, and which, by reason of its form, is selfchecking;
- missed rules and redundant rules are obviated, since the total number of rules is known beforehand;
- since each rules column is provided with a complete set of values, the single-line action row is easy to complete.

Second representation of the seat booking table

The same set of relationships is presented in an expanded form in the table in page 3. Since this table is bulkier than the original, and gives no additional information, it is not in itself of practical use. It is offered as a transitional step towards the more compact form in which such tables are usually drawn up; and to help in explaining why many practical tables have fewer than the theoretical number of rules, but more rows in the condition stub than the number of independent variables.

In this table, each variable factor has been broken down into a number of two-valued aspects. This step has certain advantages:

- we are now in the familiar and machine-compatible field of binary notation;
- we no longer require code symbols in the boxes, and a legend to explain them;
- we have performed a process of pre-analysis, so that each individual condition entry represents a less complex concept.

It should be noted that, when we break down a many-valued factor into a number of two-valued aspects, there is a minimum possible number of such aspects. If the number of values of the original factor lies between 2^{p-1} and 2^p, it requires at least p two-valued aspects properly to represent the original factor. For example, if we are analyzing a factor ith 13 possible values, we shall need at least 4 two-valued aspects, since 13 l.es between 8 ($= 2^3$) and 16 ($= 2^4$). If we arrive at a smaller number, we have not covered every aspect of the factor. This serves as a useful check.

It is always possible, although not necessarily convenient, to represent a factor by the optimum number of aspects.

It can be done by the following process: fill out the number of values to the next highest power of 2 with dummy values; then use as aspects these questions:

- Is the required value in the first half of the list?
- Is the required value in the first or third quarter of the list?
- Is it in the first, third, fifth or seventh eigth?
- . . . .
- Is it the first, third, fifth, seventh . . . . value in the list?

This will give p questions (two-valued aspects) which will in combination indicate each in turn of 2^p values. Those combinations which indicate the dummy values should be discarded.

Where the values of the factor concerned are well understood by the systems analyst, he may be able to supply a set of aspects which is more suitable for his purpose than the set produced by this process; it may occur that such a set has more than the optimum number of aspects.

As an example, let us break down the 5-value variable ticket demand in the above tables by the rules given. First fill out the number of values to 8 as follows:

S : C : S/C : C/S : N : X : Y : Z :

where X, Y and Z represent the dummy values. The aspects become:

- S, C, S/C, or C/S?
- S, C, N, or X?
- S, S/C, N, or Y?

and, representing the answers to these questions in order by y for yes and n for no, we see that yyy = S, yyn = C, yny = S/C, ynn = C/S, nyy = N. All other combinations represent dummy values.

The aspects used in the figure on page 3 are not these; they are an instance of a set selected by the systems analyst because it is simpler and more problem-oriented.

The set used happens also to be an optimum set. In more complex cases, it is frequently better to ignore special knowledge (unless there is a special reason for using it), and to use the set derived as demonstrated above. There are two main reasons for this:

- full coverage of the factor is guaranteed. Even when an intuitively derived set of aspects has not less than the optimum number, it may still be deficient, because of unrecognized overlapping in the questions;
- although it may be less problem-oriented, the formally derived set, because of its binary structure, may be more machine-oriented.

Third representation of the seat booking table

To return to the figure on page 3; here, a yes answer has been indicated by an X in the appropriate box, and a no answer by putting a dot in the box. Many of the X's and dots have been ringed; inspection will show that these answers are irrelevant, in that the action entry for the rule concerned is not affected by omission of a ringed X or dot. Such omission makes columns 2, 9 and 10 identical

	code	condition stub	1	2	3	4	5	6	7	8
			rules							
demand	Sp	stalls preferred	Y	Y	•	•	•	•	•	•
	Cp	circle preferred	•	•	•	Y	Y	•	N	•
	B	both acceptable	•	N	•	N	•	Y	Y	Y
availability	Sa	stalls available	Y	N	N	•	•	N	Y	Y
	Ca	circle available	•	•	N	N	Y	Y	•	N
		action stub								
		usage %								
	S	issue stalls tickets	x	•	•	•	•	•	x	x
	C	issue circle tickets	•	•	•	•	x	x	•	•
	T	subtract number issued from stalls availability	x	•	•	•	•	•	x	x
	U	subtract number issued from circle availability	•	•	•	•	x	x	•	•
	N	inform customer on non-availability	•	x	x	x	•	•	•	•
	V	contact customer re alternative dates	•	x	x	x	•	•	•	•

Seat booking table

Legend

conditions	Y = yes N = no • = irrelevant
actions	x = yes • = no

Note: the condition entries for rule 7 could also be: •/•/Y/Y/N.

with column 1; columns 8, 12, 16 and 20 with column 4; columns 7, 13 and 15 with column 5, column 19 with column 11; and column 18 with column 14.

Omission of these now redundant rules gives the figure on page 6. This table is now in standard form. Here Y is used for yes, and N for no. It is best to place a dot in those boxes which require no entry, to indicate that they have not been left blank inadvertently, but that the content is logically irrelevant or that a particular condition is not applicable to the rule concerned. Where programming is to be done directly from decision tables, it may be desirable to write Y or N in a box whose content is formally irrelevant, in order to obtain a uniform logic flow for all rules.

Comparison with flowcharts

It is frequently possible to represent the same decision situation either by means of a flowchart or of a decision table. In this connection, the following facts should be borne in mind:

- a decision table can be drawn up by the application of set rules. However, if the information input is exhaustive, then the action entries section is also exhaustive, and offers every possible solution;
- the production of a flowchart is a creative act; in the hands of an experienced systems analyst, a flowchart can be more economical, both in the actual effort of preparation and in the subsequent impact on the systems effort, than a corresponding decision table. But there is no guarantee of exhaustiveness;
- it is possible to complete a decision table without having an exhaustive information input. In these circumstances, a flowchart is more likely to get bogged down, and to prove difficult to complete;
  This effect can operate to the advantage of either form of presentation; where it is not realized that the information input is incomplete, the flowchart is more likely to reveal the fact; but where it is necessary to operate with information which is known to be less than exhaustive, a decision table may be easier to construct, and may also show more clearly the effect of the deficiencies of the input;
- a flowchart is time-ordered; a decision table is a simultaneous presentation. As a result, a decision table is more compact, and more flexible with respect to permissible courses of action; whilst a flowchart is less compact and more rigid;
- in any given situation a decision table is, apart from differences in representation which are fundamentally trivial, unique; a flowchart is usually not;
- a decision table is more easily understood by the uniniate — e.g. management;
- decision tables allow the systems analyst to communicate with the programmer, without interfering the latter's responsibility to handle data in the manner he considers best suited to the computer configuration; but programming can be accomplished accurately and efficiently from decision tables prepared within the prescriptions of a programming language such as COBOL or FORTRAN.

Conclusions

From these considerations we may draw the following conclusions:

- in a simple situation, or in a situation thoroughly understood by the systems analyst, use a flowchart;
- in a complex situation, or in any situation where the input information is known to be, or suspected of being, incomplete, use a decision table;
- where the situation calls for it, first prepare a decision table, and from it derive one or more flowcharts, selecting for use the most suitable;
- where the analysis of a situation has to be offered to management by the project team, a decision table, perhaps with additional annotations, is frequently the most suitable medium.

Summary of basic format

The basic format of the decision table consists of five sections:

- heading. Contains the general information necessary to identify the decision table;
- condition stub. Lists the variables or conditions that must be dealt with in the problem area or decision situation;
- condition entries. Indicates in separate columns of rules each possible combination of applicable conditions;
- action stub. Lists the actions to be taken as a result of the conditions satisfied in each rule;
- action entries. Specifies the actions to be performed as the result of the fulfilment of the conditions of each rule.

Working with decision tables

Having drawn up a decision table, it is necessary to know how to apply it.

Hit

An user will commence with the receipt of information concerning the value of each conditions in a particular instance. Working from left to right through the rules, this input information is compared with the content of each column until a rule is found which corresponds exactly. Unless the table has been improperly drawn up, each input will produce one and only one such coincidence, which may be termed a "hit". Following the rule column down into the action entries, we are led to the appropriate actions.

Result and continuation

The action entries quadrant of the table on page 6 has been considerably extended as compared with that of the earlier tables. Each possible action has been given a separate row, in order to continue the binary nature of the condition entries into this quadrant. In this figure the first entry encountered in passing downwards through an action entries column is that which is directly and immediately deducible from the rule.

The action corresponding to this entry may be called the "result". Actions corresponding to any further entries may be called "continuations". A continuation implies knowledge of the structure of the system outside the area covered by the decision table.

Order of the entries

The order of the conditions in the condition stub is —apart from optimizing the table— as such not significant, since for a rule to be satisfied all conditions relevant to that rule must be simultaneously satisfied. The order of the entries in the action stub may be, and usually is, of importance. It is always possible to arrange that the result comes first; since each rule produces an unique result, it is sufficient in this respect to write all the results in the action stub before any of the continuations. The continuations must then be entered in the appropriate order. In the cases where the order of the continuations is not the same for every rule, there are two methods: repeated entries and sequence entries.

Repeated entries
Any continuation may be entered more than once, so that that occurrence can be selected which gives the right performance order in the action entries;

Sequence entries
Instead of putting X's in the action entries, the numbers 1, 2, 3, etc. may be used. This does not invalidate the binary nature of the quadrant; the numbers are ordinals, and are merely equivalent to a series of ordered X's. Such entries are called "sequence entries". See page 20 for an example. On page 21 the same entries are arranged in performance order.

Other terms

Each entry in the action stub is a statement comprising a verb and its object, often called the "imperative" and the "target".
For data transfer, "get" and "put" are used as imperatives; "go to" is used to direct action, for example, to another decision table, or back to the same table, and should be the last imperative in any rule; "do" is used to indicate performance of another decision table, followed by return to the same table to continue with the next action of the same rule. In bookkeeping transactions, "post" is to be preferred to "enter", to avoid confusion where automatic conversion of decision tables into programs is concerned.

Practical considerations

Compound tables

The foregoing is the "pure" theory and application of decision tables. It is both sufficient and workable. In practice, however, certain modifications often occur. They arise chiefly from the necessity to produce, for the entire system, a body of tables of convenient size and number. It is sometimes desirable to lump together material which is properly the subject of two or more tables into one, or to include in the condition stub certain of the simple acts, (really trivial two line tables), which would otherwise result in a continuation reference in the action stub, thus calling up unnecessary additional documentation. Where this is done, there will be more than one result in the action entries; generally, there will be one result for each implicit table or simple act. In the next example, on a wage calculation, the condition entry "quality bonus" is of this type; the condition row corresponding to "quality bonus" and the action row corresponding to "add quality bonus" together form a complete, if trivial, decision table. It is obviously more convenient, and more efficient, to include it in the basic wage table, rather than to create a separate document for it (see the figure on page 15).

Where this procedure is adopted, the same care is necessary in ordering the results portion of the action stub as in ordering the continuations portion; and the same methods are applicable in resolving difficulties of ordering.

Limited and extended entries

An entry in a decision table which is purely binary in nature and positional in significance (X's, Y's, N's, or ordinal numbers) is called a "limited entry". When an entry carries additional information, it is called an "extended entry". Thus, the entries in the original table in page 2 are extended entries, and those in page 3 and 6 are limited entries. In an extended entry, a portion of a condition or action is transferred to the corresponding entries quadrant. If the results in overall simplification, the proceeding is justified. The chief difference between the extended entries in the first example, and those in more sophisticated tables, is that in the first case, they are forced upon us; whereas in the second they are selected, and used at the judgement of the systems analyst.

Trinary answers

A form of extended condition entry which can sometimes be used systematically, rather than by judgement and intuition, and which can affect significant reduction in the bulk of the tables, is to use trinary rather than binary answers in the condition entries quadrant, This will greatly reduce the number of aspects required when a factor has a large number of values. For example, with 200 values, we need 8 binary aspects, but only 5 trinary.

Methods similar to those used for breaking down a factor into binary aspects can be used in the trinary case also; powers of 3 replace powers of 2, and thirds, ninths etc. replace halves, quarters, and so on. But since this form of extension would normally be reserved for cases where one or more conditions had a very large number of values, the work would become long and tedious. In such cases, resort should be made to a set of tables known as Normalized Grossman Tables.

Example extended entries

The last example of the construction of a decision table in this technique is concerned with a stock control problem. This example is derived in standard form, as given in page 21 and is then shown in page 22 with extended entries. The extended entries are marked with asterisks.

Usage index

It is fundamental to the decision table technique that all possible rules are presented. It may often happen that some combinations of values are so unlikely that they do not justify the expenditure of much effort in dealing with them, whereas others may be overwhelmingly likely. In the presentation of a decision table, all rules carry equal apparent weight. It is therefore desirable to be able to distinguish the important rules from the less important; otherwise the continuation from an extremely unlikely rule may become the subject of much systems engineering and programming work, when a simple reference-out or exception action would have served.
For this purpose, an additional section may be added to the format of a decision table. It takes the form of a row between the condition and action parts of the table, and is called the usage index. Its stub carries the words "USAGE %", and its entries in each column are the probabilities of occurence of each rule, expressed as a percentage. The examples on pages 21 and 22 carry completed usage indices.

Further examples

Wage calculation

The wage structure for a certain production group within an organization can be defined as follows: Gross weekly pay = $A \times GM \times (1 + 0.05B + 0.1C + 0.1D)$ + a quality bonus; total subject to an overall maximum. A, B, C and D are "deltas", which are unity when: for A, the wage number is such as to place the employee in the group; for B, production $\geqslant 100$; for C $\geqslant 120$; for D $\geqslant 130$; and are otherwise zero. GM is the quaranteed minimum wage. The overall maximum is applicable only in the case of an employee with production $\geqslant 130$, and a quality bonus qualification. Invalid wage numbers are subjected to rescrutiny; the next step in the system is to calculate the nett wage via table 4 (deductions calculation).
We can break down the wage formula into four aspects: Valid wage number; quantity produced $\geqslant 100$; quantity produced $\geqslant 120$; quantity produced $\geqslant 130$. The quality bonus provides a fifth aspect — really an independent condition. The condition stub may now be written:

condition stub
valid wage number
quantity produced ⩾ 100
quantity produced ⩾ 120
quantity produced ⩾ 130
quality bonus

Condition entries
The figure below gives the condition entries for the wage calculation example, thus constructing the decision rules.

condition stub	condition entries rules 1	2	3	4	5	6	7	8	9
valid wage number	Y	Y	Y	Y	Y	Y	Y	Y	N
quantity produced ⩾ 100	Y	Y	Y	Y	Y	Y	N	N	•
quantity produced ⩾ 120	Y	Y	Y	Y	N	N	•	•	•
quantity produced ⩾ 130	Y	Y	N	N	•	•	•	•	•
quality bonus	Y	N	Y	N	Y	N	Y	N	•

Action stub
The required actions for the conditions previously illustrated would consist of calculating the gross pay and bonus, checking that the gross maximum is not exceeded, and making use in the case of rule 9 of an error handling decision table to correct an invalid wage number. The figure below illustrates the method of showing these actions in the action stub.

action stub
gross pay = guaranteed minimum (GM)
gross pay = $1{,}05 \times$ GM
gross pay = $1{,}15 \times$ GM
gross pay = $1{,}25 \times$ GM
add quality bonus
do table 2 (maximum check)
do table 3 (invalid wage number)
go to this table
go to table 4 (deductions calculation)

Action entries

The figure on page 15 shows the wage calculation completed.

Flowchart

The same calculation is shown for comparison in flowchart form on page 14.

Stock control problem

Further to describe the method of entering information on decision tables, a stock control problem has been chosen as a typical data processing problem.

In this example, two types of request for materials supply can occur:

- for production purposes;
- for repair purposes.

As a rule, production requirements should fit within forecast reservations, but excess demands over reservations can occur; repair demands are not forecasted. When a request falls partly within a reservation it may occur that actual stock is insufficient, owing to pending delivery of supplier's orders. In such cases reminders have to be sent to speed up delivery by supplier. Part delivery against repair demands does not occur.

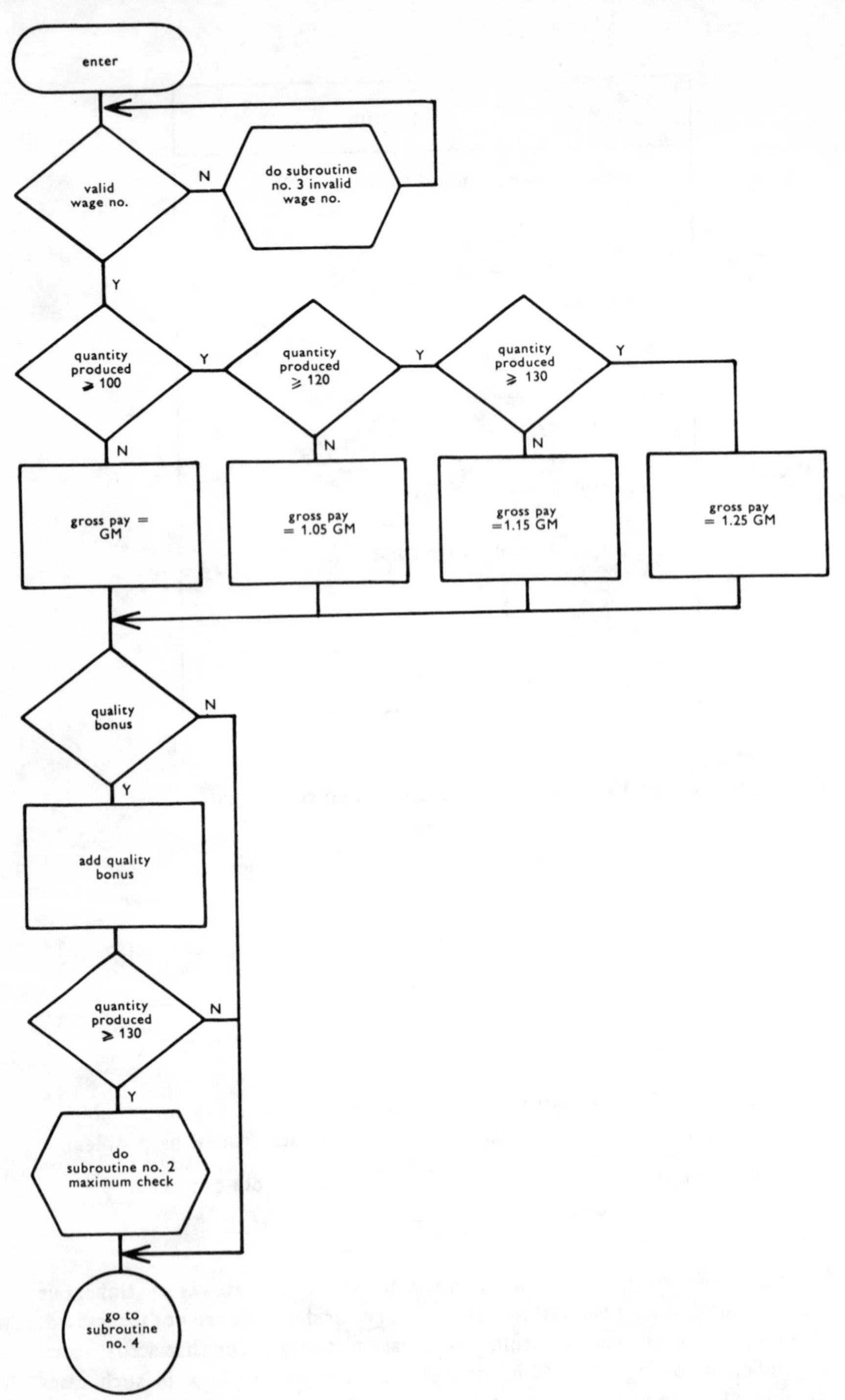

Flowchart wage calculation example
page 14

conditions		rules 1	2	3	4	5	6	7	8	9
valid wage number		Y	Y	Y	Y	Y	Y	Y	Y	N
quantity produced ⩾ 100		Y	Y	Y	Y	Y	Y	N	N	•
quantity produced ⩾ 120		Y	Y	Y	Y	N	N	•	•	•
quantity produced ⩾ 130		Y	Y	N	N	•	•	•	•	•
quality bonus		Y	N	Y	N	Y	N	Y	N	•
actions	usage %									
gross pay = guaranteed minimum (GM)		•	•	•	•	•	•	x	x	•
gross pay = 1,05 × GM		•	•	•	•	x	x	•	•	•
gross pay = 1,15 × GM		•	•	x	x	•	•	•	•	•
gross pay = 1,25 × GM		x	x	•	•	•	•	•	•	•
add qualits bonus		x	•	x	•	x	•	x	•	•
do table 2 (maximum check)		x	•	•	•	•	•	•	•	•
do table 3 (invalid wage number)		•	•	•	•	•	•	•	•	x
go to this table		•	•	•	•	•	•	•	•	x
go to table 4 (deductions calculation)		x	x	x	x	x	x	x	x	•

It is supposed that the receipt of new reservations is dealt with in another decision table, table no. 3. To the normal actions of that table belong the issue of new orders on suppliers. Issue of new orders will also take place when, on account of the receipt of requests for materials, the free stock level decreases below the re-order point.

Condition stub

To set up a decision table describing this example, the conditions which will be encountered must first be entered in the condition stub, as given in the next figure.

condition stub
1 type of request for material's supply 2 within reservation 3 actual stock available 4 free stock below re-order point

Conditions 1 and 4 are two-valued, and conditions 2 and 3 are three-valued.

Condition entries in extended form
It is necessary to fill in a separate column or rule for every possible combination of conditions. As the condition stub lines are complete statements, the condition entry rules will consist of "yes's" and "no's" or of extended entries to the questions posed in the condition lines. Extended entries are unavoidable when the conditions can have more than two different values.

There must be at least one "yes" and one "no" for each condition statement. If the condition statement is irrelevant to a specific rule, then the box applying to the statement may be left blank, or a symbol indicating that the statement does not apply may be entered.

The figure A on page 18 gives the condition entries in extended form, belonging to the condition stub in the previous figure.

Condition entries in limited form
If it is preferred to use only limited entries of the YES-NO type, than the condition stub must be enlarged from 4 up to 6 conditions, giving the alternative set of condition entries, as given in the figure B on page 19.

Action stub
Having filled in the condition portion of the decision table, it is now necessary to specify the actions that must be taken for each of the rules encountered. The action stub of the decision table could contain the following information as illustrated below.

The amount of the request will be issued when sufficient actual stock is available; part delivery, which means issuing the stock balance, takes place only in the case of a production demand. When the request is not (completely) delivered, it is annotated, held until further notice and posted in the backorder ledger. Completed requests are filed. If the request was partly reserved, it is split into a 100% reserved part and a nonreserved part which will both reenter this table. When full delivery of reserved requests is not possible, reminders must be sent to suppliers to speed up delivery of outstanding orders.

action stub
1 issue amount required
2 issue stock balance
3 subtract issue from reservation
4 subtract issue from actual stock ledger
5 do invoicing procedure: table no. 2
6 file request
7 annotate and hold request
8 post undelivered amount in backorder ledger
9 send reminder to supplier (if order outstanding)
10 split request into reserved and non-reserved amount
11 go to this table
12 go to new order procedure: table no. 3.

Action entries with sequence numbers

In completing the stock control example the appropriate set of actions to be taken for any possible combination of conditions must be indicated in the action entries part of the decision table. As the sequence in which the actions are to be performed is important, this must be indicated. In the table on page 20 numerals are entered for this purpose. Inapplicable actions are marked with a dot.

Action entries, ordered and in limited form

Page 21 gives the same decision table, but the actions are now ordered in such a way that the subsequence numbers can be eliminated.
At the bottom of this table the action pattern is indicated, demonstrating that the 16 different decision rules result in 9 different action patterns. This is an important piece of information for programming.

Action entries in extended form

Finally, page 22 gives the same table again, but this time with extended entries. The tables in pages 21 and 22 both carry usage indices.

Flowchart

This stock control example is completed for the sake of comparison, with a program flowchart showing the decision pattern only. See the figure on page 23.

condition stub	condition entries rules 1	2	3	4	5	6	7	8	9	10	11	12	13	14	15	16
1 type of request for materials supply	P	P	P	P	P	P	P	P	P	P	R	R	R	R	R	R
2 within reservation for requiring department	Y	Y	Y	pa	N	N	N	N	N	N	•	•	•	•	•	•
3 actual stock available	Y	pa	N	•	Y	Y	pa	pa	N	N	Y	Y	pa	pa	N	N
4 freestock below re-order point	•	•	•	•	Y	N	Y	N	Y	N	Y	N	Y	N	Y	N

A

Legend

P = production demand
R = repair demand
pa = partly
• = irrelevant

B

condition stub	condition entries rules													
	1	2	3	4	5	6	7	8	9	10	11	12	13	14
1 materials supply for production	Y	Y	Y	Y	Y	Y	Y	Y	Y	Y	N [1])	N	N	N
2 completely within reservation for requiring dept.	Y	Y	Y	N	N	N	N	N	N	N	•	•	•	•
3 completely without reservation for requiring dept.	•	•	•	N	Y	Y	Y	Y	Y	Y	•	•	•	•
4 actual stock available for complete delivery of demand	Y	N	N	•	Y	Y	N	N	N	N	Y	Y	N	N
5 actual stock nihil	•	N	Y	•	•	•	N	N	Y	Y	•	•	•	•
6 free stock below re-order point	•	•	•	•	Y	N	Y	N	Y	N	Y	N	Y	N

[1]) Owing to the splitting up of the conditions, the new condition no. 5 appears to be irrelevant in case of a repair demand; this reduces the number of rules from 16 to 14; colums 13 and 14 of the conditions entries, in extended form in the previous figure, disappear.

conditions	rules 1	2	3	4	5	6	7	8	9	10	11	12	13	14	15	16
1 type of request for materials supply	P	P	P	P	P	P	P	P	P	P	R	R	R	R	R	R
2 within reservation for requiring department	Y	Y	Y	pa	N	N	N	N	N	N	•	•	•	•	•	•
3 actual stock available	Y	pa	N	•	Y	Y	pa	pa	N	N	Y	Y	pa	pa	N	N
4 free stock below re-order point	•	•	•	•	Y	N	Y	N	Y	N	Y	N	Y	N	Y	N
actions / usage %																
annotate and hold request		5	1				4	4	1	1			1	1	1	1
subtract issue from actual stock ledger	3	3			2	2	2	2			2	2				
issue stock balance		1					1	1								
issue amount required	1				1	1					1	1				
do invoicing procedure: table no. 2	4	4			3	3	3	3			3	3				
post undelivered amount in backorder ledger		6	2				5	5	2	2			2	2	2	2
file request	5				4	4					4	4				
go to new order procedure: table no. 3					5		7		4		5		4		4	
go to this table				2												
send reminder to supplier (if order outstanding)		7	3				6	6	3	3			3	3	3	3
split request in reserved and non-reserved amount				1												
subtract issue from reservation	2	2														

conditions		rules 1	2	3	4	5	6	7	8	9	10	11	12	13	14	15	16
1 type or request for materials supply		P	P	P	P	P	P	P	P	P	P	R	R	R	R	R	R
2 within reservation for requiring department		Y	Y	Y	pa	N	N	N	N	N	N	•	•	•	•	•	•
3 actual stock available		Y	pa	N	•	Y	Y	pa	pa	N	N	Y	Y	pa	pa	N	N
4 free stock below re-order point		•	•	•	•	Y	N	Y	N	Y	N	Y	N	Y	N	Y	N
actions	usage %	50	5	1	5	2	5	3	2	2	1	2	15	2	2	1	2
1 issue amount required		x				x	x					x	x				
2 issue stock balance			x					x	x								
3 subtract issue from reservation		x	x														
4 subtract issue from actual stock ledger		x	x			x	x	x	x			x	x				
5 do invoicing procedure: table no. 2		x	x			x	x	x	x			x	x				
6 file request		x				x	x					x	x				
7 annotate and hold request			x	x				x	x	x	x			x	x	x	x
8 post undelivered amount in backorder ledger			x	x				x	x	x	x			x	x	x	x
9 send reminder to supplier if order outstanding			x	x				x	x	x	x			x	x	x	x
10 split request in reserved amount and non-reserved amount					x												
11 go to this table					x												
12 go to new order procedure: table no. 3						x		x		x		x		x		x	
action patterns		(1)	(2)	(3)	(4)	(5)	(6)	(7)	(8)	(9)	(=3)	(=5)	(=6)	(=9)	(=3)	(=9)	(=3)

Legend P = production demand; R = repair demand; pa = partly; • = irrelevant

conditions	rules															
	1	2	3	4	5	6	7	8	9	10	11	12	13	14	15	16
1 type of request for materials supply	P	P	P	P	P	P	P	P	P	P	R	R	R	R	R	R
2 within reservation for requiring department	Y	Y	Y	pa	N	N	N	N	N	N	•	•	•	•	•	•
3 actual stock available	Y	pa	N	•	Y	Y	pa	pa	N	N	Y	Y	pa	pa	N	N
4 free stock below re-order point	•	•	•	•	Y	N	Y	N	Y	N	Y	N	Y	N	Y	N
actions / usage %	50	5	1	5	2	5	3	2	2	1	2	15	2	2	1	2
1/2 issue amount	D	S			D	D	S	S			D	D				
2/4 subtract issue	P,A	P,A			A	A	A	A			A	A				
5 do table no.	2	2			2	2	2	2			2	2				
6 file request	x				x	x					x	x				
7 annotate and hold request		x	x				x	x	x	x			x	x	x	x
8 post undelivered amount in backorder ledger		x	x				x	x	x	x			x	x	x	x
9 send reminder to supplier		x	x				x	x	E	x			E	x	E	x
10 split request in reserved and nonreserved amount				x												
11/12 go to table no.				1	3		3		3		3		3		3	

Legend

P = production demand
R = repair demand
pa = partly
• = irrelevant

D = issue amount required (= **d**emand)
S = issue **s**tock balance
P = subtract issue from reservation (= **p**lanning)
A = subtract issue from **a**ctual
E = if order outstanding

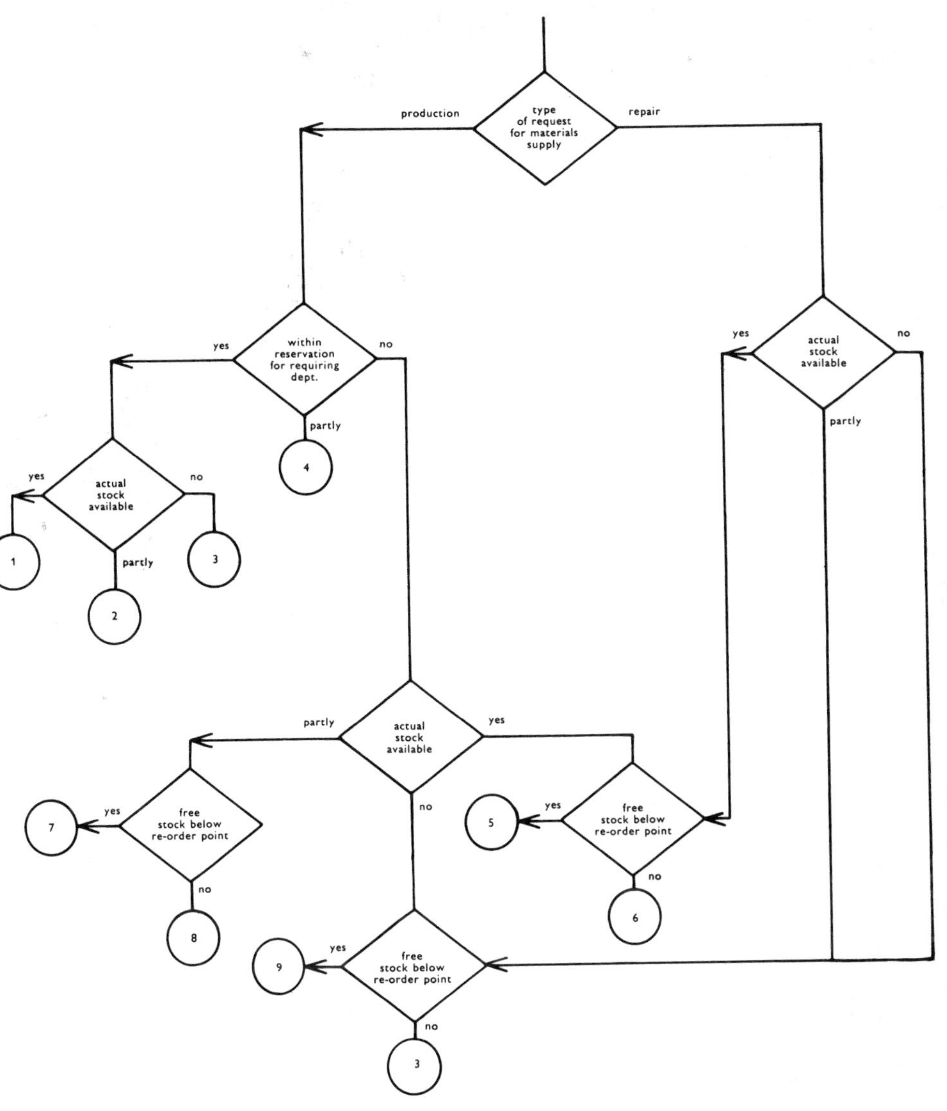

Flowchart stock control example

The connectors 1 to 9 refer to the nine different action patterns, already indicated in the decision table on page 22.

Subroutines

Instead of 9 independent routines for these different action patterns modular subroutines could be developed for the following action numbers:

- SO1: actions 1, 6, SO4;
- SO2: actions 2, SO4;
- SO3: actions 7, 8, 9;
- SO4: actions 4, 5.

The decision rules or routines will then contain:

- RO1: actions 3, SO1;
- RO2: actions 3, SO2, SO3;
- RO3: SO3;
- RO4: actions 10, 11;
- RO5: SO1, action 12;

actions/ subroutines	incorporated in												
	SO1	SO2	SO3	SO4	RO1	RO2	RO3	RO4	RO5	RO6	RO7	RO8	RO9
1	x												
2		x											
3					x	x							
4				x									
5				x									
6	x												
7			x										
8			x										
9			x										
10								x					
11								x					
12									x		x		x
SO1					x				x	x			
SO2						x					x	x	
SO3						x	x				x	x	x
SO4	x	x											

- RO6: SO1;
- RO7: SO2, SO3, action 12;
- RO8: SO2, SO3;
- RO9: SO3, action 12.

The programming structure on page 23 can also be expressed in the following gridchart.

Standard form

A standard blank for the construction of decision tables is reproduced on page 26. This form embodies all the features required for the purpose.

Summary

The basic advantage of decision tables, as compared with the more familiar techniques of problem definition —flowcharting and prose description— are that they compel the development of precise solutions to complex problems in which the values of many variables must be determined before action leading to the desired results can be taken.
Their only real disadvantage is their relative unfamiliarity; few systems analysts or programmers have sufficient experience with them to feel comfortable in their use.

DECISION TABLE

system :
subsystem :
prev. issue :

project no. :
chapter/sect. :
page :
issued :

conditions		usage % / actions	rules
			1
			2
			3
			4
			5
			6
			7
			8
			9
			10
			11
			12
			13
			14
			15

Technique 6-2.5: Forms Design

Introduction

Good forms are essential to the success of nearly every business information system. Efficiently designed forms can facilitate the entry and processing of data, and can effect a great reduction in the reporting of incorrect or irrelevant information.

Experience shows that automation — because of the great ease with which reports can be created by computers — leads to requests for more and more reports, which in turn need more clerical help in order to prepare, distribute, analyze and file them. Automation has not reduced the paperwork management problem; it has added to it. High-speed printers spew out material at a rate of a thousand lines per minute; each line is there to be read, and may call for a decision.

Lack of effective forms control leads to a rapid increase in the clerical payroll. Every time someone creates a new form, he is committing his company to an expenditure, in clerical and administrative salaries, many times the cost of forms procurement alone.

With expenditures of this magnitude, it is little wonder that programs for controlling the design and procurement of forms have gained wide acceptance in both government and industrial enterprises. Such programs usually review a company's existing and proposed forms, in order to:

- eliminate unnecessary forms, unnecessary copies of forms, and unnecessary items on forms;
- consolidate redundant and overlapping forms;
- improve form design;
- increase the usage of general-purpose forms, and decrease the number of forms whose use is limited to relatively few departments.

As the number of information systems increases, the work of the forms analyst is rapidly becoming the responsibility of those data-processing people whose job it is to plan the conversion of manual paperwork systems into automated dataprocessing systems. These people evaluate the source documents, lay out the forms which will be used, and coordinate the purchase of forms. The systems engineer examines the forms which will be part of the automated system, has them reviewed by line management, and revises or consolidates them so as to ensure efficient and economical transmission and transcription of data from form to machine and from machine back to form again.

Definition

A form is a data carrier, usually of paper, of which as many copies as necessary are available, which bears fixed data in the form of text and lines, and upon which variable data can be entered as required.

Purpose

The purpose of forms design is to produce forms which, by reason of their individual quality and their systematic coherence and compatibility, will be used efficiently. If this is achieved, the possibility of error and misunderstanding will be reduced, and the total cost of the administrative procedures in which the forms are used will be minimized.

Scope

Many systems analysts tend to underestimate the importance of forms. In fact, it is impossible to overstress the need for deep thought in all matters pertaining to forms. In this technique, we shall define the position of forms design in relation to the wider subject of forms management, and indicate the types of problems, possibilities and techniques which the analyst is likely to encounter in this area.
Forms management comprises three major subdivisions; forms analysis, forms design and forms control. The overall efficiency of a form in action depends upon all three having made their appropriate contributions. The function of forms analysis is to decide what the content of the forms is to be. That of forms design is to order the arrangement of this content, and to determine the overall structure of the form. Forms control involves the supervision of the form throughout its useful life, from the moment of its creation to the moment of its destruction. This is shown schematically, and in greater detail, in the figure below.

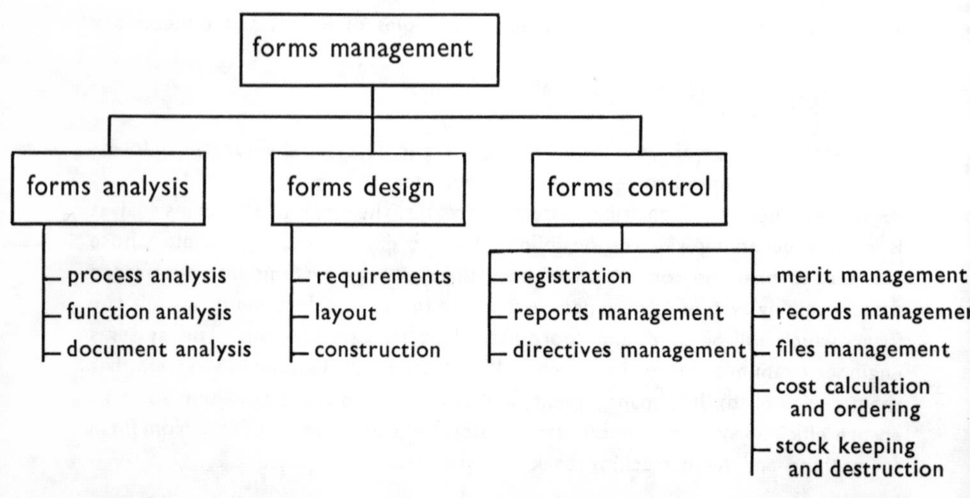

This technique confines itself to the subject of forms design. For information on forms analysis see: 3-2.3 (analysis of information flow), in particular pages 22 (data usage chart), 24 (report usage chart), 27 (function worksheet), 28 (form description sheet), 30 (document analysis and description), and 31 (document analysis checklist); 4-3.1 (procedure requirements); 4-3.2 (forms requirements). It need hardly be said that persons engaged in forms design should at all times maintain close contact with those concerned with forms analysis and forms control.

Area of application

This technique is concerned with the design of all types of forms for use within a company or externally, in manual procedures or in the data-processing department, and printed by any means including computer.

Responsibility

The forms in the existing manual system may well have been designed by a person having at best an incomplete knowledge of the appropriate techniques. The redesign of any such forms which are retained in the new system, together with the design of all new forms called for, is the responsibility of the systems analyst — who may be, at the same time, the forms analyst also. Even in an organization which employs a specialist forms designer, the systems analyst cannot afford to take any form lightly; though he may perform neither the analysis nor the design himself in detail, the ultimate responsibility remains with the project team.

The responsibility of the printer does not extend beyond that of executing the print order precisely; nevertheless, the designer would be well advised to seek his printer's advice in all matters of printing technique.

Subdivision

In this technique, forms design is subdivided into three phases; the pre-design phase, the design phase, and the post-design phase. For each phase, a checklist is provided. A fourth checklist — the forms analysis checklist — takes care of the interface between forms analysis and forms design.

Forms analysis checklist

Forms design originates in forms analysis. Only when the need for a form has been recognized, and the content and number of copies determined, can design begin. The designer then takes up where the analyst left off, determining the organization of the fixed data on the form and the overall physical make-up.
In view of the essential continuity of the activities of the analyst and the designer, it is desirable that the results of the analysis should be verified before the design begins. For this purpose, the forms analysis checklist on pages 15-16 is provided.

Pre-design checklist

In developing a form from rough draft to its final optimum arrangement, the designer must investigate and allow for many relevant factors. For example, the place of the form in the organization, and its usage, must be clarified (see 3-4, 4-1.2 and 4-2.3); the equipment required for filling-in, decollating, cutting, folding and using must be considered, and any special requirements allowed for; and the annual quantity and rate of use, and whether the form is to be temporary or permanent, will give an indication of the importance of the document.
The pre-design checklist on pages 21-24 is a tool to facilitate the task of the designer in this phase of his work.

Design checklist

All forms have certain requirements in common. Amongst these are ease of reading, ease of filling-in and ease of handling. All such requirements must be considered in relation to the specific nature and method of use of each particular form. In addition, each form will have its own particular requirements. The designer must be aware of all these requirements, and be able to estimate their influence on efficiency and economy in clerical operations, if he is to achieve the optimum end-result. For this purpose, the design checklist on pages 25-29 is provided.

Post-design checklist

When the designer has achieved a satisfactory layout and format, it is then necessary to have the form printed in the required quantities. For this purpose, a satisfactory method of specifying the form to the chosen manufacturer is required. The designer's work will have been in vain if any detail is missed in production. In order to ensure that this does not happen, the post-design checklist on pages 29-31 is provided.

Technical considerations

In entitling this section "Technical considerations", it is not intended to imply that the subject matter of the other sections is non-technical; rather that it is necessary for the forms designer to have more than a nodding acquaintance with many branches of technology outside the field of forms design itself. Printing, reproduction methods, paper, the effects of lighting and environment on the behaviour and legibility of forms, the possibilities and performance of many types of office machinery and equipment, even certain aspects of elementary physiology and psychology . . . . . . the list is long.
It must be appreciated that no work of this size can hope to give a full exposition of all matters which can possibly have a bearing on the work of the forms designer. What is included is essential; but it should be regarded as more of a guide or pointer than as an exhaustive exposition. Further reading and study are, of course, desirable; but the real value in a practitioner in one profession having a

genuine but limited knowledge of the field of a practitioner in another, is that he will be able to make an informed assessment of when to seek professional assistance.

Paper

The choice of paper will be determined by many factors. The paper selected must have a surface suited both to the reproduction method by which the form is to be printed, and to the method which will be used to enter the variable data; in addition, the question of erasures must be considered. It may be desirable to make erasure easy, or, as a protective measure, to make it impossible. Weight, thickness, durability, colour — and, of course, cost — must also be taken into account.

The cheapest papers are those known as "wood" papers; the most expensive, "rag" papers. Intermediate grades, containing various proportions of wood and rag, are available. The more rag a paper contains, the more dense and strong it becomes, and the more it is able to resist discoloration from adverse environments and age. Rag papers fold better, and erase better; it is easier to prepare rag papers with a naturally smooth surface.

Weights and thicknesses

All papers are available in varying weights and thicknesses. What is variously termed "bulk", "body" or "substance" is a measure of weight and thickness together. The bulk of a paper is the weight of a given area of the paper. Thus two papers of the same physical kind, one of which was twice as thick as the other, would have their bulks in the ratio 1 : 2; while two papers of different physical make-up, one being twice as dense as the other, and having equal thicknesses, would also have their bulks in the ratio 1 : 2.

It is a general rule that paper should never be thicker, nor heavier, nor stronger, nor more highly surfaced, nor contain more rag, than is expressly necessary for the function which the form has to perform; and it should always be white unless some other colour is expressly called for by that function. Any good printer will be happy to provide samples of various types of paper, both printed and unprinted, for the consideration of the user. While it will be necessary to take advantage of the printer's experience in respect of matters such as dimensional stability, light stability (against colour change and texture alteration) and long-term resistance to environmental factors, experiments can be carried out to determine suitability for multiple use with interleaved carbons, legibility under various lighting conditions with different inks, erasure properties etc.

Paper grain

Paper grain has sometimes to be considered. The cheaper wood papers have little or no grain; in addition, these papers are usually employed in the thinner

grades, where mechanical strength is not of prime importance. But where better quality, strongly-grained papers are used, certain rules should be observed.
Where such paper is used in a machine with a platen, the grain of the paper should ideally run parallel to the axis of the platen, to ensure a good wrapping action.
When forms are to be filed vertically in a box, the grain should be vertical to avoid curling over at the top, and thus difficult retrieval.
Where forms are to be bound in book-form, the grain should run parallel to the binding margin, for ease of turnover.

Where these rules (and the easy extensions which the reader will make for himself in specific instances) come into conflict with each other, the choice must be made on the basis of function.

Multiple sets

Multiple sets of forms frequently make use of coloured paper. Coloured paper should not be used automatically for such forms, however. If used, the colour must have a purpose. Coloured paper is more expensive than white, more likely to fade and deteriorate, and less easy to read. If used, colours should be faint; a light-coloured paper is easier to read from than a dark one, and its physical properties are closer to those of unadulterated white paper. Blue, green, yellow and fawn are generally the most satisfactory colours: pinks and reds should be avoided.
An alternative to the use of colour is the application of large size preprinted numbers or codes.
So that filling-in of all copies is achieved in one action, multiple copies are provided with a means of transferring the impression from the top copy to the other copies below. This can be achieved by interleaving the set with carbon paper, by backing each sheet with carbon, or by chemical treatment of the paper. Interleaving introduces extra paper thickness into the set, and to some extent therefore degrades the lower impressions, and reduces the number of impressions available. Carbon backing avoids these disadvantages, but adds a new one, in that the form permanently carries its finger-soiling carbon coating with it. The method does, however, permit selectivity in respect of what data is recorded on which copy, since not all of the copies need to have a complete backing. The chemical treatment method ("NCR" = No Carbon Required) possesses the same advantage without the drawback; in it, colourless substances on the back of one sheet are brought into intimate contact by the pressure of key or pencil with others on the front of another, to form black ink. The method is, however, expensive, and less efficient than carbon paper.

While certain rules may be found in various published works concerning the number of carbon copies which can be obtained under various circumstances of use, these are of only the most general usefulness. So many factors other than those associated with the weight or type of paper affect the issue; the method of filling in, the range of machines which may be used, the degree of acceptability for the last copy..... only experience and experiment can really decide the issue.

In general, it can be said that the papers should be graded in thickness, from the thinnest at the top (impress copy) to the bottom of the stack, where papers of various thickness are to be used; that all papers should be kept as thin as possible; that, for this purpose at least, the cheap wood papers, with as little grain as possible are much the best; and that if the different copies of the form in the stack are of different colours, then all colours should be as light as possible, and the lightest colours should be used for the lowest copies.

Ink

One has usually little choice in the matter of ink beyond selecting the colour. For use with the various in-house (office style) reproduction methods, the method usually determines the ink. Even the range of available colours may be limited for a given machine and/or method. Even when the form is to be produced by a professional printer, the choice of paper will restrict the choice of ink.
Where a certain finish is necessary — e.g. a matt effect in deep black for optical character reading — it will usually be necessary to subjugate the choice of paper and reproduction method to the necessity of obtaining the required result. (It is worth noting that most OCRs will read semi-matt printing such as is provided by ordinary printer's ink provided that there is no "meniscus effect" in the printing — a raising of the character in a hemispherical manner. In this respect, the choice of paper may be more important than that of the ink. A little experiment here can save a great deal of money which might otherwise be spent on special inks and processes.)

Coloured inks

If printing with coloured inks is planned, the following practical points are worth noting:

- red and orange are irritating to read, and hence give rise to errors in reading. In addition, these colours are likely to be subject to fading. Yellow is almost illegible; in addition, many papers turn more or less yellow with age;
- blue, while otherwise satisfactory, will not reproduce on many copying machines. Thus it should not be used when the form is liable to require copying;
- brown, green and grey are in most circumstances the best to use.

Where any part of the fixed data of a form must be printed in a colour, then all the fixed data should, if at all possible, be printed in that colour. To print in more than one colour is costly, and almost never justifiable.

Reproduction methods

Forms will either be prepared by in-house duplicating machinery, or sent out to a printer. If the organization is large enough to possess its own print shop, this amounts to the same thing as sending out, except that closer control may be possible. Even where the form is sent out, the printer may elect to use some form of offset printing, rather than the traditional typesetting.

The choice of printing method will have an effect upon the choice of paper, the paper size, the choice of ink, the permissible lay-out of the form, and the physical make-up. Conversely, fixed requirements in connexion with these factors will restrict the choice of printing methods. Unless a full and free choice of printing methods is available, the designer may have to make some compromises.

Offset

In the offset method of printing, the image to be reproduced is prepared in an ink-attracting medium on an ink-repellent master.
The method is versatile and economical, calls for only a small capital expenditure, and is very reliable — apart from routine cleaning and oiling, the apparatus is virtually trouble-free. The results are directly comparable with those obtained from typesetting, particularly where the better and more versatile keyboard machines are used for preparing the text.

The masters take two forms — paper (or plastic), and aluminium. The metal masters are used where more than a few hundred copies are called for. It is possible, however, to make one master from another, and this will sometimes prove convenient for medium-length runs of a few thousand copies using paper or plastic masters. This would be the case if the master were to be prepared by direct typing and drawing — neither typists nor draughtsmen work comfortably on metal, although it is possible. If the master-from-master method is to be used, the required number of secondary masters should be run off before the primary master is used for the preparation of copies of the form.

There are two methods of preparing primary masters. The first is by direct typing and drawing on the surface of a blank master. For this purpose, special inks and typewriter ribbons are required. No special difficulties are encountered except, perhaps the need for a higher than usual degree of attention to cleanliness. With paper masters, erasures are best considered non-feasible; with plastic masters, the procedures are not difficult, and are explained in the manufacturer's literature. Paper masters, which are but little cheaper than plastic, are on the whole not so satisfactory; they are usually not worth storing after one run, and do not give so many copies. The second, and generally more satisfactory method of preparing litho masters is photographic. The drawn part of the form is prepared to size (or to reduction size if required) on good white paper. The text is typed separately, also on paper, and is then cut into the required blocks and pasted up on to the drawn part. The whole composite is then photographed on to special blank masters. In this way, draughtsman and typist work with their accustomed normal materials under their accustomed normal conditions, and the master is produced under conditions ideally suited to high quality. A wide range of coloured inks is available; if several colours are to be used on one machine, spare ink-feeds and ink rollers should be obtained, both in the interests of speed and of clean work.

Other in-house methods

Other in-house (small machine) methods are in general far less useful to the forms designer than offset litho. Chief amongst such methods are stencil duplicating and hectograph. The stencil cannot give the crisp, professional result of litho. It is generally satisfactory for typed text, but, in spite of recent improvements, has a poor quality of line. The stencils themselves are messy to handle, and difficult to store. A stored stencil, upon retrieval, seldom gives as good a result as it did before storage, even though it has not been used to run its full recommended number of copies. Stencils offer no special difficulties to suitably experienced typists, although the machine used must be in good condition. This method is very economical, however, and quite satisfactory for internal forms.

Modern hectograph equipment is versatile, and offers no difficulties to typist and draughtsman. Special ribbons and inks are used, and both are available in a wide range of attractive colours. The work is done on paper having a glazed surface. The hectograph offers the only simple method of producing a multi-coloured printout in one stage — the colours used in preparing the master are reproduced in the output. There are serious limitations, however, on the number of copies that can be produced from one master, and on speed. The process is economical, but once again, the final result lacks the finish of good offset work.

Some consideration should be given to the possibilities of Xerography, dyeline printing, Thermofax, and so on. Of course, any method of office duplication can be pressed into service for the reproduction of forms; but generally speaking, only offset, stencil and hectograph are serious contenders.

Of the remainder, Xerox has the advantage in that it uses ordinary paper; but it is only workable with certain types of paper. It needs no special type of master, and gives a good quality of output. Various colours of "developer" are available, but the changeover from colour to colour is not simple. The process is relatively slow and costly. The other methods generally use a special paper to print on, and most of these papers are for one reason or another unsuitable for forms. In addition, they are nearly all very slow and expensive.

Typesetting

The ancient and traditional method of producing printed work — typesetting — is that capable of producing the most pleasing and professional end result. It is also by far the most versatile printing process, and, in some of its variations, the fastest. The speed of a high-speed line printer pales into insignificance compared with that of a rotary press. For large quantities, letterpress methods are also the cheapest — but the quantities must be large. No other methods are currently economically available for the production of multiple continuous stationery and no other method can seriously compete in the production of padded multiple interleaved forms, unless the quantity be of the order of tens or the low hundreds.

Printing possesses a vast and complex technology, and the forms designer should not attempt to acquire more than a small acquaintanceship with it. Matters of printing should be left to the printer; given a good specification, he will produce a good result. It is desirable, however, that the forms designer should have some knowledge of the subject of typefaces, so that he may be able to discuss it in the appropriate terminology, and make a knowledgeable selection from the material offered him by his chosen printer. Printed letters are divided into upper case (capitals, usually abbreviated to caps), and lower case (in lay terms, "small letters"). In a normal font (printer's term for a set), the upper case letters stand taller than the lower case. A font is sometimes provided with an additional set of upper case letters of the same height as the lower case; these are known as "small caps". Letters which stand vertical and have serifs (ticks at the end of the strokes) are called Roman letters. This sentence is set in Roman letters. Vertical letters without serifs, as in the text of this book, are sometimes referred to as Gothic, but more commonly, nowadays, Sans letters. Letters which slope to the right are called Italics. While most Italics are *Roman*, *Sans Italics* also exist. Since printers were the first artisans to require a system of precise measurement units, they were compelled to invent one. By and large, this system has survived to the present day. It is not surprising, therefore, that printers terms for sizes sound unfamiliar, and bear no simple relationship to Imperial or Metric units. Moreover, the terms and their interpretations vary from country to country. Sticks, Ciceros, Augustijns, etc. etc. . . . . . these matters are best left to the professional. Certain matters, however, are commonly the source of misunderstandings; and since they are of importance to the forms designer, they are discussed briefly here.

It is fortunate that the printer's unit called the point is international, although it, too is susceptible of some slight variation. It may be taken as about 0.38 mm. It is not, as is often thought, exclusively a unit of height of typeface; it is fundamentally a unit of height of the block which carries the type. It is thus a limiting factor for type height; a 6-point letter has a maximum height of 6×0.38 mm = 2.28 mm. It can, however, have any size whatever smaller than this.

Spacing between letters, words and lines — other than that represented by the fact that the letter is smaller than the block — is called "white", and is introduced by means of spacing pieces. White between letters or between words is called "space", and between lines "interline".

Sans lettering is to be preferred for the captions of business forms.
Roman type is the most suitable for large masses of print, while Italics should be used for brief explanations.

Use of ordinary measures

A final word to dispel another misconception - any printer will be perfectly happy to work in metric or Imperial measure if you want him to. He doesn't expect his customers to learn his trade secrets. He is perfectly accustomed to fitting his esoteric measures into spaces defined by centimetres and inches; if the designer choses a style of typeface, the printer will select the appropriate sizes and spacings to fit it professionally into the allotted spaces.

Design considerations

While ingenuity, creativity, and a "good eye" are essential to the creation of satisfactory forms, the designer is, as is any other craftsman, limited by certain rules and conventions. Forms design has been the subject of much thought and research in the past few decades, and the principles which have emerged are not lightly to be ignored.

Surviving from many concepts, the two principal methods of layout are the box arrangement and the columnar, or tabular, arrangement. The box style is used where each item of fixed data calls for the entry of one item of variable data, and the tabular method is the best suited for cases where there are several items of variable data to be entered under each fixed data entry. It is, of course, possible to combine both methods in one form, if the nature of the entries renders this desirable.

In addition to the question of layout, the actual physical presentation must be considered. This must, of course, be function-oriented. Matters to be considered include origin; destination; number of copies required; special instructions related to individual copies; equipment to be used for filling-in; methods of storage; handling and filling; environmental factors; and any special requirements. Working on these lines, the designer will be able to decide whether the form is to be single or multiple; white or coloured; large or small; presented individually, or as separate sets, or padded, or continuous; interleaved, or carbon backed, or NCR; with coloured or black ink; with this paper or that ....

Answer boxes

Answer boxes are practical for both handwritten and typewritten entries. When they are used, they are made by the insertion of vertical rules, as required, between horizontal rules extending from margin to margin. The vertical rules should be so positioned as to minimize the number of typewriter tab stops necessary. A common left margin should be used, to enable the typewriter carriage to return each time in the same position.

The printed captions detailing the required data content of a box should be set in small gothic and placed in the upper left corner of the box. In this way, the captions are always visible to the typist, and the whole width of the box is available for data entry. Good box design can increase available space by as much as 25%. (See various examples throughout Volumes 2 to 5.) Each caption should be complete in itself, but can be amplified by brief explanations in Italics. When each space is clearly defined, and each box limited to one entry, there is never any doubt concerning which box a caption applies to. Captions may be numbered for quick reference.

Blank spaces, headed "Leave Blank", may be left for future use. Where the data entry can be limited to a small number of preselected answers, these entries can be preprinted, the user indicating his choice by means of an "X". (See 4.5, page 22.) If this method is adopted, a horizontal arrangement of the choices is to be preferred to a vertical, in order to avoid ambiguity of interpretation of the answers in the event of slippage between the members of a carbon-interleaved set. If a vertical arrangement must be used, double vertical spacing (1/3") should be employed. If the form is to be filled in by hand, leave at least 1/4" spacing between boxes. An additional possibility of using "X" entries occurs when the questions can be answered "yes" or "no".

Columns

Where several entries may have to be made against each item of fixed data, the form should probably be organized in columnar fashion (see various examples throughout Volumes 2 to 5).

Column widths are determined principally by the amount of fill-in data expected. The size of the heading can be allowed to have some effect on the column width — a column could be made a few characters wider than was otherwise necessary so as to accommodate a well-set title; but if the effect of the title would be too great, or if space considerations prohibit the giving of any extra space to the title, then vertical or sloped titles should be adopted (see 6-2.3, page 3).

The matter entered on a columnar form is more often the subject of calculation than that on a box-type form. If calculations are to be made with the variable data entries, this fact should be recognized when designing the form, and all possible steps be taken to facilitate the operations. A minor point in this connexion — it is often useful to give each column an identifying letter, and each horizontal row an identifying number. Where a form is large, these letters and numbers can be with advantage repeated at the bottom and right of the columns and rows respectively. Instructions for arithmetic operations can be given very succintly by referring to the entry in column F, row 6 for example, instead of having to refer every time to the actual row and column titles.

Rules

Rules — printed lines — serve primarily as limiters of data fields. They are used to separate box or column headings from the body of the form; to break up a form into sections; and to guide the entry of data. They also provide an inexhaustible means of clarifying confusing material; help to provide visual interest; and accentuate certain parts of the form.

To be effective, and to improve readability, the variety of rules employed should be limited. Superfluous lines, or too many heavy or dashed lines, make a form difficult to read.
Five weights of rule are normally used in forms design, the hairline, the 1/2-point, the 1-point, the triple line, and the dotted or broken rule. The use of these rules is flexible, but experience has shown that certain patterns of use are more conducive to clerical efficiency than others. (See 2.2, pages 12 and 13.)
Avoid horizontal rules as far as possible; they make it difficult to adjust the form in the machine. Long narrow writing lines, as in accounting, can be divided every fifth line by a weighted rule. In the case of continuous forms, the ruled lineflow (zebra liniature) can be used for this purpose.

Layout
Certain matters of layout are of general applicability, whether boxes, columns, or some combination of these, or some other layout altogether is adopted.

Appearance
The attitude of the office staff towards the form will depend very largely upon its appearance. This in turn will depend upon both its design and its reproduction. A carelessly designed or badly produced form will engender a poor mental attitude in the user, which will have an adverse effect on his work. Such mental attitudes are subconscious rather than conscious; and well designed forms can contribute greatly to positive thinking and good morale.

Identification
Proper identification is always necessary to make the purpose and function of the form clear to the reader. Such identification includes the title, the subtitle, purpose, name, form number and date of edition.
Different readers will attach different degrees of importance to the various parts of the identification. The position of the identifying items on the form, however, is important to all readers.

Filing data
Proper attention must be paid at the design stage to the method of storage which will be used for the form during both its active and its inactive life. The item under which the form is to be filed, and which will be the basis for its subsequent recovery — name, department, serial number or whatever, — must be placed in a prominent and suitable position, normally in right upper corner.

Retention instructions
Instructions for the retention of a form as a temporary or permanent record may be printed on the form as convenient to the designer. In the case of multiple-part forms, the words “Retention Copy” may be printed on one copy only,

possibly at slight extra cost. It is, however, one of the objectives of a successful records control program to prevent the retention of more than one copy of a form which must be retained for a certain time, but which is inactive during its retention period.

Blocking and shading

Shading enhances the readability of the form when it is used to emphasize entry spaces or sections to be completed: to emphasize entries or sections to be processed (for example, a completed area might be surrounded by a screen to indicate punching into a tabulating card, thus aiding the keypunch operators by isolating the information to be punched): to reserve certain spaces for later entries: to distinguish one column of figures from another: and to emphasize column entries to be processed (see 3.2, page 13).

Blocking can be used to delete entry spaces which are not to be used. Do not use blocking or shading in a way which becomes visually irritating, or which gives too black an appearance when printed. Too much blocking or shading is confusing to the reader.

For inserting blocking or shading in the master, use a self-adhesive transparency or "mechanical tint" such as Normatone.

Margins

A margin is a blank space left all round a printed sheet. It improves appearance, and eases manual and mechanical handling. The margins of a sheet are referred to by the printer as the finger margin, the binding margin, the top margin and the bottom margin. The binding margin is that by which the sheet is gripped when bound or filed; the finger margin is that which is opposite the binding margin; the top margins are those at the top when the closed book is held with the spine to the left and the first page towards to you, and the bottom margin is opposite the top.

The area within the margins, in which the text appears, is called the "image area". Having defined the image area and the finished sheet size, it is only necessary to specify top and binding margins. In the case of a two-sided form, this should be done for each side separately. If it is desired to specify all four margins, care should be taken to see that the margin specifications and the image area specifications are compatible with the size of paper being used. The benefit of specifying only two adjacent margins is that it accommodates the possibility of slightly varying sizes of paper-stock in the print shop. If it is genuinely important that no variations whatever should take place in the overall size of the form, specify all dimensions; if you can tolerate, say, half a millimetre or so either way, then do not specify four margins, or else the printer may, on finding that the current stock of paper is slightly over- or under-size, cut you some "special" from larger stock — at higher cost.

Where paper is to be drawn through a machine by means of a pinwheel or similar drive, adequate additional margin must be left at the sides for this purpose. 20 mm is usually sufficient, but reference should be made in case of doubt to the

machine manufacturer's manual, and existing paper for the machine should be examined and measured.
A normal handling margin would be about 1 cm all around. It is sometimes desirable to take the image area to the edge of the form on one or more sides — to "bleed" the image off. When this is to be done, the form should usually be printed on larger stock than is actually necessary, and then cropped to the edge of the image area as required.

Grouping

Items of fixed data should be grouped on the form with several principles in mind. It is fortunate that these principles are nearly always complementary, and almost never come into conflict.

- The sequence of the items should be logical.
- The amount of writing or typing necessary to fill in the variable data should be kept to a minimum.
- Where filling-in of the variable data is to be done by means of a typewriter or other machine, the characteristics and advantageous features of the machine must be fully utilized (tabulation, automatic carriage return, etc. etc.).
- Good overall appearance should be obtained.

In addition to these factors, the designer must give full consideration to the fact that data may have to be copied to his new form from other forms; and from his new form to other forms. He should possess himself of filled-in copies of all such other forms, and make due allowance for the easing of the necessary copying.

The pre-design phase

Before entering upon the design itself, the designer must first satisfy himself of the completeness of the forms analysis, and must then determine in detail the forms requirements. In order to enable the designer to verify the completeness of the analysis stage, the following checklist is provided.

Forms analysis checklist

- Was the need for the form questioned?
- Was the need for every item on the form questioned?
- Was the need for every copy of the form questioned?
- Have similar and related forms been examined with a view to amalgamation?
- Is the sequence of items logical? Easy to follow?
- Are all source documents available? Does the order of items correspond well with that of the relevant items on the source document?
- Are all target documents available? Does the order of items on the form correspond well with the requirements of transcription from the form to the target document?
- Does the order of items on the form correspond well with the requirements of the associated clerical procedures?

- Is the amount of writing required for filling reduced to a minimum?
- Is the form adapted to derive full benefit from writing machine characteristics?
- Has proper consideration been given to filing data and margins in respect of the filing methods and equipment to be used?
- Are the titles, numbers and colours well adapted to facilitate dispatching, handling and checking?
- Are the captions clear and unambiguous?
- Have the space requirements for each individual item been verified?
- Has provision been made for overflow in the event of an exceptional answer?
- Has maximum use been made of the principles of speciality forms?
- Have the users been adequately consulted?
- Is there a written procedure for the use of the form?
- Has the method of transmitting the form been analyzed?

Determination of forms requirements

In addition to the material contained in TECHNICAL CONSIDERATIONS and DESIGN CONSIDERATIONS, each of the following points should be considered in detail with respect to the form which is to be designed, and the Pre-design Checklist, see page 21, should then be followed through, in order to elucidate the specific requirements of that form.

All requests for new or revised forms must bear an appropriate authorizing signature.

Originator

The name and departmental address of the originator must be stated, so that he can be contacted in connexion with any queries concerning the form.

Purpose

If the purpose of a form — and in the case of a new or revised form, perhaps its benefits also — are not made clear by the title and subtitle, they can be further explained under the heading "Purpose".

Title and subtitle

When a person uses a form for the first time, he will gain his first impression of what it is all about from the title.

The title should thus be specific and meaningful, and indicate clearly to the user the subject, operation and function of the form. The title should normally be placed in the upper left-hand corner of the form, aligned on the top and left margins, and should be in large, easy-to-read type.

Subtitle

A subtitle may be desirable in order to make the application of the form more explicit to the user, or to assist in identification.

Due date

The due date is the date on which the new forms are required in the using department. The designer should always be given an actual date. Avoid such expressions as "rush", "at once", or "as soon as possible". If, in spite of his best efforts the designer cannot meet the due data requested, he should inform the requesting department as soon as possible, and tell them the earliest date upon which delivery can be made.

Sources

During the forms analysis, all items to be included will have been described in detail on a field description sheet (3-2.3, page 29). All other sources which contribute to the content or format of the form, such as procedure descriptions, procedure flowcharts, etc. must be made available to the designer.

The information to the designer should clearly indicate and identify any other forms from which data must be copied on to the new form. Where possible, a filled-in copy of any such source forms should be supplied. In this way, the task of the designer in simplifying the copying of data will itself be simplified.

Completion by hand

To achieve ease of reading a hand-filled form, adequate space should be provided to enable the data to be written in clear, legible script. Where handwritten data will have to share a box with printed captions, the box must be of sufficient size to contain a clearly printed caption and a clearly written entry; and control must be exercised over the printing stage, to ensure that the style and position of the caption remain precisely as called for by the designer.

As a guide in determining how much space is to be allowed for handwritten entries, one should take as ideal 1/6" (4 mm) per character horizontally, and 1/3" (8 mm) vertically per line. 1/10" (2.5 mm) per character and 1/4" (6 mm) per line should be regarded as the absolute minimum.

Completion by typewriter

When the form is to be filled in by typewriter, a minimum of one space more than the maximum number of characters to be accommodated should be allowed, in order to prevent crowding.

An elite typewriter has a spacing of twelve characters per inch, and a pica typewriter ten. Both have a vertical line spacing of six lines per inch, so that the vertical spacing of the form should be in multiples of 1/6".

Certain typewriters — notably those in the Triumph and Adler series — are sometimes supplied with standard line-spacing, but with a letter spacing between Pica and Elite; approximately 11/inch. Since the typist usually considers such a machine to be Elite, difficulties could arise here.

Completion by machines

On certain printers, the line spacing is under the control of the operator, and can be changed from six per inch to eight per inch. If such a printer is to be used, careful instructions must be given in order to avoid troubles such as the misplacement or overlapping of lines.

When the form is to be filled in by means of special equipment, the reference manual for such equipment should be carefully studied before commencing the design.

It may occur that the new form is intended for use with an office machine, or in conjunction with other forms used with an office machine. Where such is the case, the designer should be given full details, and supplied with a machine-completed copy of the relevant forms and, if applicable, a machine-completed facsimile of the new form.

Destination

The destination determines whether or not certain items, such as the company name, telephone number, etc., have to be printed on the form.

Environmental requirements

The designer must have a full knowledge of the environment in which the form will be used. From consideration of such factors as lighting, spaciousness, dirtiness, temperature, humidity etc., he can determine any special requirements in respect of typeface and size, material, binding and so on.

High legibility

Where completed copies of the form are to be used with optical character readers, or subjected to some form of reduction printing, special measures may have to be taken to ensure that the standards of legibility are kept adequately high.

Numbering

Adequate forms control is impossible unless every form carries a meaningful control number. By providing a unique and systematic identification system, these numbers enable management to determine at any time the quantity, usage, purpose, and location of all forms in use, and simplify the ordering and the administration of consumption.

In order to achieve these ends, the numbering of forms must be logical and systematic. It should be controlled from a single centre. The numbers may consist of alphabetic or numerical characters, or of a combination of both. While these numbers could be arbitrarily and sequentially assigned, it might be of some benefit to allocate certain groups of characters to indicate aspects of usage such as department ordering, filing details etc. However, it should be a guiding principle to keep the numbers as simple as possible. If a number is overloaded, it tends to lose significance and therefore usefulness. Where a set of forms are closely related, they may be given the same basic number and distinguished by means of a suffix; e.g. 1543-1, 1543-2 . . . . .) It should be noted, however, that in this and in any other case where two or more forms differ by only a small detail — perhaps the suffix number and some other small variation, or the inclusion of an edition date — the printing cost may be disproportionately increased as compared with that of a consolidated version serving more than one purpose.

The serial numbering of a set of forms can present a production problem, since the forms, although functionally identical, will have a different print content. It can also present a control problem, in necessitating special measures to account for missing numbers due to spoiled or cancelled forms.

With respect to the production problem, consultation with the printer is called for. Certain printers, specialising in the production of forms, tickets and such, have installed special equipment which renders the production of serially numbered batches an economic proposition. Single-cylinder offset processes would necessitate the introduction of a second operation for numbering; numbering methods are available, however, for use with multi-cylinder offset or rotary press printing machinery.

The numbering of multiple-part forms calls for the inclusion in the print specification of an instruction to the printer to set his numbering device to trip every second, third, etc. impression, according to the number of forms in the set.

With respect to the control problem, it may well be that the need to prevent misuse of the form, and therefore to compel users to account for every copy, was the very reason for deciding to use serial numbering.

Indeed, unless some such consideration exists, it would be unwise to undertake serial numbering. Unless a form is liable to be misused, the added cost of serial numbering in terms of printing charges and extra control effort will seldom be repaid.

Effect on other forms

The introduction of a new form, or a change or revision of an existing form, may call for the revision of existing forms. Where it is known that this is the case, the identification of all such forms, and, if possible, filled-in copies, should be supplied to the designer.

Relations with other forms

When data has to be transcribed to or from the form, the organization of the data items on the source or target document must be coordinated with the corresponding arrangement on the form. If, for example, the target document is a punched card, the items to be punched must be organized on the form, and if possible on the card also, so as to achieve the proper order for punching.

Disposal of superseded forms

Where the new form supersedes an existing form, there has to be a decision concerning the disposal of all copies of the old version. These may be used to a fixed date, or until finished, or destroyed as soon as the new form becomes available. It must be borne in mind that in addition to the quantity in stock, there may be many copies of the old form held in user offices.

Duplication after completion

When completed copies of the form are to be duplicated, allowance should be made in so far as the duplicating method to be used affects the design of the form. Where a large number of copies is to be made by some such method as hectograph or offset litho, consideration should be given to preparing the form directly on a hecto or litho master, or even by computer printer, or typewriter.

N-up printing

Where the total character-width of a printer or tabulator exceeds the maximum character-width of a given printout by a factor of two or more, it may be considered desirable to arrange the printout in columns, two-or-more-up across the paper.

Window envelopes

Window envelopes, while slightly more costly than the ordinary type, possess many advantages. In eliminating totally the need for addressing envelopes, they eliminate also the commission of errors in transcribing names and addresses from forms to envelopes and the insertion of forms into wrong envelopes. They thus contribute greatly to the prevention of delay and non-delivery of forms.

A window four inches wide by one inch deep will accommodate most addresses, and will not detract from optimum utilization of the area of the form.

If window envelopes are to be used, economic considerations dictate that the number of different types in use be kept to a minimum. Before designing a form to be used with a window envelope, all details of the envelope must be known to the designer, so that he can ensure that the address area on the form will be correctly aligned with the window when the form is folded and inserted. The provision of a preprinted folding guide will assist in expediting the despatch of the form.

Filing data

When, in filling in the form in use, a number of copies are made, each separate part (copy) is given an appropriate colour or part number. All data relevant to the filing of the various copies of a multi-part form must be known. For example, different copies may be filed according to date, customer, and order number. The retrieval key should be printed in an easily readable position — preferably on the upper right corner.

In order to be able to determine the physical size and shape of the form, the number, shape and position of the perforations etc. the designer must know the type of storage in which the filled-in copies are to be kept.

Instructions

Well-thought-out instructions enable the reader to interpret the form in such a way that he can give accurate and appropriate answers, or process the form efficiently. In this, as in any other branch of writing, the writer should put himself in the position of the reader, and should try to criticize his own work from the reader's point of view.

Brief general instructions are placed close to the title, preferably immediately beneath it. Brief instructions to amplify items of information or column headings should be placed in parentheses immediately after the item or heading. Brief instructions which relate to a specific section should be placed close to the section heading. Where an instruction is required which is too lengthy to be so located, it should be printed outside that part of the area of the form which is devoted to the entry of variable data — in a reserved area at the bottom, on the reverse side, or in a separate sheet or booklet. A clear note referring the reader to such an instruction should be placed where the instruction itself would have gone, had it been brief. In the printing of a lengthy instruction, the normal printing precautions for securing easy legibility should be observed; in particular, a mass of single-column small print extending across the whole reverse side of the form is unlikely to be read.

Instructions for filling out the form

Such instructions should not be used where the other fixed data on the form render it self-explanatory. Where they are necessary, they should be placed at top of the form, so that the user sees them before he starts to write data.

Routing instructions

Routing instructions for complete forms can be placed either at the top or at the bottom, at the convenience of the designer. Where each member of a set of forms has a different routing procedure, printing costs can be reduced by printing all routing instructions on each copy, and using coding or colour to identify the copies. In such cases, the routing instructions should refer to each copy.

Further details in completing the work of forms design are stated in the Pre-design Checklist.

PRE-DESIGN CHECKLIST

Check on:	*Examples of detail questions*
The originator	• Who is the originator? • What is his department? • When did he request the form? • Has the design been authorized?
The user	• Who will use the form? • External or only internal use? • What are the departments of the users? • Have all users been informed of the development of the form?

The purpose	• What is the purpose of the form? • Is it necessary to state the purpose on the form?
Name	• Is the name of the form in keeping with the purpose? • Does the name explain the content? • Can the name go in the normal place — top left corner? • Is the name authorized and registered with the forms control department? • Is a subtitle necessary?
Quantity	• What is the estimated quantity? • Is the quantity an indication of the importance to be attached to the development? • Is the estimated quantity in keeping with the expected use? • Is it desirable to reduce the quantity in anticipation of improvements arising from actual use?
Delivery time	• What is the requested delivery time? • What is the promised delivery time? • How much time does the printer need? • How much time is left for design?
Format	• Which of the following standard breadths can be used? 18 cm; 24 cm*, 28 cm; 33 cm**; 38 cm; 40 cm. * 21 cm (A4), with pinfeed left and right ** 29.7 cm (A3), with pinfeed left and right • Which of the following standard heights can be used? 4″; 5½″ (A5); 6″; 8″; 11″ (A4); 12″. • STANDARDIZATION CUTS COSTS
Margins	• Front: top ..... cm; bottom ..... cm; left ..... cm; right ..... cm. • Back : top ..... cm; bottom ..... cm; left ..... cm; right ..... cm. • Leave 20 mm for pinfeed holes if used; leave at least 1 cm handling margin all round.
Make-up	• Single or multiple form? • If single, then single or double-sided? Units or padded? Continuous? • If multiple, then unit sets or padded? Continuous? Carbon interleaved, carbonized or NCR?
Matching	• Is matching necessary with other forms? • Is matching necessary between the forms of the set?

Facts	• Are all the necessary source documents available? • Are all the necessary facts available?
Method of filling in	• By hand: Pen, pencil, ballpoint? Writing lines to be provided or not? Allow about 6 mm between lines and 3-4 mm per letter horizontally. • By typewriter. Elite has a letter-spacing of 12/inch, and a linespacing in multiples of 1/6 inch. Pica has a letter spacing of 10/inch, and a line-spacing in multiples of 1/6 inch. Some German typewriters have an intermediate letterspacing, approximating to 11/inch. • Other machines. Usually line-spacing in multiples of 1/6 inch and letter-spacing of 10/inch. But check maker's handbook. Are the name and model of the machine known? Are the size and position of the spaces provided in keeping with the capabilities of the machine? • Stamps. Is the allocated space in keeping with the size of the stamp?
Place of use	• Office? • Factory? • Lighting conditions? • Damp? • Dirt? • Temperature? • Humidity? • Likely contamination? • Any other special environmental characteristics?
Readability	• Are there any special readability needs? • Is this true for all copies?
Utilization	• How frequently is the form referred to? Daily, weekly, monthly, seldom? • Expected lifetime? • Retention time?
Form number	• Does the form have a form number? • Can the number in the normal place - bottom left corner? • Should the form have a serial number? • Must the forms be numbered consecutively? If so, has the number series been made as small as possible? What must the first and last numbers be?

- Is there enough room to build the numbering device into the printing forme? (A 'forme' is a metal frame used by the printer to hold the typesetting for a page together.)
- Must each copy of the set carry its own serial number? Is the benefit of doing this sufficient to justify the cost?

Effect on other forms

- Does the introduction of this form eliminate the need for any other forms?
- Reduce or increase the usage of any other form?
- Duplicate in part the content of any other form?
- Simplify the utilization of any other form?
- Make demands upon machinery already more or less fully loaded?
- Make demands upon people or machines at the same time that other forms would normally be making such demands?
- From what other forms must data be copied onto this form? Is there any effect as a result on the operation of the other form?
- To what other forms must data be copied from this form? Is there any effect as a result on the operation of the other form?
- Is there any other foreseeable way in which the introduction of this form will affect the operation of other forms?

Having determined the forms requirements, and obtained all the necessary source documents, the designer is now in a position to commence the step-by-step design of the form. This section is designed to assist him in this process, and to help him in assessing the quality of his design.

Step-by-step design

The designer's first task should be to make a rough draft, with the aid of a guide sheet (see page 24A), embodying as much as he can of the known requirements. His basic job at this time is to effect a logical ordering of the fixed data on the grid sheet, approximating as closely as possible to the required finished form. He will then proceed, step-by-step, to bring the rough draft to a true representation of the final form.

Counting for space

On the rough draft, count across boxes or columns, allowing 1/10 or 1/12 inch per character as appropriate for entries which will be made by typing and 1/6 inch for characters which will be entered by hand. Set totals at right hand edge, at appropriate level. Count vertical lines, using 1/6 inch for typed lines and 1/3 inch for handwritten. Enter totals at bottom of page. Count text (fixed data) content, using printer's rule or character count chart. Compute space needed for each fixed data entry.

Determining size
The longest line across the form, as seen from the results of counting for space, will determine the width of the form. The greatest number of lines vertically will determine the height of the form. This height and width are for the image area. Adjust by adding any necessary margin sizes. This gives the overall size.

Adjustment
Note the amount by which each other line measure or height measure falls short of the longest. Decide where the adjustments are to be made. Use this step to line up as many tab stops as possible. Decide upon the actual size of paper to be used — use standard sizes — and make any further adjustments necessary to accommodate.

Outlining
On a fresh guide sheet, lay out the overall form area. Mark off image width and height by means of Xs on top, bottom, right and left scales; mark off form margins by joining appropriate Xs.

Plot down
Using right and left scales, mark off the position of all vertical rules. Draw all full-height rules by joining marks. Complete the plot entering all incomplete rules, horizontal and vertical.

Letter
Enter all fixed data text by hand, including instructions, to approximately the size required.

Mark up
Having determined the method of typesetting, and the weights of rules required, enter the appropriate printing instructions, using a different colour of ink. Prepare an additional specification to the printer if necessary, using Post Design Checklist (pages 29-31).
To emphasize the aspects of readability, filling-in and handling the form the following checklist is provided.

DESIGN CHECKLIST

READING THE FORM

Check on:	*Examples of detailed questions*
The title	• Does the title clearly indicate the nature and function of the form? • Is it displayed in a suitable position? • Does it interfere with other data, or with filling-in of the form?

The captions	• Are the captions easily understood? • Are they as short as possible?
The wording	• Is the wording clear and unambiguous?
The instructions	• Are instructions concerning completion placed at the top? • Are the lengthy instructions legibly printed? • Are any of the instructions on the face of the form too long, requiring removal to another place? • If there are any lengthy instructions printed on the back of the form, or separately, are there appropriate references to them in the proper places? • Are general instructions grouped together? • Are the specific instructions placed close to the related data items? • Are the disposal instructions at the end of the form?
Typefaces	• Are the typefaces appropriate? • Are all words legible under all conditions of use?
Rule weights	• Do the rule weights guide the eye appropriately? • Do they give good emphasis?
Boxes	• Have the possibilities of boxes been fully used? • Are all box captions in the top left corner of the box?
Identification	• Is the form correctly identified by code number? • Are all copies of the form correctly identified? • Are all items correctly identified?
Blocking and masking	• Is unused data and space appropriately blocked out? • Is the blocking and masking quiet, inoffensive and non-irritating?
Filing data	• Is the filing data present? On each copy? • Is the filing data correctly placed?
Ink	• Is there sufficient contrast between ink and paper? • Is there sufficient contrast between fixed and variable data?
Appearance	• Is the appearance neat? • Is the appearance quiet?

FILLING IN THE FORM

Check on:	*Examples of detailed questions*
Quantity of writing	• Has the amount of writing called for been reduced to a minimum?
Order	• Does the order of the items correspond as closely as possible with that of the order of the items on the source documents? • Does the order of the items correspond as closely as possible to that of the order of the items on the documents to which it is transferred? • Are the items in the most logical order for entering? • Are items to be entered by the same user well grouped?
Captions	• Are the captions correctly placed to facilitate filling-in?
Space	• Has sufficient space been allowed for each item of variable data?
Starting points	• Does the typing start, as far as possible, from a common left margin?
Vertical alignment	• Are vertical rules aligned to reduce the number of tab stops?
Columns	• Has the use of columns been considered? • If columns are used, are they correctly proportioned? • Have vertical or sloped headings been considered?
Overflow	• Has provision for overflow been made in the case of exceptional answers?
Machine compatibility	• Does the form take advantage of writing machine characteristics? • Horizontal and vertical spacing correct? • Maximum paper width established? • Maximum writing width established? • Is bottom inch of form clear of entries?
Help lines	• Are dotted help lines necessary? • If so, are they so placed as not to impede typing?

Margins	• Have the margins been correctly specified? • For both sides? • Are they consistent with the filing method?

HANDLING THE FORM

Check on:	*Examples of detailed questions*
Handling sequence	• Does the order of the items follow the order of the clerical routine?
Equipment	• Has consideration been given to the available equipment for folding, cutting etc.?
Facilitation of handling	• Do titles, numbers, colours etc. facilitate routing, dispatching, handling and checking?
Speciality forms	• Has maximum use been made of the principles of speciality forms?
Efficiency	• Does the overall physical make-up of the form lend itself to efficient handling in all expected working conditions?
Features	• Have the following possible features been considered? • Registration? • Serial numbering? • Perforation? • Scoring? • Punching? • Rounding corners? • Collating? • Padding?
Filing	• Has due consideration been given to the method(s) of filing which will be used to store the various copies of the form?
Folding	• Will the form be folded for filing, self-mailing or insertion into an envelope? If so: • Have the various methods of folding been duly considered? • Have the various possibilities of printing for two-sided folding forms (head-to-head, head-to-side, head-to-foot) been considered? • Have folding marks and instructions been correctly given on the form?

Numbering	• Is the form identified by a form number? • Is this number placed in the bottom left corner? • Are pages of a multiple form numbered?
Self routing	• Are copies of the form identified to make them self routing? • Are "To" and "From" boxes used?
Updating	• Is the form organized to facilitate the more foreseeable types of update? • In particular, does the form permit users to notify a change of address?
Accounting	• Are accounting requirements met?
Company name Department name	• Does the Company name appear on a form used by people outside the firm? • Does the originating department's name appear on an internal form?
Originator's approval	• Has the originator cleared the final draft?

The design is now complete, but remains to be carried into effect. In the larger companies, the forms designer does not have direct contact with the printer, but must place his order via the purchasing department, or perhaps the forms control department. The post-design checklist serves not only to check all aspects of the finished design, but also as a source from which, in conjunction with the results of the step-by-step design, the print order may be directly prepared.

THE POST-DESIGN CHECKLIST

Check on:	*Examples of detailed questions*
Facts about each sheet	• Type of paper. • Weight of paper. • Colour of paper. • Ink colour — front and back of sheet. • Carbon (full or partial? Define) — carbonization (define areas) NCR? • Vertical perforations. • Filing holes. • Date of issue. • Date.

Direction of movement	• Define with respect to print area. • If relevant, define with respect to grain also.
Printing	• One side or both? If both, • Head-to-Head? • Head-to-foot? • Head of front to right of back? • Head of front to left of back?
Margins	• Front top? • Front left? • Back top? • Back left?
Numbering	• Form number correctly allocated? • Serial numbering required?
Perforations	• Required? • Margin allowed for?
Folding	• Required? • Type of paper suitable? • Window envelope used? • Folding guide?
Punching	• Required? • Measurements correct?
Round corners	• Required? • 1, 2, or 4?
Sets	• How organized? • Print problems solved? • Collation? • Handling?
Packaging and identification	• Arranged?
Delivery date	• Arranged?
Proofs	• Delivered on time? • Returned corrected on time?

Continuous forms
- Packaging method?
- Handling method?

CONVERSION

General

The difficulties of conversion — the change from an existing system to a new system, which may be more suited to new business needs or better fitted to handle old ones — must not be minimized. The principles which have been emphasized throughout ARDI, and which are summarized in 1-4, "The ARDI approach to the systems effort", are as important here as in any other aspect of systems work.

"Conversion" is the standard name for this type of activity. In this technique*, we shall use the term in its normal sense; but in addition, where we wish to imply a wider view — not merely conversion in its technical sense, but all possible aspects of the transition from one data processing environment to another — we shall speak of "change-over".

Purpose

The purpose of conversion is to make current data-processing projects operational in a new data-processing environment. In terms of change-over, everything has to be accommodated to the new environment — resources and results as well as specifications and procedures.

Scope

This technique covers the three basic situations which call for conversion. These are the transition from one generation to another; the adjustment to the specifications of a different system, perhaps of another manufacturer; and the transition from one programming language to another.

Transition from one generation to another

The most radical form of change-over is the transition from an earlier generation to a third- or post-third-generation system. In such a case it may well be that not only do specifications and requirements change, but whole concepts and philosophies. There will be large differences in method and degree of I/O support; in manner of data handling and performing work; in the amount of operator intervention required; and many of the methods and procedures developed for the old system will become obsolete, and will have to be replaced by improved or totally new ones.

---

* This technique is based largely on a paper by A. J. v. d. Korst (Information Systems and Automation Department, Philips Gloeilampenfabrieken, Eindhoven), and P. K. Schrammel (Philips, Austria), presented at the Diebold Research Program conference in March, 1971.

Adjustment to specifications of another system

Circumstances may arise in which the use of another type of machine, of the same generation but having different hardware or software concepts, becomes necessary. This will call for modifications in file construction, and in programming and control facilities. It will not be necessary to develop a new method of thinking, but only to accept and accommodate to new specifications.

Transition from one programming language to another

The transition from one language to another presents fewer problems and difficulties than either of the other transitions. There are several reasons for undertaking this type of conversion, amongst the commonest of which are the need to improve programming facilities by adopting a more powerful language; to improve program maintenance by changing to a language well suited to program standardization; and the fact that support is being withdrawn from the language in use.

Methods available

A number of methods is available to assist in achieving operational status in the new environment. To select those most suitable in a particular case, it will be necessary to analyse the present projects individually, in order to decide whether or not they can be transferred, and if so, by what means. When this has been done, it will then be necessary to determine if the appropriate tools are available, or whether they must be specially developed.

The methods available for transferring projects from the old environment to the new are:

- translation;
- conversion;
- simulation;
- emulation;
- restoration;
- reprogramming;
- redesign;
- reconstruction.

Each project should be considered in relation to each of these methods, to decide whether it can, in whole or in part, be thereby suitably dealt with.

Translation

Translation is transfer without logical adjustments. It is never in itself sufficient. In human language, it is necessary to consider a whole sentence or even a whole passage in terms of content and logical relationships before a good translation can be attempted; similarly in computer language, the mere translation of individual words and statements will produce errors and difficulties. Program translators are useful aids, but will leave much to be done by men who know the meanings and purposes of instruction sequences within a program.

Conversion

Conversion goes beyond mere translation. It includes the automatic performance of changes and additions in such a way as to lead to a complete translation. Language conversion programs will delete obsolete definitions and add new ones, and will change program parts to bring them into conformity with the new specifications.

File conversion programs will not only make the data physically readable to the new equipment, but will also add logical information such as new labels.

Simulation and emulation

Simulation is the imitation of the old machine by means of a software program which interprets and simulates on the new machine every instruction of the program to be executed.

Emulation is supported by what is called a "compatibility feature", whereby all the instructions available to the old system are included in the hardware of the new processing unit.

Each of these methods permits the user to run projects unchanged on the new machine, without any alteration to programs, files or procedures. Such projects will, of course, not be making full use of the facilities of the new system; performance will depend largely upon the extent of the differences in structure between the old and new systems, and may even be degraded.

In addition, the files used for simulated and emulated projects will not, in general, be compatible with those designed for the new system, so that old and new projects will not be able to be directly connected.

Thus these two methods, while they may be useful in getting a quick start in running projects on the new machine, have distinct disadvantages.

Apart from projects with a low running frequency, and obsolescent projects which it is considered not worth while to transfer, any projects which have been temporarily dealt with by these methods should be transferred to the new system by other and more suitable methods as soon as possible.

Restoration

Restoration is the improvement and updating of programs in the light of modern standards and know-how. Every D.P. department has its "old-timers"-programs which were developed in the early days of the installation, and which are still running, although it is often difficult so see why or even how. They have been changed many times, and are probably highly inefficient. These are the programs which should be the subject of restoration. Change-over time is a good time for the removal of old-fashioned and inefficient coding.

Reprogramming
In this method, the programs concerned are not transferred, but are directly rewritten in new languages and in accordance with new specifications. The method is particularly suitable for programs which are so tailored for the old system — written in languages which cannot be translated perhaps, or which are dependent upon features which no longer exist — that it is unreasonable or impossible to transfer them.

Redesign
Redesign is indicated when the program as written falls far short of making good use of the facilities of the new system. The new I/O possibilities, for example, may render the external I/O specifications out-of-date; or altered data-management concepts may permit complicated jobstreams, resulting from the use of sequential files, to be simplified by employing direct-access facilities, or program maintenance procedures to be improved by the use of library facilities not hitherto available.

Reconstruction
Reconstruction should be employed when the external I/O specifications are still valid, but where the programming method adopted in solving the problems is not good enough for the new situation. For example, it may be possible to improve the program structure and the sequence of the processing steps by making use of features such as overlay, dynamic program loading, etc., which are available in the new system but were not in the old.

Problem areas

In order to be able to determine which of the methods of the preceding section should be employed in any given instance, an accurate inventory of the installation must be made. For this purpose, division into the following problem areas has been found the most effective in use:

- user programs;
- application packages;
- operating system facilities;
- files;
- hardware.

User programs
In evaluating the user program problem area, we must find out what programming languages are available in the new system, and whether or not they are compatible with those currently in use in the old.
Various high-level programming languages, such as COBOL, ALGOL and FORTRAN, have been developed by independent international committees to ensure widespread compatibility. In adopting the use of such languages, however, dif-

ferent manufacturers embody variations in the specifications and features; each manufacturer uses modifications which are oriented towards his own particular requirements, and, of course, builds these changes into his compilers. Thus the so-called compatible languages are in reality no longer compatible. Even if the new system offers the same languages which you were previously using, therefore, care will be called for if you are changing to the products of another manufacturer.

If no language similar to that which you have been using exists in the new system, then either reprogramming or simulation/emulation will be necessary.

From the foregoing, it can be seen that there is considerable advantage in the employment of uniform, compatible high statement level programming languages throughout a project.

A second and even more delicate problem within the user program problem area arises when use has been made — and, in particular illegitimate use — of special hardware or software features of the old system. As a user grows familiar with a system, he learns to make increasing use of its special facilities. This ultimately leads to the invention of many ingenious "dodges", some of which amount virtually to abuses of the system components. Such deviations from standards and illegitimate employment of system peculiarities offer a serious obstacle to effective conversion. Such "dodges" should be removed to subroutines for reprogramming, while the rest of the programs can undergo standard conversion procedures.

It is worth noting here that all "tricky", too-ingenious programming should be avoided; apart from the difficulties which it presents at conversion time, it is seldom well-documented, lacks generality, is frequently unreliable when cases crop up which were not envisaged at the time of writing, and in general can defeat itself by reason of its own particularity.

Application packages

Almost every system makes use of one or more application packages. These may derive from the equipment manufacturer, from program exchange associations such as user clubs, and from software houses. Very often, the user of such software is not in possession of the full source text; and even if he is, modifications and conversions may be barred by patents, registered designs, copyrights, service agreements . . . . . .

In such cases, the best course is to seek an equivalent package which is available for the new equipment. It may be necessary to make some changes in the application itself in order to accommodate the new package. In the worst case, where no possibility exists of converting the existing package, and where no equivalent package is available, it will be necessary to develop a suitable package or specific user program.

Operating system

The operating system of the new installation will differ, to a greater or lesser degree, from that of the old.

The consequences of changing from a limited to a more extended O.S. are not so extreme as those of changing from a system with no O.S. at all. In the former case, the new system will contain all the old, although differences in specifications may call for some adjustments.

The least troublesome type of O.S. transition is the case where the same O.S. is to be used, but with extensions in respect of level improvements. Such a change calls for little more than jobstream and control card adjustment, with perhaps some re-arrangement of program structures. This type of transition corresponds to system changes such as the introduction of multiprogramming or multiprocessing. Wherever applicable it will be necessary to determine whether the O.S. support programs used in the old system will be available in the new, and if so, whether they will work in the same or a similar way. If not, and if it is found that the function which they fulfilled is still necessary, equivalent programs for the new system will have to be developed. Such would be the case if the principles of operation and maintenance were to remain unchanged in the new system, and depended upon text facilities, utilities and library support programs no longer available.

File conversion

File conversion is a particularly complex problem area. The choice of means for performing the transition will be affected by the methods of storage, access and file management, and by the space requirements. In general, a new system will offer new and additional storage and access methods. This is particularly true when new I/O units offer new concepts and facilitaties. If the methods used in the old system still exist they will be changed to improve and simplify file handling. As a result of these factors the files of different systems are almost never compatible, because labelling will be changed, data representation may be in another code, and space requirements may be altered. It will often be impossible to recognize the data of the old I/O directly on the new, or to simulate a file on the old machine to make it readable to the new system. In many cases, the only way to convert a file will be via another medium, e.g. cards. It will sometimes be possible to write a generator program for the new equipment to create the necessary files.

While this is a particular complex and sensitive problem area, in practice it should not give rise to too much trouble. It will be necessary to invoke the more tedious methods of conversion for only a few files; perhaps even only for one. Having fully converted the minimum necessary number of files, the remainder will be produced from these masters by subsequent program steps directly on the new machine.

Hardware

For our purposes the hardware can be divided into the central processing unit (C.P.U.) and the input-output (I/O) equipment. With respect to the differences between the old and new C.P.U.s, the difficulties of conversion will depend upon the extent to which assembly language was used in programming. Since assembly language programs are coded at machine instruction level, they are very closely tied to the special pecularities of the machine. Where large differences exist between the old and new C.P.U.s, it will not in general be profitable to attempt conversion of such programs. Reprogramming or simulation/emulation will be the best solution.

For programs written in compatible high-level languages, differences between the old and new C.P.U.s will generally call for no more than corrections in respect of field allocations and data formats.

Characteristic differences

Some characteristic differences to be expected between the old and new C.P.U. are as follows.

One machine is byte or octad oriented, the other word-oriented. This will affect space utilization and field formats.

The third generation machines make a distinction between blanks and zeros, where second generation machines normally accepted these as equivalent. When blanks are used in numeric operations, third generation machines produce program checks.

The old and new machines may make different uses of registers for purposes such as arithmetic operations, base addressing, floating point operations, decimal point location, and indexing for table searches.

Addressing methods may vary; for example, one machine may use absolute addressing, while the other uses relative addressing with base registers.

The instruction repertoires of the two machines will differ. Many of the instructions of the old machine will not be present on the new, or will work in another way, or perform different functions, or differ in their privilege status. This will be especially true where there are large differences in the methods of handling I/O operations.

The differences between the old and the new I/O equipment will affect file conversion procedures, and may require changes in the programming and procedure design. Specific examples are as follows:

- When tape units differ in density or track-mode, or disk units differ in capacity or storage concept, file conversion can be performed only on a machine configuration which can handle both versions. If this is not available, the files must be converted via another medium.
- Programming will be influenced by differences in disk concepts, and by the introduction of printer forms control.
- Procedures design will be affected by the availability or non-availability of stacker selection.

Tools

When you have made thorough inventory of all problems arising in the problem areas of the proceding section, you can then list the conversion activities which you will require for the performance of the change-over. From this list, you will able to determine what aids and support facilities will be called for. Normally, some of these instruments will be available, while others will have to be prepared.
Instruments for assisting with the change-over can be grouped into three categories: processors and aids, support facilities, and methods.

Processors and aids
Processors and aids are instruments for conversion or translation. Processors operate with a minimum of human intervention, while aids only support the change-over and call for a considerable amount of manual work.
Processors and aids are the most important instruments in effecting change-over, because program conversion forms the greater part of the work. The manpower and machine-time called for are in inverse ratio to the degree of automatic translation or conversion employed. The success of a change-over, therefore, will depend very largely upon the availability of appropriate processors and aids, and upon the power of the processors and aids which are available.
In general, file-conversion processors can be divided into two classes; those which can be run on either the old or the new machine, which read in the old data, and reorganize and rewrite it in accordance with the new specifications; and those which operate in two steps, the data being first dumped from the old machine on to an intermediate device which is then used as an input generator for a file generator on the new machine.
Processors for the conversion of programs written in high-level languages are relatively simple. Because of this fact, most of these processors are readily available.
Less simple is the transfer of a program to a language of a different level; e.g. from RPG to COBOL, or from AUTOCODER or ASSEMBLER to COBOL.
The chief problem in such cases is the difference in language structure and philosophy. Some processors are available in this area, but in many cases the choice will lie between using a less comprehensive instrument or, if circumstances so indicate, creating a suitable processor.
The most difficult case is the conversion of programming written in machine-oriented languages. Such programming is very difficult to translate automatically, since a great number of instructions will have to be simulated or replaced by their equivalents in the new system — if such equivalents exist. It may even be necessary to effect changes in the program logic order to achieve the desired result in the new language. Automatic processors for this form of translation will seldom be available, and it will not often be economical to create them. In this area, a great deal of manual translation can be expected.

Support facilities
In addition to program conversion, a wide variety of other activities is necessary to the performance of a change-over. These include checkout, investigation, analysis, project control, the handling of emergencies and the design of procedures. Many of these can be performed, and most of them at least supported, by the use of suitable auxiliary programs and subroutines. Such programs and routines are called support facilities.

Checkout
Checkout is the comparison of the output from original and converted programs. It can be accomplished by screening and file-compare programs.

Investigation and analysis
Investigation and analysis of the present situation, in the sense of summarizing the facilities in use and building up cross-references and statistics, is effected by means of count/sort/merge/combine operations. This is data processing in the original meaning of the term, and is therefore appropriate work for the computer.

Project control
Project control can be greatly assisted by the use of accounting routines in its effectiveness in managing the change-over.

Emergency utilities
Emergencies which can lead to panic situations include the destruction of files and the unreadability of a library file. To overcome these and other similar disasters, emergency utilities are necessary to every installation. Such utilities must be capable of reading, interpreting and correcting data which cannot be read by standard software.

Pre- and post-processors
Procedures can be designed, including pre- and post-processors, for the purpose of handling and linking those parts of a change-over which cannot be effected by single programs, but must be performed as a series of steps.

Methods
For the purposes of this section, methods are guidelines which offer predefined procedures to be used in the performance of the change-over. They deal principally with conversion streams, handling procedures, and the ordering of procedure steps. They comprise descriptions of the various approaches which can be used to achieve the goal of getting the application operational on the new system, and of the methodology appropriate to these approaches; give hints for the efficient processing of given workloads; and present flowcharts of transition techniques.

Methodology

This section deals with the practical approach to an actual change-over. It presents tested methods for attacking the problem, with illustrations drawn from experience.

Investigate the current state

The present state should be investigated in terms of the following particulars.

- Number and size of programs.
- Packages used.
- Libraries and standard sub-routines.

The first step should be to prepare a list of all the programs which are to be considered for conversion. This list should include program identification, size, language, and type of file organization. If the program employs any specific features of the current system, this must be indicated. It is important to indicate which programs originate from packages.

Where large quantities of programs are involved, it is useful to have a special program to perform the listing and analysis automatically. In an actual case, a program was succesfully developed for the handling of COBOL programs. This provided a "where-used list", and a survey per program of the quantities of source statements, data names, procedure names, and the use of reserved words. One result of subjecting all programs to such an analysis is to provide in advance a very good picture of the nature and extent of the work involved before conversion is actually started.

At this stage, it is useful to examine the information obtained with a view to making the optimum use of the library facilities which are such a valuable feature of third and post-third generation methods.

Visualise the future state

The next step is to make a preliminary visualisation of the future. This should be done in terms of the following possibilities.

- Conversion — translation.
- Restoration — reprogramming.
- Redesign — reconstruction.
- Simulation — emulation.
- Improvement.
- Replacement.

Each program in the list should be examined, in the light of the information provided in the list of programs, in order to determine what steps are appropriate in order to make its function available to the new system. One or more of the possibilities given above should be either tentatively or definitely selected.

Although it is inadvisable to make major structural modifications to a program in the course of conversion, some changes will nevertheless appear desirable. In particular, where old and inefficient programs are still in use, consideration should be given to rewriting them, if time and capacity can be made available. Of

course, every opportunity should be taken to replace old selfwritten utilities with modern software.
Undoubtedly, new packages will be available. The introduction of a standard package should be given precedence over the conversion of a self-written package, even though this introduction will itself cost time and capacity.

Requirements planning
The results of the investigation of the current state and the visualisation of the future state should now be brought together. This confrontation will permit an assessment of the requirements of the change-over.
We should be able to determine accurately at this stage what instruments will be called for. Enquiries will ascertain which of these instruments are actually available from the various sources — the manufacturer, and possibly software houses, users' clubs, and so forth.
Any instruments not available from any discoverable source will either have to be created or done without. The decision as to whether to create an instrument or operate manually in its absence will depend upon the relative quantities of work involved in the two courses, and here again the results of the current and future state enquiries will provide a basis for estimation.

Checkout
Checkout is not merely ascertaining that a program works; it is determining that the output from the running of a program is either precisely the same as that from the corresponding program in the old system, or that it differs only in specific and intentional aspects.
Checkout can proceed only when suitable test data is available. The test data employed must not be too extensive; otherwise the demands in time and cost will be too high, and control too difficult. Therefore it is necessary to choose the test data with care.
A good file-compare program is of great help in checking test results. It must be so constructed that it is capable of recognizing inserted and deleted records; otherwise a record-by-record compare will go out of step whenever a missing or additional record is encountered in either file.

Assessing the value of the available instruments
The determination of what is desirable is not too difficult. But in the determination of what is available, much care must be exercised. Indeed, true processors are rare, and prospective users must be very wary. Similarly, all Support Facilities offered should be closely scrutinised before any aspect of the overall planning is made to depend upon their performance.
The best procedure is to run a test shot, to determine whether or not the instrument under consideration operates as represented. Conviction arises from actual practice. Mere operation is not necessarily fully satisfactory; the speed and core efficiency of the converted programs are also important.

In this respect, it should be borne in mind that a reduction of the core requirement is not in general to be looked for. Indeed, an increased core demand is more likely, although where this occurs it should be the reflection of advantages in other respects, such as flexibility, versatility, improved performance, or speed. There should, however, be no substantial increases in throughput times, particularly in respect of programs written in high-level languages. Here again, however, the wise course is to try it out, observe what happens, and draw conclusions from the results.

Planning

Having reached this point, an estimate can be made of the machine hours and man capacity required for the conversion. In this respect it is important to optimize for the workload, the time-scale and the manpower.

Merely employing more people on the project will not automatically guarantee a faster change-over; the team must be properly balanced in respect of the various skills called for.

One should take into account the necessity for the maintenance of converted programs, which will make demands upon a certain section of the already too small available force, thus depleting it even further and unbalancing it ......

Manpower

Ideally, most or all of the manpower required should come from existing staff. This would ensure that all concerned were given an adequate opportunity to learn about the new system before it became operational. It would also mean that new development, and possibly the operation of the current system, would be brought almost to a standstill. The opposite side of the coin would be to put the job of conversion out to contract. This has a superficial attractiveness, but if adopted will result in the hardware, programs and system software being insufficiently familiar to those who must subsequently use it.

A middle course is advisable; selected positions can be filled from software-house personnel, and perhaps extra outside programming assistance can be acquired for the change-over itself.

Machine-capacity

In general, it is often difficult to find in-house machine capacity. The existing system is normally so fully loaded that preparatory work for the conversion must be done elsewhere. In this connexion, it should be noted that familiarisation with the new computer and the carrying out of conversion work is without doubt an integral part of the provision of the new system, and should therefore be eligible for assistance and tools offered by the manufacturer.

Training

It is important to consider the training aspect during the planning stage. The skill of the personnel involved is of the highest importance for a successful change-over, and a good knowledge of both the old and the new systems will improve the conversion tempo.

This should not be taken to mean that as many people as possible should be sent as soon as possible to as many courses as possible. The existing skills and experience of the people who are running the current system must on no account be overlooked or underestimated. Operators and programmers are not really interested in continually starting over again. An operator with plenty of experience in operating a third-generation system knows what an operating system is, and, in general, how it must be used; he will have little difficulty in accommodating to a new one. After all, a man does not learn to drive all over again each time he changes his car, and a pilot who moves to a different type of aircraft receives a specific conversion training, not a complete new pilot's course. Conversion training, preferably organized and carried out by an experienced operator on the present staff, is both cheaper and more efficient than complete retraining. It is also more popular.

The same is true for programmers. It is foolish to send an experienced COBOL programmer on a COBOL course. He is quite capable of learning from a manual and a list of recommendations and differences. Likewise, of course, for ALGOL, FORTRAN, etc.

Scheduling

The time-scheduling of the various conversion activities is conditioned by a number of considerations.

In general, programs which make either heavy or frequent demands on the schedules production time of the new system should be given high priority of conversion. But these programs — those which are long-running, or which are run daily or several times a week — are frequently amongst the most complex of the programs to be converted, and therefore most likely to encounter difficulties and delays in the conversion. If a long or frequently-used program happens to be relatively simple, and/or to offer little difficulty in conversion, it is a natural candidate for very early conversion. But if the entire manpower available for the program conversion effort is set to work at the very beginning on a set of tasks which for a long time produce no output at all in terms of finished programs available for running on the new system, this is bad both from the viewpoint of efficiency of change-over and from that of morale. So, while it is not a good idea to keep *all* the problems to the end, the above general recommendation must be tempered in its application by judgement and expediency.

Another determining factor in scheduling is the availability of test data. A converted program is valueless until it has been tested. But it is usually prohibitively expensive, and sometimes impossible, to provide appropriate test data directly for every single program. The solution is to group the programs into sets in such a way that test data has to be supplied to only the first program in each set, and the output of each program in a set can be used as test input for the next.

While this method avoids the necessity of providing large quantities of test data, and makes smaller demands upon computer time and the usage of tape reels, disc packs etc., it does to some extent dictate the order in which the program conversion can be done.

Frozen period
During the period in which a program is being converted, it is necessary to "freeze" it — to declare that during the actual conversion time no program changes can be accepted. The length of time for which a program can be frozen, and the time scheduling of its frozen period, will naturally have a considerable effect on the overall scheduling of the change-over.
From this point of view, it is also recommended not to include the most recently finished programs in the first conversion projects, since these programs are those most likely to require a substantial number of changes.

Change-over preparation

Before the change-over proper, a number of points require attention. The most general and important of these are dealt with in this section; in any specific case, other points of a similar character may exist. Such points will become obvious from a careful inspection of the results of the work accomplished to date.

Collecting source programs
It is necessary to make sure that all available source programs have been located. These programs should be examined for error. In particular, it is necessary to discover whether any core-image programs have been patched or otherwise altered without the corresponding corrections having been made in the source program; this condition, if it goes undiscovered and uncorrected, is deadly to conversion.

Library facilities
A good library system is necessary for the successful accomplishment of the change-over. This system should enable the user to correct programs as easily and efficiently as possible. In this connexion, it must be stated that the handling of large quantities of programs in card form is virtually impossible. It is desirable that all conversion tools employed in the change-over should accept this library as input.

Jobstreams
At this stage, the overall jobstream structure of the change-over should be made up. The complete preparation of individual jobstreams should not be attempted, because the feedback resulting from their use would lead to difficulties and unduly high correction costs. Where — as is, of course, desirable — the conversion tools available make possible the simultaneous conversion of large quantities of programs, the principle of jobstream generation plays an important role.
In practical cases, the conversion processors have been designed to convert the

input programs, return them to library in source form, and generate a jobstream containing all the jobcontrol statements required to macro-process, compile, linkage-edit, and catalogue these programs in the new system. If these activities are not performed by the conversion processors, they must be done manually at this stage, usually at the cost of much manual work, many re-runs and a good deal of frustration due to mistakes and mispunching.

Conversion of standard parts

Before converting the programs, it is recommended that all associated subsidiary routines be first converted.

Where COPY and INCLUDE statements have been included in COBOL programs, the SSL books should be converted first. If this is not done, then any corrections required will have to be made each time the book is called for.

Macros have to be carried over into the new system. For the standard software macros (I/O macros etc.) suitable new equivalents will be selected and built into a conversion routine, so that replacement can be done automatically. Where self-written macros are concerned, experience shows that these should always be rewritten; this makes for simplicity and a more efficient conversion.

The principal difference between macros and general subroutines is one of flexibility. Macros are generated on-line in the source decks, and the source statements generated can be varied within wide limits by use of the parameters in the macro call; general subroutines are fixed entities which are added to the program at link-edit or execution time. What has been said concerning macros is applicable also to subroutines; it is normally profitable to replace the standard software with selected equivalents, and to rewrite the self-written examples in accordance with the requirements of the new system.

Utilities must also be carefully considered. In general, redesign and/or reprogramming will be appropriate for the self-written utilities; but the situation should be examined to determine whether or not the utilities offered with the new hardware are capable of replacing some or all of the self-written utilities.

Change-over

The actual conversion period can sometimes run into many weeks. The more thoroughly the preliminary work, up to and including the final change-over preparations, has been done, the fewer will be the difficulties encountered during this period. The following factors are important.

A realistic and comprehensive time-schedule must first be drawn up. This schedule must not only allow for the influences of many opposing factors, but must be so constructed that it is capable of being continuously corrected and updated as a result of feedback from the current state of achievement as the change-over proceeds.

This feedback is a part of the very necessary activity of process control. In practice, regular progress-control meetings have been found indispensable. At these meet-

ings, achievement is compared with plan, and the differences are examined both to discover their causes and to estimate their effect on the possibility of fulfilling future targets.
Results obtained from the job-accounting system must be recorded in such a way that they contribute to the progress control function.
In the beginning, when little comparative quantitative information is available, these figures form valuable yardsticks. When standards have been established, the accounting-system figures can be compared with them, and the differences noted and acted upon.
In this area, graphical representations are generally preferable to long lists of complicated figures. In any case, both the form of presentation and the method of collecting data must be fixed beforehand, and not left until the conversion has been started.
The entire change-over should be carefully documented as it progresses. The reference material thus obtained will prove invaluable later.

Consolidation

At the moment when the conversion is nominally complete — i.e., when the old system has been phased out, and the new hardware and software are ready to accept the work-load, much still remains to be done. One of the most important things is the preparation of the new procedures. The general form of these procedures has, of course, been mapped out already, almost as a by-product of the planning stage; but the formalization cannot usefully be accomplished until the new system is ready to be operated. The first period of operation with the new system will lead also to the streamlining of many aspects, in particular the job-streams. All the considerations of 5-5 and 5-6 apply to some degree in this phase of the change-over.
This is also the time to attend to the documentation of the new system. In practice, this often turns out to be a lighter task than might have been expected. Much depends upon the quality of the documentation of the old system, and even more upon the thoroughness with which the documentation of the preparation for change-over and of the change-over itself have been performed.
It is very important that the documentation should be made as system-independant as possible.
When making block-diagrams, preference should be given to macro diagrams. The more detailed the block diagrams, the more likely is it that they will have to be substantially changed to meet a new situation (e.g. a subsequent change-over).
While computer flowcharting can sometimes be useful, experience to date tends to show that it is of but limited helpfulness. This does not mean that the employment of good flowcharting programs should be ruled out if any are available; merely that too much should not be expected from their use. On the other hand, I/O analyzers and system flowchart programs which portray the jobstreams can prove extremely useful.

Experiences and recommendations

This final section comprises a set of hints and tips, arising from much actual experience in change-overs, which, it is hoped, will prove useful.

- COBOL is ideally suited to conversion. It has proved possible to design a COBOL converter which calls for an absolute minimum of manual correction to the converted programs. Difficulties can arise, however, when changing to a random-access system, because of the technical differences between direct addressing and any other form of address.
- Almost 100% success has been achieved in converting automatically from RPG to COBOL, and in the conversion from the COBOL of one manufacturer to that of another.
- Difficulties are likely to be experienced in the conversion of second generation Autocoder into COBOL, in spite of the availability of certain programs to assist. Better results can be expected in the conversion of second generation Autocoder to third generation Autocoder.
- While file conversion (see 5-4) sometimes seems at the outset an intimidating task, it is a fact of experience that it seldom turns out to be as difficult as was thought. The appearance of difficulty arises from the fact that so many files are large and extensive; but the new system's files are not likely to differ greatly from the old in their fundamental characteristics. File conversion almost never produces a bottleneck.
- As a rule-of-thumb for progress measurement, one program converted per programmer-day is a useful figure to bear in mind. It is, of course, an average figure, and cannot be applied to specific programs or particular days.
- It is sometimes alleged that a converted program is necessarily less efficient than the program as originally written. Experience does not bear this out. Depending upon the circumstances, it can occasionally happen; but when full use is made of the possibilities of the new system, the converted programs are, in general, more efficient than the originals.
- Difficulties may be encountered in connexion with members of the staff who are unable to cope with the new system. This can arise from two circumstances; there are the people who were so busy working until the last moment on the old system that they had no time to be trained on the new, and there are the people who are simply not capable of coping with the new situation. The existence of people in the first category is a fault of the change-over planning. All personnel who are to work with the new system must receive training during the change-over, whether they are employed on the change-over itself or not. It is all too easy to forget this in respect of people who are deeply involved for example, in maintaining the old programs up to the last moment; but to do so is to build trouble into the plans. The existence of the second category is unfortunate, but if it occurs no amount of planning could have avoided it. Nevertheless, the possibility of its occurrence must be taken into account at the planning stage, and provision which is seen by all to be fair and reasonable should be made to deal with it. If the introduction of a

new phase of computer operations achieves the reputation of having caused harsh and unfair decisions, then there will probably be personnel troubles the next time changes are called for.

Next time

It may seem premature to commence thinking about a future change-over during the performance of the present one. It is not. It is a common experience at change-over time to find oneself wishing that certain things had, in the past, been done otherwise. There is, in fact, no time better than change-over time for thinking about the next change-over. The following recommendations should be kept in mind throughout the whole process.

Avoid "tricky" programming. If a programmer sees a highly ingenious solution to a specific problem, he will often use it for the intellectual satisfaction it offers him, without reference to the overall effect on the system. But such solutions are usually rather specific, and not capable of extension to other problems in the same group. It is usually better to stick to house standards and to adopt uniform methods, even where these mean that the actual method of programming a small number of problems suffers in brilliance for the sake of uniformity. This should not be taken too far, however. A method should not be rejected simply because it is ingenious. If a programmer comes up with a method which is economical, ingenious and of good generality, but not in accordance with the house standards, then due consideration should be given to changing the standards to accommodate it. Due and full consideration; do not forget that adoption of new standards may mean retrospective action on existing programs. What is essential is that similar problems are solved throughout by similar methods.

- If a certain task occurs frequently, provide for its solution by means of macros, routines or standard programs. For example, take the case of table-handling in a COBOL program. COBOL does not provide for table-handling; thus, in the absence of other arrangements, the programmers will have to solve this program each time it occurs. It would be far better to supply a standard binarysearch routine, written perhaps in Autocoder. If a system is well provided with such help routines, then at conversion time, these can be dealt with first; this will lessen the amount of manual work required, and improve the core and timing aspects of the conversion process.
- Ensure that, at all times, programming is carried out according to the rules. It is not only ingenuity which can cause programmers to depart from house standards; sometimes it is lack of proper understanding, and sometimes just laziness. Non-standard programming is deadly for change-over.
- Standardize. Standardization of methods, procedures and programs offers the best chance of approaching 100% success at change-over time. Ideally, standardization should be taken to the point where there is only one solution to any problem.
- I/O is always a complicated business in change-overs. Numerous difficulties arise in connexion with the incompatibility of peripherals. There is much benefit to be drived from writing programs with separate I/O routines or macros, or even separate I/O programs.

Activity 6-3: Data gathering

Technique 6-3.1: Interview

Purpose

The purpose of interviewing is to obtain quantitative and qualitative data regarding policies, procedures, and practices, either existing or planned for the future.

Areas of application

The interview technique has application in all phases of the systems effort, from obtaining costs and savings information to determining functional requirements and securing agreement with user management.

Scope of interviewing

The object of an interview is to elicit frank and complete answers from the respondent. In attempting this, the interviewer[1]) faces an individual who will react both to the personality of the interviewer and to the subject matter which is discussed. The interviewer must, therefore, concern himself with the goals, attitudes, beliefs, and motives of the respondent, if he is to make the most efficient use of the interview.

Respondent motivation[2)]

This section surveys some of the motivational factors relevant to the planning, conducting, and analysis of a fact-finding interview.

The degree of motivation required to carry an interview to a successful completion is directly related to the demands made on the respondent. Interviews differ in the amount of time required, in the effort of recall required, and in the threats and fears which are generated. These factors define the weight of the interview task on the respondent which must be overcome by motivation.

The initial motivation in many interviews is no more than courtesy — the custom in our society that strangers are to be treated politely. This motivation is of very short duration, and the time thus gained must be used by the interviewer to bring other motives into play, principally by making the interview meaningful in terms of the respondent's goals and needs. This means obtaining

1) The interviewer is described as being a teammember participating in the project as an outside consultant. If the interviewer is already familiar with the user organization some of the more formal points in this technique are not applicable.

2) The theorical material in this paragraph is extracted from: R. L. Kahn and C. F. Cannell, *The dynamics of interviewing: theory, techniques and cases*, John Wiley and Sons, Inc., 1966 (368 pp). This book is recommended reading for anyone attempting to become professionally proficient in the interviewing area.

prior knowledge of the respondent, so that appropriate language can be used, and the purpose of the interview expressed in terms meaningful to the respondent. The tenor of the interview must be directly and explicitly determined by the respondent's goals.

A frequently useful motive is the desire to "influence important activities". The respondent will be motivated to participate if the purpose of the interview is suitably presented — that is, if the respondent is made to feel that he can be instrumental in causing a change or action that he considers desirable. It is important, therefore, to relate the context of the interview to the change desired, and to make clear how the interviewer can have a role in bringing about this change. This motive also helps to keep the discussion focused on relevant topics, and to probe deeply into the subject.

The desire of the respondent to talk about topics which are of interest to him, but which he is not usually able to discuss with a responsible person, can be another strong motive. This factor can be strong so long as the interviewer maintains an atmosphere in which the respondent feels that he is fully understood, that he is not being juedged or criticized, and that he can trust the interviewer not to betray confidences.

The interviewer will find that, even in an atmosphere of trust and acceptance, the respondent will present his ideas only when he feels they will significantly affect the systems effort. Consequently the respondent must be made aware of the importance of his cooperation; respect for his opinion and status must be evident throughout the interview. If the respondent is antagonized, or made to feel defensive about his participation in the system, a valuable source of information will be lost.

Procedures[1)]

Because the interview is so basic a form of communication with such a variety of purposes, dependent upon the nature of the systems effort, it is impossible to establish a list of specific questions to be asked. Instead, general guidelines for effective interviewing are presented below:

Interviewer's need for interviewing skills

Interviewing is a technique which can be used by each team in nearly all the activities of the systems effort. The team members who do not originally come from the user organization will have little or no knowledge of how this organization operates. Therefore, in addition to background research, they will have to talk to people in the organization.

---

1) This section is the result of research performed for the U.S.A.F. System Command's Project 465L. It was originally made avaible by: M. I. Bolsky, *Guide to gathering information for system analysis.* Unpublished Note LO-2864, S.D.C., 1964.

The training of an interviewer in talking to people — interviewing — is very important. He should be aware that there is more to interviewing than merely making conversation. Interviews which do not produce the desired information leave both the interviewer and the respondent frustrated.

No user wants an outsider to come in and tell him how to run his organization; and indeed no outsider can do so, because he has not lived in the organization, and will not have to use the system he designs. The real job of the project team is not so much to design a system as, through skilled interviewing, to enable user personnel clearly to define for themselves the most effective and efficient system for their needs. This is the way to achieve a truly workable system. The user's personnel, having enjoyed full participation in the definition and development of the system, will regard it as their system, and not as a system arbitrarily imposed by someone from outside.

Interview-appraisal criteria

Psychologists have discovered that a person can listen to verbal material, and comprehend what he hears, at over double the rate at which most people speak (average comprehension rate = 300 words/minute; average speaking rate = 125 words/minute). This means that the average person can listen to a conversation and think about something else at the same time. This is the cause of much mind wandering; and once the listener lets his mind begin to drift, he tends to end up not listening at all. The remedy that most psychologists recommend for this, is not to let the mind begin to wander in the first place. Instead of using the extra comprehension time to think about unrelated subjects, it should be used to analyze and evaluate what the respondent is saying. This will reinforce listening, instead of ruining it, as does mind wandering.
Below are suggested some questions which the interviewer should ask himself while listening:

- What supporting facts does the respondent have for his main points?
- How recent is his information?
- How complete is his information?
- Do I really understand what he is saying?
- Are some areas being omitted from the discussion by the respondent?
- If so, what areas, and why?
- Have I already discussed this topic with someone else?
- How do the respondent's information and ideas compare with what I was told previously?
- How important is this topic? Is much time being spent on something of minor importance?
- Is the respondent using logical reasoning?
- Are irrelevant or inconsequential side-topics being connected with the main topic under discussion?

Deciding whom to interview

It is important that the project team schedules sufficient interviews with personnel at all levels of the user organization. The easiest and most straightforward interviews to arrange and to manage are likely to be those with people in the middle echelons of the organization. It is nevertheless essential to interview, in addition to such people, those at both the highest and the lowest levels. The reasons for this are given in the following paragraphs, and details of the particular methods applicable to such interviews are presented in the appropriate sections of this technique.

Personnel at the lower levels of the organization

Much is to be learned from employees at the lower levels; in fact, there are usually many practical items which can be learned only from personnel at these levels. Furthermore, those below the executive and professional level will almost certainly be playing a significant and perhaps major role in the operation of any new system. If they have not been consulted, or made to feel that their ideas and knowledge were taken into consideration, there is bound to be difficulty when the new system is implemented. No matter how efficient a system may be from a theoretical standpoint, it cannot work properly if the people who are to use it are not sympathetic.

Personnel at the higher levels of the organization

It is important that the project team schedules at least a few interviews with personnel at the highest levels of the user organization; for instance, the managing director. This does not mean simply "briefing" that person, but having true discussions with him.

A newly designed system which does not operate to the satisfaction of the management of the user organization presents serious problems both to the organization and to the project team. However short the time which they can afford to devote to interviews, top management will therefore readily appreciate the need for their cooperation from the earliest stages. "Briefings" are useful, but far from sufficient in themselves; they usually allow little time for true discussion, and may thus not accurately convey the objectives and progress of the project team's work.

Preparing for the interview

Terminology

In addition to general knowledge obtained by background research, the interviewer should learn the language used in the organization; he should study the jargon and abbreviations from all available glossaries, introductory brochures training documents, and reports. If there are no glossaries, he should make one up himself. Virtually every profession, business, and trade has words peculiar to itself. If the interviewer has not taken the trouble to understand these specialized words, he cannot hope to understand what respondents tell him. Sometimes considerable misunderstanding and difficulty is caused by the failure of the interviewer to learn the appropriate jargon before he starts the interviews.

Coordination
One of the complaints that users often have is that, when several interviewers are working on a project, each asks the same questions that others have already asked. The users feel, perhaps justifiably, that the interviewers have not been coordinating among themselves. Some duplication is, of course, unavoidable, and is often desirable; but excessive duplication of this sort can be avoided if each interviewer takes notes at the interviews, writes up a report, and routes it to the other interviewers working on the project.

Conducting an introductory group meeting
If possible, supervisory personnel should tell prospective respondents in advance that they will be interviewed, giving reasons. One way of doing this is by means of an introductory group meeting, where the supervisor introduces the interviewer and explains who he is and what he is doing; and the interviewer then speaks for a few minutes about his duties.

Scheduling specific times for interviews
The approach to personnel at any level should be courteous and reasonable. At top level, this would imply providing well in advance explicit details of the ground which it is intended to cover on each particular occasion; and allowing the executive concerned to select, within reason, his own time for the interview. If the matter is approached in this way, difficulties will seldom be encountered. Specific times for the interviews should always be scheduled in advance; the interviewer should not unnecessarily interrupt people in the course of their duties.

To give prior notification several days (or at least hours) before an interview enables respondents to prepare themselves for it. It is best that this notification should come from a supervisor in his capacity as an official of the organization. If the interviewer comes without advance notice the respondent may not have time to talk. Furthermore, an unpleasant feeling may be established, so that future interviews may not go well even if scheduled in advance. Alternatively, the respondent may attempt to talk, even though he has insufficient time; as a result, the interview may be rushed and tense, and possibly lead to misunderstandings and erroneous information. Most important, scheduling in advance will allow the respondent to organize his thoughts, and collect any background information that should be discussed.

Late interviews
No interviews should be scheduled late in the day or just before lunch. As far as possible, interviews should not be scheduled for after 4:00 p.m. People are apt to be tired by this time, and a tired person is not likely to be very informative.

Starting the interview

Business cards

The interviewer should give the respondent his business card at the beginning of the interview. This is an additional and tangible means of introduction. It will help put the respondent at ease if he has some sort of record to keep, showing to whom he has been speaking. Also, if he has the card at the start, he will have the interviewer's name right, and will know how to address him during the interview. To be ignorant of the interviewer's name might make him uncomfortable during the entire interview. Finally, if he has the card, he will know where to reach the interviewer later on, if necessary.

Making clear the reason for the interview

At the beginning of the interview, the interviewer should take a few minutes to clarify the reason for the interview, even if there has been some prior notification, in order to relieve any fears or suspicions. If the respondent feels that the interview is a personal test or criticism of him, his remarks may be of little value. Such an explanation is especially inportant when interviewing a person low in the user organization, such as a clerk or mechanic, who may have absolutely no idea of what the purpose of the interview is. This initial explanation should be repeated, although perhaps in abbreviated form, at subsequent interviews with the same person. People need to be reminded, and to be reassured that their jobs are not at stake.

Beginning the interview

It has been found, through research into interrogation techniques, that successful interviewers frequently ask broad general questions at the beginning of an interview. This permits the communication of important information; in addition, it provides the respondent with an opportunity to digress into those areas with which he may be particularly concerned. This broad questioning may then be followed by specific inquiry.

Conducting the interview

Pertinence

Interviews must be kept to the subject; that is, the system to be defined. Extraneous comments and conversations should be kept to a minimum. The interviewer is leading the interview, and must not introduce irrelevant topics. If the person being interviewed introduces such topics, the interviewer will try to lead the interview back to the main subject.

The people being interviewed are busy with routine duties. If the interviewer becomes known for wasting time in long, irrelevant conversations, he will seriously impair his ability to work effectively. Sometimes people initiate conversations in order to show friendliness, but in this context the best way to show friendliness is for each participant to respect existing demands on the time of the other.

"Yes" or "no" questions

The interviewer should not ask, "Do you like such-and-such feature of the present system? This question might be rephrased, "Please tell me the particular aspects of such-and-such feature of the present system that you do like, and those that you don't like". Questions which can be answered with a "yes" or "no" elicit snap judgements which do not stimulate thought. However, if the respondent is asked for specific, itemized facts or opinions, he is forced to consider what he actually thinks, and why.

Absence of criticism

If the respondent has no criticism at all of the existing methods in the organization, he is probably being defensive. The interviewer should try to put him at ease, and then find out whether there actually is something wrong with those methods. No organization is perfect, and the human tendency is to criticize. Frank talk, including criticism, is one sign of a healthy organization. If there is no criticism at all, it may be because things are so seriously wrong that personnel are afraid to criticize. This situation usually arises, not in an entire organization — it could hardly have survived if it was so inefficient — but rather in a particular group or section. When this is encountered, it calls for close scrutiny to determine the true situation. Of course, it is possible that the group really is working at top efficiency.

Thinking time

The respondent should be allowed periods of silence in which to think. If a question is asked and the respondent does not immediately reply, the interviewer should refrain from suggesting answers, or asking another question. He should give the respondent a reasonable time in which to think. Many interviewers assume that silence must be avoided at all costs. This assumption is wrong. Occasional periods of silence are desirable in an interview; the respondent may recall vital bits of information, ideas, or analyses which would otherwise have been lost.

Outside distractions

Freedom from distractions is imperative in an interview. Distractions may include such things as outside noises, telephone calls, and people coming to see either the interviewer or the respondent. Every effort should be made to eliminate such distractions. They are not merely temporary annoyances, costing a few seconds or minutes; they seriously interfere with the thinking processes of both the interviewer and the respondent. Frequent distractions can totally ruin an interview.

Internal distractions

Distractions from the outside are bad enough, but those created by the interviewer himself — fidgeting with papers, glancing at papers while the respondent is talking, looking out of a window or door, playing with a pocket knife or a paper weight, rearranging articles on his desk — are even worse. Such actions not only distract the respondent, they also show a lack of respect for him, and for what he is saying. Even though this lack of respect is not intentional, it nevertheless has its effect.

Fact or opinion?
If the matter raises the slightest doubt in his mind, the interviewer should ask the respondent whether he is stating a fact or a personal opinion. Sometimes the respondent will give an opinion, confident that the interviewer will recognize it as such; while the interviewer assumes that it is a statement of fact. It is important to have people's opinions, but it is equally important to be aware that they are opinions.

Encouragement of elaboration
A good way of getting a person to elaborate on something he has said is to rephrase or summarize the gist of his last few statements. This prevents an immediate change of subject, and gives the respondent more time to think about it. It also permits him to hear his ideas voiced by someone else, which may stimulate his own thoughts.

Sarcasm and humour
Sarcasm should never be used in an interview. Jokes or other types of humour should also be avoided unless the interviewer is positive that the repondent realizes he is joking. The interviewer sets the tone of the interview, and if he is sarcastic, he simply lowers the whole image of his work in the eyes of the respondent. Jokes or humour are occasionally permissible, provided that humour is harmless and that it is clearly humour. However, the interviewer should be certain that what is intended as a harmless joke is not taken by the respondent as a sarcastic or otherwise negative attitude or comment.

Background of the organization
The interviewer should ask about past behaviour in the user organization, in order to get a feeling for the background conditions giving rise to current practices. Many of today's needs stem from yesterday's conditions. It is thus important to understand earlier problems and requirements thoroughly, so that the routines embodied in current operations may be understood.

Respondents' questions
The interviewer should answer courteously, and record, all questions asked by the respondent except for those dealing with user-organization management plans, or personalities. One of the principal aspects upon which to concentrate in all interviews is that of bringing to light any questions the respondent may have regarding what the new system is supposed to do or not to do; how it will operate; how it will be produced; how various problems and obstacles will be overcome, and so on. These questions should be given very careful attention, and should be written down. Questions stimulate thought. Sometimes questions

which appear obvious — or even rediculous — uncover areas about which everyone is making unexamined assumptions; therefore, no question that is raised by a respondent should by lightly dismissed. Sometimes a person who asks questions is more helpful than one who supplies a large number of facts.

Showing of interest
It must be clearly evident that the interviewer is really listening to, and interested in, what the respondent is saying.

The unfamiliar
The interviewer should concentrate on the difficult and unfamiliar, rather than the obvious, aspects of the topic under discussion. Most people have a tendency to dwell on topics which are straightforward and clear. Often a discussion or meeting will spend much time on things which everyone knows, and then hastily skim over topics that are unfamiliar, or difficult, or complex, or which involve many questions and conflicting ideas. Obviously, this tendency must be avoided if the interview is to be conducted efficiently.

Verbal confusion
One of the things that an interviewer must be alert for is the inconsistent or incorrect use of words. For instance, in the computer industry, a man may use the following words interchangeably: computer, hardware, data processing machine, digital computer and system. It is most unlikely that the interviewer can bring about any substantial changes in the vocabulary in use; the next best thing is for him to be aware that there are areas in which local usage may be confusing him; to seek to learn the meaning of such usage; and to speak at once whenever he is in doubt about the meaning of a term.

Handling disagreements

The interviewer must never directly contradict or interrupt the respondent, even if he strongly disagrees with what is being said. When the respondent has expressed his views, the interviewer should then employ whichever of the methods of this section he considers most appropriate, perhaps even turning the disagreement into a useful exchange of ideas.

Proper humility
Admit that he is not an expert in the user organization's work. Most important, admit that he is not as expert in the respondent's job as the respondent himself, and that he is not trying to tell the respondent how to do his job.

Postponement
Say that he will take the matter up later in the interview, or at a subsequent interview, and drop it completely for the present. If such a course is adopted, then, on resumption, the respondent must be allowed his full say.

Appreciation of the other opinion
If for some reason the matter can not be dropped, then this rule should be followed:
"Each person can speak up for himself only after he has first restated the ideas and feelings of the previous speaker accurately and to that speaker's satisfaction".[1])

Stimulation of questions
Try to stimulate the other person into asking questions, and ask him questions in turn. When two persons disagree with one another, they have really broken off communication; if the interviewer can initiate the asking of questions, this will tend to restore communication.

Definition of the cause
Once the cause of disagreement is defined, the disagreement will be half solved. Is the disagreement a difference over:

- fact? Then the obvious solution is to refer to some authority — either a book or a person;
- opinion? Be sure that each participant clearly understands the other's opinion. If there is still no agreement, then both opinions should be included in the report, with reasons in support of each.

Termination
If there is a clash of personalities, the interview should be terminated quickly and courteously. If there is an important reason for continuing the interview, it must be rescheduled for another day.

Note-taking

Points in favour of note-taking

- Note-taking tends to keep the mind on the subject and alert for items to be recorded;
- note-taking helps to keep the interview on the subject under discussion;
- if the interviewer has a poor memory, note-taking may be necessary in order to retain specific facts;
- notes, however, short and incomplete, permit the subsequent recall of the major trends of the interview, and details heard but not recorded.

Points against note-taking

- If too much time is spent in taking notes, the interviewer becomes more of a stenographer, and loses effective control of the interview;
- some respondents may become hesitant to speak if the interviewer starts taking notes; when such a reaction is observed, the notebook must be put away;

[1]) R.G. Nichols and L.A. Stevens, *Are you listening*, McGraw-Hill, New York, 1957.

- note-taking may cause excessive attention to facts, with little attention given to ideas, opinions, questions, etc.

The interviewer should take out his notebook and pencil at the start of the interview, before the conversation has begun. He should also immediately inform the respondent that a copy of the notes will be sent to him before they are published or routed to others.

Taking the notebook out at the start will immediately get the respondent used to the idea that notes are to be taken; taking it out later may surprise and disturb him.

Telling him at the start that he will see the notes before they are published or routed to others will relieve him of any anxiety about their accuracy or completeness.

Of course, this promise must be kept; this will prevent any misunderstandings or inaccurate information.

Writing the notes

A minimum of time should be spent in the actual writing of notes during the interview, since note-taking impedes the normal flow of discussion. If necessary the respondent should be asked, at the end of the interview, to review the main points of what he has said, so that they can be written down at this time.

Writing the report

The interviewer's report should be written immediately after the interview. If this is not possible, at least a few minutes should be spent in amplifying the notes. Memory of what was said is freshest immediately after the interview; it will begin to fade away with the passage of even a few hours.

In the report, any items not clear should be mentioned specifically. One of the most important functions of the written report after an interview is to point out specifically:

- any assumptions being made;
- any items which are not clear.

The interviewer must give detailed reasons for any such confusion or ambiguity; for example, he should not write, "I had trouble understanding the XYZ function"; but should describe the exact nature of his difficulty.

Reviewing the report

The draft report must be reviewed with the respondent at the follow-up meeting arranged for this purpose. This will ensure that the respondent's statements have been correctly understood and interpreted. Thus any misinterpretations, omissions, or unwarranted assumptions can be corrected immediately.

Concluding the interview

Interview proper

Interviews should not be closed abruptly. A few minutes should be allowed for some informal talk and summarization at the end of the interview — it has been discovered that people sometimes keep the most significant bits of information to the end.

Getting a lead

The respondent should be asked to recommend other persons who should be interviewed, or documents or reports which should be read. He should also be asked to give the specific reasons why the person or report is being recommended. This should be asked after the interview is over, since it signifies an end to the interview; if asked too early, it would tend to break up the interview. In this way, the compass of the interview may be greatly extended at little cost in time. No interviewer can hope to cover everybody and everything concerned with the subject, but respondents can refer him to specific people and reading material that may help him considerably.

Following up after the interview

A minimum of two interviews should be scheduled with each respondent — preferably more.

The first interview will bring the interviewer's work to the respondent's attention, and will allow the respondent's subconscious mind to start considering the problem. Only in subsequent interviews will the full benefit of his ideas and knowledge of the subject be obtained.

The interviewer should let the respondent know what he has done with the information the respondent gave him. In addition, the respondent should be apprised of the general progress in the system definition process. This will give respondents a feeling of participation in what is being done. Only in this way can wholehearted cooperation be expected.

General comments

The following are precepts to be observed while interviewing.

The interviewer should:

- not believe everything he hears. Some people will attempt to mislead him and present a distorted picture of their own contribution to the organization, and of events, needs and procedures;
- double-check allegations by actually following, say a paperflow; and by interviewing more than one person on the same topic;
- verify quantitative data whenever possible. People who work closely with

processes tend to over- or under-estimate volumes of work to suit their own purposes;

- beware of artificial system requirements. A person may feel flattered by the receipt of computer-prepared reports even if he neither needs nor uses them. The interviewer must investigate the contribution the report will make to the overall operation, and then make his own evaluation of the actual need for it;
- try to distinguish between emotionally motivated statements and statements of fact. A person may unwittingly allow emotional considerations to obscure factual issues.

Technique 6-3.2: Measuring and estimating

Purpose

The purpose of this technique is to enable the systems analyst to determine when and how the application of statistical metods can help him in his work. To this end, methods are described and illustrated by means of examples. Tables and charts are provided, so that many of the simpler statistical problems can be solved by an analyst without specialist mathematical knowledge. For those who wish to proceed further in the study of statistics, a comprehensive bibliography is supplied.

In addition to offering the means for the solution of certain types of statistical problem, a knowledge of the material in this technique will permit the systems analyst to recognize other problems which, while amenable to statistical treatment, require the attention of a professional statistician. In such cases, this knowledge will enable the analyst to discuss the matter with understanding, and will give him an appreciation of the nature and value of the results obtained.

Areas of application

The methods of this technique are applicable in any circumstances where sampling has to be employed. It serves to provide a speedy answer of known reliability where large numbers of objects or large masses of figures must be analyzed. It is thus likely to find application at all phases of the systems effort, and to be particularly useful in the preparation of reports during the earlier stages of a project, in the handling of records and data elements, and during post-implementation evaluation.

Introduction

Basic to the theory of statistics is the idea that it is possible to select a group of entities from a larger assemblage in such a way that the properties of the group are related in a known manner to those of the assemblage. In this context, the assemblage is known as the "population", and the group as the "sample". The act of selecting the sample from the group is known as "sampling", and the branch of statistics which deals with the relationships between samples and their parent populations is called "sampling theory".

Sampling theory

The purpose of taking samples is to save time or material. If the population under consideration is too large for us to examine every member, or if the type of examination required would damage or alter the member examined, we must deduce the properties of the population from those of samples. In this connexion, we must bear three important facts in mind:

- the samples must have been drawn from the population in such a way that the propositions of sampling theory are applicable;
- the results obtained from a sampling investigation are of necessity approximate;
- we must know quite a lot about a population before we can take valid samples.

In order to understand the relevance of these facts, we must consider in some detail the nature of populations and samples.

Populations

The members of a population must have at least one characteristic in common. This is necessary so that we can define the population. If they are to be of statistical interest, they must also have at least one characteristic in respect of which they differ. It is in connection with such a characteristic that we shall wish to examine them.

The inhabitants of a certain town may be regarded as a population, having the common characteristic that they all live in the same town, by means of which they are defined as a population, and differing in many respects, such as for example height, income, intelligence and accident-proneness.

The positive numbers less than one are a population defined by the fact that they all lie between 0 and 1 exclusive, but differing in that some are rational and some irrational, some algebraic and some not, and so on.

Populations can be actual or conceptual. The inhabitants of a town are an example of an actual population, the positive numbers less than 1 of a conceptual population. Actual populations are always finite, whilst conceptual populations may be finite or infinite. The population of a town is finite; there is an infinite number of numbers between 0 and 1.

These distinctions are of importance when we come to consider sampling, and in respect of the appropriate methods to apply to samples drawn from various populations.

Samples

If it is to serve its purpose of saving time or material, a sample must be small compared to the population from which it is drawn. In what follows, we shall assume that a sample is less than 10% of its population.

The term "sampling" can cover several different types of activity. We can sample a population by merely considering some of its members; or by subjecting some members to an examination; or by withdrawing some members for examination and return; or by withdrawing some members for an examination of a kind which will result in their alteration, consumption or destruction, in which case they cannot be returned. Sometimes we shall withdraw members and fail to return them simply for reasons of convenience, although we have not altered them in any way.

Sampling without replacement will in the end exhaust any finite population. In addition, the removal of each sample or member of a sample alters the probabilities associated with the drawing of further samples. When the sample size is small, this effect may often be neglected. If the total of all samples taken from a population does not exceed 10%, the errors incurred will in most cases not be serious, while if it does not exceed 1%, they will be negligible.

Simple sampling

Sampling in which the composition of the population remains constant throughout the process is called "simple sampling". All sampling from infinite populations is thus simple, as is all sampling with replacement. The methods described in this technique are those applicable to this form of sampling. They are applicable without serious error in all cases where the composition of the population remains substantially unaltered.

Sample size

Within the context of relative sample size outlined above, samples of the order of 10 may be regarded as small, samples of the order of 100 as of moderate size, and samples of the order of 1000 or larger as large. If this seems arbitrary, it should be reflected that a sample of 100 has precisely the same information content whether it is drawn from a population of a thousand, a million, or of infinite size. It is a common misconception that a sample of 100 from a population of 1000 gives information of the same reliability as a sample of, say, 1000 from a population of 10,000. This is not so; provided that the population is much larger than the sample, it is the actual size of the sample which determines its information content, and not its relative size.

Sampling methods

In most cases, the method of drawing a sample is of great importance. If the distribution of population characteristics in the sample is to be a good representation of that in the population itself, then every member of the population must have an equal chance of being selected as a member of the sample. A sample so selected is called a random sample.

Random number method

If a population consists of a finite number of discrete objects, a random selection can be made by allocating a number to each member, and then selecting the sample by means of a table of random numbers [1]).

[1]) A table of random numbers for this purpose is available in the Journal of the American Statistical Association, Vol. **48**, No. 264, Dec. 1953; or see *A Million Random Digits*, Rand Corp., the Free Press, Glencoe, Illinois. A useful though smaller collection of random digits may be achieved by using the second and third digits of each four-figure entry in a table of four-figure logarithms.

In this method of selecting a random sample, two factors are important:

- the numbers must be assigned to the members of the population in a systematic manner; no attempt should be made to do this "randomly";
- the numbers from the table of random numbers must be taken consecutively; any attempt at random selection will surely introduce bias.

Practical use of random number tables

In tables of random numbers, the digits are normally arranged in groups of five. This is for convenience of reading only. A table of random numbers should be regarded as a continuous list. The method of use is as follows:

- ascertain how many members the population possesses; this determines the digit length of the random numbers required. Say, for example, that the population numbers 17.846; then we need five-digit numbers;
- start at an arbitrary point in the table of random numbers. It is sufficient to open the book "at random" and to select a starting point with finger or pin;
- read the first five digits, neglecting the manner in which they are divided in print. If in the example the number is between 00.001 and 17.846, we regard the member of the population so indicated as selected. If the number is 00.000 or greater than 17.846, we discard it and take the next five digits;
- proceed in this manner until the required sample size is achieved.

Ticket method

In the random number method of taking random samples, we accept any degree of ordering which may exist in the population itself, and utilize an independently achieved randomization embodied in a table of random numbers.

The principal alternative method is called the "ticket" method. In one realization, that from which the method derives its name, we make out a ticket for each member of the population, shuffle the tickets thoroughly, and select the first "n" tickets to indicate a sample of size "n". In this form, it is applicable only to small populations for which the ticket-making activity is practicable; and, as any card player will realize, the degree of randomization achieved will be poor unless the shuffling is lengthy and thorough. However, the principle involved, which is randomization of the whole population followed by a systematic choice, is a powerful one.

The ticket method is widely used by market researchers and mail-order houses via the medium of alphabetically ordered lists of the names of the inhabitants of towns, cities or even countries. The inhabitants of a city are likely to be non-randomly distributed in respect of many characteristics. The wealthy live in one sector, the poor in another; there is a concentration of academics about the university, of technicians about the electronics factory, perhaps of farmers about the perimeter. Thus characteristics such as income, education, intelligence and physique will be unevenly distributed. But there is no reason to suppose that a man whose name begins with "A" is likely to be wealthier, better educated, more intelligent or stronger than one whose name begins with "K". Thus an alphabetically ordered list of the inhabitants is likely to be random in respect of all characteristics which are independent of name.

In the basic ticket method, we select the first n items from the randomized population. This is because the population has been "absolutely" randomized, and not ordered with respect to any particular characteristic. If a market researcher wants a 1% sample from an alphabetical list, he will usually take the 1st, 101st, 201st, and so on. This is because the list is very non-random with respect to names, and therefore with respect to characteristics which are not name-independent. Now, families have the same name, and also share many characteristics; thus the first n names on an alphabetic list, which would contain many whole families if n were large enough, would not be a good random sample. Hence the skipping method of selection.

Practical use of ticket method

The procedure for the ticket method is as follows:

- determine whether the population can be randomized arbitrarily, either by means of physical tickets and actual shuffling or by some alternative method (possible methods include deriving some arbitrary function of quantities arbitrarily associated with each member, e.g. the first five digits of the square of the stock number plus the drawing number reversed);
- if this is impossible, or impracticable, determine whether the population can be ordered with respect to some characteristic which is actually or virtually independent of the characteristic under investigation. Alphabetical listing is frequently applicable;
- if ordering of the latter type has been used, examine the circumstances for the possible existence of the "family effect";
- draw sample accordingly.

Population - sample relationship

We take samples for the purpose of deducing something about the population from which they were drawn. In order to understand the relationship between a population and the samples drawn from it, it is simpler if we consider at first a population of known characteristics, and make deductions about samples.
Let us suppose that our population is the items in a store, and that the characteristic we are investigating is whether or not a member of this population has been requested in the past year. We will call all articles not requested in the past year non-current. Let us further suppose that we have fixed the sample size at 10, that the actual percentage of non-current items in the store is 10%, and that the total number of items is ten thousand.
The first thing to notice is that a sample of 10 can consist entirely of current items, or entirely of non-current items, or can be any one of the nine possible mixtures. But obviously not all sample compositions are equally likely. The most likely proportions for a large number of samples are approximately as follows.

All C (= current)	35%
9 C, 1 non-C	39%
8 C, 2 non-C	19%
7 C, 3 non-C	5½%
6 C, 4 non-C	1%
All others combined	½%

This table is an example of a probability distribution. Whenever the members of a population are discrete entities which either do or do not possess a certain characteristic, then the distribution of the presence or absence of this characteristic in a derived population comprising all possible samples of a given size is what is called a binomial distribution. The reason for the name, and the method of calculating the probability figures, will be found in the section headed "The binomial distribution".

Inspection of the table shows that the most likely sample (39%, or 0.39 probability) has nine current articles and one non-current article. This corresponds exactly to the composition of the parent population. But this is the most likely single sample. The total probability of all other samples is 0.61. We should therefore be unwise to assume that the composition of the population was the same as that of any single sample; the odds against us being right are in this case nearly 2 : 1, and when we are wrong the error may be of any possible size.
Further examination of the table shows us that the samples having the largest deviation from the composition of the population have also the smallest probabilities. Indeed, while a sample consisting of 10 non-current articles is possible, its probability is 0.000 000 000 1, or 1 in 10^{10}. It therefore appears likely that we shall be able to interpret the evidence of our samples in such a way as to give us a high degree of certainty in association with a wide range of values for the composition of the parent population, or a low degree of certainty with a narrower range of values. If we reflect that each of the samples in the table could have come from some other population, in which the ratio of current to non-current articles was other than 10%, and that it would then have had a different probability associated with it, we shall see that this is in fact the case.

Confidence limits and level

These two factors — a range within which the answer is thought to lie, together with a degree of confidence which we are willing to accord to the assertion that it does lie within that range — are found in all sampling analyses. In one form, they are called respectively the confidence limits and the confidence level. It is necessary to understand clearly the meanings of these terms if error in the interpretation of statistical results is to be avoided.

Suppose that, as a result of our investigation of the store, we arrive at the conclusion that the percentage of non-current articles is between 7% and 15%, with a confidence level of 90%. The confidence limits thus are 700 and 1500.

We do not state that the true value lies between these limits, but only that we are 90% sure that it does. There is no presumption that the true value occupies any particular position within the range; in particular, it is dangerous to assume without additional evidence that its most likely value is the arithmetic mean of the limits, in this case 1100. This may be so, or it may not.

The meaning of "a confidence level of 90%" requires careful attention. It does not impose a sort of additional tolerance on the limits; it expresses the probability that the true value should lie completely outside the limits. Thus, if the confidence level is 90%, there is one chance in 10 that the limits do not contain the true value at all. It is meaningless to give the results of a sampling investigation without quoting both the confidence limits and the confidence level. They jointly represent the actual information which can be bought for the information content of the sampling; we can chose to buy more of one kind only at the expense of getting less of the other, because a given sampling exercise, carried out in a given way, will produce a fixed amount of information. Thus for a given sample size we can narrow the limits only if we are willing to accept a lower confidence level, and vice versa. This emphasizes the necessity of taking as large a sample as possible; the accuracy of the results is directly dependant upon the sample size.

It is worthy of note that this characteristic is not to be considered a "flaw" in the method of making estimates by sampling methods. All measurements are in fact statistical estimates. If we make several measurements of a quantity, say the length of a steel rod, they are unlikely to be all identical. The various values, all close to the true length if the measuring instrument is a good one, are samples of the population of all possible measurements of that rod with that instrument; they possess a distribution, from knowledge of which we could calculate confidence limits for the true answer for any required confidence level. But for most physical measurements, the confidence level for the stated or expected limits is so close to 100% that we omit to give it.

If the measurement undertaken is simple, and if there exist expected limits for that kind of measurement, we often omit to state the limits also; thus a "pound" of butter or a "yard" of cloth. Measurements of this latter type are invariably made from a single observation — they are deductions from a single sample, made with confidence because the circumstances are known to be suitable. There is a continuous graduation in type of measurement from simple single-shot estimates of this sort to the most complex statistical sampling investigations; they differ only in the complexity of the entity on which measurements are being made, and the amount of information which can be obtained from each sample. Whether we notice it or not, they all have confidence levels and confidence limits.

Distributions

It has been stated that, when the parent population is a collection of entities each of which either does or does not possess the characteristic being investigated, then the distribution of this characteristic in a second population comprising all possible samples of a given size is a binomial distribution. There are many other distributions, each applicable to specific circumstances, type of population, sampling method, etc. The most generally useful, other than the binomial, are the Poisson and the Normal (or Gaussian) distributions. Before describing these three distributions in more detail, and giving methods for deciding which to use and charts and tables to permit the employment of each without detailed statistical calculations, it will be necessary to define certain terms and symbols.

Definitions

Variate

The characteristic which is the subject of the investigation is called the variate. A variate which can adopt only certain specific values is called discrete variate. Thus the characteristic of being non-current in our store example is a discrete variate, taking the values yes and no (1 and 0), and the numbers of non-current items in a sample of 10 is a discrete variate which can adopt any integral value from 0 to 10. A variate which can take any value within a given range is called a continuous variate. Thus all possible measurements of the length of a steel rod are a population with a continuous variate. It is often convenient to regard a variate which is actually discrete as though it were continuous. All possible measurements of a steel rod using a digital measuring instrument (predefined resolution) is an example of such a variate.

Population parameters

Measures of the characteristics of a population are called population parameters; we shall denote the total number of members of a population by N, the variate by X, and the individual values which X can assume when it is a discrete variate by X_1, X_2, X_3, . . . and so on to X_N. In defining the way in which a characteristic is distributed in a population, we need two sorts of information:

- a measure of central tendency; a quantity which gives information about the value around which the measures of the variate tend to cluster;
- a measure of scatter; a quantity which gives information about the extent to which values of the variate are dispersed about the central value;.

As a measure of central tendency, we shall choose the mean. The mean is defined by the formula:

$$\overline{X} = (X_1 + X_2 + X_3 \ldots + X_N)/N$$

where X is the symbol for the mean.

As a measure of scatter, we shall choose the standard deviation. The standard deviation is defined by the formula:

$$S = \sqrt{\{(\overline{X} - X_1)^2 + (\overline{X} - X_2)^2 \ldots + (\overline{X} - X_N)^2\}/N}$$

where S is the symbol for the standard deviation.

Example

In order to fix ideas in respect of these definitions, consider the following example. The population concerned has four members, whose weights are respectively 5 kg, 6 kg, 8 kg and 9 kg. Thus, if weight is the variate, $N = 4$ and $X_1 = 5$, $X_2 = 6$, $X_3 = 8$, $X_4 = 9$. Then $X = (5 + 6 + 8 + 9)/4 = 7$, and

$$S = \sqrt{\{(7-5)^2 + (7-6)^2 + (7-8)^2 + (7-9)^2\}/4} = \sqrt{(4 + 1 + 1 + 4)/4} = \\ = \sqrt{2.5} \simeq 1.58.$$

Sample statistics

Measures of the characteristics of a sample are called sample statistics. We shall denote the total number of members in the sample by n, the variate as represented in the sample by x, and the values of x in the sample by $x_1, x_2, x_3, \ldots, x_n$. The mean of the sample values of the variate will be denoted by x, where

$$\bar{x} = (x_1 + x_2 + x_3 \ldots + x_n)/n$$

and the standard deviation of the sample by s, where

$$s = \sqrt{\{(\bar{x} - x_1)^2 + (\bar{x} - x_2)^2 \ldots + (\bar{x} - x_n)^2\}/n}.$$

Discrete and continuous distributions

M is sometimes used for the mean of the population, and m for that of the sample. N, M, S, m and s are used only when the variate is discrete; in the case of a continuous variate, N no longer has a significant meaning, since it has of necessity become infinite, whilst S and s are replaced by σ, and M and m by μ. The binomial and Poisson distributions refer to discrete, and the normal distribution to continuous variates.

The probability of the variate taking a specific value, or, in the case of a continuous variate, lying within a specific range of values, we shall denote by p; the probability of it not doing so by q. Since the variate in any particular case is certain either to adopt or not to adopt any named value whatsoever, the chance associated with this event is 100% — a probability of 1. Thus $p + q = 1$.

Relationships between confidence limits and confidence levels

For all probability distributions which are symmetrical, we can define the following confidence levels and confidence limits:

- the confidence level for M to fall between $m + s$ and $m - s$ is approximately 68%;
- the confidence level for M to fall between $m + 2s$ and $m - 2s$ is approximately 95.5%;
- the confidence level for M to fall between $m + 3s$ and $m - 3s$ is approximately 99.7%.

De Moivre's approximation

Also applicable to many symmetrical distributions, and to most distributions which are only very approximately symmetrical, is de Moivre's approximation. This states that the confidence level for M to lie between x_1 and x_2, where x_1 and x_2 are more or less equally spaced about m, is equal to the percentage of the area of the normal curve which lies between the ordinates at

$$(x_1 - m - \tfrac{1}{2})/s \text{ and } (x_2 - m + \tfrac{1}{2})/s, \; x_1 \text{ being greater than } x_2.$$

Areas of the normal curve are to be found in mathematical tables. The graph of page 11 gives areas and ordinates of the normal curve to a sufficient degree of accuracy for most of the applications likely to be met within systems work.

Whilst there is a unique confidence level for any stated confidence limits, it should be noted that there is no unique pair of confidence limits for a given confidence level. In a symmetrical or near-symmetrical distribution, the narrowest limits are those which are symmetrical about the mean; but it is also possible to obtain other limits. In particular, we can always find a value X_1 of X for which, at a given confidence level, we can state that M lies between 0 and X_1 (i.e. does not exceed X_1), and a value of X_2 of X for which, at a given confidence level, we can state that M lies between X_2 and infinity (i.e. is not less than X_2). To find these values, in a symmetrical distribution and with a large sample size, we take the area of the normal curve, page 9, from zero to the required confidence level, or from 100 minus the required confidence level to infinity, locate the sigma value at the indicated ordinate, multiply by the value of the actual standard deviation, and add or subtract the result from the actual mean, as appropriate.

The binomial distribution

The table in page 6 gives the probability distribution for the composition of samples of ten from a population in which 10% of members have the characteristic under investigation — i.e. where $n = 10$ and $p = 0.1$. This table can be presented in graphical form, as shown in page 13. Such a graph, called a histogram, is often useful in visualizing the facts in a problem dealing with a discrete variate.

If we make the column width our horizontal unit, the area of each column of the histogram will be equal to the probability of obtaining a sample of the composition shown at the foot of the column. Thus the total area of the histogram is equal to the probability of a sample having any one of its possible compositions, and is therefore 1. (For similar reasons, this is true of the graph of any probability distribution, whether it is a histogram, a polygon or a continuous curve.)

The following facts about the binomial distribution are given without rigorous proof. For textbooks offering such proof, reference should be made to the bibliography.

$(p + q) = 1$ represents the chance of either obtaining, or not obtaining, an

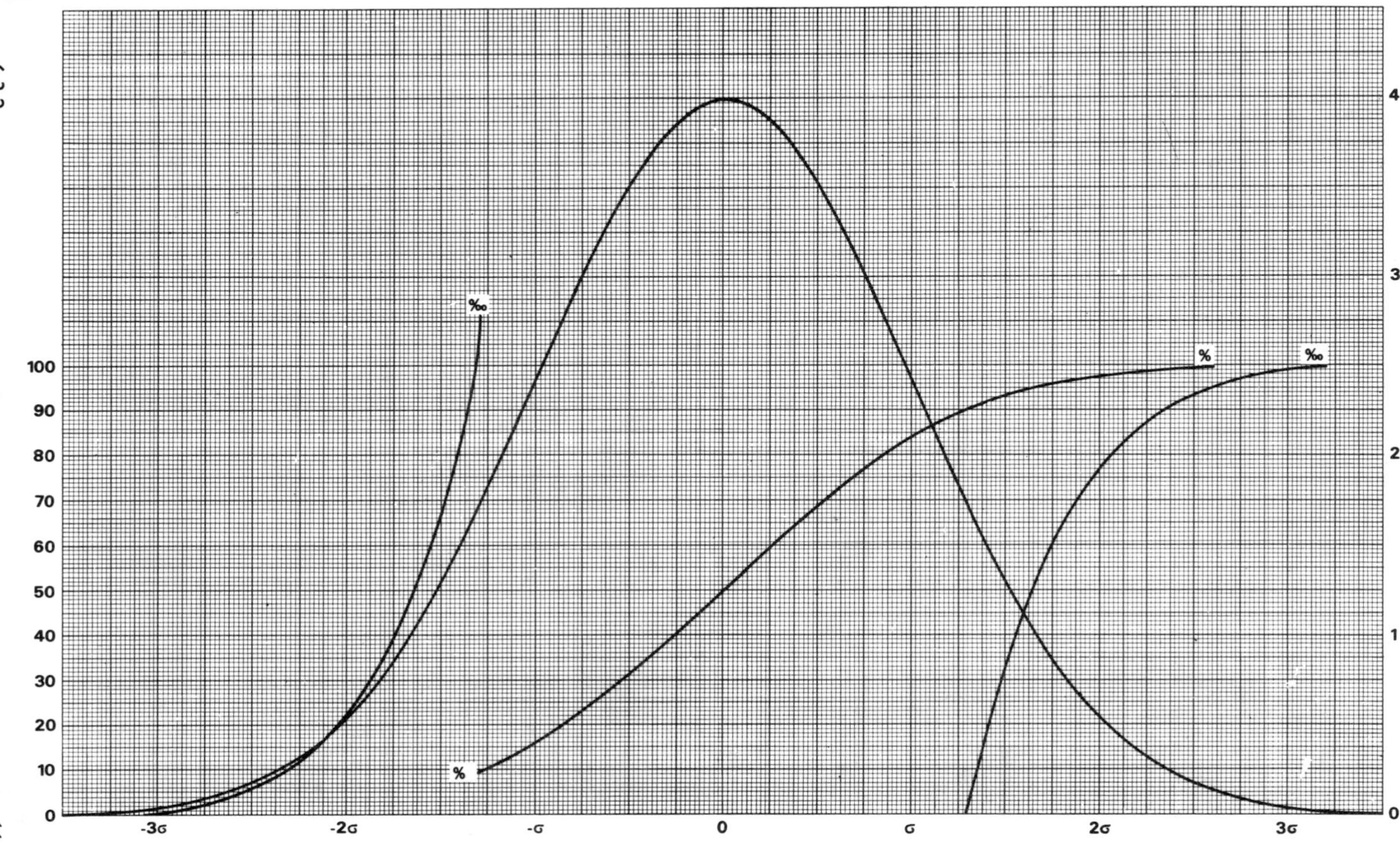

Areas and ordinates of normal curve

example of the characteristic sought when selecting a single member of the population. Thus, in the store example, $(0.1 + 0.9)$ represents a ten percent chance of selecting a non-current article, a ninety percent chance of selecting a current article, and a one hundred percent chance of selecting one or the other.

$(p + q)^2 = 1$ represents the chances of selecting, in two choices, two p-probability articles, or one of each, or two q-probability articles. If we multiply out the expression, we get

$$p^2 + 2pq + q^2 = 1$$

where p^2 gives the probability of selecting two p-probability articles, $2pq$ that of selecting one of each, and q^2 that of getting two q-probability articles. To apply this to the store case, we have

$$(0.1)^2 + 2(0.1 \times 0.9) + (0.9)^2, \text{ i.e.}$$
$$0.01 + 0.18 + 0.81,$$

so that the chances of two non-currents in two choices are 0.01, of one current and one non-current 0.18, and of two currents 0.81. Addition of these probabilities will produce, as anticipated, 1.

In general, the expression $(p + q)^n$ will, if expanded, give in consecutive terms the probabilities for all possible compositions of samples of size n from a large population in which the probability of having a certain characteristic is p, and the probability of not having it is q. This expression is the binomial from which the binomial distribution derives its name.

Mean and standard deviation

The average number of p-probability articles per sample of size n will, for a sufficiently large number of samples, be np. This is the mean of the distribution, $\overline{X}$ Since the probability pq represents the chances of two consecutive choices being different, we should expect it to give some measure of the scatter of the distribution. In fact, the standard deviation turns out to be $\sqrt{npq}$ for samples of size n.

Symmetry

The histogram in page 13 is asymmetric. In page 14 appears a histogram for a binomial distribution with $p = \frac{1}{2}$, $q = \frac{1}{2}$ and $n = 6$. It will be seen that this histogram is symmetrical. Whenever the probabilities p and q are equal, i.e. whenever the population contains 50% of articles with the distinguishing characteristic, the histogram will of necessity be symmetrical. It is true also, but less obvious, that as n increases the histogram tends towards a symmetrical shape. $(0.2 + 0.8)^{50}$ is to all intents and purposes symmetrical, as is $(0.1 + 0.9)^{100}$ So for equal probabilities or for large samples, the binomial distribution is symmetrical. The vertical line which is the axis of symmetry then corresponds to the mean.

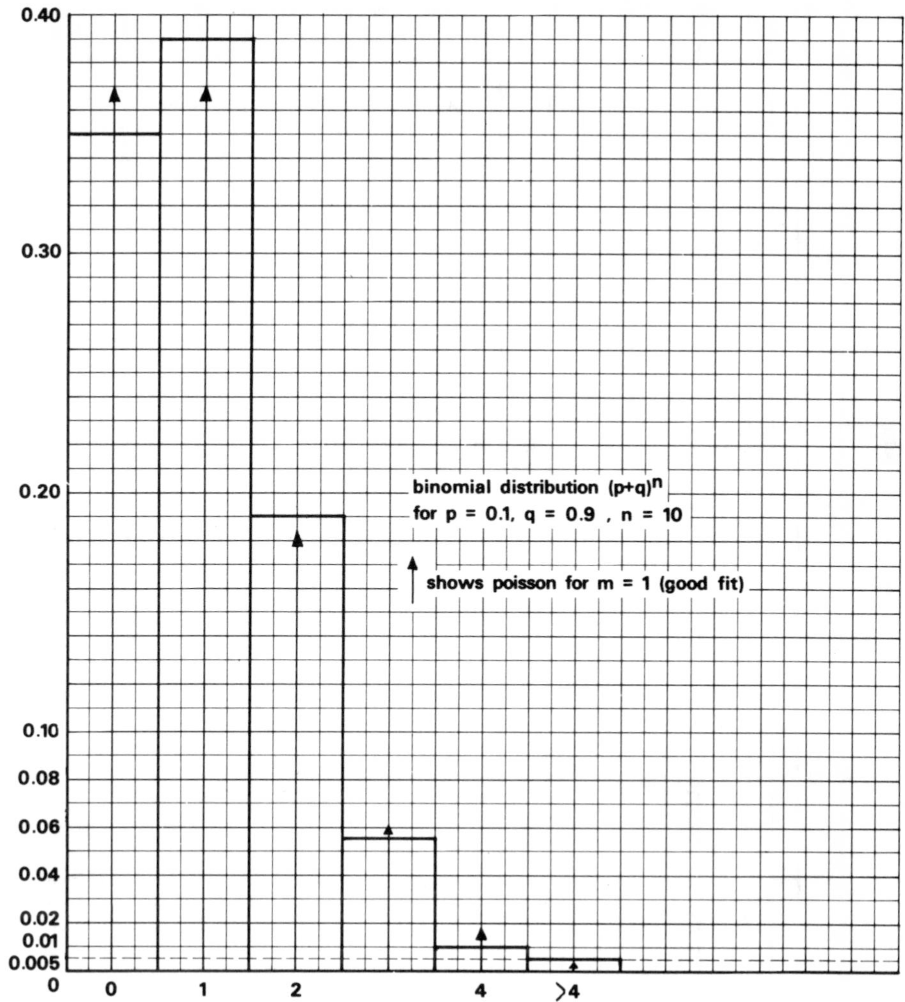
0.40
0.30
0.20
0.10
0.08
0.06
0.04
0.02
0.01
0.005
0
probability of sample
binomial distribution (p+q)ⁿ
for p = 0.1, q = 0.9 , n = 10
shows poisson for m = 1 (good fit)
0
1
2
4
>4
number of non-current articles in sample n (n = 10)

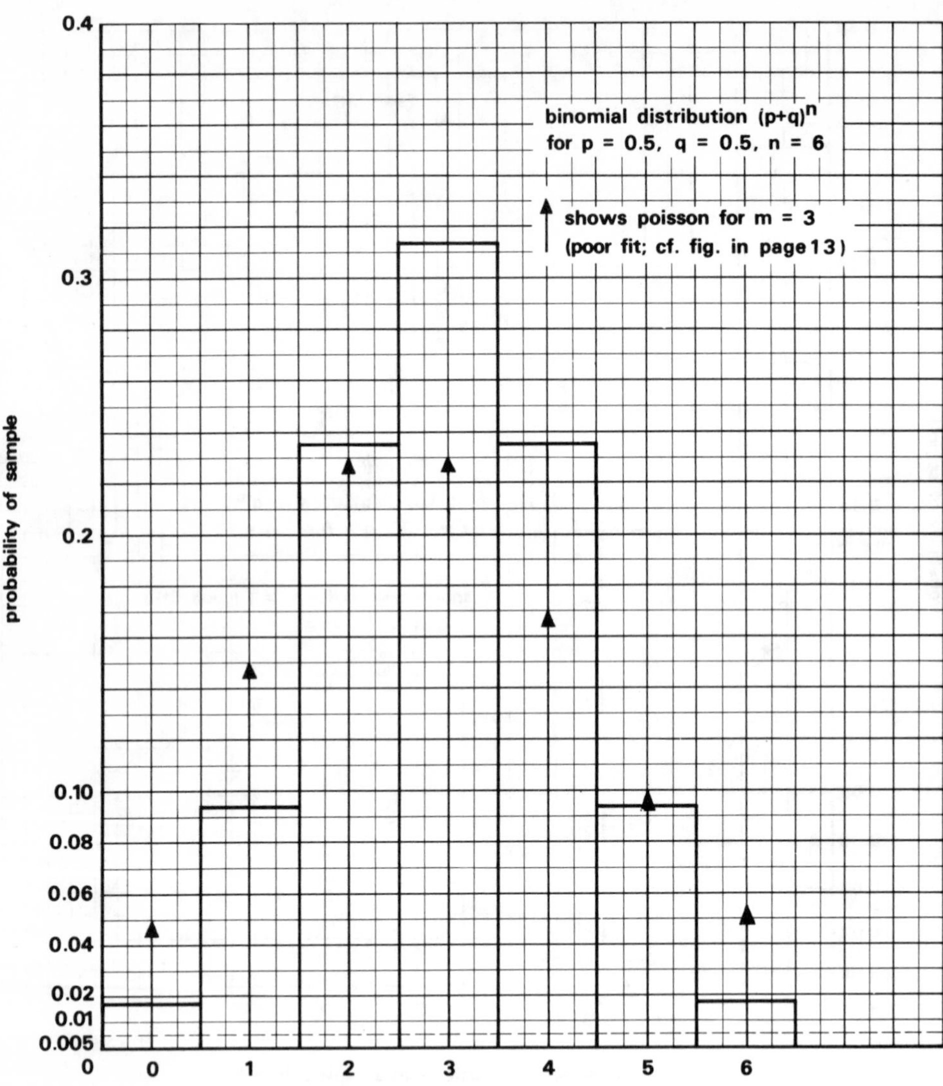

binomial distribution $(p+q)^n$
for p = 0.5, q = 0.5, n = 6
shows poisson for m = 3
(poor fit; cf. fig. in page 13)
probability of sample
0.4
0.3
0.2
0.10
0.08
0.06
0.04
0.02
0.01
0.005
0
0
1
2
3
4
5
6
number of 'sought' articles in sample (n = 6)

Characteristics and interpretation

M is the mean number of "wanted" articles per sample in the derived population of all possible samples of the chosen size. It is therefore precisely equal to np, where n is the sample size and p the probability of selecting single article having the required property. m is the average number of occurrences of the required property per sample in the samples actually drawn. The larger the number of such samples, the more closely does m approximate to M. The answer we are looking for is the number of articles in the parent population which possess the required property. This is equal to the total number of articles in the parent population multiplied by p, so that to find p is to solve our problem. The method is to accept m as a good approximation for M, and divide it by n to obtain an estimate of p. The total number of items in the parent population multiplied by this estimate of p gives us our estimate of the number of items in that population possessing the property under investigation. If the distribution is approximately symmetrical, we can then use either of the methods of page 10 for deriving confidence levels and confidence limits. If the distribution is strongly asymmetric, we must adopt other methods. We can increase the sample size until the distribution is nearly enough symmetrical; we can have recourse to the Poisson distribution (see next section); or we can make use of the graphs in pages 16 and 17. These graphs give confidence limits at the 90% and 95% confidence levels for sample sizes between 10 and 500 and sample content up to 20%. These figures will cover all the asymmetric binomials likely to be encountered in practice, and a very large proportion of the near-symmetric as well. It will be appreciated that an asymmetric binomial of the form $(p + q)^n$ where q is less than 0.2, can be brought within the scope of the graphs by treating it as $(q + p)^n$, and regarding the absence of the distinguishing feature as the characteristic under investigation. Binomials in which the smaller probability is greater than 0.2 may be regarded as approximately symmetrical if the sample size is greater than 50.

The Poisson distribution

The important mathematical quantity e is defined by the relationship

$$e = \lim_{k \to \infty} (1 + 1/k)^k,$$

which means that if successive values of the quantity $(1 + 1/k)^k$ are taken with increasing values of k, then as k approaches infinity, the values of $(1 + 1/k)^k$ approach e. The expansion of this binomial gives for e the value

$$1/0! + 1/1! + 1/2! + 1/3! \ldots = 2.71828 \ldots$$

where $a! = 1 \times 2 \times 3 \times 4 \times \ldots \times a$, so that $1! = 1$, $2! = 1 \times 2 = 2$, $3! = 1 \times 2 \times 3 = 6$, etc. It will be seen from the definition of $a!$ that $(a - 1)! = a!/a$; thus $0! = (1 - 1)! = 1!/1 = 1$.

It is a property of the above limit that

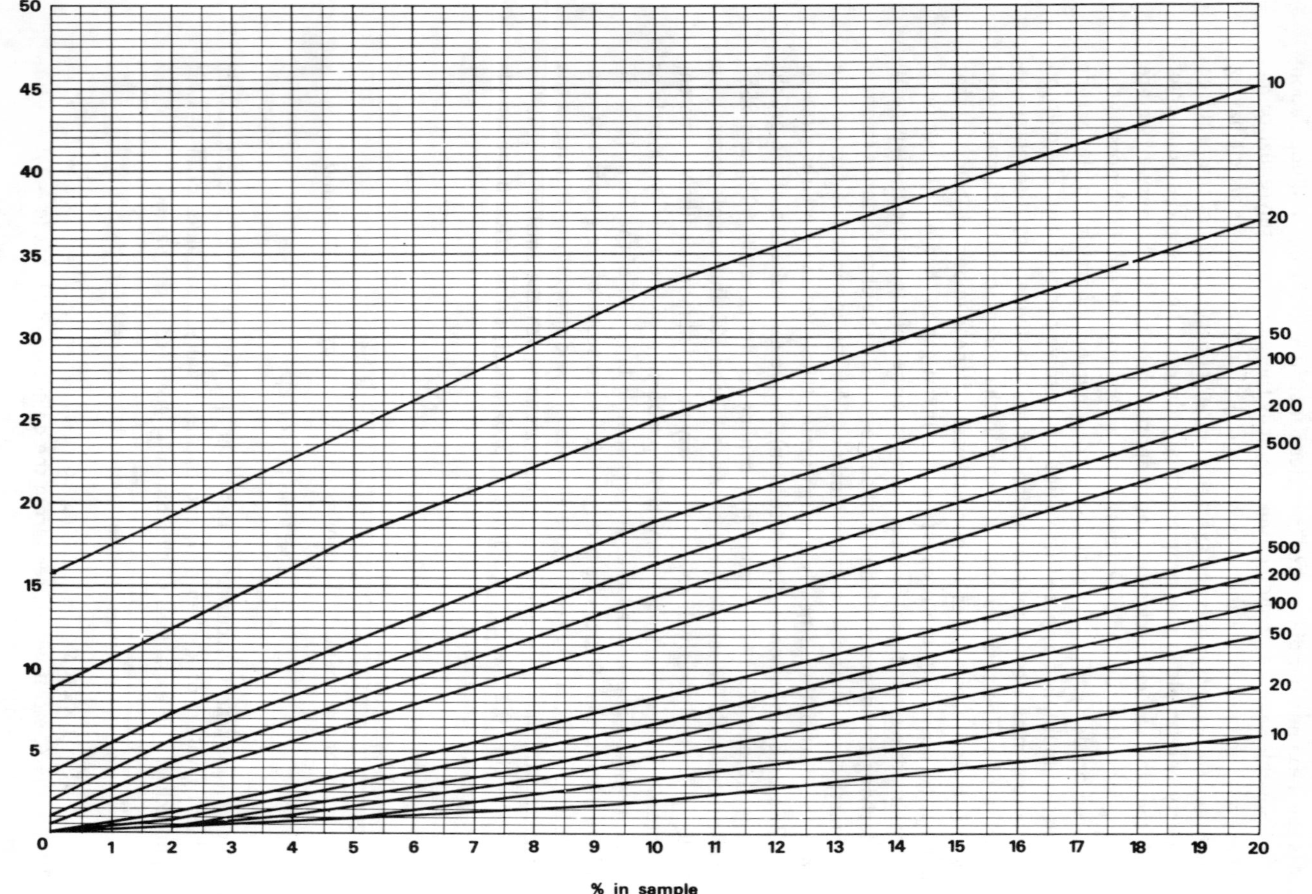

Binomial distribution - 90% confidence level

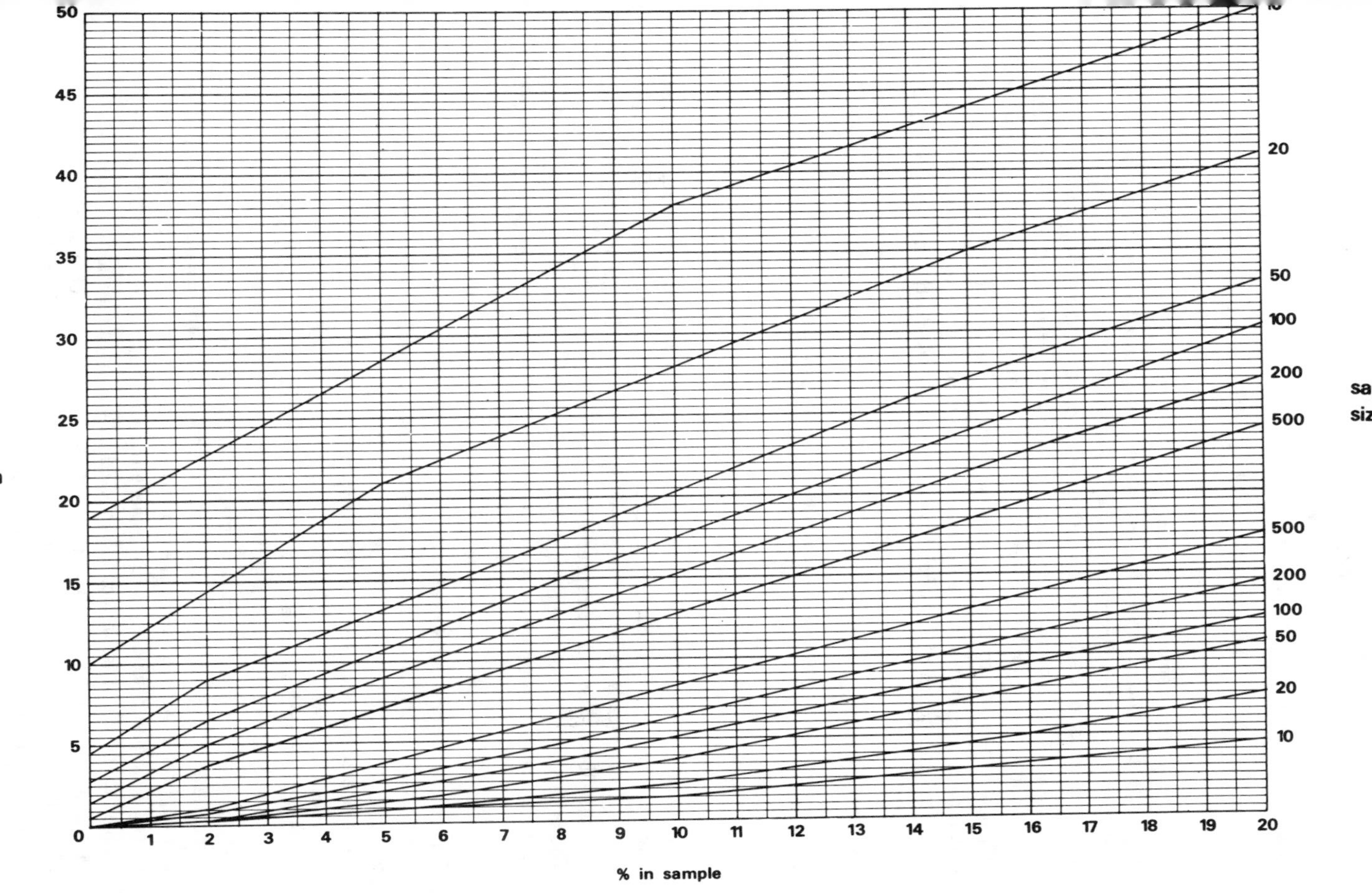

Binomial distribution - 95% confidence level

$$e^z = \lim_{k\to\infty} = (1 + z/k)^k,$$

and expansion here gives for e^z the value

$$1/0! + z/1! + z^2/2! + z^3/3! \ldots$$

Relationship to binomial distribution

If in the binomial distribution we have a very small value of p, then since $p + q = 1$, q will approximately be 1. Now our binomial $(p + q)^n$, for very large values of n, begins to look like the binomial in the definition of e^z. Since $m = np$ for the binomial distribution, we can put $p = m/n$, getting for our total probability the binomial $(1 + m/n)^n$. From the above formula, this is equal to e^m, if n is allowed to tend to infinity. Since the value of this function is not equal to 1, we must adopt a device to make it so before we can regard it as a suitable description of a probability distribution. We do this by multiplying by e^{-m}, thus;

total probability

$$= e^m\, e^{-m} = e^{-m}(1 + m + m^2/2! + m^3/3! + m^4/4! \ldots) = 1.$$

Multiplying out, we get

$$e^{-m} + me^{-m} + m^2e^{-m}/2! + m^3e^{-m}/3! + m^4e^{-m}/4! \ldots$$

The successive terms of this expression give the probability of no occurrences, one occurrence, two occurrences . . . . . of a rare wanted characteristic in a very large (theoretically infinite) sample which is nevertheless of known fixed size. The distribution which it represents is the Poisson distribution.

The points on a line of given length, or in a given area or volume, or the instants of time in a fixed time interval, are examples of infinite samples of known fixed size.

Characteristics and interpretation

The Poisson distribution is suitable for the investigation of events whose probability is numerically very small, by means of samples large enough to ensure that there are some occurrences. It is a special, or limiting, case of the binomial distribution, in which n has become very large and p very small. It is thus suitable for investigating isolated events in time, (incidence of reports, orders, faults), or in a linear, a real or volumetric array, (units of information of a specific but rare type in a store, dropouts in magnetic tape, subdivisions of a tape or disc store viewed as arbitrary or random occurrences in a linear continuum). It is also applicable without serious error to any investigation which properly calls for the binomial distribution, but where the value of p is less than 0.01 and n is greater than 100. It is, in fact, often used as an approximation in cases where p is greater than 0.01 and n less than 100, because it is much easier to calculate $m^ke^{-m}/k!$ than the corresponding terms in the binomial distribution.

In a Poisson investigation, we do not expect to derive a value for p, since we have already assumed at the start that p is virtually zero. The answer will take the form of "so many occurrences can be expected in a given time (area, volume, length)". If we are dealing with an infinite population, this is what we shall want, but if we are for reasons of simplicity substituting Poisson for binomial, we shall get the answer "so many per sample size" i.e. np, which will in fact be equivalent to obtaining a value for p.

It must be noted that the Poisson distribution is valid only when the circumstances are such that the average number of occurrences per sample of selected size can reasonably be expected to remain constant. Thus we could use it to investigate the number of faults per week in the mid-life of a computer system, but since the number of faults is likely to be higher immediately after installation (bugs) and towards the end of the useful life (deterioration), it should be applied to these periods only by a competent professional mathematician.

Mean and standard deviation

Since we derived the Poisson distribution from the binomial by putting $p = m/n$ and letting n tend to infinity, we can derive the related sample statistics by the same procedure. Thus $\lim_{n \to \infty} np = \lim_{n \to \infty} n \cdot m/n = m$, and the m in the Poisson expression is still the sample mean; and $\lim_{n \to \infty} \sqrt{npq} = \lim_{n \to \infty} \sqrt{n(m/n)\ (1\ m/n—)} = \sqrt{m}$, so that the standard deviation of a Poisson distribution is the square root of the mean.

The shape of a Poisson distribution can be shown either in tabular form, or graphically, as for the binomial distribution. The graphical representation can take the form of a histogram or a "probability polygon". The Poisson distribution can, like the binomial, be symmetrical or asymmetric. It is substantially symmetrical if m is greater than 10, in which case the methods for the derivation of confidence levels and confidence limits already given are applicable. For other cases, the table in page 6 gives the lower bound (L_B) and the upper bound (U_B) for the confidence limits in terms of number of occurrences per sample time (length, area, volume) for confidence levels of 90% and 95%. The figures in pages 13 and 14 show Poisson polygon for $m = 0.1$ and 3.

Normal distribution

The binomial and Poisson distributions deal with discrete variates — with countable things. The normal distribution deals with continuous variates — with measurable things which are not countable. It is not possible to count all possible measurements of a given steel rod with a given measuring instrument. Just as the Poisson distribution was derived as a special case of the binomial, so the normal distribution may be regarded as a particular sort of binomial distribution.

Relationship to binomial distribution

Let us imagine a binomial distribution in which we are taking very large samples from a near-infinite population. The histogram will have a very large number of columns, and the difference in height between one column and the next will be very small. In the limiting case, there will be an infinite number of columns, each of zero width, and the rectilinear outline of the histogram will become a smooth curve. We must now remember that each column of a histogram represents the probability of occurrence of a sample of a certain composition — a sample of *one* from the derived population of samples. Thus the infinitely thin columns of the smooth-curve limiting histogram represent the probability of obtaining a single measurement corresponding to the value of the variate at the foot of the column. Now, the area of an infinitely thin column is, of course, zero; so that the probability of the variate taking any specified single value in its range is also zero. This is what we should expect, since the variate has, being continuous, an infinite number of possible values. Nevertheless, the area under the curve remains 1 throughout the development from a histogram to continuity. The probability of the variate lying between any two selected values is equal to the proportion of the total area of the curve which lies between the verticals (ordinates) corresponding to the two selected values.

Characteristics and interpretation

Strictly speaking, the normal distribution as usually defined is a symmetrical distribution. Some continuous variates, however, have a distribution which is represented by a smooth curve which is not symmetrical. The distribution of wages in an organization is an example of such a distribution — the mean wage is determined more by the large number of small wages than by the few large ones, whilst wages can, theoretically at least, adopt any value. If the asymmetry — "skewness" — of such a distribution is not too great, it may be treated as a normal distribution; if, however, an example of a strongly skewed continuous distribution is encountered, the services of a professional statistician should be sought.

The graph in page11shows a normal distribution curve. The second curve is the integral of the normal (bell-shaped) curve. The ordinates of the integral curve give the corresponding areas of the normal curve. These values, while not so accurate as those obtainable from a table of areas, will be useful in making rough calculations. In this graph, the mean of the curve has been set at zero, and the horizontal axis has been marked off in terms of σ, the standard deviation, instead of in terms of the variate. In this form, the curve is of general use; all normal curves are of the same shape, differing only in the values of μ and σ; to put $\mu = 0$ is equivalent to working in terms of differences from any particular mean, and to put the divisions of the horizontal axis in terms of σ enables a generalized curve to be used to determine actual values once σ is known [1]).

Although the variate under investigation is continuous, we can take only finite samples. The results of sampling in an investigation which concerns a normal distribution can be shown in the form of a histogram. Since, however, we are

[1]) $x_i' \,(0;1) = \frac{x_c \pm \mu}{\sigma}$.

very unlikely to get many values repeated exactly, we group the values together according to the range in which they fall. Thus, if we find for a set of measurements of the length of a steel rod that we obtained as part of the set the values . . . 100.012, 100.013, 100,015, 100.017, 100.0175, 100.018, 100.02, 100.02, 100.02, 100.025 . . ., we might decide to take as ranges 100.010 to 100.019, 100.020 to 100.029 . . . . In the part set quoted, there are six members of the first range, and four of the second. Such ranges are known as "class intervals", and the number of measures of the variate falling within a class interval is called a "class frequency". (The above measures might equally well be measures on the lengths of separate rods made by the same machine; if they are measures of the length of a single rod, we are more likely to be investigating the behaviour of the measuring instrument than measuring the rod.) One benefit of drawing such a histogram is that it enables us to visualise the degree of skewness of our distribution; it also enables us to make rough and rapid estimates of m and s for the corresponding binomial distribution, often a useful preliminary check, and to test the "fit" of the normal curve, when derived, by superimposition.

Mean and standard deviation

σ and μ for the normal distribution are derived from samples in much the same way as s and m for the binomial distribution;

$$\mu = (x_1 + x_2 + x_3 + x_4 + \ldots + x_n)/n,$$

and

$$\sigma = \sqrt{\{(\bar{x} - x_1)^2 + (\bar{x} - x_2)^2 + \ldots + (\bar{x} - x_2)^2\}/n};$$

but since the mean of the sample is not likely to be exactly the mean of the population, we must introduce a correction for the value of the standard variation. Whilst the expression above is correct for the standard deviation of the sample, what we need is an estimate of the standard deviation of the population; this is obtained by dividing by $(n - 1)$ instead of n, thus:

$$\sigma = \sqrt{\{(\bar{x} - x_1)^2 + (\bar{x} - x_2)^2 + \ldots + (\bar{x} - x_2)^2\}/(n - 1)}.$$

The quantity thus calculated is read as "sigma cap", and is what is called an "unbiassed estimate" of σ for the population.

Confidence limits for the results of an investigation of a normally distributed population at the required confidence levels can be obtained by the methods of page 5, or directly from tables or graphs giving areas under the normal curve.

Practical rules

Practical rules will now be given, both general (applicable to all statistical enquiries) and specific to the three distributions described.

General

- Ascertain which distribution is applicable:
  - — if the enquiry deals with a finite number of objects, each of which does or does not possess a specific characteristic, in general use the binomial distribution. But if either p or q is of the order of 0.01, consider the use of the Poisson as a speedier alternative;
  - — if the enquiry deals with the occurrence of isolated events in time or in space, use a Poisson distribution;
  - — if the enquiry is clearly of the binomial type, but if either p or q is very small indeed (of the order of 0.001) do not consider the use of the binomial distribution; use the Poisson;
  - — if the variate is continuous, use the normal distribution; but first ascertain that the distribution is at least approximately symmetrical;
  - — if the variate can adopt any of a very large number of values, then, although it may be actually discrete, treat it as though it were continuous and employ the normal distribution.
- take the largest possible (number of) sample(s) permitted by circumstances;
- take all possible precautions to ensure that the sample(s) is (are) randomly selected. (This is often impossible in Poisson investigations, where it may by necessary to inspect consecutive time periods, lengths etc. Under these circumstances, it is still necessary to ensure that there is not likely to be any abnormality in the field inspected);
- determine the sample statistics;
- deduce the population parameters;
- check the deduced population for "fit" with the observed sample statistics by superposing its distribution over the histogram or polygon of the measured values (see appendix).
- if in doubt or difficulty, enlist the services of a specialist;
- never forget the confidence limits and the confidence levels — without them the result is meaningless.

Binomial distribution

In any sampling investigation, we must have some idea about the likely answer before we can properly choose the method. If we suspected that the number of non-current items in the store in our earlier example was less than 1%, we should use Poisson methods; let us assume that we believe it to be greater than 1%, but less than 20%. We shall therefore be dealing with a skew binomial distribution, and the skewness will prevent us from using the methods of symmetrical distributions unless our sample size is large relative to the actual value of p.

Let us suppose that we can afford to take a sample of 200 items. Proceed as follows.

- select the most appropriate sampling method:

— if the ticket method is chosen, note that this is not simple sampling; an article once chosen has no chance of being selected again, and is thus effectively removed from the population. Observe appropriate ratios (page 3);
— if the random number method is employed, this is simple sampling. It is unlikely, but not impossible, that an item should appear twice in the sample. If this does occur, there is no reason to reject the second (or subsequent) appearances of an item; randomness decrees that the unlikely will sometimes happen;

- apply the selected method to obtain a sample of 200;
- count the number of times the characteristic under investigation (in this case non-currency) appears in the sample. This number is m for the sample;
- divide this value of m by the sample size, here 200. From the relationship $m = np$, this gives us an estimate of p;
- from the graph in page 16 determine the lower confidence limit for p at the 90% confidence level. Call this value p^*, and derive $q^* = p^* - 1$. If $(p^* + q^*)^n$ is approximately symmetrical, we may use any of the suggested methods for deriving confidence levels and limits; if not, we must use the graphs of pages 16 and 17;
- derive confidence levels and limits as appropriate.

Example

Let us suppose that the sample of 200 yielded 23 non-current items. Thus $m = 23$, and $p = 23/200 = 0.115$. From page 16, $p^* = 0.08$, thus $q^* = 0.92$. From page 12 we can see that $(0.08 + 0.92)^{200}$ is substantially symmetrical. We may therefore use any of the given methods for the determination of confidence levels and limits.

For purposes of illustration, we shall use each in turn:

- graphical method; the sample p of 0.115 is equivalent to an estimate that the population contains 11.5% of non-current articles. Drawing a vertical line across the 95% confidence level graph at 11.5%, we see that it cuts the 200 sample-size lines at 7% and 17%. We state our result as "The total percentage of non-current items in the store is estimated to lie between 7% and 17%, with 95% confidence;
- $s - 2s - 3s$ method; for a binomial distribution, $s = \sqrt{npq}$. In this case, $n = 200, p = 0.115$, and therefore $q = 0.885$, so that $s = \sqrt{200 \times 0.115 \times 0.885} = \sqrt{20.355} \simeq 4.5$. For a confidence level of 95.5% we take $m + 2s$ and $m - 2s$, i.e. 23 + 9 and 23 − 9, giving as the limits for m 14 and 32. These values are respectively 7% and 16% of the sample size, and lead to the result that the store is estimated to contain between 7% and 16% of non-current items, at a confidence level of 95.5%.

  The discrepancy between this and the previous result is not significant; it is an error of the magnitude to be expected with this type of investigation, when conducted by relatively unsophisticated methods;
- de Moivre's method; This method enables us to select our confidence limits,

and to determine the applicable confidence level, whereas the two previous methods first chose a level for which limits were then determined. This fact makes de Moivre's method particularly valuable in cases where limits are predetermined.

For illustration, let us chose the limits obtained in the previous example, for which we already know the confidence level. Thus we have $x_1 = 32$ and $x_2 = 14$, corresponding to the limits of 16% and 7%. Substitution in the de Moivre formula gives

$$(32 - 23 - \tfrac{1}{2})/4\tfrac{1}{2} = 1.9,$$

and

$$(14 - 23 + \tfrac{1}{2})/4\tfrac{1}{2} = -1.9.$$

From the graphs in page 11, we see that the percentage of the area of the normal curve between −1.9 and +1.9 is approximately 90%. We thus state that "the store contains between 7% and 16% of non-current articles, with 90% confidence".

There are two things to observe in connection with this answer. In the first place, the two parts of the formula gave numerically the same answer. This is the case only when the chosen limits are symmetrical about the sample mean. Had we taken the values 7% and 17% from the first example, we should have obtained +2.3 and −1.9, for a confidence level of 92%. And in the second place, the result of 90% (or even 92%) is significantly different from the 95% already obtained for the same limits.

In the form given, the de Moivre approximation is always slightly pessimistic when the distribution is symmetrical or very nearly so. It is better applicable to cases where there is a slight but appreciable skewness, and continues to give good results even in the presence of considerable skewness.

For the determination of level from given limits where the distribution is actually or virtually symmetrical, it is better to use

$$(x_1 - m)/s \text{ and } (x_2 - m)/s,$$

and it is no longer necessary to stipulate that the limits chosen are nearly symmetrical about the mean.

Using these formulae, which are in fact an extension of the $s - 2s - 3s$ method, we have for the values $x_1 = 32$ and $x_2 = 14$,

$$(32 - 23)/4.5 = 2,$$

and

$$(14 - 23)/4.5 \quad = -2,$$

and the percentage of the area of the normal curve from −2 to +2 is 95.5%.

This pair of formulae is applicable also to finding absolute upper and lower bounds for a given confidence level (page 00). Suppose that we wish to find the limit above which, with 90% confidence, we may assume that the percentage of non-current articles does not lie. This is equivalent to finding a value of x, say x_1, such that there is a 90% confidence level that M lies between 0 and x_1.

Substituting in the first formula, we get

$$(x_1 - 23)/4.5$$

now, from the table of areas of the normal curve, we find that, starting from 0, the ordinate corresponding to 90% area is +1.27. Therefore we put

$$(x_1 - 23)/4.5 = 1.27,$$

from which $x_1 = 28.7$. A similar calculation by means of the second formula gives us a 90% confidence that M does not lie below 17.3. It would be very wrong, however, to assume that this gave us reason to state that we were 90% confident that M was between 17.3 and 28.7; each of these figures allows values of M forbidden to the other, and so they cannot be thus combined.

Poisson distribution

Although the formulae concerned look complex, the Poisson is by far the easiest to deal with.

Example

Let us suppose that a computer system, in mid-life, produces in consecutive weeks the following number of faults;

4, 0, 2, 3, 5, 1, 3, 2.

From these 8 samples, we find that $m = (4 + 0 + 2 + 3 + 5 + 1 + 3 + 2)/8 = 2.5$. Hence the standard deviation $= \sqrt{2.5} \simeq 1.58$.

We immediately observe that we are not going to be able to apply any of the methods for symmetrical distributions, since the Poisson distribution is not symmetrical for $m = 2.5$; indeed, since 3s is greater than m, we should get not merely wrong answers, but ridiculous answers.
Substituting in the Poisson expansion

$$e^{-m} + me^{-m} + m^2e^{-m}/2! + m^3e^{-m}/3! + m^4e^{-m}/4! + \ldots$$

we get

$$e^{-2.5} + 2.5e^{-2.5} + (2.5)^2.e^{-2.5}/2! + (2.5)^3e^{-2.5}/3! + \ldots$$

Now, this is much easier than it looks; observation reveals that, after the first term, each term is obtained from its predecessor by multiplying by m (in this case 2.5) and dividing by the next whole number (i.e. using 1, 2, 3 . . . in turn as divisors). Thus, from mathematical tables the first term, $e^{-2.5}$, is 0.08. The second term is $2.5 \times 0.08/1$, i.e. 0.2. The third term is $2.5 \times 0.2/2$, i.e. 0.25. The fourth term is $2.5 \times 0.25/3$, i.e. 0.13; and so on.

The work may be conveniently laid out as follows:

$$
\begin{array}{lrr}
T1 = e^{-2.5} & & 0.08 \\
\hline
\quad \times m & & 2.5 \\
\cline{3-3}
 & \div 1 & 0.20 \\
T2 = & & 0.20 \\
\hline
\quad \times m & & 2.5 \\
\cline{3-3}
 & \div 2 & 0.50 \\
T3 = & & 0.25 \\
\hline
\quad \times m & & 2.5 \\
\cline{3-3}
 & \div 3 & 0.625 \\
T4 = & & 0.208 \\
\hline
\quad \times m & & 2.5 \\
\cline{3-3}
 & \div 4 & 0.520 \\
T5 = & & 0.130 \\
\hline
\quad \times m & & 2.5 \\
\cline{3-3}
 & \div 5 & 0.325 \\
T6 = & & 0.065 \\
\hline
\quad \times m & & 2.5 \\
\cline{3-3}
 & \div 6 & 0.1625 \\
T7 = & & 0.0271
\end{array}
$$

And so on, for as many terms as we require.
For the present case, we get for the probabilities of the indicated number of breakdowns per week the figures given in the following table

Breakdowns per week	0	1	2	3	4	5	6	7 or more
Probability	0.08	0.20	0.25	0.208	0.130	0.065	0.027	0.040

The column for "7 or more" was filled in by making the sum total of all the probabilities equal to 1.
From this table, we can estimate that the probability of not more than three faults in any week is 0.08 + 0.20 + 0.25 + 0.208, i.e. 0.738; or that the probability of a week with more than four faults is 0.065 + 0.027 + 0.040, i.e. 0.132.

These are useful results, but we wish to be able also to quote limits and levels. Since we know that the distribution is asymmetric, we are confined to the de Moivre and the tabular methods.

- Tabular method; from the table in this page which is the Poisson equivalent of the binomial graphs of pages **16** and **17**, we can derive limits for the probable number of faults per week at confidence levels of 90% and 95%. We see that the sample mean is quoted in whole numbers from 0 to 20. Since the Poisson distribution deals with statistical rarity, we do not expect m to achieve high values. Nevertheless, it is often desirable to take samples in such a way that the mean is greater than 20; in such cases, however, m is appreciably greater than 3s, and the distribution may be treated as symmetrical. In the present example, we derive our 95% limits for a 2.5 mean by linear interpolation between the values for 2.0 and 3.0, getting 0.64 and 7.21. Since there is no physical meaning to 0.64 of a fault, or for 0.21 of a fault, we could state this result as "the number of faults in any given week will lie between 1 and 7, with a confidence of 95%"; or we could more accurately say that the average number of faults per week in any period will be between 0.64 and 7.21, with a confidence level of 95%;

- de Moivre method; chosing the limits 0.5 and 7.0, we get:

$$(7 - 2.5 - 0.5)/1.58 = 2.52, \text{ and}$$
$$(0.5 - 2.5 - 0.5)/1.58 = -1.58;$$

  and the percentage of the area of the normal curve between the ordinates -1.58 and $+2.52$ is 94.4%.;
- $s - 2s - 3s$ method; this method, while not applicable to the present example, is suitable whenever m is greater than 20.

Normal distribution

In dealing with the normal distribution, we shall consider only symmetrical or moderately skew distributions. If the conditions or the preliminary results suggest that the distribution under consideration is grossly skew, then the services of a professional statistician should be sought.

Example

A typical example of a normal distribution is offered by the measures of the time taken to perform a well-learned task. Let us suppose that a new procedure has been designed and implemented, and that sufficient experience has been gained in its use for us to believe that its time of performance has stabilized. It is important to the systems analyst, because of the interrelationships between this procedure and other parts of the system, that he shall be sure that even under the most adverse conditions this procedure shall take no longer than six minutes. He is interested also in the present mean and standard deviation of the measures, for comparison with a set of measures made just after implementation of the procedure. At that time, the mean was 4.9 minutes and the standard deviation 0.55.

The following 20 measurements were made on the time of performance of 20 consecutive occurrences of the procedure;

Time in minutes: 2.7, 2.7, 3.5, 3.1, 3.0, 3.0, 3.7, 2.4, 3.7, 3.5, 3.2, 3.2, 2.7, 2.4, 2.7, 3.1, 3.4, 3.4, 3.5, 3.1.

In order to determine the sample statistics, we must add all these values, divide the result by 20 for the mean; subtract each value from the mean, square the results, add the squares, divide the sum of the squares by $(n - 1)$, in this case 19, and take the square root of the answer for sigma-cap.

In order to save work and avoid confusion, it is necessary to adopt a methodical procedure. Many such have been invented; the following is an adaption of a standard layout, suited to investigations of the type likely to be encountered in systems work:

- set the measures in order of magnitude;
- guess a mean. Call this the "working mean";
- write in a column headed "—ve" the differences from the working mean of those measures which are less than the working mean. Add the column;
- write in a column headed "+ve" the differences from the working mean of those measures which are greater then the working mean. Add the column;
- divide the difference between the two column totals by n. If the negative total was the larger, subtract the result from the working mean; if the positive total was the larger, add. This gives μ, the sample mean. The larger the actual measures, and the more accurate the working mean, the more work is saved;
- write in a single column the differences between the measures and the sample mean. To check the work up to this point, see that the sum of the negative differences is equal to the sum of the positives, i.e. that the column total is zero;
- write in an adjacent column the squares of the differences obtained in the last step;
- add the column of squares;
- divide the sum of the squares by $(n-1)$;
- take the square root of the result of the last step. This gives $\hat{\sigma}$ (sigma cap), an unbiassed estimate of the standard deviation of the distribution.

This work can be laid out as shown on page 29.
In this table, the working mean was taken as 3. The differences summed at 2.4 negative and 4.4 positive, a total of 2.0 positive. Thus the working mean was too small by 2.0/20, = 0.1; and the value of sample μ is 3.1. The column headed d gives the differences between each measure of x (the time for a performance of the procedure) and this value of μ. Checking the work so far, the total of this column is zero. The column headed d^2 contains the squares of the quantities in the d column. The total of this column is 3.04. Dividing 3.04 by $(n-1)$, where $n = 20$, we get $3.04/19 = 0.16$. To find the best estimate of the standard deviation, we take the square root of this quantity, thus:

$$\sigma \simeq \hat{\sigma} = \sqrt{0.16} = 0.4.$$

For a normal distribution with $\mu = 3.1$ and $\sigma = 0.4$, the confidence levels and limits may be found as follows:

- $s - 2s - 3s$ method: this would now more properly be called the $\sigma - 2\sigma - 3\sigma$ method. The confidence level that x shall lie between $\mu - \sigma$ and $\mu + \sigma$ is 68%. In this example, these limits are 3.1 — 0.4 and 3.1 + 0.4, i.e. 2.7 and 3.5. The corresponding 99.7% confidence limits are 3.1 — 1.2 and 3.1 + 1.2, i.e. 1.9 and 4.5. For a confidence level of 99.994 — one chance in 16,666 of being wrong — we can take $\mu - 4\sigma$ and $\mu + 4\sigma$, giving 1.5 and 4.9. Since this is still well within the six-minute limit, we need go no further; application of the area-of-the-normal-curve method would, while appropriate to the distribution, give no more information.

It should be noted that the use of a $\hat{\sigma}$ for σ leads to small errors which can be minimized by taking large samples, and which can be virtually eliminated by the use of more sophisticated methods.

The change of the performance characteristics from $\mu = 4.9$, $\sigma = 0.55$ to $\mu = 3.1$, $\sigma = 0.4$ is clearly an improvement. If there has been a less clear difference, particularly if there had been a small decrease of the mean associated with an increase of σ, it would have been necessary to have employed some criterion of significance. For such tests, the reader is referred to any of the standard works named in the bibliography. The matter is raised here in order to sound a warning concerning "improvements". A small change in the mean derived from a relatively small sample taken over a relatively short period of time, is a very unreliable indicator of improvement. This is especialy true if the standard deviation is large (greater than $\mu/4$), if several successive estimates of σ show a tendency to fluctuate, or if the sample sizes are small.

x	—ve	+ve	d	d^2
2.4	0.6		—0.7	0.49
2.4	0.6		—0.7	0.49
2.7	0.3		—0.4	0.16
2.7	0.3		—0.4	0.16
2.7	0.3		—0.4	0.16
2.7	0.3		—0.4	0.16
3.0	0.0		—0.1	0.01
3.0	0.0		—0.1	0.01
3.1		0.1	0.0	0.00
3.1		0.1	0.0	0.00
3.1		0.1	0.0	0.00
3.2		0.2	+0.1	0.01
3.2		0.2	+0.1	0.01
3.4		0.4	+0.3	0.09
3.4		0.4	+0.3	0.09
3.5		0.5	+0.4	0.16
3.5		0.5	+0.4	0.16
3.5		0.5	+0.4	0.16
3.7		0.7	+0.6	0.36
3.7		0.7	+0.6	0.36
	2.4	4.4	0.0	3.04

Conclusion

This technique is not, and does not purport to be, a comprehensive course on statistics. It places the systems analyst in possession of a number of methods likely to be useful in his work; but, possibly even more important, it gives a picture of the nature of a statistical enquiry, and indicates the sort of result which can be expected, and what sort of pitfalls may be encountered. It should enable the analyst to do two things at least:

- to recognize the occasion for a statistical procedure when encountered;
- to determine whether such an occasion calls for outside assistance.

Appendix

In most statistical problems we are interested in questions such as:

- what is the percentage of bricks which are too small;
- what is the probability that the stock will be insufficient for the orders of next week.

In all these problems we are interested in the probability that a variate will have a specified value. If the distribution of the variate is known, we can calculate this value (possibly with the aid of a table). In statistics however we are usually concerned with random variables having unknown distributions, and therefore most statistical techniques are directed towards the problem of determining distributions by means of observations. There are two possibilities:

- nothing is known of the distribution;
- it is known that the distribution belongs to a special class, e.g. the normal distribution.

In the first case the distribution can be estimated, but it is impossible to determine the disparity between the estimated and real distributions. Therefore, the estimating function can only be used to get an idea of the distribution. If with the aid of this estimating function, a known distribution function is chosen to be representative for that under consideration, a statistical test can be used to decide if this known distribution corresponds with the unknown one.

Histogram

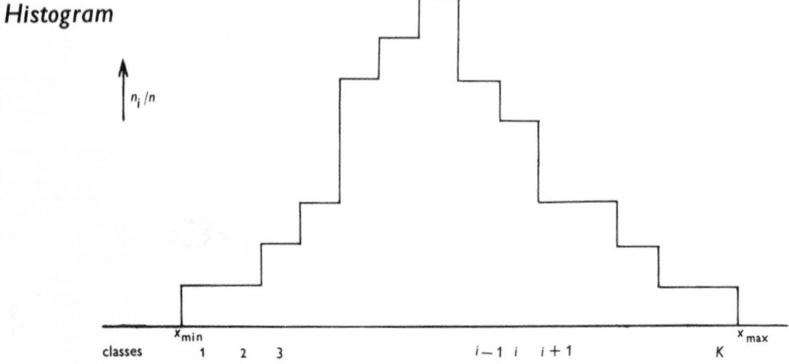

The n observations are placed in decreasing order; their range is divided in K equal classes. The number of observations are counted for each class, divided by n and then a diagram is made of relative frequencies. See figure on page 30. Sometimes it is more practical to take a fixed range of the variate in advance, so that one incorrect observation cannot cause a histogram of the type in the figure below. In addition, histograms of the same class width are directly comparable. See figure below.

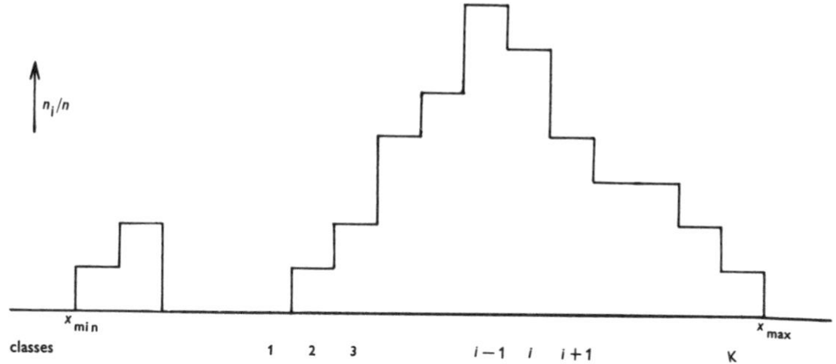

Although the class width — and so the number of classes — is arbitrary, there are certain practical rules:

- if the class width is large, all observations are counted in only a few intervals and therefore the information contained in the values of the observations is lost. The histogram will have the form shown below;

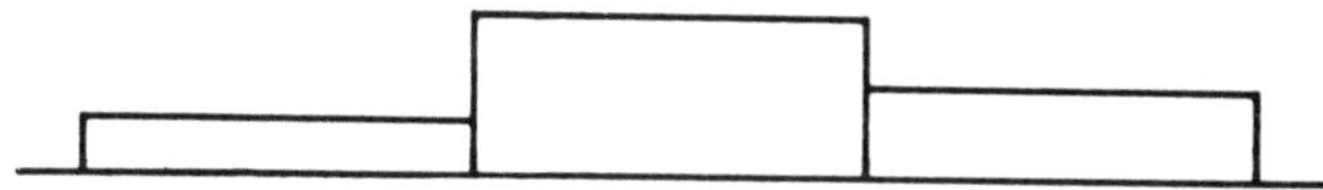

- if the class width is very small rounding-off errors may have a great influence on the form of the histogram as shown in the figure below.

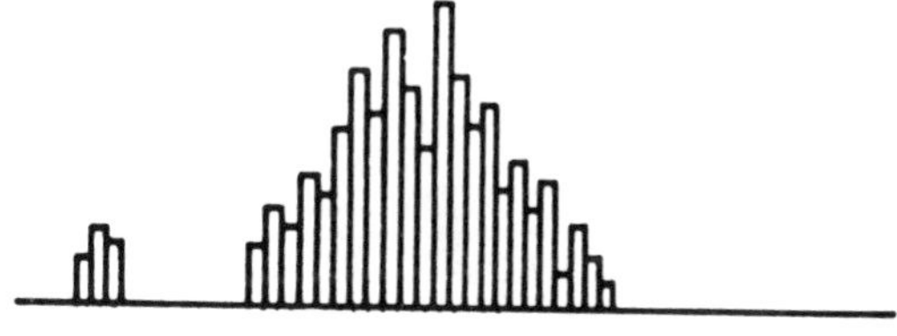

It is not possible to give a universal rule for selecting the class width, so that the histogram is the best estimator of the density, for this depends on the unknown density; whatever the best estimating criterium will be. However an empirical rule often quoted is: the number of classes should be equal to the square root of the number of observations. In addition, the class width must be chosen so that observation values, which have to be rounded off, do not fall in the neighbourhood of the boundaries between two classes.

Activity 6-4: Design and development

Technique 6-4.1: Identification of system elements and data objects

The identification of data objects is an important element of the systems effort. With many people working under conditions in which improvisation or the slightest misunderstanding could cause delay, a standard method of identification is essential.

This chapter shows, by means of a few general remarks and a detailed example, how standardization could be set up in this field. It is certainly not the last word on this subject, but it is put forward with the expectation that the suggestions and recommendations will prove helpful.

Purpose

The purpose of this technique is to recommend methods of uniquely identifying each element of, and the data objects encountered in, an information system.

Responsibility

The responsibility for laying down standards for the identification of system elements and data objects is that of the information systems department.

Application

The standards laid down apply to all personnel involved in the systems effort, to the personnel of user organization, and to the maintenance team.

Scope

The identification standards should cover all items used in a systems effort, and all the means by which data is processed.

Data objects include:

- files;
- logical records;
- fields;
- forms;
- areas;
- texts;
- constants.

System elements include:
- systems;
- subsystems;
- procedures;
- programs;
- routines;
- subroutines;
- switches;
- indicators;
- labels (references within a routine or subroutine);
- storage media.

Principles

It is necessary to identify every element of, and data object used in, a system in order to be able to locate it, or to refer to it. This reference could be either physical, e.g. finding a particular tape in the library of the computer centre, or a form in a procedure; or it could be abstract, e.g. accessing a specific file by a program, or displaying a particular message on the console.
The most convenient identifiers are strings of alphanumeric characters. This is because:
- a small number of characters can identify a very large number of objects (6 characters give over one thousand million possibilities);
- objects can be classified by means of an initial letter, e.g. file-identifiers could all start with the letter F;
- it is possible to construct meaningful names, recognizable abbreviations or mnemonics by which objects can be identified e.g. CSTA for customer's address;
- it is possible to use recognizable parts of identifiers of one or more objects or elements to construct identifiers for related objects or elements. For example a subsystem number, a file number and a run number could be combined to form the identifier of a storage medium.

Some programming languages, such as COBOL, permit the use of very long character-strings (usually up to 30 characters) as identifiers. In many cases such lengths are unnecessary and may even be undesirable since they permit too much inventiveness on the part of individual programmers. In any case, in the interests of consistency and standardization most data names will need to be established at subsystem or system level, before programming actually starts.

Example

The remainder of this technique consists of an example of the type of standards for data object identification that the information systems department of an organization should establish early in the systems effort. The example refers to a medium-sized information system i.e. one containing up to one hundred files and one hundred programs.

When defining the strings of characters that constitute the identifiers of system elements or data objects, the COBOL convention for specifying character-types in picture description is used, i.e.:

- the letter X represents an alphanumeric character;
- the digit 9 represents a numeric character;
- the letter A represents an alphabetic character.

It is usual to reserve certain characters for special applications, e.g. the letter "X" as the first character of the identification code of a standard program or routine of the computer centre itself.

Files, logical records and fields

The file, logical record and field are used in this standard in a strict hierarchy:

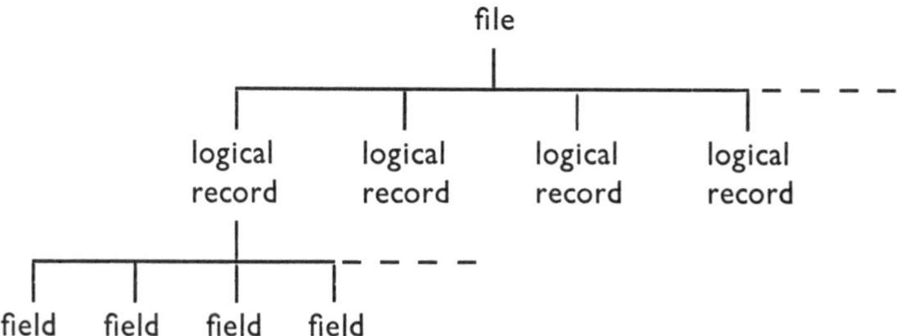

Files

A file is a collection of related records treated as a unit (ASA definition). The related records should have one characteristic in common.
Every file in the system is identified by a 5-character code, having the format: A9999 in which:

* the letter F for file;
 ** sequence or serial number of the file: 01 to 99;
  ** state number, 01 to 99; indicating the state of the file concerned, e.g. sorted, unsorted, etc.
 **** for a file stored on any storage medium these four characters correspond with the 4th to 7th positions of the storage medium code.

Examples: F2101 transactions on punched cards;
F2103 transactions on magnetic tape — unsorted;
F2104 transactions on magnetic tape — sorted;
F2102 invalid transaction cards;
F2201 system file on magnetic tape.

Note: these numbers are allocated during the system design activity. Even if the file is to be used in several subsystems it retains its original file number.

Logical records

A logical record is a collection of related items of data, treated as a unit (ASA definition). Logical records can be defined separately (i.e. without special provisions) in COBOL.
Every logical record in the system is identified by a 4-character code having the format:
A99A in which:
* letter L for logical record;
** sequence or serial number, 01 to 99;
* phase indication; one of the letters A to Z.

Example: L35B = order records sorted.

Note: the sequence numbers (01 to 99) are independent of the files in which the logical records are used. They are, however, completely system-dependent. A logical record always bears the same identifier even if it is used in several files.

Fields

A field is a specified area in a record used for a particular category of data, e.g. a group of card columns used to represent a wage rate or a set of bit locations in a computer word used to express the address of the operand (ASA definition).

Every field used in the system is uniquely identified by a 4-character code of the form AAAX. The letter "X" must not be used for the first character.
Example: CSTN = customer code number.

Even if a field occurs in more than one logical record it always bears the same identifier.

Forms

Every form used in the organization is identified by a 6-character code having the format:
999A99 in which:
*** reference number of department by which the form is used (or the originator department if the form is used by more than one department);
* the letter D for document;
** sequence number 01 to 99.

Areas

It is usually necessary in a program to identify input and output areas and working areas to facilitate reference to them.

Input and output areas

An input area is a storage block to which input takes place. An output area is a storage block form which output takes place (IFIP-ICC definitions).
The method of identifying input and output areas is entirely dependent on the type of computer used.

Working areas

A working area is a number of usually consecutive store locations used by a program for temporary storage, e.g. of intermediate results (IFIP-ICC definition).
Working areas can be either coupled or not coupled with a field.

Working areas not coupled with a field are identified by a 4-character code having the format:
AA99 in which:
*   letter A for area;
 *   letter indicating the type of area e.g.:
       C = creation in the program;
       T = counting area;
  **   sequence number 01 to 99.

Working areas coupled with a field are identified by a 6-character or 7-character code having the format:
AAAAAA(9) in which:
*   letter A for area:
 **** standard name of the field;
     * letter indicating the type of area e.g.:
       C = creation;
      * if a field is identified in more than one working area the format is extended by one digit in order to be able to distinguish between them.

Example: ACSTNC = area for customer code number, created in the working storage.

Texts

A text is an ordered set of characters intended for ultimate printing or display. Any text in a program can be identified by a 4-character code having the format:
AA99 in which:
*   letter T for text:
 *   letter indicating the final output device, e.g.:
       C = console, P = printer, D = display;
  **   sequence number 01 to 99.

Example in COBOL:

```
DATA DIVISION.
WORKING-STORAGE SECTION.
77 TP01 PICTURE X(23) VALUE IS
        "START INVOICING ROUTINE".
77 TL02 PICTURE X(33) VALUE IS
        "TOTAL AMOUNT OF DEBTORS PROCESSED".
PROCEDURE DIVISION.
    DISPLAY TC01 UPON CONSOLE.
    MOVE TL02 TO L08T.
```

Constants

AX(X . . . . . X) = format, consisting of:
* C = constant;
********** absolute value of constant.
In COBOL constants are defined in the WORKING STORAGE SECTION.

Examples: constant 01 = C01
constant 1 = C1
constant 115 = C115
constant "page" = CPAGE

(Sub)system

999 = format, sequence number 001 to 999.

Procedures

Every procedure within the organization is identified by a 6-character code having the format:
999A99 = format consisting of
*** (sub)system number;
* the letter P for procedure;
** sequence number 01 to 99.

Program

99999 = format, consisting of:
*** (sub)system number;
** sequence number 00 to 99.

Program description

999 = format, consisting of:
** sequence number of program (4th and 5th characters of program identification code);
* sequence number 0 to 9 (allowing 10 chapters per program description).

Routines

A routine is a set of instructions arranged in proper sequence to cause a computer to perform a desired task (ASA definition).
A99 = format, consisting of:
* letter R for routine;
** sequence number; 00 = main routine; 01 to 99 = other routines.

Examples: R17 REBATE calculation;
R23 REORDER decision;
R49 PRINT routine;
R51 PAGE OVERFLOW routine.
The routine number may be used as a SECTION-name in COBOL.

Subroutines

A subroutine is a routine that can be part of another routine (ASA defintion).
A99 = format, consisting of:
* letter S for subroutine;
** sequence number 01 to 99.

Subroutines, once written can be executed in several parts of a program e.g. by the PERFORM instruction in COBOL.

Switches

A switch is a point in a routine at which two courses of action are possible, the decision as to which one to follow having been determined previously by a condition prevailing elsewhere in the routine.
A99A9 = format, consisting of:
*** identifier of routine or subroutine in which the switch is used;
* letter W denoting a switch;
* sequence number 1 to 9.

Switches are as a matter of fact, always routine or subroutine bound. Should there be more than nine switches in a routine, it would be very difficult to understand. A different breakdown of the program into routines and subroutines should therefore be attempted.

Indicators

An indicator is a device which may be set to a prescribed state, possibly according to the results of a previous process, and which subsequently may be used to determine the selection from alternative processes (IFIP-ICC definition).
A99 = format, consisting of:
* letter I for indicator;
** sequence number 01 to 99.
In COBOL the indicators are defined in the WORKING-STORAGE SECTION.

Labels

A label (also known as a symbolic address) is an address expressed in symbols convenient to the programmer (ASA).

A99AA = format, consisting of:

*** identifier of routine or subroutine in which label is used;

   ** AA for entry; ZZ for exit; AB to ZY for other references.

Storage media

A storage medium is a data carrier intended for the retention of data for subsequent usage.

Apart from the specifications given by the manufacturer for identification additional (header) labels can be given for usage in the system.

Depending on the size of this label, the coding could be structured as follows:

9999999999 (suppose a 10-digit format)

*** (sub)system number;

   **** numerical part of the file code (2nd to 5th position);

       *** run number (see later);

***** note: the first five characters correspond with the program number.

Run number

For situations in which it is possible to code runs in terms of processing frequency, the following method is suggested:

- daily 001 to 366
- weekly 601 to 653
- 3 times per month 701 to 736
- twice per month 751 to 775
- monthly 801 to 812
- quaterly 901 to 904
- four-monthly 911 to 913
- half-yearly 921 to 922
- annually 931
- incidentally 999

If this interval coding is not possible the last three characters of the storage medium identification code could be used as cycle sequence numbers.

Technique 6-4.2: Data organization

This techniques chapter about data organization provides fundamental information about file organization methods, criteria for the selection of a file organization and the organization of data within a file.

Purpose

During system design the effort is first directed to the production of a machine independent design. The purpose of organization of data in physical files and records is:

- determination of the kind of storage devices which best serve the data processing required in the system and which, under the selected or available hardware and software configuration, enables the most efficient execution of the processing. No description of store units is given in this technique section. For explanation of typical characteristics and definitions the reader is refered to manuals of the hardware manufacturers;
- determination of the relationships between records of a file and records in the same and/or different files. The relationships are given with respect to the physical location by means of record keys, also called control fields;
- the definition of the various data and data identification elements and their allocation to the various files.

Areas of application

The data organization techniques are applicable to the activities of system design and subsystem development. The organization of data is a complex subject and can have a profound effect on system efficiency. File organization usually effects more than one program and frequently also the efficiency of related manual operations. Therefore, the requirements of the whole system must be known before any selection of data organization can be attempted.

Definitions

file or data file: a collection of logical records which have at least one characteristic in common and which are organized in such way as to permit retrieval.

logical record : the basic unit of information for a processing program. A record contains identification (record key) and descriptive information.

physical record: a group of logical records treated as an entity for the purpose of storage on, or retrieval from an external storage device.

A physical record is also known as a block. A block may contain only one logical record.

blocking : the process of grouping together a number of logical records to form a physical record, or a block.

field : the smallest element of data that can be referenced by a program.

record key : the element of data in a record which identifies that record. In general, record keys must be short and non-duplicating e.g. customer number, partnumber, order number.

Subdivision

The subject of data organization is dealt with under the following headings:

- file organization methods, which discusses sequential, index sequential and random organization methods in detail and briefly describes a number of other organizations;
- criteria for the selection of file organization, which presents the advantages and disadvantages of the various methods of organization to facilitate making a choice between them for any particular application;
- additional possibilities in file organization, which presents a number of variations and extensions of the basic methods which, in many systems, can lead to better performances;
- record organization, which deals with the process of identifying, sizing and sequencing the individual or hierarchical data elements at the field, logical record and physical record (block) level.

File organization

Introduction

File organization, or structure, deals with the relationship of the record key of each record in a file to the physical location of that record in the storage medium.

The most widely used methods for file organization are:

- sequential;
- indexed sequential;
- random

File processing

Note that the terms random and sequential, as applied to file organization should not be confused with the same terms when applied to file processing.

Random processing involves processing the records of a file in random order whilst sequential processing involves processing the records in ascending or descending order of record key.

Sequential

In a sequentially organized file, the records are stored in ascending or descending order of record key. Sequential organization is the only satisfactory method of organizing files held on unit record equipment i.e., cards, papertape, magnetic tape etc. but it can be used on all types of storage device.
On unit-record equipment the physical nature of the recording medium requires that each record be processed as it is encountered, and therefore the records must be organized in a sequential manner.
Since files on magnetic tape must be organized sequentially it follows that all associated transaction files, regardless of the storage medium, must also be sequentially organized.
A major disadvantage of sequential organization is that it is impossible to delete or insert records without rewriting all subsequent records.

Indexed sequential

The indexed sequential organization can be used only on direct access storage devices. This method is basically sequential in that it involves storing the records in record key sequence so that records with successively higher record keys are stored in higher address numbers.
The method, however, takes full advantage of the ability on direct access storage devices to locate an area of the storage medium quickly. Thus, if there is some correspondence between record key and record location, any record can quickly be found. This correspondence is provided by an index.

Index to storage location
The index system may be likened to the index system used locating an item in a conventional multiple-volume dictionary. The index on the cover of each volume gives the last item it contains. In an indexed sequential file organization the master index performs this function. The thumb index in a dictionary is similar to a cylinder index, while the upper-page index is analogous to the track index. The required item is located by searching the page in the dictionary or the track in the direct access storage device. Each of these indexes may be considered as a level.
The number of levels and the size of the index is dependent on the record length and the total number of records and the storage capacity of each level in the file. The indexes are usually contained on the same storage device as the in file itself. When the file is processed, the master index and, if possible, the cylinder indexes are read into core and retained whilst the file is processed. The indexes take the form of tables containing at least two elements per entry: the group address and the key of the last record contained in that physical group (volume cylinder, track).

The figure below shows the general arrangements and the operation of an index system.

read record 01712

master (volume) index; stored on track 0 of cylinder 000 of volume 01

record key	volume no.
00910	01
05612	02
11710	03
—	—
—	—
—	08

cylinder index for volume 02; stored on track 00 of cylinder 000 of volume 02.

An index of this type is stored on track 00 of cylinder 000 of each volume of the file

record key	cylinder no.
01012	001
01420	002
02016	003
02585	004
—	—
—	—
05612	119

track index for cylinder 003 of volume 02; stored on track 00 of cylinder 003 of volume 02.

An index of this type is stored on track 00 of every non-zero cylinder of the file.

record key	track no.
1510	01
1612	02
1710	03
1787	04
—	—
—	—
2016	09

required record is on track 04 of cylinder 003 of volume 02.
Search track for specified record key and then read record 01712.

Generalized indexed sequential file-organization system

Overflow
An addition is inserted into the file in its proper sequential location by replacing an existing record and shifting the remaining records on that track to the right. If the track is already full this causes an overflow.
Depending on the suppliers data management either the newly added record or the record which falls of the track is stored in an overflow area.

An overflow requires the use of a linkage field in the record to maintain the sequential nature of the file.
In the second solution, in which the displayed record from the end of the track is moved to the overflow area, requires an update of the track index to show the new last item on the track and to indicate the overflow track in which the overflow record (the previous last record) is now located. Thus the records in the prime area are in sequence and their record keys are always lower than those of any records that have overflowed that area (track).

Overflow areas may be designated for each different level e.g. for disk every cylinder can have its own overflow track and one or more cylinders can be reserved to hold the records that overflow the overflow tracks.
As the number of overflow records increases, however, the access time also rises, and it is customary, therefore, to reorganize the file periodically, in order to incorporate all overflow records into the prime area.
The overflow area contains records in sequence by time of arrival only, but they can be retrieved in record key sequence by use of the sequence linkage field.
The figure below gives a simplified arrangement of the method of index updating and overflow organization for the displaced record overflow method.
Records can be deleted either physically, or by appending a marker or tag to the record to indicate that it is no longer applicable. A disadvantage of physical deletion is that it necessitates updating the appropriate index(es).

before insertion

record key	track no.
1510	01
1612	02
1710	03
1787	04
—	—
—	—
—	—

after insertion

record key	track no.
1510	01
1612	02
1709	03
1787	04
—	—
—	—
—	—

track index cyl. 003

record key	data	sequence link addr.
—	—	
—	—	
—	—	
1706	x—x	
1708	x—x	
1710	x—x	

record key	data	sequence link addr.
—	—	
—	—	
—	—	
1706	x—x	
1708	x—x	
1709	x—x	00

track 03 content

record key	data	sequence link addr.
1512	x—x	02

record key	data	sequence link addr.
1512	x—x	02
1710	x—x	04

overflow area (track 00) content

Note: This area occupies that part of track 00 which is not taken up by the track index

Insertion of item with record-key 1709

Random

In a random file organization the records are stored without regard to the sequence of their record keys. The location of the record is determined by transforming the record keys (also called the symbolic key) into a physical called the actual key. This process is called "record key transformation". This actual key specifies e.g. for a disk the sector or track in which the record will be placed.
There are two methods of doing this. One, known as record key transformation, entails mathematically converting the symbolic key into an actual key by the computer itself. The other method, known as direct addressing allowing the allocation of the actual address by having this address made available in the input to be processed

Address conversion
To select the best address conversion routine, an evaluation of the calculated addresses must be made to determine the proportions of unique addresses and synonyms that will be generated and to assess the packing factor (= percentage of the allocated file actually used for records) and the average and maximum record retrieval time. The most popular methods of address conversion, such as division by a prime number, and folding are described in technique 6-6.4.

Because record key conversion (transformation) routines normally create duplicate addresses (synonyms) a method must be found to store and to retrieve these synonym records. The usual method of achieving this is by chaining.

Chaining of synonyms
The first (or "home") record is stored in the actual address developed by the record key conversion routine. This address is known as the home address.
The address of the first overflow record is placed in the home record, the address of the second overflow record is placed in the first overflow record etc. A field for the overflow address must therefore be reserved in every record and is used in every synonym record except the last in the chain. The diagram below illustrates the principles of chaining. To reduce seek time, it is best to store synonym records in overflow locations in the same cylinder as the home record.

Method of use
To locate a record, its symbolic key is processed either by the record key conversion routine or by direct address look up to derive the actual address, and a search and seek is then made to this address. The home record is read and its symbolic key compared to that of the record being sought. If these keys are unequal, the next record in the chain as determined by the chain address is read and the symbolic keys are compared again. These steps are repeated until the desired record is found. Each link in the chain requires a read and, usually for long chains, one or more seeks. Therefore the time needed to find a record depends upon its position in the chain.

actual key	(record-key) symbolic key	data	chain address
01716	16781	XXX----------XXX	01721
(home-address) initial seek and read		1st link	
01721	15811	XXX----------XXX	01745
		2nd link	
01745	33817	XXX----------XXX	
			unused until another synonym for address 01716 occurs.

Example of accessing chained unbinned records

The number of synonyms should be as small as possible; also the most active records should, wherever practible, be stored early in the chain to minimize retrieval time. In an existing file it may be possible to determine activity by carrying a count in each record and incrementing this by one for each access. The file could then be reorganized on the basis of these counts. It should be borne in mind, however, that carrying this count uses file space and updating it takes time.

Another method of minimizing access time is to place a number of synonimous logical records side by side to make up groups. This method is known as binning and is fully described later in this technique. Each seek and read makes available a number of synonyms, as shown in the diagram below. Binning reduces access time because it reduces the likelihood of overflow

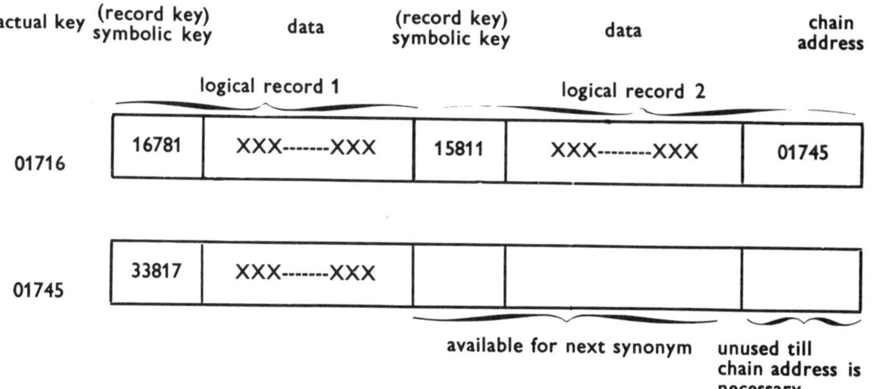

Example of chained binned records

Other file organizations

The sequential, indexed sequential and random methods of file organization are at the present time (1968) the most widely used. Many other methods of organization are of course possible including very complex organizations such as those offered by "I.D.S." (integrated data store). The two most popular alternative methods of organization, viz. relative and partition, are described here.

Relative organization

In a relative file, the record key defines the relative position of the record within the file. The key is transformed into an actual address by dividing the key by the number of records in a cylinder to obtain the cylinder address and then dividing the remainder by the number of records in a track to obtain the track address. This calculation is made by the program.

A consequence is of course that all records of a relative file must have the same size. The relative file organization may be used e.g. for files that only contain detail records.

Partition organization

A partition organized file is fundamentally a file which is broken down into a number of sequential organized subfiles or members. A member index is maintained to permit access to the beginning of any member. This kind of organization is particularly useful for filing programs.

Partition organization is possible both on direct access storage devices and magnetic tape. With direct access storage devices any member can be accessed directly using the index.

Criteria for the selection of file organization

In situations where a choice can be made between files on tape or disk, file size can be an important consideration. Until about 1967, disk files were prohibilitively expensive. Current progress in disk design, however, particularly the introduction of removable disk packs, is making disks more competitive with tape.

For batch processing, at the present time (1968) however, large tape files are usually the more economical as storage medium and are likely to remain so. In the selection of computer hardware however, direct access storage devices may have to be chosen if system performance requirements can be met only by the use of file organizations other than sequential.

File activity

File activity is quantified in terms of the relative frequency of referencing each record in the file. If the majority of file update transactions or output reports reference the most current records in the file, it may prove more beneficial to

place all new records on the end of the file in chronological sequence. Using this approach, the older portions of the file may often be split off into a historical file, thereby reducing the size of the active file, and at the same time permitting substantial economies in processing.
If the above solution is not practical indexed sequential or random file organization can offer a solution as only accesses have and can be made to records involved. In this case the access times should be compared with reading and writing a complete sequential file.

File turnover

File turnover is expressed in terms of the number of additions and deletions of records, or changes of address keys that have occurred, or can be expected to occur in a master file.
When these changes are relatively low in volume, the master file may be sequenced in such a way as to reduce output sorting requirements.

For example: employee numbers could include department number, thereby reducing sorting requirements when reports showing labor distribution are to be prepared. If file turnover is relatively high, however, the reduction in output sorting time must be weighed against the time that would be required to resequence the file should changes in employee department be made.

Access time

The access time to a record is relatively slow in comparison with the internal speed of the central processor.
For disk units the access time consists of two elements: seek time (head positioning time: 50-200 milliseconds) and latency time (rotation time: 15 to 25 ms). This time is large compared with the start-stop time of magnetic tape units: 5 ms is not uncommon. When a file is accessed randomly, the average access-time is the sum of the average seek time and the average latency time.

For this reason it is important that the file be organized in such a way as to minimize access-time. The following methods are possible:

- if a program accesses more than one file, time can be saved if these files can be accessed in overlap. With direct access devices it is usually possible to store more than one file on a device, but unless the device concerned has more than one access mechanism, no device should hold more than one of the files to which the program requires access;
- another consideration in this connection is the blocking factor of the master file. When the transaction or input file is in the same sequence as the master file it is likely that the next record is to be processed will already be in core so that the access time is zero.
  When the master file is organized in a blocked indexed sequential manner this method can give excellent results.

Indexed sequential versus random file organization

Advantages of random organization

- Access time is normally shorter for random input/output. There is no need to look in a directory, so that, in general, only one seek is required to locate a record;
- periodic reorganization of the file is not normally necessary;
- since there is no index, there are no maintenance problems and no disk or core storage requirements for an index.

Disadvantages of random organization

- Random key analysis and development of record key transformation routines are necessary;
- any changes in record keys will entail file reorganization to maintain access requirements;
- sequential processing in record key sequence is normally impracticable. If sequential processing is necessary a chain must be maintained in record key sequence.

Advantages of indexed sequential organization

- Sequential and random input of transactions can be handled. Reports arranged in record key sequence can be obtained without sorting;
- when sequential processing is carried out the entire file need not to be on-line simultaneously.

Disadvantages of indexed sequential organization

- For random input/output, searches in the index tables give rise to large access times;
- periodic reorganization is necessary, depending on the number of record additions to the file, especially when the usage of available storages capacity approaches 100%;
- chaining techniques are possible only with symbolic addresses. This causes either longer processing time or requires a bigger internal store capacity.

Core storage and external storage capacity

- Random organized files require core storage for the key conversion routine;
- indexed sequential files require core storage for the directory interpreting routines and cylinder index tables;
- random organization can make use of between 20% and 85% of the capacity of the storage medium — indexed sequential organization can utilize up to 100% of the available storage medium. Since about 10% of the total capacity is required for track index tables, however, the available capacity is only about 90% of the total capacity.

Additional possibilities in file organization

Splitting files

There are several reasons for splitting a file:

- access required by means of other than the primary key. This may require the use of inverted files (see later);
- different processing cycles may make it worthwhile to place seldom-accessed records in a separate file;
- limitations of an available configuration (in terms of coding capabilities and/or storage capacity) may require multiple passes. In such cases the establishment of separate files may reduce I/O, and/or processing time.

Processing cycle files

In most applications, files contain both current and historical information, and data needed for cyclical — i.e., daily, weekly, or monthly — processing. Sometimes, the seldom-used fields occupy a high percentage of the file and cause the frequent cyclical processing to be input/output-bound. In such cases the fields of the records should be divided over two files: a file containing only those fields that are necessary during the frequent processing, and a file containing the fields that are seldom accessed.

As an example, suppose that in a large, real-time, information retrieval application, it is discovered that only a portion of the information requested requires immediate response, whilst the remainder can be returned on a four-hour cycle. The fields required for immediate access are stored on a random access storage devices, with several inverted file indexes established for ease in locating them. The fields that remain are stored on a multi-reel tape file which is updated at regular intervals.

On receipt of a transaction, which requires immediate response the record is located (either directly or through inverted index files). The required response is made, and the update material caused by this transaction is chained to the record.

When the file on tape is read and the record which matches this transaction is reached, it is updated and written to the new file, and a complete response is then generated and transmitted to the requestor.

Split Files

In a split file the records remain the same but the file as such is divided into an active and nonactive part. This method can be used to save memory space and reduce calculation time. The diagram below illustrates the use of this method used for a master file with high activity but low updating rates with a program having tape limited processing. During the weekly or monthly processing run the file with updated records is merged with the master file and a new master file is written.

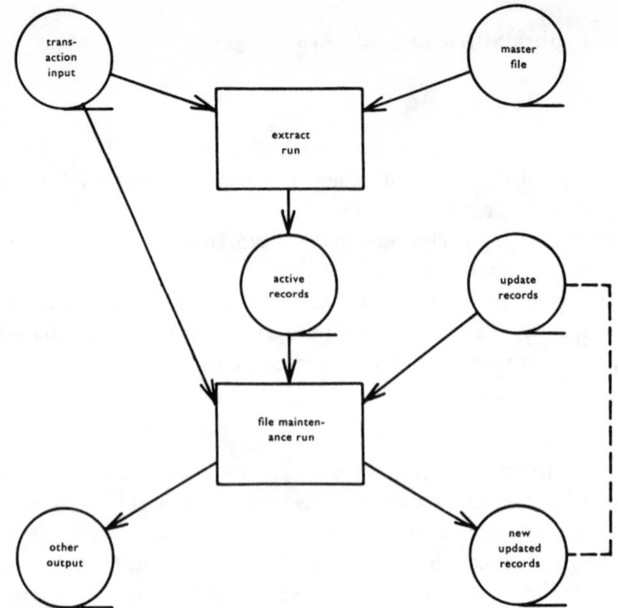

Split file (extraction method updating)

Inverted files

For retrieval applications where the records required for display or reporting must be located by matching a combination of search criteria, the use of an inverted file may be advisable particularly when the object data file is large. An inverted file consists of a number of indexes, each of which relates one of the frequently referenced search criteria (document descriptors, reference data, size, shape, method of processing, etc.), to the actual address of the appropriate master file records.

Example

Suppose it were necessary to select the proper production process for a new part which might be similar to one that has been produced at some time in the past. Instead of laboriously searching all previous orders for a similar part, a description of the new part could be matched against the descriptor-oriented inverted file, to determine which order, if any, dealt with a similar item.
A flow for product design data retrieval using an inverted descriptor file is given on page 13.

Applicability

The inverted file is most commonly used for fairly heavy retrieval applications, since extra costs are inevitably incurred in the construction and maintenance of the multiple indexes.
Inverted files used in high-volume retrieval applications are most flexible and require the least access time when they are random organized. This is particular-

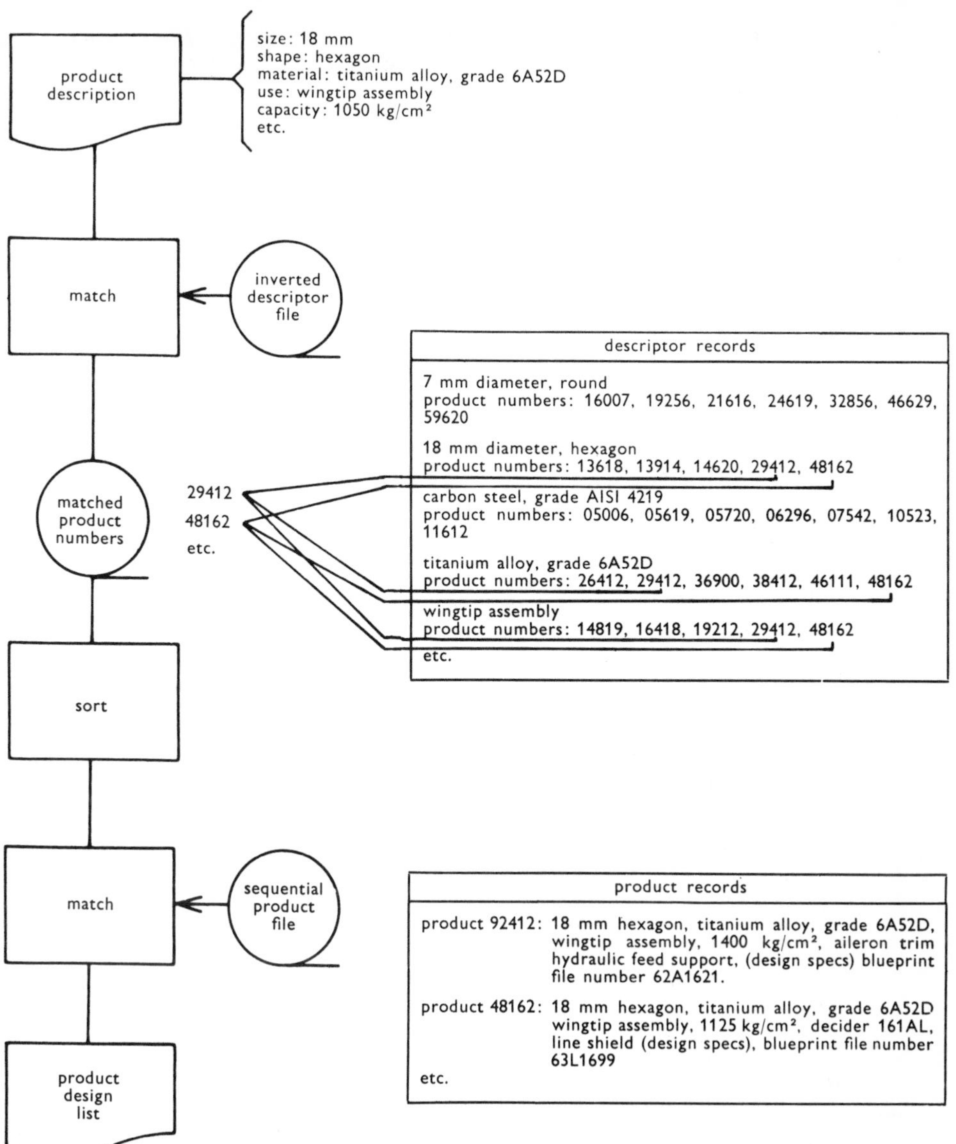

Inverted file for product design retrieval.

ly true when there are many descriptors per record, many descriptors in the file but few entries for each descriptor.

It then becomes possible to process each descriptor in a search problem separately and completely without matching. Random organized inverted files are therefore frequently used when response time requirements are highly critical, e.g. in online information retrieval systems.

For specialized applications in which an inverted file is entered only for search problems, it is possible to add all new records to the end of the file, and chain them into their appropriate groups.
Inverted files may have simple or complex hierarchical structures. They usually allow swift, efficient access to records. Their major disadvantages are:

- they use valuable core storage;
- they require complex maintenance.

In some information retrieval applications, the indexes can occupy more space than the master file to which they refer, and the maintenance procedure can be longer and more complex than the processing programs.

Alternatives for indexes

In inverted files the alternatives to the use of indexes are scanning and chaining. If only a small proportion of transactions do not use the primary key of the file, scanning could be used.
For a larger proportion of non-primary key transactions the chaining possibilities presented below can frequently be used provided that chains are few in number and reasonable in length.
Normally, however, the need for indexes is immediately apparent, and the only parameters are the number of indexes and their exact sort.
To a lesser extent, chaining may also be used in such applications, but only when the number of chained descriptors for each parts master record is low. Since access to individual records within a file is possible only through the inverted file or by tracing the chain, the selection of records by other criteria must be accomplished by scanning the contents of the entire file, as would be necessary in a tape operation. For files used for information retrieval applications only, or for small files where total file scanning can be accomplished quickly, inverted-file/chained-entry methods are used only where this type of organization gives better file maintenance efficiency.

Chaining

Chaining within a file

A powerful method of retrieving records from files on direct access storage devices by keys other than the primary key, is the use of a chaining, or threading, technique. In this technique a field in each record indicates the address of the next record in the desired grouping.
In addition to this a starting index containing for each group key, the address of the first and last record in each chain must be established. When a new record is inserted, a new link is added to the chain by storing the address of the new item in the "link" field in the current last item, and then placing the address of the new item in the "last-item" address field in the relevant record in the starting index.

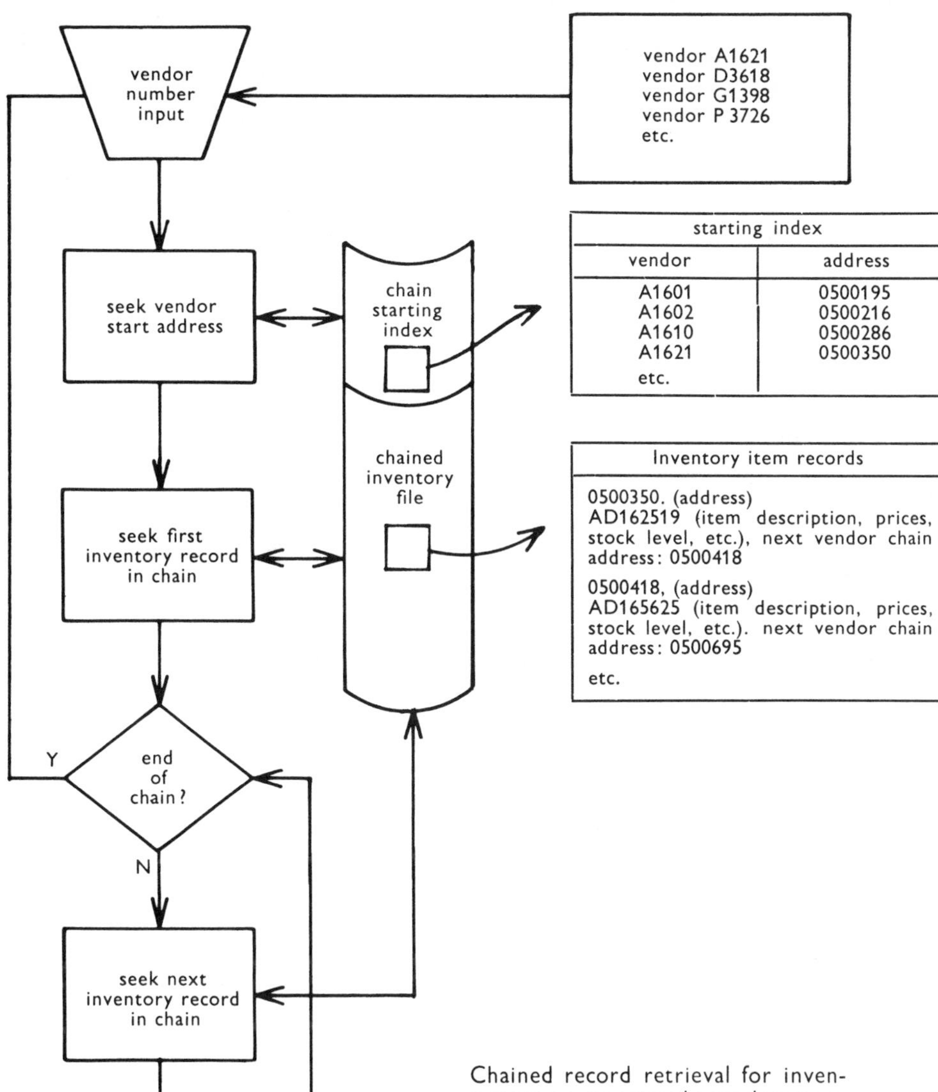

Chained record retrieval for inventory status reporting by vendor group

Insertion and deletion of records is greatly simplified if bidirectional chaining is used. In this case there are two linkage fields in each record; one to the next record and the other to the previous record in the chain. When a record is deleted the "next record" address from it is transferred to the next record field of the previous record and the "previous record" address from it is transferred to the "previous record" field of the next record. This relinks the chain.

Although this method is most often used with random access files, it is often advantageous for indexed sequential files. In this case, the feasibility of using chained records depends upon a comparison between the processing time required to find and analyze the group key (vendor number, etc.) in unchained records, against the time required for the complex task of maintaining a chained file.

Implications, advantages and disadvantages

Chaining can be used as an alternative to an inverted file over which it can sometimes offer savings in processing time. This is because it substitutes a single, relatively simple index for the multiple indexes. Chaining can also increase file maintenance efficiency, since only one file need be maintained. The chaining of indexed sequential files can be a very efficient means of accessing records within a desired grouping, and is a widely used method of gaining additional retrieval power.

Some constraints exist, however, in using chaining:

- each record must be involved in only a small number of chains. Each time a record is added or deleted, the preceding and succeeding record in each of the chains of which the subject record is a component must be updated. This makes updating both complex and time consuming, particularly if many chains are threaded through each record.
- changes to the groupings within a file must be held to a minimum. Every time a group key (e.g. stock classification) is changed the chain base point and many records in the associated chain must usually be altered;
- chains must be long enough to make the method worthwhile. For a given volume of data the shorter the chains the greater their number and this requires a much larger starting index. In extreme cases it might be more practical to use an inverted file. A good balance between the size of the starting index and the size of the file itself is necessary;
- response time requirements must be non-critical to a degree permitting a methodical search through the relevant chains, particularly if these are long.

The chained file is initially interrogated at its starting index, which contains fields relating all major file groupings (vendor number, stock classification, etc.) to the address of the first record for that group. The specified record in each group contains the address of the next record in that group.

Example

Most inventory status reports must be grouped by stock classification or by vendor, so as to speed reorder review and processing. In order to provide the capability of selecting stock items within desired stock categories and vendors (to the exclusion of all others) the items in each category are chained.

The diagram on page 15 shows the method of retrieving items by vendor number from a chained stock file. It is important to note that a system using chaining is considered to work well when chaining is used as little as possible.

Chaining of records in a hierarchical structure

Chain addressing can also be used to relate in a hierarchical structure parent-records to component records and vice versa. A parent or detail record contains individual information serving to identify and to characterize an object, whilst a relation-record contains relational information, presenting the connections between two or more objects.

For example: An article is identified and characterized by its code number, description, size, price, etc., and therefore this information will form the parent record. If an article is made up of a number of components, this information will be held in component records while the hierarchical structure is given by the relation records. Note that there exists a chain of relation records connected to the parent record. Each relation record points to a component record. An example of simple structure is given below.

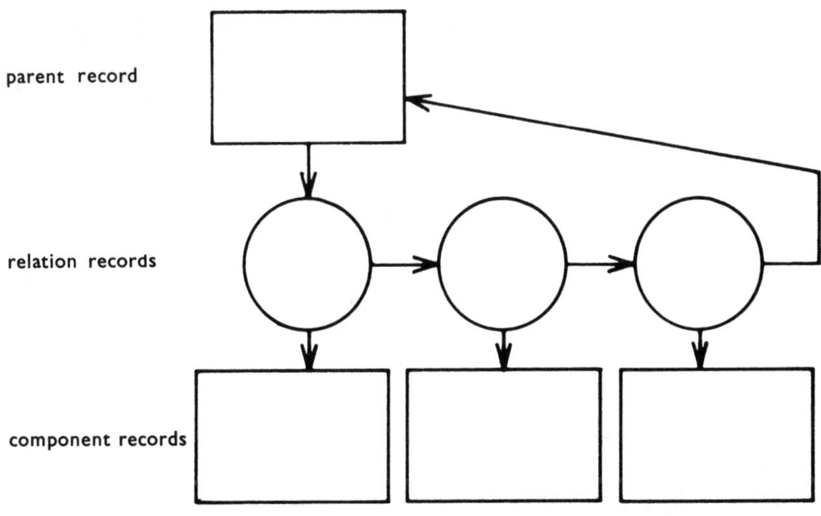

Simple structure

In the above figure a one-way structure (parent to component) is given, but more complex structures are possible. The figure below shows a multiway structure with forward (parent to component), backward (component to parent) and both a foreward and backward relation chain.

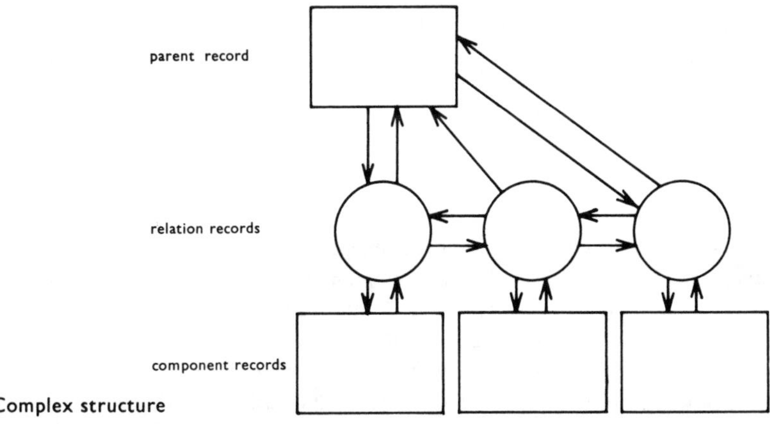

Complex structure

The chain addressing method has the following advantages:
— once-only recording of information on each object reduces file size and permits better control of updating;
— relatively simple updating procedures;
— rapid access to grouped data.
Disadvantages are:
— more core storage capacity needed for complex updating routines and I/O buffers;
— when chaining is accomplished by means of actual keys severe updating problems can arise when one or more of a set of chained files are changing frequently;
— access times can become very long when chains are lengthy and poorly organized.

Overflow Chaining
In files on direct access storage devices, chaining is used to connect a sequence of overflow records, and thereby provide an access path. When the home address for a record is already occupied, a sequential scan can be made through the file until an empty location is found, and the new record inserted at this location. The record is chained to the relevant record in the home address. When deleting records, care must be exercised to re-link the chain.

In record retrieval operations, a comparison of address keys must be made along the chained path in order to locate the desired record; this will result in a short scanning operation. When overflows start to occur frequently, the storage area allocated to the file should be increased, to allow more efficient operation.

Record design

Record design is the process of placing data in fields, assembling fields into logical records, and building logical records into blocks (physical records). The following part is therefore divided into three main sections:
- field design;
- logical record design;
- block design.

Field design

A field is defined as the smallest element of data that can normally be referenced by a program. Since it is also the basic element from which logical records are built up, however, it follows that good field design is essential to good record design. Field design can have a profound effect on file size, input/output time and processing time and complexity. The main factors to be considered when designing a field are its length, its coding and its position within a record.

Field length

The length of a field is the number of characters it contains. Fields can be fixed, incremental or variable in length:

- fixed length fields. As the name implies, fixed length fields are fields which contain a predetermined, and invariable, number of characters. The field length is equal to the maximum number of characters that the field could possibly require. Because of this, fixed length fields can be extremely wasteful of storage space. The greatest waste occurs with alphanumeric fields such as those for customer or employee names and addresses, where the maximum field length is usually many times the average. Fixed length fields are, however, by far the easiest to process, particularly when they are used directly, in edited format, on output reports, because the editing information is, in effect, carried permanently in the field. Also, the use of fixed length fields greatly simplifies the task of estimating file size.
- incremental length fields. This type of field contains a variable number of fixed length segments, the actual number of segments being specified, for each individual field, by a count, usually carried in the first segment. This type of field is far less wasteful of storage space than fixed length fields, but requires more processing time to interpret the count and expand the field to reference format in core.

  In order to select the optimum length for a segment, it is usually necessary to carry out a statistical analysis of the expected field lengths. If it is found that most fields will have a length within a few characters of the average length, then it is best to make the segments slightly longer than this average. If the field is highly variable in length then a compromise must be made between short segments, which are less wasteful of storage space, and long segments, which require shorter processing time. The segment length is usually made an integral multiple of the smallest addressable unit of internal storage;
- variable length fields. Variable length fields contain a variable number of characters, the actual number in a particular field being specified by a count, usually carried in the first two or three characters. It is also possible, insteed of carrying a count, to mark the end of the field by means of a field terminating character or sentinel. This type of field is, in effect, an incremental length field in which the segment length is one character.

  Variable length fields make the most efficient use of storage space. Savings over the other types of field are greatest when the average number of characters plus one is less than the maximum field size.

  Their great disadvantage is that they require the longest processing time of all, assuming that the processing must be carried out by software. If, however the computer instruction set contains macros capable of dealing with variable length fields, then this method of field organization can be very efficient indeed.

  An advantage of variable length fields over incremental length fields is that no statistical analysis is necessary, although of course the average length is required for estimating file size and the maximum length is required for designing the reference format. The reference format is the format into which the field is transformed when it is transferred into core in order to facilitate reference by the processing program.

Field compaction techniques

Because the length of a record is the sum of the lengths of the individual fields it contains, and because the longer a record the fewer the number of records that can be accommodated in a given space and the greater the input/output time needed to transfer it to or from core, it follows that there are advantages to be gained by reducing field size.

A proposed compaction technique must be evaluated for:

- core capacity required to hold the encode-decode instructions;
- encode-decode execution time;
- compaction percentage achieved;
- compatibility with programming systems;
- retention of collating sequence;
- retention of fixed field length (where applicable);
- effect on the overall system, including related clerical functions.

The method of reducing field size given in the preceding paragraphs have been directed towards assembling the characters comprising the field into the most economical format. The purpose of this section is to present methods of reducing the number of characters required to carry a given amount of data.
The methods available are:

- scaling;
- bitting;
- coding;
- substituting;
- converting into binary;
- packing.

Scaling

When storing fixed point numbers, that is to say, whole numbers (integers) or numbers with a fixed number of digits after the decimal point, it is often necessary to store a large number of zeroes to the right or left of the significant digits purely for the purpose of decimal point positioning.
It is often possible, however, to omit some or all of these zeroes by scaling the number by an appropriate positive or negative power of ten. For example if the range of values of the field were from .0000000 to .0000999 the field could be scaled by 10^{-7} so that it would be stored as 000 to 999 which requires only three characters instead of the original eight.

Two conditions must be satisfied for scaling to be an efficient method of field compaction. First, all the values that the field can assume in any record of a file must either be integers which are multiples of a power of ten, or must be decimal fractions of the same order of magnitude, for example:

number range	scale	characters required
10,000 to 9,999,900 in steps of 100	10^2	5
10,000 to 9,999,000 in steps of 1000	10^3	4
10,000 to 9,990,000 in steps of 10,000	10^4	3
.000001 to .000009	10^{-6}	1
.000001 to .000099	10^{-6}	2
.0001 to .9999	10^{-4}	4

It would not normally be worthwhile to scale the last example since only one character (the decimal point) is saved.

The second condition that must be satisfied is that the value of the scaling factor must be communicated to all the programs that will process that field. This can be done either when the program is written, or by including a field specification record into the file, and causing the program to read this record before processing any scaled field.

Bitting
Many items of data can be stored in one or more characters by assigning to each bit of each character a specific value or control function.
Thus, bit 1 could represent male (1) or female (0); bits 2 and 3, one of four credit ratings; bits 4, 5 and 6, one of eight age classification etc. Care must be taken to ensure that none of the possible combinations of bits are invalid to the hardware to be used.

Coding
Coding may be used to replace a larger field. During processing, the codes can be interpreted or translated to the constants they represent. For example: a one-position code may represent the unit of measure of inventory items, e.g. 1 = dozens; 2 = ounces; 3 = pounds.

Substituting
Substituting makes use of the number of free bits that appear in a given character set or, in the case of EBCDIC, some of the lesser used combinations, such as the lower case letters. Each of these characters could be used to represent one or more other characters. This method is particularly suitable for converting numeric pairs, such as month number, to a single character by using the letters A and B to represent November (11) and December (12).

- Binary. In most of the latest computer peripheral devices, each character, whether alphabetic or numeric, is represented by eight bits. Thus twenty-four bits (three characters) are required to represent a number in the range 000 to 999. In binary, however, an eight-bit number ranging from 00000000 to 11111111 can represent decimal numbers ranging zero to 255. Twenty-four bits (three units of core or media store) can represent numbers from zero to 16,777,215. Binary notation is therefore a very effective compaction technique for numeric data, but it can be used only when the computer is capable of handling such data efficiently.

- Packed numeric format. Decimal data can be represented in the binary coded decimal (BCD) code, which requires only four bits (numeric value, 8, 4, 2, 1) to represent each digit. In storage units capable of handling eight bits per unit of storage, two decimal digits can be packed into each unit of storage. To illustrate:

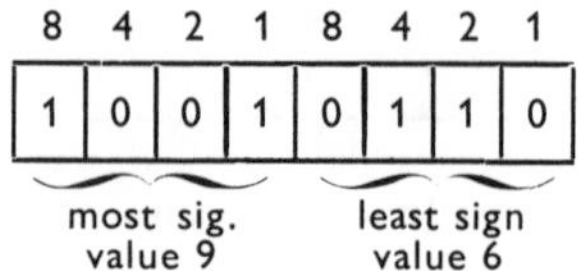

In order to be able to operate efficiently in packed format, the computer must contain in its instruction set, codes to pack and unpack, as well as to operate arithmetically when in the packed mode.

Field coding

Planning the coding to be used in a field entails the selection of the radix (binary, decimal or alphanumeric) of the stored data, and its precise format. Coding decisions are dependent on the various usage frequencies and types of data, and the space saving made possible by means of judicious code selection. Some of the factors to be considered are shown in the table below.

	binary	decimal	character
conversion to/from external formats	slow	moderate *	none
speed of arithmetic processing	fast	moderate *	slow
compactness of information storage	good	moderate	poor

*) Good if computer contains hardware for processing packed decimal data.

This table assumes a computer with the octad (8-bits-per-character) decimal, and binary characteristics of the typical third-generation computer.

A similar chart could be produced for any other computer. The following examples will illustrate the type of analysis required to select the proper coding method.

Example 1

A highly transient numeric field is introduced into the system from an input tape, and is listed in an edited format on several reports, with the entries in each report in the same order as in the master file. The field, therefore, is not processed extensively in sorts, or carried for long periods on a master, so that storage compactness is not a major factor. The field is not used for arithmetic, but is used in external format only. The field therefore should be carried in character (octad) format.

Example 2

A rate field that is seldom changed is carried in the master record of each item in mass storage. It is used for the multiplication of other fields which are transient. If the rate field is stored in binary format, it will need less than half the

space required for decimal format, but it would then require that every transaction item stored in character format be converted to binary format for calculation.
The correct decision depends on the requirements of the specific installation with regard to balancing conversion time against storage space.

The discussion so far has referred to fields whose contents when stored in the computer consist of an image paralleling their recorded form; for example, a number in binary format is still unquestionably the same number as soon as the format is specified. A field can also be stored in the computer so that a specific code or data configuration represents some other, totally different data configuration on the reports produced, such as the arbitrary assignment of specific numbers to certain patterns of transaction codes, or carrying a duplicate sort key in a record in which each character has been translated to the binary pattern representing the collating sequence required in a special report. Careful translation of fields on entry into the computer system can reduce both storage space and processing time required.

Field start position
The position of the start of a specific field within a record can influence processing time especially on word-oriented computers. The question of whether to pack the content of a field against that of the adjoining fields, or to leave it synchronized to a computer word is often critical. The storage space wasted by synchronizing must be determined and weighed against the time lost in reading and storing the unused characters. In computer systems where the reading time is overlapped with computing, however, the cost of the extra storage is the only relevant factor.

Field position
A field's position within a record is often selected to accomodate sort key requirements, or to satisfy a requirement that a group of fields also be capable of being treated as a single field, or to satisfy the display requirements of specific output reports. If possible all the conceivable uses of a field should be established before its position is determined. This should minimize the possibility of having to rearrange the fields later, at painful cost in file conversion and personnel adaption.

Logical record design

A logical record is the basic unit of information for a processing program. Fields are grouped together into logical records to accomodate as efficient as possible processing of:
- input;
- output;
- arithmetic or administrative operation.

The consideration of object oriented grouping, i.e. product or customer oriented, will lead to a consolidated file in which practically any element is stored only once.

Since not all elements will be present in any logical record — they will not always be applicable — logical records have basically a variable length. However, the logical records will for practical reasons in most cases be stored in a fixed length physical area (record). Maintaining the fixed length format in the physical organization can lead to the following methods of dividing a logical record into more logical records:

- split files;
- processing cycle files,

  which coincide with a division over more physical records.

Another method is chaining. The chaining method is usually applied for separating the invariable and variable part of the logical record. The variable part of the record is either partially or completely stored in one or more overflow areas.

Blocking

The storage of records in an unblocked form normally lowers the gross data capacity of the storage medium due to the presence of inter-record gaps.

Blocked records (also called physical records) are two or more logical records grouped together and treated as a whole for reading, writing and storage purposes. Each logical record within the block is processed individually by the program.

The blocking factor is the number of logical records contained in a block.

Blocking permits more efficient use of the storage medium and reduces input/output time. However, logical (unblocked) records require the minimum core storage and no deblock routines are required.

Physical records on magnetic tape are separated by blank tape (gaps). When records are blocked, fewer gaps are created so the storage capacity of the tape is increased. Moreover I/O-time is saved because the tape must stop and restart at each gap.

When blocks are short, the time taken for the tape to reach writing/reading speed and subsequently stop at the end of the block can exceed the time taken to write or read the data. If the processing is I/O limited this will increase the job-time; long blocks can also decrease the number of reels of tape required, thereby achieving savings in tape handling and storage costs:

e.g. for a tape of 2400 feet, gap 0,6 inch, 800 bits

no. of characters per block	total no. of characters per reel in millions	percentage of tape used for data
100	3,97	17.2
1000	15,02	67.2

Binning

Binning techniques are those methods used to design multiple-record "bins" for use on direct access storage devices. Probability theory indicates that, for random organized files, the overall storage and retrieval efficiency can be improved by keeping more than one record at an address. The reason for this is that minor overflows and underflows at adjacent addresses tend to cancel out. The table below gives the percentages of overflow from bins of given sizes, assuming a random distribution of addresses. The load factor is computed as the number of records divided by the number of storage locations available. The

bin size	load factor							
	20%	40%	50%	60%	70%	80%	90%	100%
1	9.4%	17.6%	21.3%	24.8%	28.1%	31.2%	34.1%	36.8%
2	2.2	7.3	10.4	13.7	17.0	20.4	23.8	27.1
3	.6	3.6	6.0	8.8	12.0	15.4	18.9	22.4
4	.2	2.0	3.8	6.2	9.0	12.3	15.9	19.5
5	.1	1.1	2.5	4.5	7.1	10.3	13.8	17.6
6		.7	1.7	3.4	5.8	8.8	12.3	16.1
7		.4	1.2	2.6	4.7	7.6	11.0	14.9
8		.3	.8	2.0	4.0	6.7	10.1	14.0
9		.2	.6	1.6	3.4	5.9	9.3	13.2
10		.1	.4	1.3	2.9	5.3	8.6	12.5
20				.2	.8	2.3	5.0	8.9
30					.3	1.2	3.5	7.3
40					.1	.7	2.6	6.3
50						.5	2.0	5.6
60						.3	1.7	5.1
70						.2	1.4	4.8
80						.1	1.2	4.5
90						.1	1.0	4.2
100							.8	4.0

Notes:

- Bin size is the number of records stored at an address
- Load factor is the percentage of the primary area of the storage medium actually occupied by records. It is expressed as:

$$\frac{\text{total no. of records} \times 100}{\text{record storage capacity of prime area}}$$

Overflow must be stored in separate overflow area.

figures assume that, when overflow occurs, a separate area receives the overflow items. Bin size represents the number of records that can be stored at any single address. With a typical load factor of .8, a bin size of 5 gives a 3 : 1 improvement over the one-record-per-address method, while a bin size of 10 gives an improvement of 5-1.

Bins can therefore offer a reduction in search time, but only when access to the records in a bin is faster than access to adjacent or overflow bins. This is true for cylinder/track storage equipment, where bin size is usually taken as the space available without movement of the read/write head.

There is an alternative to the use of bins and separate overflow areas. When access to any location requires approximately the same processing time and single or multiple records are stored at each address, an overflow condition necessitates a sequential search of the storage medium in order to find an empty storage location. The record is then stored and chained in the sequence stemming from the location originally referenced. If overflow has already occurred, the search starts at the last record chained to the referenced storage position. This method should only be used with load factors below approximately .8; otherwise, too long a search would be required. Many modifications of these methods are possible but the correct choice for any situation is dependent on the characteristics of both the file itself and of the computer to be used.

When track search hardware is available and the record keys in a track can be abbreviated so that each is unique but still fits within the search hardware limitations, track size bins usually prove optimum. If a good key transformation method has been developed, the distribution of record keys is genuinely random, bin sizes of 2-4 will usually prove to be optimum.

Technique 6-4.3: Application software

Purpose

The purpose of application software is to provide the user with proved and tested designs for at least a part of the information system he requires. Depending upon the extent to which suitable packages are available, the use of application software can effect substantial saving of time in the design, development and implementation phases of the systems effort.

Areas of application

Application software can be a source of ideas during the system design stage. If available, application packages cover functions to be incorporated in the new information system; their structure should be taken into account when making the division of the system into subsystems. During the development phase, application packages can provide detailed information and solutions ranging from routines ready for the realization of functions to aids for conversion.

General characteristics of application software

Avialable application packages vary widely in their characteristics. This variety arises not only from the differing purposes of the packages, and from the methods adopted for overcoming the difficulties inherent in achieving a real general-purpose package, but also from the different incentives which prompt the various manufacturers to produce application software.

Product

To make these differences clear, application software is classified below first by type of product, and then according to the degree of hardness with which it appears on the market.

Type of product (category)
The type of product is greatly influenced by the technical constraints which govern the definition and realization of a generalized package. The types which can be identified are:

- modules or routines. This class includes scientific routines such as functionals, square root etc., intended for a program library from which they can be called up as required by the programmer;
- packages which cover a wide variety of data processing functions, and which are customizable by means of a "generation" program. These packages contain an extensive range of options which can be suppressed if not required.

In general, the package will perform rather elementary functions such as creation and maintenance of a set of complex files;

- packages which are expected to require a significant amount of adaption to specific user requirements. The package will offer a complete design consisting of a main line to which a set of routines are connected. The logic itself will be of general applicability, but the routines should be exchangeable.
  The supplier of such packages will usually be in a position to offer alternative routines for selection;
- packages which do not offer problem solutions, but are closer to compilers. These packages, by making use of a set of macros, permit the use of normal forms of expression in describing the solution of a problem, thus avoiding the necessity of employing a higher statement level language.
  Examples of this type are file processors, preprocessors to convert decision tables into a COBOL program etc.;
- packages for specific purposes, such as conversion of programs written for one type of equipment to another type of equipment. An example of such a package is EXODUS I and II, developed by Computer Sciences Corporation, which can convert programs written for 1410 and 1401 to 360 programs.

"Hardness" of the product

The hardness of the application software can be made clear by the division into the following:

- packages which will be maintained and updated (manufacturers and software consulting companies);
- packages for which the manufacturer accepts no responsibility for maintenance and updating. This type of package will be more subject to changes originating from organizational and operational requirements in a typical application;
- packages which are not developed beyond the design level, identification of requirements applicable to typical solutions, and block diagrams for these solutions (application description).

Implementation support

The application package as a product is not complete without adequate training services and documentation of the package.

Training services

To facilitate the implementation of application packages, representatives of the user organization should participate in courses devoted to the subject of the package.

At the end of the design stage or early in the development phase, it is necessary to obtain an understanding of the decision rules and logic applied in the design, and to learn how and where the program package should link up with the procedures to be executed by line personnel in the organization.

Towards the end of the system development phase, a second course should provide experience in exercising the implementation procedure and in the use of the package.

Documentation
The documentation of the application package should provide at least those details which, at the time of implementation, are to be included in the user documentation. If the available documentation is not sufficient to permit changes and adaptions to be made, the value of the package is reduced to that of an application description.

Implementation assistance
In addition to the documentation and training courses, the package designer's organization should be preferably provide implementation assistance on the spot.

Suppliers of application packages

Application packages are put on the market by computer manufacturers and software consulting companies.
Manufacturers develop and make packages available as part of their activities because they have recognized that the user organizations are in need of new systems, and not merely of new equipment. Experience acquired in design of new information systems is evaluated and applied in making a generalized design.
Software consulting companies take, to a certain extent, the same approach. However, they generally charge the user of the application packages, so that they tend to fill the gaps left by the manufacturers.
Also, software consulting companies (software houses) are forming user circles which are interested in certain types of application. The software house accepts the responsibility for development and, after implementation, the maintenance of the package. Consultancy in this respect is further developed in the USA then in Europe.

The value of application packages

The value of an application package is determined by its category, its level (hardness) within its category, and the stage of design or development which has already been reached in the prospective user organization.

Advantages

- An application package at the highest level of "hardness" provides the user with a tested and documented set of programs;
- the ideas implemented in the solution can serve as idea generators for the potential user.

By applying the structure of the package, the user will be able to shorten the duration of his design stage. If the package covers only a part of the planned system, it nevertheless helps to draw the overall design concept;

- if the package is accepted in toto, the time necessary for development and testing will also be shortened.
  In addition, the time-consuming job of preparing documentation is eliminated;
- application packages enable the user more speedily to reduce his backlog relative to other organizations in the same type of industry, by applying advanced methods to the operation of his organization;
- change over to a new equipment entails the necessity of programming existing applications in cases where emulation is either impossible or undesirable. In such cases, the use of application packages may well reduce the time and effort required to effect the change over;
- it is in the nature of a well-designed application package that any necessary additions and modifications can be made relatively easily;
- both manufacturers and software consulting companies employ specialized personnel; in consequence better efficiency can be expected from software packages than from typical user-made prôgrams;
- in some instances application package designers have succeeded in making available packages which contain a wide range of features and alternatives. The user can generate a typical version of the package by specifying the required functions; the version thus generated contains only what has been specified, and will consequently require the same space in internal storage as an efficient user written program.

Limitations

Application packages suffer from certain limitations. If the use of these packages is to be successful, it must be ascertained that the additional effort required to overcome the constraints imposed by these limitations is less than that which would be required for the design of a completely new system.

- If the application package covers only a part of the planned system, the functional specification of the package, if accepted, may put constraints on the overall design of the system;
- use of the package may imply the usage of predescribed inputs and outputs not compatible with those envisaged for the rest of the system;
- application packages are mostly manufacturer-oriented. Even software houses make their packages only for a very limited number of types of equipment. This problem is becoming less significant for the software houses, as the use of statement level programming lanugages eases the conversion to other equipment lines;
- in non modular designed packages the efficiency can be diminished because of generalities which are built into the program but not employed by the user.

How to proceed in selection (methodology)

- Make a survey of the packages offered, the environment in which they have been used, and the success with which they have been implemented;
- visit and discuss one or more actual applications;
- determine the functions covered in the application packages;
- compare the functions offered, and their relationships and decision rules, with those laid down in the system specification;
- evaluate the possibilities of either adapting the system specification or modifying the application package;
- determine impact on operating performance, required effort and throughput time;
- evaluate documentation, availability of training courses and on-the-spot support during implementation.

Technique 6-4.4: Data transmission[1])

Purpose

Transmission of data between remotely located terminals and a computer installation via public switched networks or leased lines (both telephone and telegraphic lines).

Areas of application

This material is needed as a part of the basic technical orientation during the design and development of information systems which require remote terminal access to the computer.

Introduction

Both analogue and digital data can be transmitted over "common carrier" lines (telephone and telegraph networks) in many ADP applications. The messages to be transmitted are translated by common carrier equipment into a form suitable for transmission (tone or d.c. pulses or modulated tones) and restored to system-compatible form by similar equipment at the other end.

The figure on page 2 outlines the component parts of a typical computer-based data communication system [2]). The computer system has connected to one of its input/output channels a data communication control unit (each manufacturer has his own name for this unit; other representative names are "data transmission unit", "data line terminal" and "data transmission controller"). The control unit is the translation stage between the standard formats of the computer and the standard format and signal type used by the "plug in" interface with the common carrier's equipment. In many cases the data communication control unit also works as a reduction stage between a number of transmission lines and one computer channel.
The "plug in" unit, with which the data communication control unit interfaces, is the data set (modem) supplied by the systems manufacturer, private communications company or a public T & T company.
The data set provides the transmission frequencies and wave-forms needed to operate the communications network.

At the remote end of the link, an equivalent data and terminal control unit accomplishes the transformation of the transmitted data back into readable or computer sensible format.

---

[1]) This technique is based on an internal paper, written by A. Wolters, Philips — Electrologica, Apeldoorn.

[2]) A basic introduction to data communication technology can be found in the A.T. & T. sponsored book by Edgar C. Gentle Jr., *Data communications in business*; A.T. & T.; 1965 available from Publishers Service Company (Room 600) 75 Varick St., New York 10013.

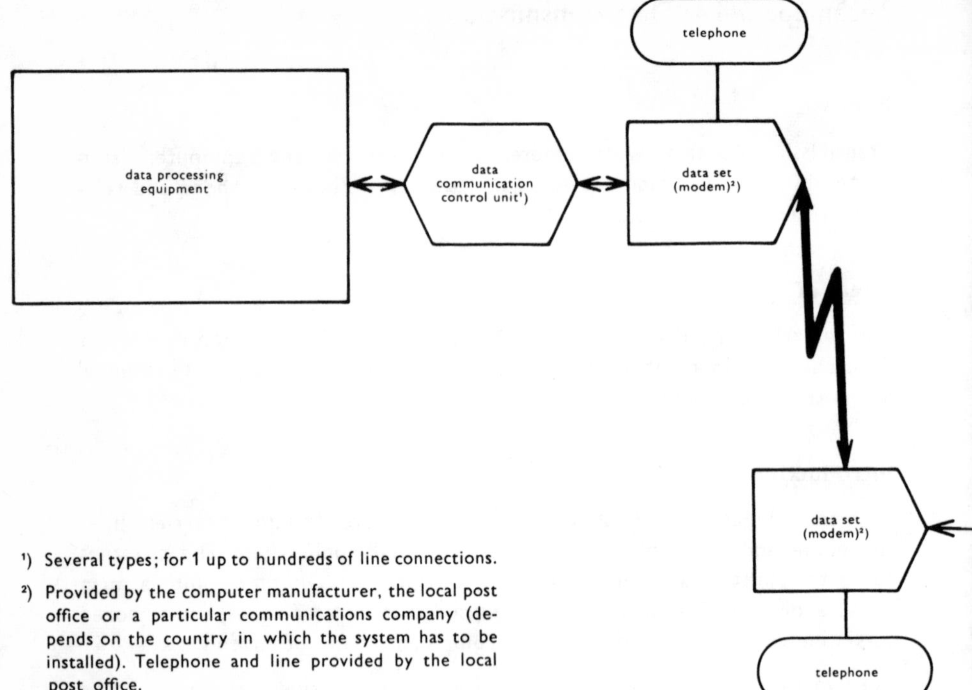

¹) Several types; for 1 up to hundreds of line connections.

²) Provided by the computer manufacturer, the local post office or a particular communications company (depends on the country in which the system has to be installed). Telephone and line provided by the local post office.

³) This control unit is a part of the terminal or a separate unit that controls a number of terminals.

Remark: in place of the terminal control unit a data communication computer can be applied also.

Data communication system

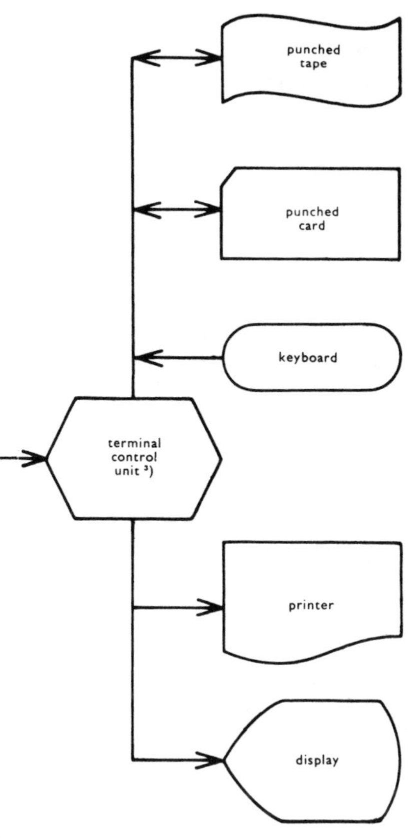
punched
tape
punched
card
keyboard
terminal
control
unit ³)
printer
display

Transmission facilities

A communication circuit consists of a physical transmission path varying in form from a wire to a microwave relay network. The circuit is divided into a group of channels, each capable of offering a specific service. Some of the transmission facilities normally available in a channel are described below.

Directional capability

Three basic types of channels are available. A "simplex" channel can carry information in only one direction. Simplex is used in many low-activity applications because of relatively simple and economical types of sending and receiving units which can be used in such applications. A "half-duplex" channel can carry information in either direction, but only in one direction at a time. This is the type of data channel most commonly in use. A "duplex" channel can carry information in both directions simultaneously. The communications network can consist of any combination of these, according to the requirements of the application.

In planning half-duplex circuits, allowance must be made for "turn-around time" (normally 0.2-0.5 seconds) for reversing the flow of data. Since most systems use "answer back", a coded data-receipt confirmation at the end of each unit of transmission for error checking, the turn-around time can significantly reduce overall system performance if the data blocks are not of a large enough average size.
The turn-around time is also influenced by a response time in many applications. This response time depends on the data check methods used, and exists also in full duplex circuits.

Capacity

Channels are of various "grades" depending on their data transmission capacity, i.e. the maximum rate of which they can transmit data with an acceptably low incedence of transmission errors. This is normally specified in "bauds" (bits or unit pulses per second).
In Europe the channel grade has been defined by the CCITT (Comité Consultatif Internationale Télégraphique et Téléphonique) and recommended to the different national T & T companies. Three grades of channel are normally available, broad-band, voice-grade and telegraph-grade.
It is possible to tailor system capacity very closely to application needs by combining circuits of differing grades to provide almost exactly the channel capacity required.
The next figure lists the most important characteristics of a number of transmission facilities.

facility	type	capacity in bauds *)	operation **)	remarks
telex network	switched	50	HDX	restricted to a 5 unit code (CCITT alphabet 2)
datex network	switched	200	DX	available in Germany and comparable with the American TWX network supplied by A.T. & T. Usually used as HDX only
telegraph circuits	leased	50 100 200	DX DX DX	
telephone network	switched	200	DX	
		600/1200	HDX	comparable with the American WATS network supplied by A.T. & T. (capacity: up to 2000 bauds)
telephone circuits	leased	600/1200	DX	
special quality circuits	leased	2400 4800	DX DX	possible when using special data sets (modems)
high speed circuits	leased	up to 40.000	DX	comparable with the American Telpak. In some very special cases television circuits (up to 3 megabauds) are available

Legend:
*) The approximate capacity in characters/sec. depends on the code set used and the method of transmission (start/stop or synchroneous). In telex for instance the capacity is $6\frac{2}{3}$ char./sec.
**) HDX: Half-Duplex
DX : Duplex

Narrow-band channels (usually called telegraph channels) offer transmission rates of upto 200 bauds. However, in a number of countries the telegraph channels offered by the T & T companies are capable of a maximum rate of 150 bauds.

Voice-band channels are provided by the T & T companies through their telephone service. Such channels offer data transmission capability of up to 1200 bauds (in America up to 2000 bauds) on regular lines, and up to 2400 bauds on private wire services. Higher transmission speeds are possible using special data sets.

Broad-band channels may be supplied in various degrees of frequency response and freedom from transmission errors—achieved by hardware bases equivalent to those of a number of voice-grade channels—depending on user requirements.

Network types

The various networks available include exchange systems and private wire systems. The private wire networks can be used in either a switched (dial-up) or a party-line mode, i.e. several users, of whom only one can use the facilities at a time. Exchange networks are usually, but are not necessarily, dial-up systems.

Exchange data services
These services provide for the transmission of data using normal telephone or teletype dial-up networks.

Private-line data services
These services provide for a fixed configuration of channels connecting two or more points. Rates for these channels are dependent on the grade and type of service offered and on the distance covèred.

Switched networks
Switching services normally use regular dial-up access techniques. Special equipment is available for:

- allowing the terminals to answer automatically;
- allowing unattended operation of terminals; and
- allowing the computer to dial or answer automatically (not available for all switched networks in Europe).

Party-line networks
In party service the computer and several terminals are connected to the same line. Selective calling and polling units and methods are available to ensure that only the desired station is active at any one time. Each terminal has a specific address number consisting of one or more characters. In the party-line network one station (usually the computer) controls the transmission. When the control station transmits a special alert code followed by the proper identifiers, only the station addressed is activated. If the control station is calling to request a message, it transmits a special code which either starts transmission from the station addressed, or causes it to send a no-message code. If the control station is calling to send a message, it waits for an answer-back indicating "unit ready" and then transmits the message.

Conclusion

Specific types of data sets and terminal equipment currently available are not discussed in this technique, since technological change is rapid in this field, and current descriptive literature is available from many suppliers and other sources [1,2]). Data gathering and dissemination applications based on transmission over common-carrier facilities are becoming an integral part of many new systems. Some specified benefits of these systems are that they:

- reduce the time, effort, and expense required to get information into the data processing system, by capturing the data at its source;
- increase the effectiveness of the information system in meeting the objectives of the organization, by permitting more rapid reporting, processing, and control of information;
- increase management effectiveness by supplying more timely reports, and by allowing remote monitoring.

---

[1]) Auerbach corporation, *Auerbach data communications report*, Auerbach Info. Inc., Philadelphia, Pa, USA, 1967.

[2]) Adams associates, *The computer display review*, Adams associates Inc., Bedford, Massachusetts, USA, 1967.

Activity 6-5: Control techniques

Purpose and scope

This chapter provides sufficient knowledge to enable the systems analyst to decide which control techniques should be applied for a specific system, and to determine the relationships between them. Also the systems analyst should recognize the need for consulting control or auditing specialists in difficult situations, and for verification and approval of the control network.

Area of application

This chapter describes techniques for ensuring the reliability of an information system. It covers the aspects of accuracy, completeness, timeliness and retrievability to the extent to which they are stipulated in the design for the new system.
The control techniques described constitute a basis for setting up a control network covering all aspects of the information system.
It is not possible to provide a standard control network which can be applied to all systems. The selection of controls must be performed in accordance with the specific requirements of the information system envisaged.
A reliable information system is not created merely by means of a sensible choice of controls. The organization of the company has to be structured according to accepted accounting and control principles providing a favourable environment for establishing a high degree of reliability.
Examples are the separation of duties, the principles for the organization of automatic data processing work and some of the control principles regarding system design.

General

Controls should be considered an indispensable part of an information system. In circumstances when core capacity and processing time are scarce — and in practice this is always the case — the tendency to limit the extent of the controls, which inevitably occupy part of these scarce facilities, should be avoided. This is one reason why controls should be planned for and established during the initial stage of the design.
The same is valid for organizational measures, which take even more time and effort before they are accepted and effective.

Cost of control

Before determining the extent of the measures to be undertaken the appropriate standards of completeness, accuracy, timeliness and retrievability necessary for

the various functions in the information system should be agreed upon. These goals can sometimes be met only at the expense of additional processing time, more core capacity, or more people involved.
The costs of executing controls should be balanced with the damage which could occur as a result of operating and making decisions on the basis of false information.

Degree of control

The degree of reliability required will depend on the type of application. Tight control should be maintained over data and systems which may materially affect the financial condition of the company, such as accounts payable, accounts receivable, payroll and customer billing. Physical precautions should exist to safeguard cash, inventory and other assets, and unused forms such as blank checks.
Rigid controls are far less necessary in applications which can tolerate a reasonable incidence of minor inaccuracies. For example, in tabulating the results of a public opinion poll results would not be materially affected if one or two questionaires were lost. However, even in such mass-input applications some degree of control must be exercised, in order to prevent many minor errors from distorting the final result.

Sampling

In some applications, the reliability of the information system is guaranteed sufficiently if not all transactions are checked, but only a sample. The extent to which sampling can be used depends mainly on the volume of transactions, their variability and the system requirements for accuracy and completeness. The nature of the transactions should be studied before decisions on the use of sampling can be made.
More information can be found on this subject in 6-3.2.

Integrations of controls

Owing to the increasing use of automatic data processing, the possibilities of intermediate human checks are rapidly diminishing. More and more operations are performed without interruption. In such situations it becomes imperative to be certain of the quality of the data that are processed. This places strong emphasis on pre- and post-processing control, and should also focus attention on controls that prevent errors entering the system, as well as on programmed controls incorporated in the information system as an inseparable part of the processing.

Control schemes

Control schemes are a valuable tool for depicting the control procedures involved in an automatic data processing system. They enable the relationships

between e.g. manual and programmed checks to be specified, and the responsibilities of the personnel acting in the information flow to be laid down.
The example of a control scheme on page 4 is one of a number of related schemes concerning the input control in an actual application. The other schemes concern the control of the contents of the converted punched tapes and the control of the first processing results of the input transactions.
These latter schemes are concerned, among other things, with predetermined record and batch totals and the recording of control balances.
The control scheme given in the example covers only a single procedure; it will in practice be accompanied by procedural comments, concerning for example the measures to be taken when header and/or trailer labels of the punched tape become mutilated or get lost during computer processing.

Subdivision in techniques

Control techniques cover many areas of the organization and its data processing operations, and many of the techniques have more than one application.
The following groups of techniques will be dealt with:

- organizational measures;
- overall system controls;
- production controls
- hardware checks
- software checks
- program controls
- input preparation controls
- input acceptance controls
- processing controls
- file controls.

This chapter should be thought of as a preliminary survey of the many control techniques which can be incorporated in an information system. For more detailed discussions reference is made to the extensive bibliography given in 6-8.

Organizational measures

In any user organization a number of organizational principles must be followed if an acceptable environment for a reliable information system is to be created.

Responsibilities

Well defined responsibilities are necessary concerning input preparation and delivery, system output usage, data processing operations and system maintenance, including change control procedures.

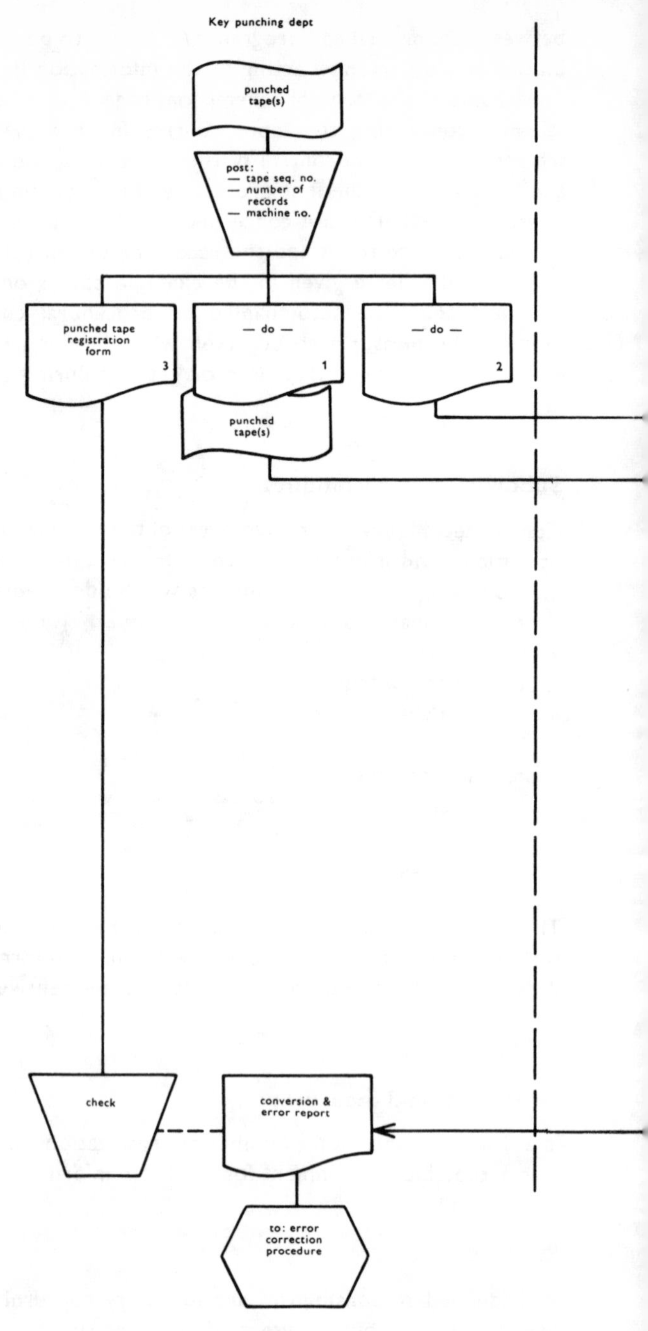

Control scheme example

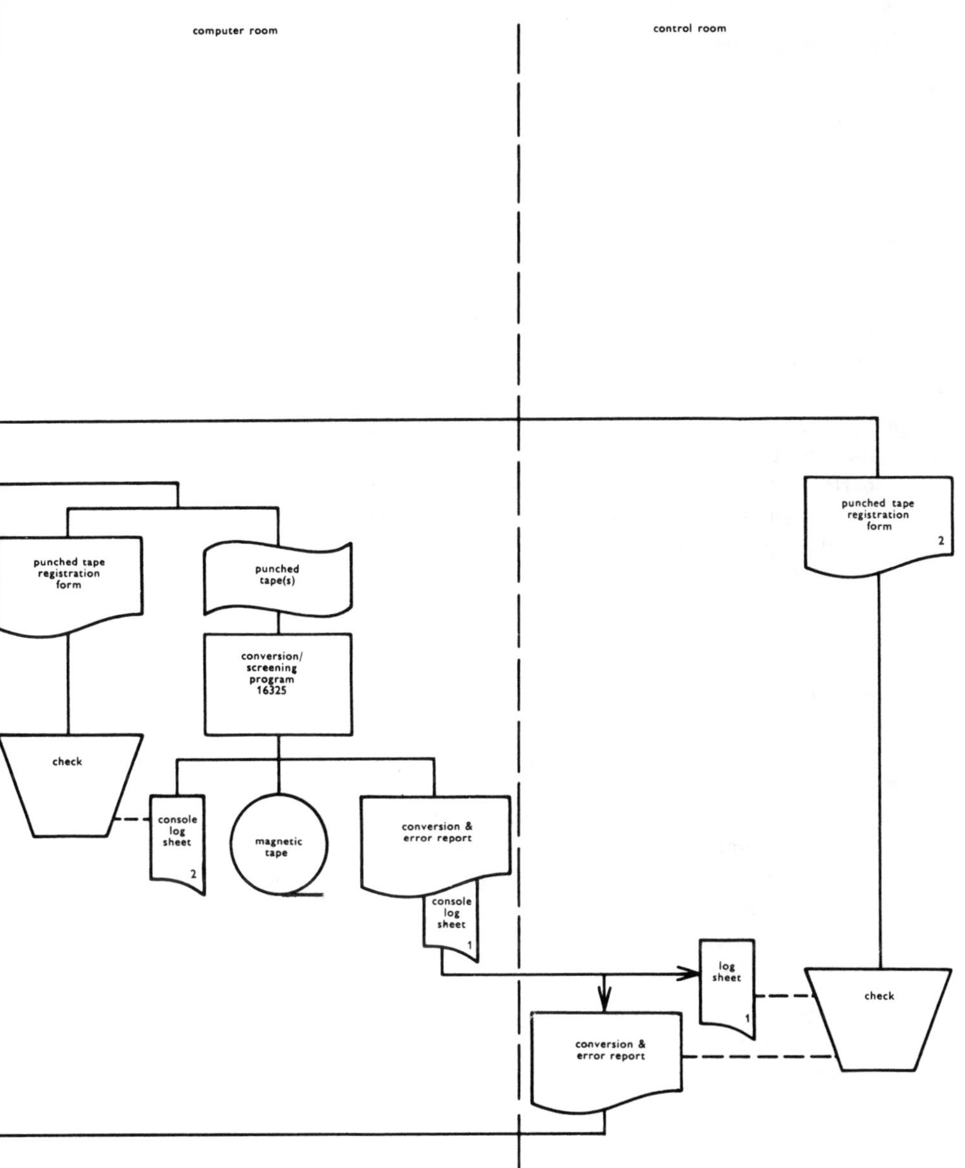

Check on processing of the correct number of punched tapes. The key punching dept is daily preparing punched tapes; it is located 10 miles from the computer centre. The computer centre is performing weekly runs.

Separation of duties

In any enterprise we can observe the phenomenon of division of labour, the fact that people in such an organization have different tasks but are working towards a common goal. In designing an organizational structure, the various functions must be distinguished and assigned according to the following principles:

- management, retention of assets or valuables, operation, registration and internal auditing as a subdivision into major groups to facilitate the introduction of control measures as well as to guarantee objectivity in control work;
- tasks, responsibilities, and authorities at various levels must be assigned to the appropriate personnel levels in the hierarchy;
- job specialization; in assigning tasks, the capacities of the people involved must be taken into account;
- performance of prescribed procedures or decision making.

Although all these considerations have an influence on the establishment of a properly organized allocation of duties within an organization, in this context we shall deal with the matter from the viewpoint of internal control.

System operation

The first recommendation is that the performance of operations must be distinguished from the recording of these operations, and that these functions must be placed in different hands. For example, a payment to a creditor has to be balanced with an accounts payable entry; the latter should not have been made by the person who will perform the balancing. Even within the recording function, separation of duties is advisable, so that we can make use of the possibilities of comparing related information. For example, information about received quantities of goods, which originates in the warehouse, should match the information which is supplied by the department that handles the supplier invoices. By comparing the information contained in records made by different employees, a reliable control on the correctness of the process can be created.

Separation of duties is important in the computer centre also. Responsibilities for the supply of data to the computer centre, for the processing in the computer centre, and for the use of information, must be clearly distinguished.

System maintenance

Strict control of the procedures for modifying any element of the information system is essential. A standard change control procedure must be used during design and continued during the development and implementation phases and also after turnover of the system.

See 2-4.1 for change control and 4-6 for the error reporting procedure.

These procedures cover directives for standard format of documentation, and for dealing with any maintenance problem. This includes analysis of the problem, considering the impact on user organization and system performance; approval of the alterations; authorization of the execution of the alteration; updating of

user documentation and check on the adequate implementation of the system change or correction.
Strict discipline in dealing with change requests and in program maintenance will be facilitated by unambigious procedures embodying the responsibilities for changes and maintenance.
The standards presented in ARDI must be used if maintenance is to become an efficient operation.

Conclusion
Summarizing: No one person should have full responsibility for any one transaction. The execution of successive steps in dealing with transactions must be in the hands of different people.

Reporting

Overall system operations should be watched carefully, and the occurrence of bottlenecks and clearly unfavourable situations should be prevented by means of timely reporting to management.

Overall system controls

A number of main control aspects have to be taken into account during system design such as:
- audit trail — leap frog and listing;
- field check;
- checkpoints;
- standardization;
- error handling;
- parallel running.

Audit trail

In an information system with its integrated processing of data and use of only machine readable data carriers the problem may arise of the locatability and retrievability of alterations in the status of all the data collected by and kept in the system. In conventional accounting this problem hardly existed because all transactions were recorded and maintained in directly human readable format.
An integrated system must be designed to permit the performance of auditing procedures in such a way that individual transactions or alterations can be traced through to the final outputs, and that backtracking from the outputs to the originating transactions is possible.
The information system must possess these capabilities not only for error tracing purposes, but also for meeting internal and external auditing requirements.

Leap frog

A technique which is useful in designing an audit trail is the "leap frog" method, which provides a chaining of alterations affecting e.g. a single file record. See for a more elaborated discussion R. H. Matzken, *Toepassing van leap frog bij computers*, Philips Administration review, **17** (1963. 11) no. 4, pp. 11-16.

Listing

Another technique is to create listings containing the old balances, the alterations and the new balances of specific fields in file records.

Field check

An early check on the quality of a system design is to take each field to be produced or maintained by the system, assume it is in error, check how the error condition would have been reported, and determine whether the audit trail produced, would allow the systems analyst to pinpoint where and how the error could have occurred.

Checkpoints

Lengthy runs can be divided by means of checkpoints in order to avoid the necessity of re-running the whole job in the event of an error occurring. The programmer must decide how many segments the run has to be divided into. When a checkpoint is used, the core contents together with all related information (such as reading/writing positions in inputs, outputs and files) will be dumped on high-speed store units (disk or tape).

Standardization

One of the most effective control techniques is the standardization of such items as procedure and program description, forms, program testing requirements, system maintenance and error correction procedures, and many other components of the user documentation.
The use of such method standards is a mark of good management as well as of a system under firm control.

Error handling

Upon detection of mistakes, many information systems simply list error records, punch a card for correction and later re-entry into the system, and delete the record from further processing. Error cards and listings are then routed to the user for correction and later re-entry into the validation and updating runs.
Another approach to error handling is the suspense file method. In this method, error records are placed in a separate file and listed. Corrections are made by

means of transactions affecting the suspense file. If the correction is acceptable, records are corrected, validated, removed from the suspense file and re-entered into the regular processing. Both the manual procedure and the computer run for error correction require careful development and checkout. The training of the people to this job must be thorough. In general, the error handling procedure will give a reliable indication of the quality and completeness of the system design effort.
An adequate error handling system should indicate the origin of each error. This makes it possible to feed back an error to the place where it was caused, so that experience may be gained and repetitions prevented.
It is useful to build up statistics of errors, in order to evaluate the performance of the user in delivering his input and to evaluate the effectiveness of the programmed checks.

Parallel running

In 5-4 several methods of starting the operation of a new information system were discussed.
In most of these methods at least part of the data is processed twice, once by the existing and once by the new information system.
In such cases, the following control methods become possible:

- the new information system can be checked with live instead of artificial data;
- erroneous transactions can be entered in order to check what happens in the system, and to practice the error correction procedures.

Production controls

Although present-day software has reduced the amount of operator intervention, most applications still require a substantial amount of human participation during production, thus introducing the possibility of human errors.
In order to keep the efficiency of computer use as high as possible, it is essential that the likelihood of operator errors is minimized. This requires carefully planned and thoroughly documented operating procedures.
The following considerations are applicable:

Organization structure

- Clearly defined tasks, responsibilities and authority of departments and officials.

General housekeeping rules

- Rules about smoking, work-times, restrictions for visitors, etc.;
- emergency procedures in case of fire, power cut-off or other accidents.

Production planning

- Capacity planning and machine loading;
- preparation of operating schedules;
- work progress reporting;
- run order (4-5.6) and run summary preparation; issue of jobs to the production departments.

Operating instructions

All the programs which are released for production should be controlled by the instructions for the computer centre (4-5.6).
These instructions must specify adequately the types and unit number of I/O equipment as well as the types of data carrier (paper, forms, cards etc.) to be used.
In addition, in-house instructions for special cards, switches etc., necessary for correct running of the program can be issued.
The use of non-standard instructions should be kept to a minimum, because they are error-creating and time-consuming.
The amount of programmed halts should be kept to a minimum. The meaning of any unavoidable halts should be made sufficiently clear to the operator to ensure that his reactions are fast and correct.

Logging machine usage

The running of the computer should be recorded, independently of human intervention, bu the computer itself. The items recorded should include:
- time spent for specific jobs, programmed halts, machine waiting times;
- input files processed and output files produced;
- irregularities in the processing such as errors, interrupts, operator-machine conversations.

Comparison of the operating schedules (5-3) with the actual running times can give a valuable indication of the performance of the computer centre and of the input-supplying departments.

General machine handling instructions

The operator should be thoroughly instructed in the handling of the machine (see 5-1.4).

Computer centre library

Functions include the storing of program decks, program tapes, tapes, disks and card files, and the recording of their issue for use in computer runs.

Hardware checks

To avoid duplications or omission of checks, it is necessary for the system analyst to know what machine-oriented checks are built into the computer he is using.

Input and output equipment

The following checks are for instance possible:

- Double reading (card reader, punched tape reader);
- hole count (card punch, punched tape punch);
- echo check (printers, punches);
- read after write (tape, disk);
- protection ring (tape);
- address checks (disks);
- non-operating conditions such as no power, no paper, no punched tape, etc.;
- input interlock check;
- parity check.

Central processor

- Parity checks;
- message length check;
- validity checks;
- programs checking the circuitry.

Hardware installation checks

- temperature;
- power alterations;
- humidity.

Software checks

Third-generation computers are largely dependent on built-in "hard" software such as monitors. Therefore this type of software for the equipment under consideration should be analyzed to determine which signals are communicated to the monitor under erroneous conditions of the hardware and its software. The software will usually offer exits to execute either user-written routines or built-in routines for dealing with off-normal situations.
Exits of these types are usually offered both for hardware and for software initiated signals.

Hardware initiated signals

Examples of hardware initiated signals are:

- card jam;
- specified device not ready;
- no printing paper available;
- device address non existent;
- parity error;
- invalid core address;
- invalid instruction code.

The first three situations will normally generate a message to the operator instructing him to take the appropriate corrective action. In the other cases however, the monitor could follow the standard "built-in" solution — generally print-out and stop — or follow a user-written routine.

Software initiated signals

Software initiated signals can be communicated while the execution is continued as if nothing had occured. Such a case is the detection of a non serious syntax error in a procedural language; the error causes a warning message to be printed on the output listing.
Most of the software available from computer manufacturers contains software checks of various types, e.g. automatic read after write on disk. Usually software checks of this type can be deleted, or modified or augmented by user-written subroutines at the option of the user. If such a check fails it is normal practice to provide a suitable message to the operator and then either suspend execution of the program or transfer to a special user-written subroutine.

Examples are:

- checking the record key sequence during sequential input or output;
- accepting or rejecting either unlabelled or wrongly labelled files;
- checking the userlabels and version numbers of files.

Program controls

Some general controls on application programs are:

- testing procedures prior to turnover of the program to the user (see 4-2 and 4-5.4);
- console and/or display testing. The program is controlled while actually running in the computer to detect whether malfunctioning exists other than that which will be reported in printed outputs;
- tracing. The program is run in combination with a tracer program. After each execution of a program instruction the contents of the registers are printed to determine for control purposes whether or not the correct program path has been followed.

- memory dump. At prescribed moments during program execution the contents of the registers and the core store are printed;
- path providing codes. To ensure the completeness and accuracy of a program, when it is transferred within the machine or read into the machine on punched cards, it can be accompanied by one or more control totals, e.g. as hash total of the instruction codes of the program. A check on the correct sequence of the instructions may also be useful.

Input preparation controls

This category of controls is extremely important, not only because it contains those techniques which will ensure the reliability of the input at its sources, but also because a substantial foundation should be laid during input on which to erect a systematic structure for the control of subsequent actions such as input conversion, input screening and acceptance by the information system, data processing, file updating and output preparation. The control measures initiated during preparation offer a guarantee of the quality of the data content of the system.

Types of techniques

The following list gives a number of control techniques applicable during input preparation:
- sequence numbering;
- prepunched cards;
- turnaround documents or dual cards;
- batch numbering;
- coding of types of input;
- predetermined totals;
  - horizontal,
  - vertical or batch,
  - hash,
  - record count;
- visual checking;
- control punching;
- redundancy checks;
- selfchecking numbers.

Input acceptance control

Input acceptance control, as the first computer processing of file alterations and transactions, covers any necessary medium conversion, input screening, acceptance, and input error reporting. It concentrates on checking the accuracy, validity and completeness of the input data.
Many checks for which the basis has been laid during the input preparation

stage are now repeated by the acceptance program to enable the comparison of the results of those checks and the drawing of conclusions.

Types of techniques

Examples of input controls are:
- character check;
- field length check;
- limit check;
- plausibility check;
- existence check;
- control punch testing;
- validation;
- predetermined totals.

Processing controls

After acceptance of the input data, various types of processing are possible, e.g the performance of calculations, the creation and updating of files, the preparation of output, and data transmission.

Types of techniques

Examples of processing controls are:
- checkpoints;
- checks on multiplication and division;
- square totals;
- standards for output listings;
- historical comparison;
- two-way check; the difference between old and new balance of a data element can be compared with the algebraic total of the transactions affecting that data element;
- relationship check; when a pre-known relationship between two data elements exists and one of them is correct, then it is possible to check the other by means of a relationship check. For example, if the manual sales figure is $ 1,000,000, and the discount rate is 5%, then the rebate account must show the figure $ 50,000.

File controls

Files must be carefully protected and controlled. Security arrangements for system files should cover at least those used for manual files. Despite the often-heard comment that no one can read them, it is almost as easy to obtain information from tapes or disks as from manual files, and probably easier to destroy them. Security arrangements should tighten when vital records in the information system are involved.

Types of techniques

Examples of file controls and file protection measures are:

Physical protection
- use of depositories;
- microfilming of file dumps;
- dispersal;
- fireproof data carriers;
- separation between essential and non-essential file records;
- formal procedures to prevent premature re-use of file data carriers, e.g. magnetic tapes.

Labels
External tape labels, with standardized contents, containing:
- reel number;
- serial number;
- number of reels in the file;
- program identification code;
- creation date;
- retention date;
- density;
- drive number.

Standard header labels with:
- program identification code;
- file identification code;
- reel number;
- creation date;
- retention date.

Standard trailer labels with:
- block count,
- record count,
- hash totals,
- end-of-reel or end-of-file code.

Automatic testing of contents of header and trailer labels should be performed each time a tape is used in each program run.

Retirement
Retirement procedure for tapes with excessive read or write errors;.

Reconstruction
Reconstruction procedures for files in case of accidents (computer or I/O unit faults, fires, security failures):
- grandfather-father-son generation retention in case of magnetic tape. Especially in case of files which are frequently updated, this retention of a generation, accompanied by the retention of all input records which were processed

during the last two updating runs, provides an effective tool for reconstruction should the current tape become unusable;

- duplication of files kept on any kind date carrier, when files have a more or less permanent content, e.g. tables or reference documentation. Before using of such a file, it should be ascertained that an identical copy is kept at a different location. The copy can be on any medium;
- dumping of files which are kept on direct access stores such as disk, drum etc. This dumping should be done periodically, on a similar medium or on another machine readable data carrier. In the same way as for dynamic files on magnetic tape, all the input records processed since dumping should be kept for use, should an accident with the current file occur.
- dumping of files combined with duplication of updated records in the current file, e.g. on magnetic tape. This eliminates the necessity for retaining the transactions and file alterations after the moment of dumping.
  Reconstruction can take place by replacing the record in the file dump by the latest updated record.
- dumping of files combined with flagging of updated records in the current file, followed by dumping of the flagged records in a subsequent run. This technique is useful when no output units are available for duplication of the updated records during the normal processing run.
  It requires a new write instruction to the current file to remove the flag;

Other techniques

- Predetermined totals;
- control listing for visual checking, especially in case of file conversion;
- leap-frog method;
- manually kept control balances on the basis of periodical transaction batches, due dates, subscription periods etc. Manually calculated running totals will be used to check the correctness of computer processing and file listings;
- temporary manual files, e.g. of inventory records to check the accuracy of computer file updating and, if no record is kept by the information system, to permit checking of the results of physical stock taking against stock records in cases when a considerable number of pre-invoiced deliveries have still to be performed;
- additional identification; this method is especially useful in connection with files where it is necessary to guarantee to the highest degree the updating of the correct record. The normal identification key must be checked by some means, such as determining if the product number of the transaction is equal to the identification of the file record. An extra identification, or other data fields such as descriptions, are used for checking identity between input and file records.

Activity 6-6: Programming

Technique 6-6.1: Methods of computer programming

Areas of applications

The techniques described are applicable to the activities of program development and conversion which are carried out in the development, and implementation phases of the systems effort.

Modular programming

Modular programming is a technique by which a program is divided into independent logical sections or parts. The technique permits the efficient development and maintenance of programs. It enables the repeated use of such parts in the same or a different program (with or without modification) and the use of parts taken from other programs. Program parts which are called independently of their physical location in core, are called routines or subroutines.

Applicability

Whether or not a solution to one problem can be used for the solution of another problem depends on:
- the degree of similarity of the problems;
- the accessibility of the problem solution;
- the possibility of modifying the problem solution.

To some extent problem solutions can be made to satisfy these requirements by standardizing set-up and details. The following pages give general recommendations for a standard set-up of subproblems. For the sake of simplicity a problem solution is in this connection identified with a subroutine although the same rules apply to subsystems, programs, routines and macro-instructions.

Degree of similarity

Any program will contain three elements:
- the inputs to be processed;
- the operations to be performed upon these inputs;
- the outputs to be produced.

When two problems are compared the degree of similarity may be assessed as: identical, similar, dissimilar.

In relation to the data element, both input and output, the comparison is concerned with: the number of fields, their significance and formats.

For the comparison of the operations to be performed not only the operations themselves but also their sequence must be taken into account.

The resulting classifications can be represented in a table, as follows:

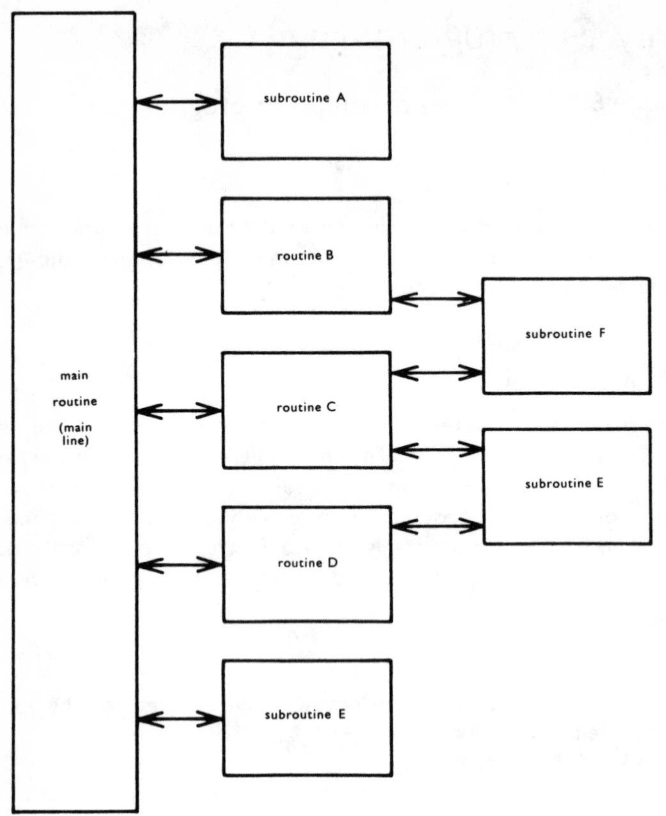

Modular set up of a program.

comparison of two subproblems		data		
		identical	similar	dissimilar
operations	identical	1	3	5
	similar	2	4	6
	dissimilar	7	8	9

Out of these nine possibilities only 1 to 4 inclusive are of practical value. The significance of the possibilities 1, 2, 3 and 4 are shown in the following table:

comparison of two subproblems		data	
		identical	similar
operations	identical	1 fixed subroutine	3 variable subroutine with parameters for data
	similar	2 variable subroutine with parameters for operations	4 variable subroutine with parameters for data and operations

The general form (group 4) develops into the macro instruction.

Advantages of modular programming

- Program logic is more closely related to problem-logic;
- complex problems can be divided into relatively simple parts;
- every routine can be designed, coded and checked-out virtually independently of other routines;
- programmers of appropriate skill and experience can be assigned to the different parts;
- programs become more accessible, which simplifies maintenance;
- it greatly facilitates the use of overlay-techniques.

Some rules and remarks

- Define the logical structure and sequence of the operations to be carried out;
- design the main routine of the program so that it divides the operations to be performed into logical parts or routines and clarifies the relationships between these parts; each part can in itself be a structure of routines;
- arrange the main routine so that the most frequently occuring transactions are processed first;
- at the beginning of each routine make a short description of its purpose; use the rule of thumb "one line of coding, one line of comment".
- obtain (or make, if one is not available) a list of standard names and abbreviations, and the layouts of the data.

Example of data and indicator transfer

A technique of transfer could be as follows:

- reserve locations in the routine for the data to be processed;
- reserve locations for indicators showing whether or not an operation is to be carried out;

- transfer of data and indicators from the main routine to other routines should be carried out via a common area;
- reserve locations for the results of the operations;
- make the operations dependent on the indicators concerned.

The operational part of a program flowchart prepared on these lines will look like this:

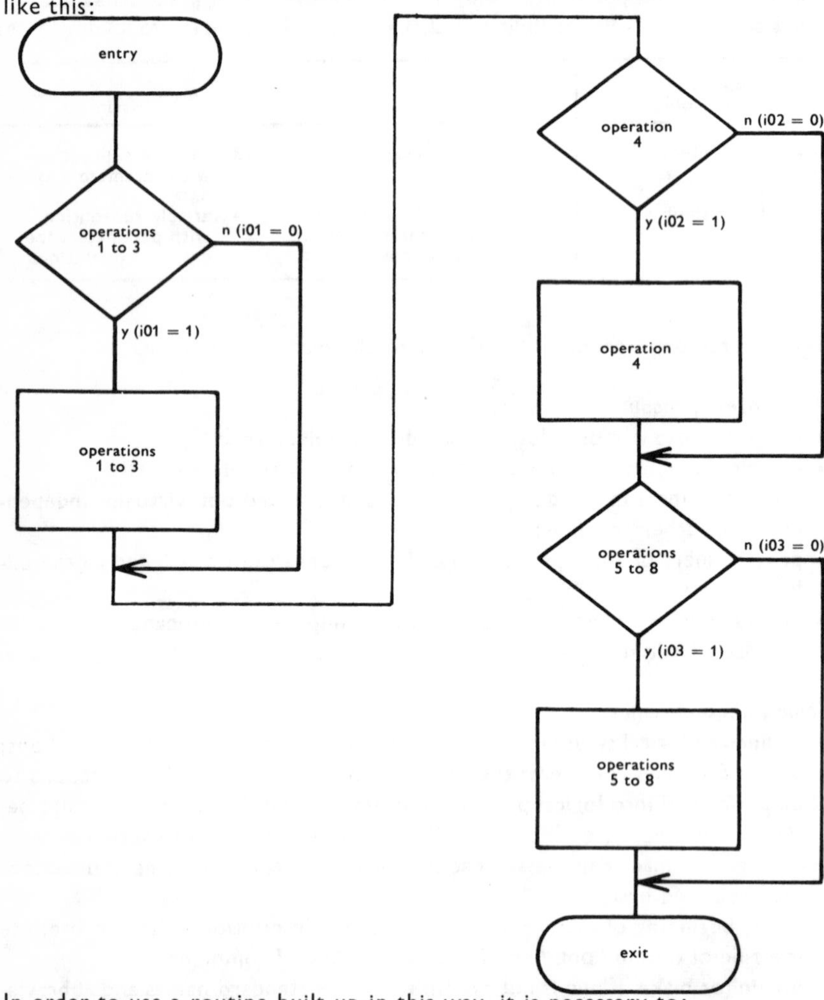

In order to use a routine built up in this way, it is necessary to:

- transfer the data to be processed to the routine;
- transfer the indicator for the operations to the routine;
- transfer the return address to the routine;
- call the routine;
- transfer the results obtained from the routine to the processing branch being executed.

Reference table for routines

The division of a problem into subproblems, i.e. into a structure of routines and macro-instructions, creates a need to know which routines are used where in order to simplify program maintenance.

It is recommended that this information be given by a grid chart of the type shown below.

	occurring in								
(sub)routine	R00	R01	R02	R03	R04		S01	S02	S03
R00 (main routine)									
R01 (initializing)	x								
R02	x								
R03	x								
R04			x						
S01		x		x				x	
S02		x	x						
S03					x		x	x	

"Balance line" method of sequential file processing

The balance line method is used for programming problems involving the processing of a number of input files which are in the sequence of the same record key. In what follows the record key(s) will be referred to as TAG. The standard set-up may best be illustrated by means of the following simplified flowchart.

Notes:

B_1: first file

B_i: one of following files, not being B_n

B_n: last file

If necessary the write indicator in a file routine is put in the "ON" position.

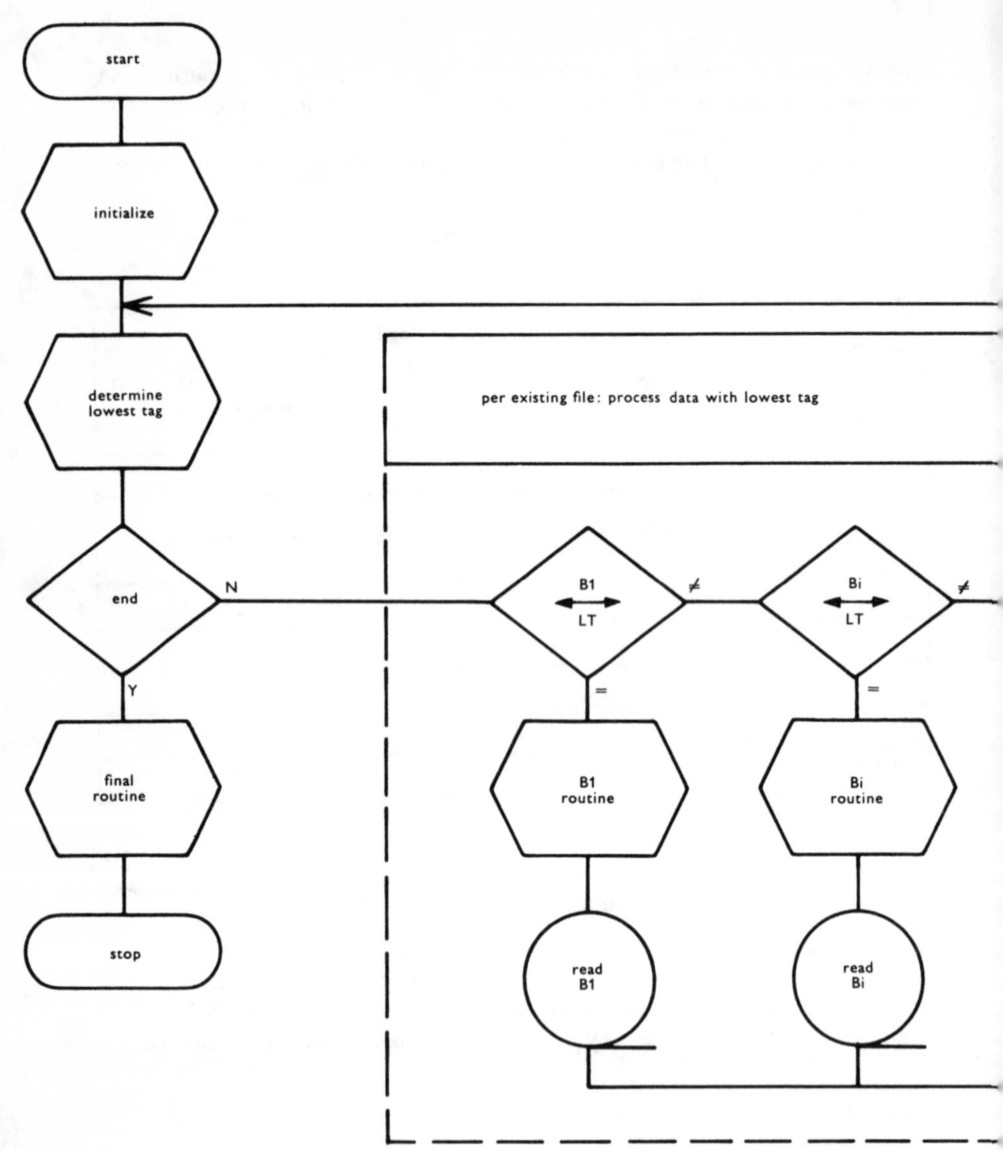
start
initialize
determine lowest tag
end
N
Y
final routine
stop
per existing file: process data with lowest tag
B1
LT
≠
=
B1 routine
read B1
Bi
LT
≠
=
Bi routine
read Bi

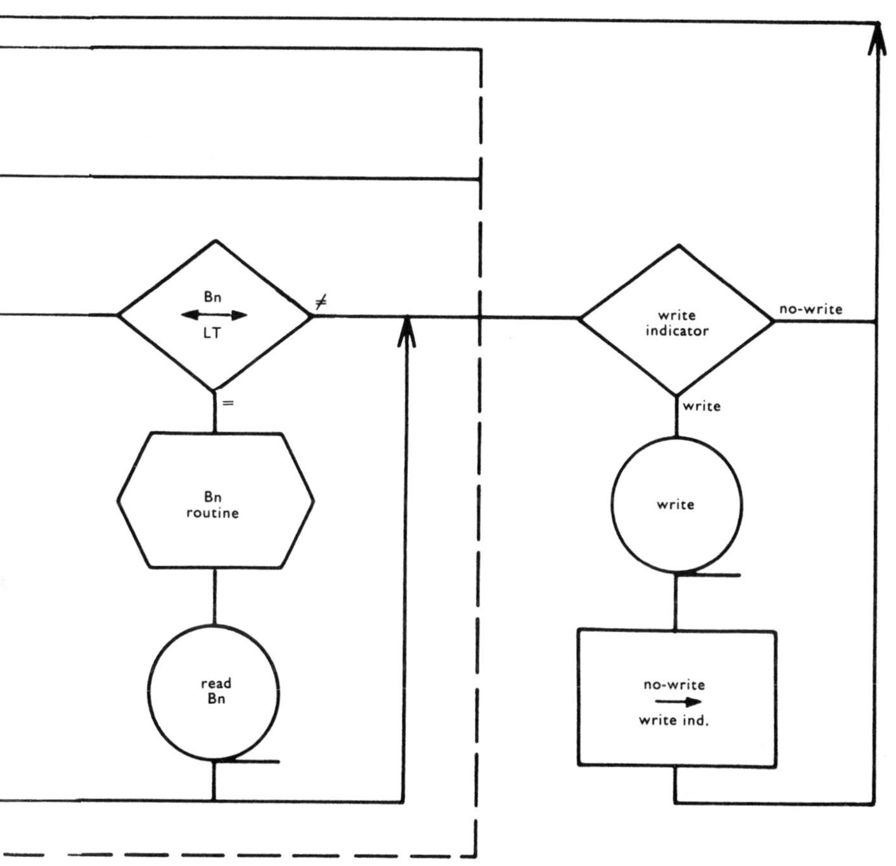
Bn
LT
≠
=
Bn
routine
read
Bn
write
indicator
no-write
write
write
no-write
write ind.

From the foregoing chart a number of characteristics can be inferred:

- one record of each of the files to be processed is read. The lowest TAG of these records is determined and stored;
- each file is tested for coincidence between the last record read in and the stored LOWEST TAG:
  - — if there is coincidence, the record is processed and a new record from this file is read in;
  - — if there is no coincidence, the record is not processed.

  This means that the annotation: "per file: process etc." consists per file of the following operations:
  a comparison with the LOWEST TAG;
  a processing routine;
  a read instruction.
- when in a certain run of the program the record containing the LOWEST TAG has been processed (and, therefore, a new record is read in) the LOWEST TAG is determined again.
- assuming that the last record in each file has an all-nines TAG, the reference to the final routine is tested by comparing the LOWEST TAG with nines. Equality indicates that all records have been processed.

Fields of application

- Merging two or more files into one, e.g. creating a new master file from an old master file and a transaction file;
- pricing mutations by means of a price file;
- computing materials requirements from product quantities ordered and specification per product.

Example 1, Merging

Forming a single ordered tape by combining five similarly ordered tapes.
The flowchart in page10shows the operations characteristic of any chart formed in accordance with the B.L.M. It consists of:

- initializing (i.a. to open all input files and to read in the first record from each file);
- determining LOWEST TAG (LT);
- determining the entry to the final routine;
- determining the entry to and operations on each file;
- writing output.

Explanatory notes

— It is advisable to carry out a sequence check for the file concerned after reading in a new record, so as to detect incorrect ordering of an input tape. In a sequence checking routine the TAG of the record read in must be equal to (if there are several records carrying the same label) or greater than the LOWEST TAG;

— the LOWEST TAG can also be used to determine whether all input tapes have been processed and the program can, therefore, be terminated (writing trailer label, closing tapes, printing control sheets etc.).
The procedure is as follows:
- as soon as the end-of-file signal is given by e.g.:
  a padding record;
  a tape mark;
  an end-of-file indicator;
  a final record with highest TAG.

  The highest value is stored in the TAG space of the reading area. This effectively blocks the entry to the branch concerned, because in the routine "DETERMINE LT" the sorting value of this file no longer qualifies as LT;
- this situation continues until all tapes show the highest sorting value in their respective reading areas. At that moment the stored lowest TAG is equal to the highest value of the TAG. The program can then be terminated.

The question represented in the chart by "END" is, therefore:
Is the LT equal to the highest TAG? If so, carry out the final routine. If not: all records to be processed have not yet been dealt with.

Assumptions:
Contents tape 1: 1, 2, 3, 5, √ (tapemark);
Contents tape 2: 2, 4, √;
Highest TAG : 9

In tabular form:
Each line represents a program run with contents of reading and writing areas.

input area		LT	end of job (LT = 9)	if tape 1 = LT		if tape 2 = LT		write on output tape
tape 1	tape 2			to output	read tape 1	to output	read tape 2	
1	2	1	N	1	2	—	—	1
2	2	2	N	2	3	—	—	2
3	2	2	N	—	—	2	4	2
3	4	3	N	3	5	—	—	3
5	4	4	N	—	—	4	√	4
5	9*	5	N	5	√	—	—	5
9*	9	9	Y	—	—	—	—	

* Enter highest TAG after reading.

Example 2
General structure for several sub-balances.
The example illustrated in page 12 is a general model and serves the purpose of illustrating the over-all structure of several sub-balances. The various sub-balances are shown by thick lines.

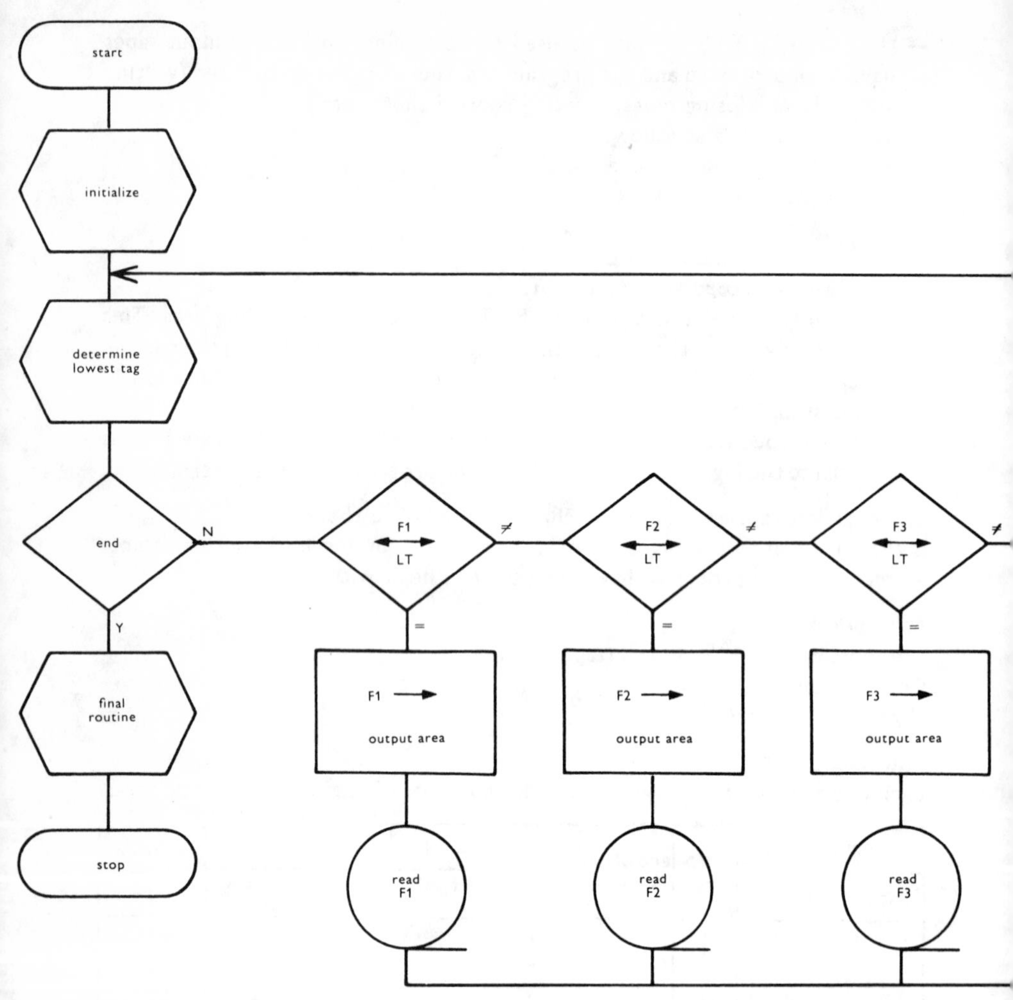

start
initialize
determine lowest tag
end
N
Y
final routine
stop
F1
LT
≠
=
F1
output area
read F1
F2
LT
≠
=
F2
output area
read F2
F3
LT
≠
=
F3
output area
read F3

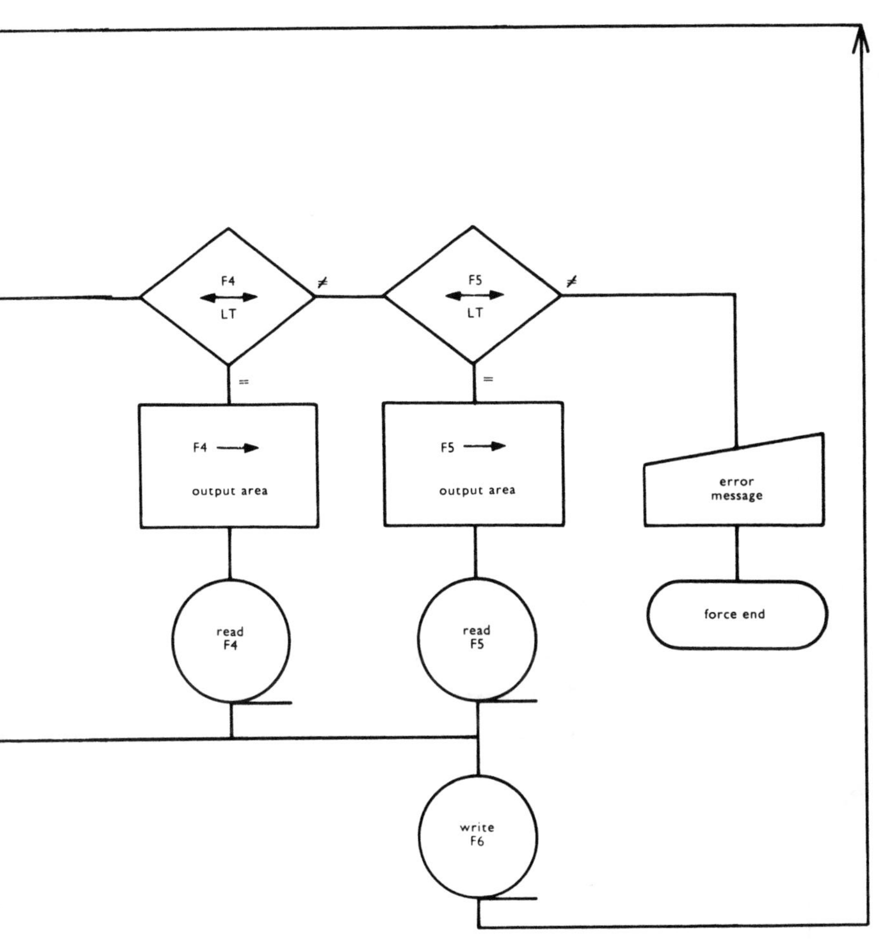

F4
LT
≠
=
F5
LT
≠
=
F4
output area
F5
output area
error
message
read
F4
read
F5
force end
write
F6

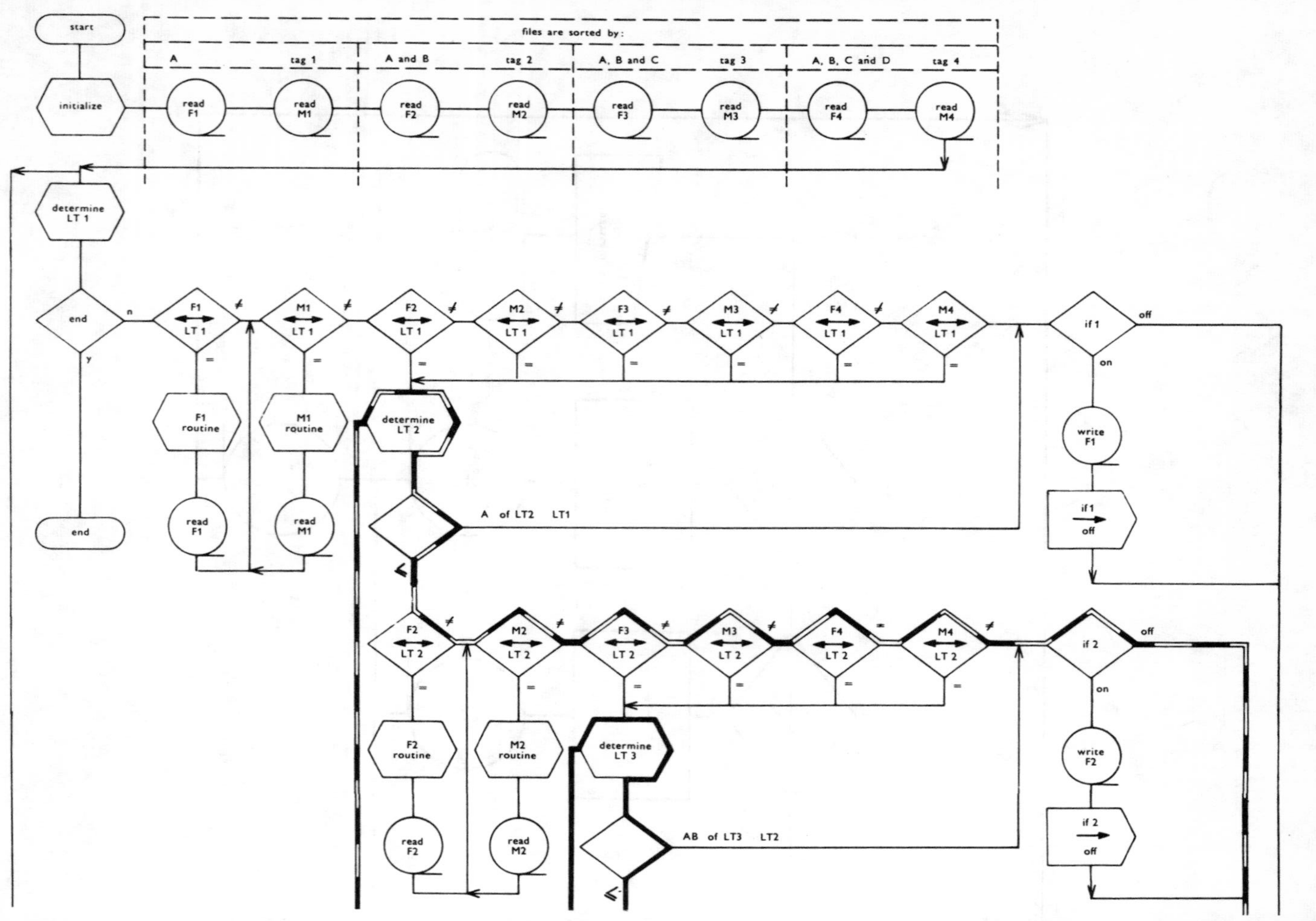
files are sorted by:
A
A and B
A, B and C
A, B, C and D
tag 1
tag 2
tag 3
tag 4
start
initialize
read F1
read M1
read F2
read M2
read F3
read M3
read F4
read M4
determine LT 1
end
y
n
end
F1 LT 1
M1 LT 1
F2 LT 1
M2 LT 1
F3 LT 1
M3 LT 1
F4 LT 1
M4 LT 1
=
≠
F1 routine
read F1
M1 routine
read M1
if 1
on
off
write F1
if 1 off
determine LT 2
A of LT2 LT1
F2 LT 2
M2 LT 2
F3 LT 2
M3 LT 2
F4 LT 2
M4 LT 2
F2 routine
read F2
M2 routine
read M2
determine LT 3
AB of LT3 LT2
if 2
on
off
write F2
if 2 off

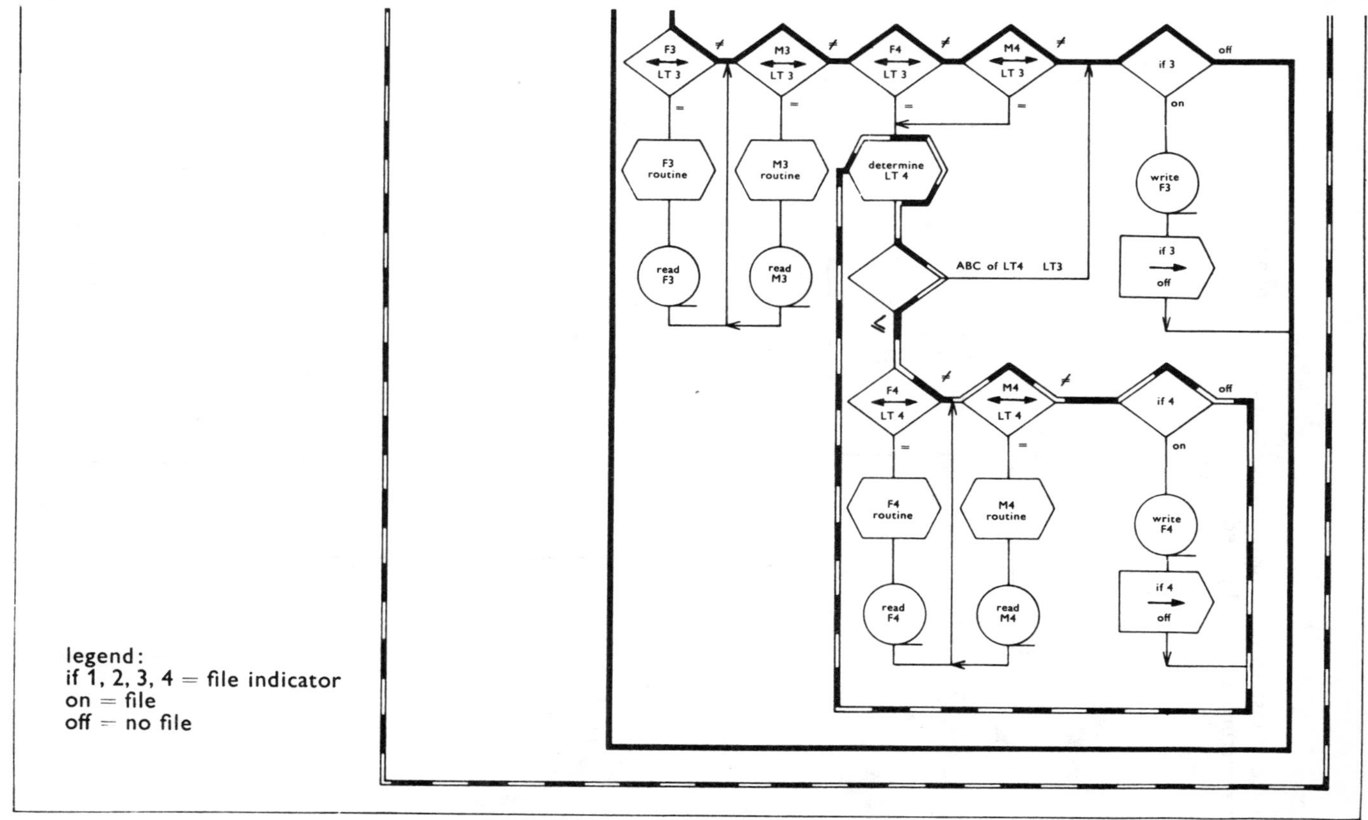

F3 LT 3
M3 LT 3
F4 LT 3
M4 LT 3
if 3
off
on
≠
=
F3 routine
M3 routine
determine LT 4
write F3
read F3
read M3
ABC of LT4 LT3
if 3 off
≤
F4 LT 4
M4 LT 4
if 4
F4 routine
M4 routine
write F4
read F4
read M4
if 4 off
legend:
if 1, 2, 3, 4 = file indicator
on = file
off = no file

Loops

Single loops

If a sequence of instructions must be obeyed a specified number of times the following structure is generally used:

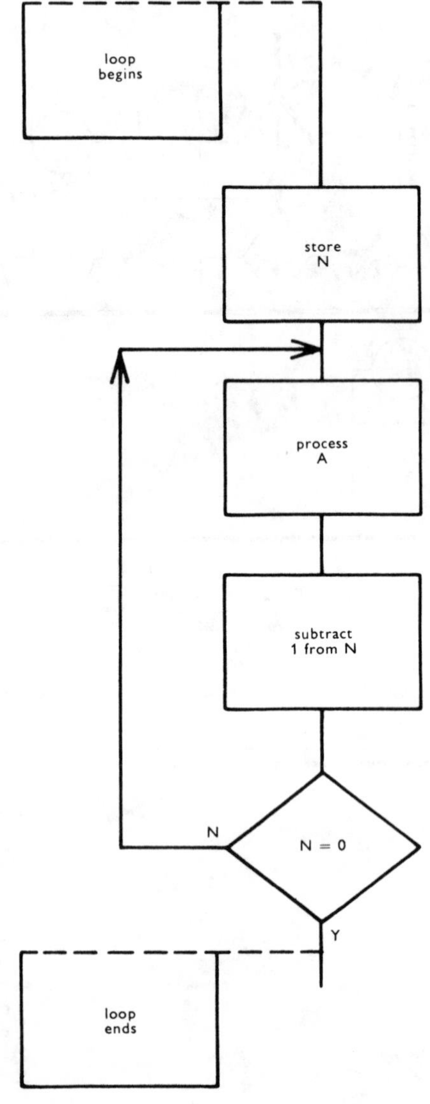

N: number of times a sequence of instructions *A* must be executed.

This pattern is usually the simplest form for coding purposes, because

- the end of the loop, since it is reached when the operations counter is zero, can be both detected and acted upon by a simple "jump if zero" instruction;
- the number of times the sequence of operations has yet to be carried out is always available.

Nested loops

The following example illustrates the flowchart structure containing loops within loops (nested loops).

Assumptions

- During processing thirty totals have been built-up in core storage in the sequence: total no 10, 9, . . . to 1; 20, 19, 18, . . . to 11; 30, 29, . . . to 21;
- on termination of the operation the totals are to be printed on a control sheet on 3 lines, each line containing 10 totals;
- the significance of the totals is given by a header line on the control sheet;
- each total requires eight printing positions;
- the printing positions are:

  totals 1, 11, 21: positions 33 to 40
  totals 2, 12, 22: positions 43 to 50
  totals 3, 13, 23: positions 53 to 60
  totals 4, 14, 24: positions 63 to 70
  totals 5, 15, 25: positions 73 to 80
  totals 6, 16, 26: positions 83 to 90
  totals 7, 17, 27: positions 93 to 100
  totals 8, 18, 28: positions 103 to 110
  totals 9, 19, 29: positions 113 to 120
  totals 10, 20, 30: positions 123 to 130

Solution

It is essential for the solution of this problem to indicate:

- which total is to be handled. For this purpose the address of the total concerned is stored in a working area T. After each run this working area contains the address of the next total;
- on which line and in which position a total is to be printed. For this purpose two nesting loops are maintained:
  - one for the number of lines to be printed. This loop is controlled by the content of working area R;
  - one for the position on the line in which the last-character of the current total is to be printed. A constant K is set at 30 and a variable quantity V at 100. Working area V controls the second loop.

The flowchart now looks as follows:

The values of various quantities per iterations are shown in the table.

R	V	address T refers to total no.	K + V	next address (T) refers to total no.	V-10	print line	R-1
entry							
3	100	10	130	9	90	N	
3	90	9	120	8	80	N	
3	80	8	110	7	70	N	
3	70	7	100	6	60	N	
3	60	6	90	5	50	N	
3	50	5	80	4	40	N	
3	40	4	70	3	30	N	
3	30	3	60	2	20	N	
3	20	2	50	1	10	N	
3	10	1	40	20	0	Y	2
2	100	20	130	19	90	N	
⋮	⋮	⋮	⋮	⋮	⋮	⋮	⋮
2	10	11	40	30	0	Y	1
1	100	30	130	29	90	N	
⋮	⋮	⋮	⋮	⋮	⋮	⋮	⋮
1	10	21	40	—	0	Y	0
							exit

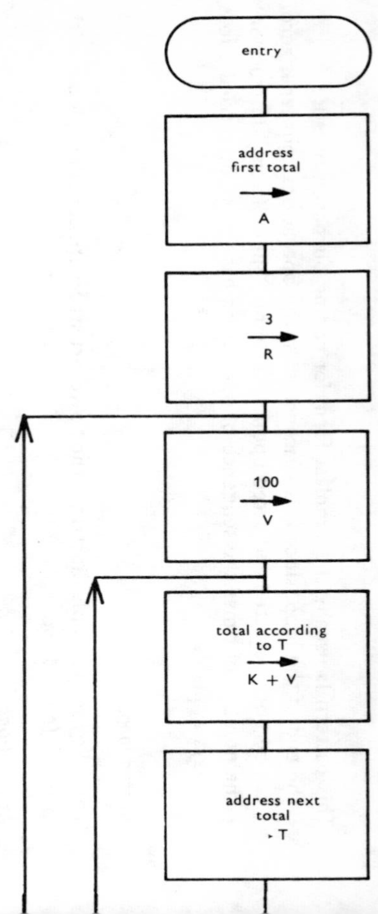

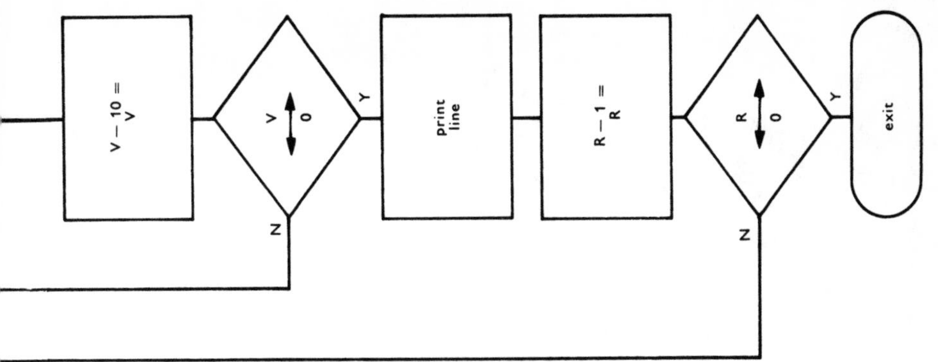

V — 10 = V
V
0
Y
N
print line
R — 1 = R
R
0
Y
N
exit

Technique 6-6.2: Programming language selection

Purpose

The purpose of programming language selection is to choose the most appropriate programming language for a system development effort, taking into consideration both developmental and operational efficiency.

Areas of application

Selection of the programming language or languages to be used is made during the step prepare hardware and software requirements, 3-4.4.

Introduction

Before final file, report, and processing specifications are complete, the programming language in which the various system elements are to be written must be selected. This selection is usually made jointly by the system engineer and the senior programmer; it requires a detailed knowledge of the proposed application, and a good understanding of the software languages available, their implementation efficiency, the characteristics of the specific machine to be used, the capabilities of the programming staff, the expected maintenance on the system, the compatibility requirements arising from planned future equipment changes and the expected life-time of the program or system.

This section presents some of the characteristics of the most widely used languages. The system engineer, if he understands the various factors outlined in this section, will be able to play an active role in the language selection, and to fashion the system he is designing to exploit fully the capabilities of the selected language.

Types of programming language

There are three types of programming language: assembly languages, procedure oriented or compiler languages, and system-oriented languages.
A particular computer configuration usually has available one assembly language-together with either a business-oriented or a formula-oriented procedural, language, or both. The system-oriented languages are not yet widely available, except in specialized areas such as simulation and machine tool control.

Assembly language translators

In third-generation computing systems, the assembly language usually includes an assembler capable of translating a basic set of mnemonic instructions into machine language; an associated high-level language-processing structure, such

FORTRAN and ALGOL characteristics

Commercial problems are data-structure-oriented, in that a fairly restricted range of available computational operations must be ordered compatibily with the organization of the working data. Scientific problems, however, are generally procedure-oriented; each such problem has a definite (and often unique) series of computational steps, many involving calculation formulae. The FORTRAN and ALGOL languages permit compact, efficient specification of calculation formulae. These languages have the disadvantages that only simple (matrix type) data structures can be specified, and that data fields are fixed in length, without provision for efficient packing or blocking. Many of the compilers currently available do not incorporate proper facilities for accomodating remote terminals or direct-access, mass-storage devices. Despite this limitation, and despite the fact that many of the available compilers are not as efficient as the current state of the art would allow, most programming today is accomplished using procedural compilers.

Characteristics of programming languages

Systems language compilers apply to a specific class of applications, such as text information retrieval or list processing, rather than to a particular application. Typical system languages include, IPL, APT and the Iverson ALgorithm Language. When this type of compiler can be used, it may reduce programming effort to a tenth of its former scope. To date, however, the available languages are applicable to strictly limited areas, and often produce inefficient object code.

Systems language compilers

The selection of a specific programming language for a specific application depends on a careful balancing of capacity and efficiency required in various areas. The figure below tabulates the characteristics of three popular languages, assuming a good implementation of the translating or compiling program. Each of the factors for which the languages are evaluated is discussed in the following paragraphs, in terms of systems design criteria.

	FORTRAN [1]	COBOL	assembler
Capability (capacity)			
calculation	excellent	good	good
data management	poor	excellent	good
field formats	fair	good	excellent
Efficiency (cost/performance)			
object program	good	fair	good
re-assembly	good	good	poor
implementation	good	excellent	poor
design	good	good	fair

[1] This column applies to scientific applications.

Programming language characteristics.

as MACRO or PROC system, which allows the programmer to develop and name (with his own assembler-type mnemonics) special subroutines to be used only at his installation; and a comprehensive library of input/output and utility routines available as part of the manufacturer-supplied operating system. Assembly-language programming, while slow and expensive, is capable of high precision. This precision is not automatic, however; the efficiency of the method is dependant upon the experience and skill of the programmer.

Although an expert using assembly language can produce faster running routines with fewer instructions than he can in a compiler language such as FORTRAN (FORmula TRANslater) or COBOL (COmmon Business Oriented Language), the average programmer will work better in one of the high-level languages, which call for the use of a compiler. The usual reasons for deciding to program in the assembly language are:

- no compiler giving efficient object programs is available;
- necessary computational, data handling, or input capabilities are not possessed by the compiler;
- a special requirement exists for maximum running speed or minimum core-storage usage in a particular program.

Most large-scale, third-generation operating systems include a routine-coordinating program, or "linkage editor", which is capable of assembling a complete program from individual routines and programming segments written in different programming languages. This allows the programmer to write only a small portion of a complex program in assembly language, and to use the appropriate compiler language for most of the programming.

Procedural language compilers

Procedural compilers include such language processors as: COBOL, FORTRAN, ALGOL (ALGOrithmic Language) and PL/I (Programming Language, first version, intended to include the capabilities of both COBOL and FORTRAN). COBOL is the compiler language most widely used for commercial, and FORTRAN for scientific applications; for the latter in Europe ALGOL is frequently employed.

COBOL characteristics

COBOL possesses an advantageously flexible data-dèscription system, enabling data to be packed into records and blocks for efficient use of the available data storage. The characteristics of the language force it to produce relatively lengthy, inefficient object programs when complex calculations are involved. COBOL does not allow the use of convenient free-form input data streams (fields of variable length separated by delimiters such as commas).

Calculation capability

Calculation capability is the characteristic which permits easy rapid definition and use of complex calculation sequences. This characteristic is important primarily in scientific applications.

Data management capability

Data management capability is the ability to specify and perform file-oriented tasks, such as record maintenance, item selection, sorting and display editing, easily and efficiently. This characteristic is important primarily in routine commercial applications.

Field format capability

This is the characteristic which permits a language to handle single or multiple bits, or variable length syllables and word-length fields with ease and precision. It is important for efficient data coding and packing in any application where large volumes of data have to be processed.

Object program efficiency

The quality of the object code produced determines the speed at which the application can be processed. This characteristic is important in high production applications, where each program will be run a great many times.

Re-assembly efficiency

This characteristic defines the ease and rapidity with which corrections can be incorporated in an existing program, and a new working program produced. It is important when changes to a system approach in frequency that of production runs.

Implementation efficiency

The efficiency of the programming and program check-out functions are termed the implementation efficiency. Since experienced programmers can produce an almost constant number of lines of code per hour in any reasonably straightforward language, the implementation efficiency of a language is directly proportional to the number of lines of code needed to program any given application. Although COBOL looses some efficiency by reason of its English entrance structure, the documentation produced is superior to that of other languages.

Design efficiency

Design efficiency refers to the impact of the language on the system design effort. System oriented languages can be used to impose a discipline on the documentation of the system design, while language capability limitations will increase the system design effort by entailing the preparation of alternative methods of meeting objectives.

Summary

A systems engineer cannot complete the design of an information system without an adequate knowledge of the programming language in which the system is to be implemented. Many detailed specifications, especially in the file design area, require this knowledge. The specific capabilities of the language must be thoroughly understood.

Technique 6-6.3: Practical rules for COBOL programming

Introduction

One reason for developing COBOL was to improve the readability of the source program. Even with COBOL, however, it is still possible to write an unreadable program. The following points give ideas of how to write neat COBOL programs which are easy to understand and to maintain.

List of standard names

At the start of a project a systems analyst or senior programmer should prepare a standard specifying the data names and abbreviations to be used by all programmers concerned with the information system. In preparing this standard the suggestions contained in the technique identification of system elements and data objects (6-4.1) should be followed wherever possible, and the field description sheet should be used.

Practical rules

Use meaningful names only when a meaning is expected e.g. for data names; and in these cases use as little abbreviation as possible, whilst keeping the names to a reasonable length. For non-meaningful names i.e. names of items such as files, routines, paragraphs etc. which are necessary for technical reasons of programming rather than for explanation, try to restrict their length to seven characters as this will save compiling time. The use of short basic names enables the programmer to append a few characters whilst still keeping the name to a reasonable length. Characters may need to be added for purposes such as redefinition or for indicating the page number etc. on which the name is used.
Those names which are used in lengthy formulas after a COMPUTE should be kept as short as possible to serve readability of the formula. In these cases it is recommended to use a comment card to clarify the information contents of the field.
Ensure that none of the data names selected is the same as any of the COBOL reserved words.
As far as possible avoid the use of the letters G, I, O, Q and Z for the initial letters of names as they can be confused with digits.
Use the letter N for the first letters of the identifiers of subscripts (where possible defined as binary) as this is the normal procedure in other languages (FORTRAN, PL/1).

Filling-in the coding sheets

Page line and program numbers

Numbering of divisions and sections

Begin each new division or important section at a page number (cols 1 to 3) which is a multiple of one hundred, for example:

identification division	000
environment division	100
data division	200
working storage section	300
procedure division	400

Page numbering

When writing the program use even page numbers to facilitate insertions later on, for example:

routine RO0	400
routine RO1	402
routine RO2	404
subroutine SO1	700
subroutine SO2	702

Line numbering

Line numbers (cols 4 to 6) should be preprinted on the COBOL coding sheets and should always be multiples of 10 in order to facilitate insertions. The line numbering for routine RO0 in the previous example would therefore be:

400 000
400 010
400 020 etc.

Filling in COBOL statements

Program number

The technique identification of system elements and data objects recommends that a five-digit number be used to identify any program in a system. These five digits should be entered in columns 73 to 77 at the top right hand corner of the coding sheet. The remaining three columns (78 to 80) can be used, if necessary, to indicate different versions of the same program.

Lines

The start of each new logical block should be easy to find and identify. The major divisions and subdivisions of the program should always be started on a new page as described previously. Each minor division should be made clear by preceding it by a blank line. Such a line, and consequently the punched card for that line, will therefore contain only the page and line number (cols 1 to 6) and the program number (cols 72 to 80).

Continuation lines
Although COBOL allows the breaking-off of words and their continuation on the next line, this should be avoided as much as possible in the interests of readability. Only in the case of literals (header lines and the like) it is permissible.

Identification division
In addition to the division name and the program identification (program number) which are required by the COBOL language, this division should contain sufficient information to enable the program to be uniquely identified by both the programming and the user organizations. It is suggested that this information should be as follows:

- purpose of program;
- name, address and telephone number of programmer;
- date written;
- date compiled;
- number and version of compiler program.

Environment division
The required items and available options for the environment division will vary with the COBOL compiler to be used. It is suggested therefore that the senior programmer studies this specification and then draws up a standard for the layout and content of the environment division and ensures that this standard is adhered to by all programmers under his control. This standard should specify which options may be used and which may not and the format of the entries in the various sections. In addition, if details of the source computer and object computer, files etc. are available from the system library tape or disk, full information, together with the library reference numbers should be made available to all programmers concerned.

Data division
It is recommended that the standards for coding the data division should be along the following lines:

- in the file description section each clause should start on a new line at column 12. Clauses should contain enough optional words to make them readable;
- in the file description, working storage and constant sections, entries bearing level numbers should be indented in accordance with their level numbers to emphasize their hierarchical structure. If an entry bears a higher level number than its predecessor indent it four spaces so that:
  - — level 01 start at col 12;
  - — level 02 starts at col 16;
  - — level 03 starts at col 20;
  - — level 04 and higher (except level 88) start at col 24;
  - — a level 88 entry (condition) should start at the same column as the entry to which it relates;
- clauses should start only at the following positions, even if this entails transferring to a new line:

— REDEFINES; immediately after the data name;
— PICTURE; col 41;
— VALUE; if possible, on the same line as PICTURE starting at col 56; otherwise at col 12 on the next line;
— USAGE; col 41;
— OCCURS; col 41. The optional word TIMES must be used in an OCCURS clause;
— DEPENDING ON; col 41;
— other clauses; col 41;

- in the working storage section:
  — all entries which can legitimately be assigned a level number of 77 (non-continuous working storage) should be given one starting at col 12. Level 77 entries must precede all other entries in the working storage section;
  — all other entries, i.e. those referring to storage for data having a hierarchical structure, should be entered and indented to show the hierarchical structure as described previously;
- whenever possible use a PICTURE clause in preference to other clauses to describe data items. Start the PICTURE clause at col 41. Note that the example on page 8 does not follow this recommendation in order to save space;
- in PICTURE clauses, use the "packed" format by adding, after the picture specification, a COMPUTATIONAL clause (see implementors manual), for files and binary format for subscripting. Ensure that the value of a subscript can never be zero and always remains within the boundaries of the table;
- the illustrations on pages 5, 6 and 8 show filled-in coding sheets for the working storage section of a data division and a record layout for the structure of the records specified.

Procedure division

For writing the procedure division of a COBOL program it is recommended that the following standards be observed:

- start each new paragraph on a new line under A at col 8;
- start each new statement on a new line under B at col 12;
- OPEN and CLOSE. Write each file name on a separate line in the sequence of input, input/output, output. Each file name should start at the same columns. Example:

```
OPEN
        INPUT            F 1209
        INPUT-OUTPUT     F 2701
        OUTPUT           F 2806
                         F 3700
                         F 3303
```

- where complicated statements are necessary it is essential to improve readability and understandability by good layout. It is good practice in such cases to write each clause on a new line, and indent the subordinate clauses by four spaces.

RECORD LAYOUT

system :
subsystem : invoicing; program 15123
prev. issue :

project no. : 151
chapter/sect. : 238
page : 2
issued :

101b

artnr, art gr, filler, artype, arprice, arstpric, artax, armismov, artnet, arreord, arrecv, arsales, arbo, arclist

01 02 03 04 05

article record 101b

keydeb, debkey, filler, keyart, artkey, filler, borep, border, bo, bocode, boprice, bo1, bo2, bo-P3, filler

01 02 03 04 05

working storage areas

gross, net, tax

01 02 03 04 05

01 02 03 04 05

01 02 03 04 05

N.V. PHILIPS' COMPUTER INDUSTRIE APELDOORN

PROBLEM ______________________________

Page (1–3)	Line (4–6)	-	A (8)	B (12)	(16)	(20)	(24)	(28)	(32)	(36)
302	000		01	BØ						
	050			02	BØREP					
	100			02	BØRDER					
	150			02	BØCØDE					
	200			02	BØ-P3.					
	250				03	BØPRICE.				
	300					04	BØ1			
	350					04	BØ2			
	400				03	FILLER				
	450									
	500									
	550									
	600									
	650									
	700									
	750									
	800									
	850									
	900									
	950									

COBOL

IDENTIFICATION 15123
73 80

PROGRAMMER ______ PAGE ______ OF ______

40 44 48 52 56 60 64 68 72

```
PICTURE XX.
PICTURE X(10).
PICTURE X.


PICTURE 999.
PICTURE 999
SIZE 12.
```

40 44 48 52 56 60 64 68 72

N.V. PHILIPS' COMPUTER INDUSTRIE APELDOORN

PROBLEM ______________________

Page (1–3)	Line (4–6)	A (8)	B (12)	16	32
300	010	WØRR	ING-	STØRRGE SECTIØN.	
↓	020	77	CRØSS	S	PICTURE
↓	030	77	NET		PICTURE
↓	040	77	TAX		PICTURE
↓	050	77	I01		PICTURE
	060	77	I02		PICTURE
	070	77	I03		PICTURE
	080	77	C01		PICTURE
	090	77	C28		PICTURE
	100	77	C1248	3	PICTURE
	110	77	CINV	ØICE	PICTURE
	120	77	CFRE	E-REMPLACE	PICTURE
	130				
	140	01	KEYD	EB.	
	150		02	DEBKEY	PICTURE
	160		02	FILLER	PICTURE
	170				
	180	01	KEYP	RT	
	190		02	ARTKEY	PICTURE
	200		02	FILLER	PICTURE

COBOL

IDENTIFICATION 73 80

PROGRAMMER ________ PAGE ________ OF ________

```
40  44  48  52  56  60  64  68  72

9(4)V99.
9(4)V99
9(4)V99
9  COMPUTATIONAL-3 VALUE 0-
9  COMPUTATIONAL-3 VALUE 0-
9  COMPUTATIONAL-3 VALUE 0-
99 COMPUTATIONAL-3 VALUE 1-
99 COMPUTATIONAL-3 VALUE 28-
9(5) COMPUTATIONAL-3 VALUE 12483-
X(7) VALUE 'INVOICE'
X(13) VALUE 'FREE-REMPLACE'


9(6)
9


9(6)
9

40  44  48  52  56  60  64  68  72
```

Example:

```
PERFORM A THROUGH B VARYING C FROM
D BY 1 UNTIL F AFTER G FROM H
BY 2 UNTIL K.
should be written as:
PERFORM A THROUGH B
    VARYING C FROM D BY 1 UNTIL F
    AFTER G FROM H BY 2 UNTIL K.
```

- when writing subordinate clauses, start each one on a new line and indent it four spaces. In the case of an IF statement the actions to be taken when the condition is satisfied should be written on a new line indented four spaces from the start of IF. The actions to be taken when the condition specified is not fulfilled should be introduced by the word ELSE on a new line starting at the same column as the IF.
Example:

```
IF A MOVE B TO C GO TO RO3 ELSE MOVE B
TO E GO TO RO4.
should be written as:
IF A
    MOVE B TO C
    GO TO RO3
ELSE
    MOVE B TO E
    GO TO RO4.
```

- for other conditional or quasi-conditional statements such as ON SIZE ERROR; AT END etc., indent the conditional clause four spaces from the start of the main clause and start the "condition not satisfied" clause immediately below the start of the "condition satisfied" clause.
Example:

```
READ A AT END MOVE B TO C GO TO RO5.
should be written as:
READ A
    AT END MOVE B TO C
        GO TO RO5.
similarly.

MULTIPLY A BY B ON SIZE ERROR ADD
A TO C GO TO RO6.
should be written as:
MULTIPLY A BY B
    ON SIZE ERROR ADD A TO C
                      GO TO RO6.
```

Relationships between program coding and flowchart

It is vitally important that each processing operation shown on the program flowchart can be easily identified in the program coding and vice versa. This means that, as far as possile the identifiers used on the flowchart should be either the same as, or recognizable abbreviations of, those used on the coding sheets. Also the operations to be performed must be as explicit and unambiguous in the flowchart as they are in the coding. Comments should be used freely; wherever there is a comment on the flowchart, there should be a corresponding comment in the coding, and wherever possible the wording should be the same.

Examples

Routines and subroutines

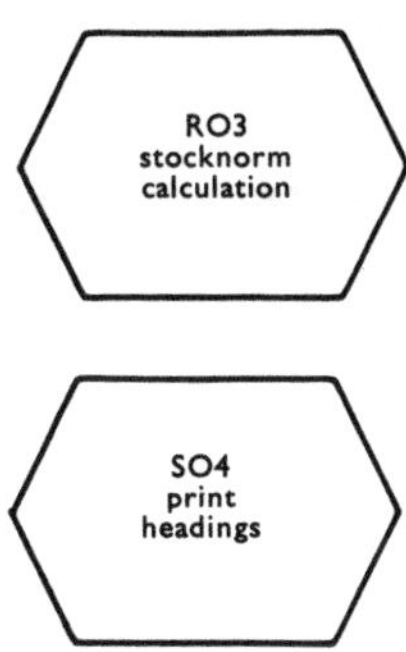

Action:
Execute a routine or subroutine.

COBOL:

(a) If the routine or subroutine is in the same program.

PERFORM RO3.
PERFORM SO4.

(b) If the routine or subroutine was compiled separately, or forms part of another program, even if this was compiled from another source language e.g. FORTRAN, PL1.

ENTER RO3.
or CALL RO3.
depending on the COBOL compiler.

Console messages

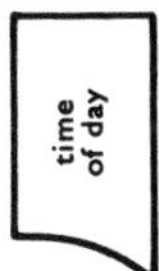

Action:

Message from operator to program.

COBOL:

ACCEPT TCO1 FROM CONSOLE.

NOTE: TCO1 IS TIME OF DAY.

Action:

Message from program to operator.

COBOL:

DISPLAY TCO9 UPON CONSOLE.

NOTE: TCO9 IS "START 35054 AGP"

Processing operations

On the flowchart the operation must be clearly specified. On the coding the operation may consist of any number of COBOL statements.

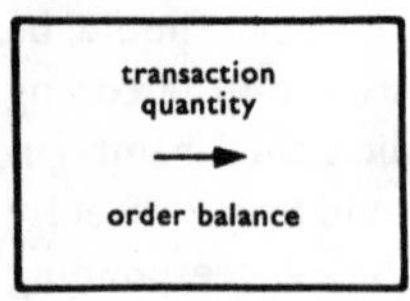

COBOL:

MOVE TRANS-QUANT TO ORDER-BALANCE

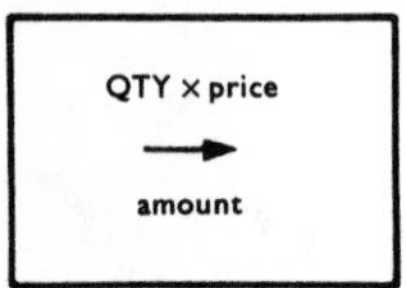

Action:

Determine amount as the product of quantity and price, i.e. multiply the content of the storage area called QTY by the content of the storage area called PRICE and place the result in the storage area called AMOUNT.

COBOL:

MULTIPLY QTY BY PRICE GIVING AMOUNT.

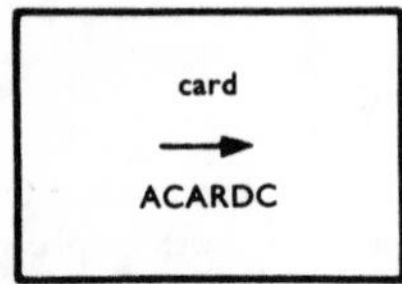

Action:

Store card code in the storage area called ACARDC.

COBOL:

MOVE CARD TO ACARDC.

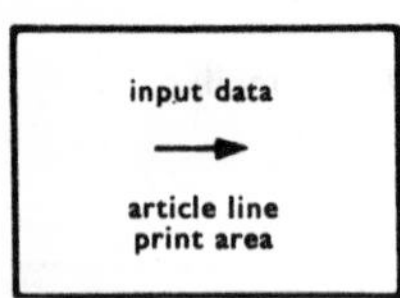

Action:

The action of this statement is self-explanatory.

COBOL:

MOVE CORRESPONDING LO1B TO LO2A.

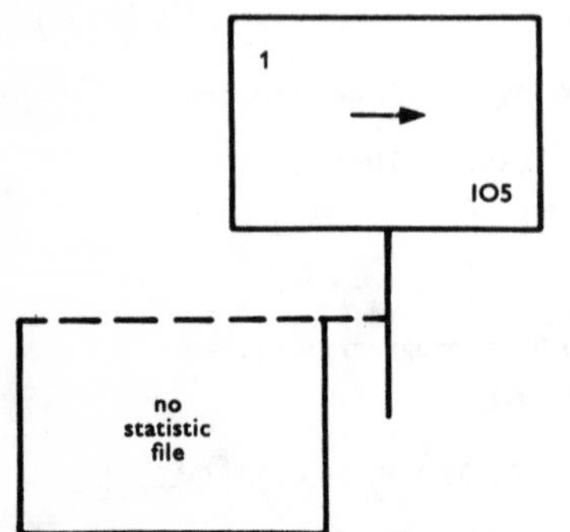

Action:

Store the constant 1 in indicator IO5.

COBOL:

MOVE 1 TO IO5.

NOTE: NO STATISTIC FILE UPDATING

WHEN IO5 = 1.

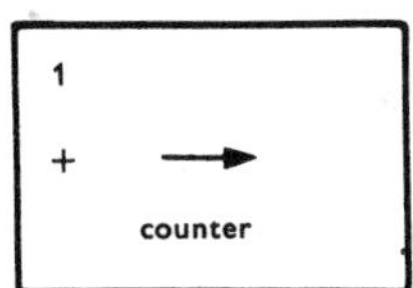

Action:

Increase the content of the storage area called COUNTER by 1.

COBOL:

ADD 1 TO COUNTER.

Action:
The complete storage area called MATPOS is set to zero.

COBOL:

MOVE ZEROES TO MATPOS.

Inquiry
The answer can only be "yes" or "no".

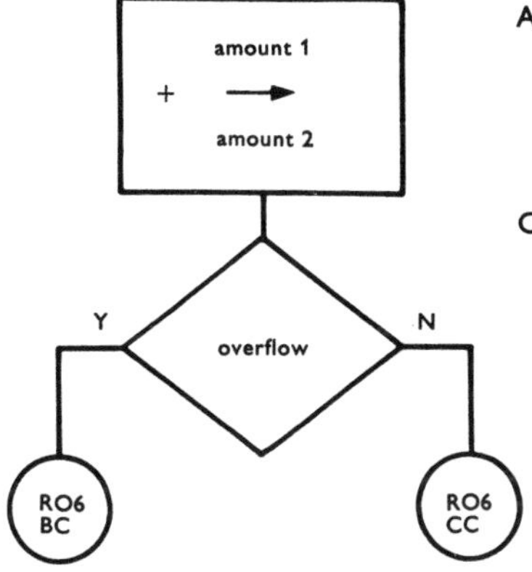

Action:
Inquiry to test whether or not an overflow condition has occurred as a result of a previous operation, and a specification of the action to be taken in each case.

COBOL:

```
ADD AMOUNT-1 TO AMOUNT-2;
ON SIZE ERROR GO TO RO6BC.
                  GO TO RO6CC.
```

Comparison
Comparison of two values (data and/or constants); the results can only be combinations of $>$, $<$, $\geqslant$, $\leqslant$, $=$ and $\neq$.

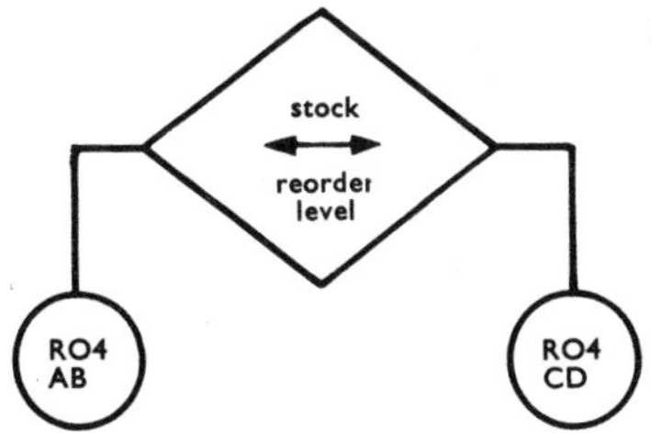

COBOL:

```
IF STOCK LESS THAN REORDER-LEVEL
      GO TO RO4AB.
ELSE GO TO RO4CD.
```

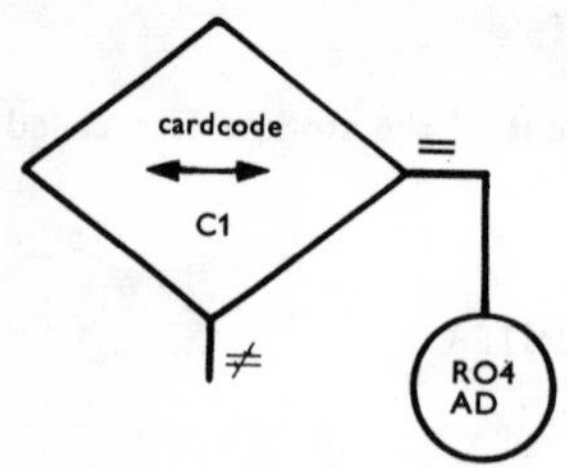

COBOL:

IF CARD = C1 GO TO RO4AD.

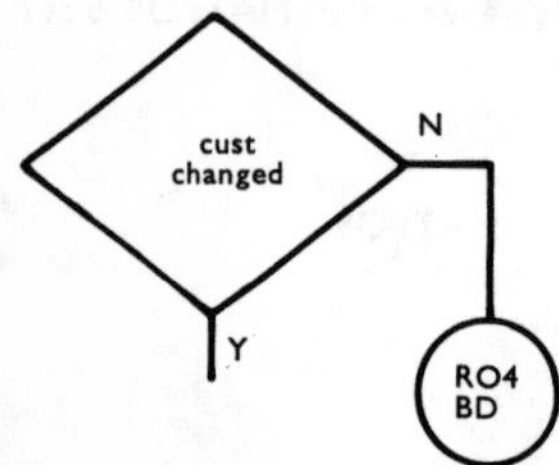

COBOL:

IF CUST IS EQUAL TO ACUSTC GO TO RO4BD.

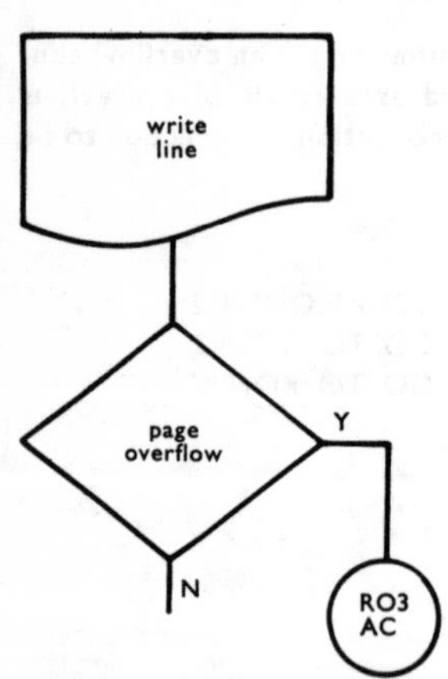

COBOL:

WRITE PRINTRECORD;
AT END-OF-PAGE GO TO RO3AC.

Compare and subroutine

Suppose that, in a particular file, articles can appear with an old material code as identifiers and it is required to convert such identifiers into a new 12-digit code (= 12NC). The old code is identifiable by the first character being alphabetic.

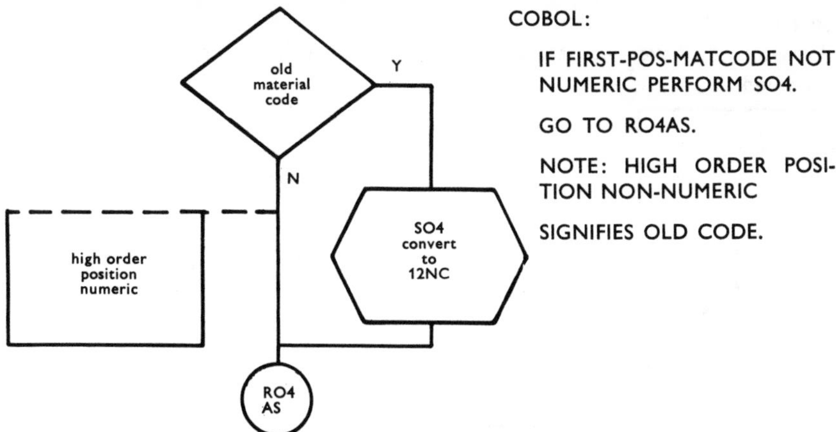

COBOL:

IF FIRST-POS-MATCODE NOT NUMERIC PERFORM SO4.

GO TO RO4AS.

NOTE: HIGH ORDER POSITION NON-NUMERIC

SIGNIFIES OLD CODE.

Programmed indicators with two or more exits

A programmed indicator is a working area, usually of one character or octad, whose state can be changed by program. Subsequent action of the program is dependent on the state of the indicator.

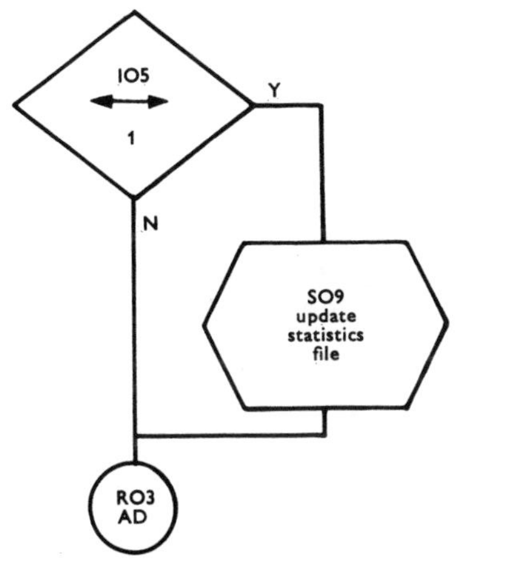

single indicator:

COBOL:

IF IO5 IS NOT EQUAL TO 1 PERFORM SO9.
GO TO RO3AD.

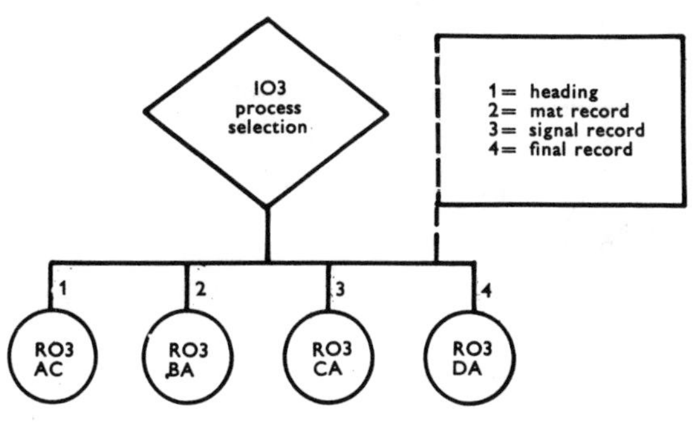

multiple indicator:

COBOL:

GO TO RO3AC RO3BA RO3CA RO3DA DEPENDING ON IO3.

NOTE: STATES OF IO3;

1 = HEADING
2 = MAT RECORD
3 = SIGNAL RECORD
4 = FINAL RECORD.

Switch

A switch can have two states; it indicates a program instruction that can be modified.

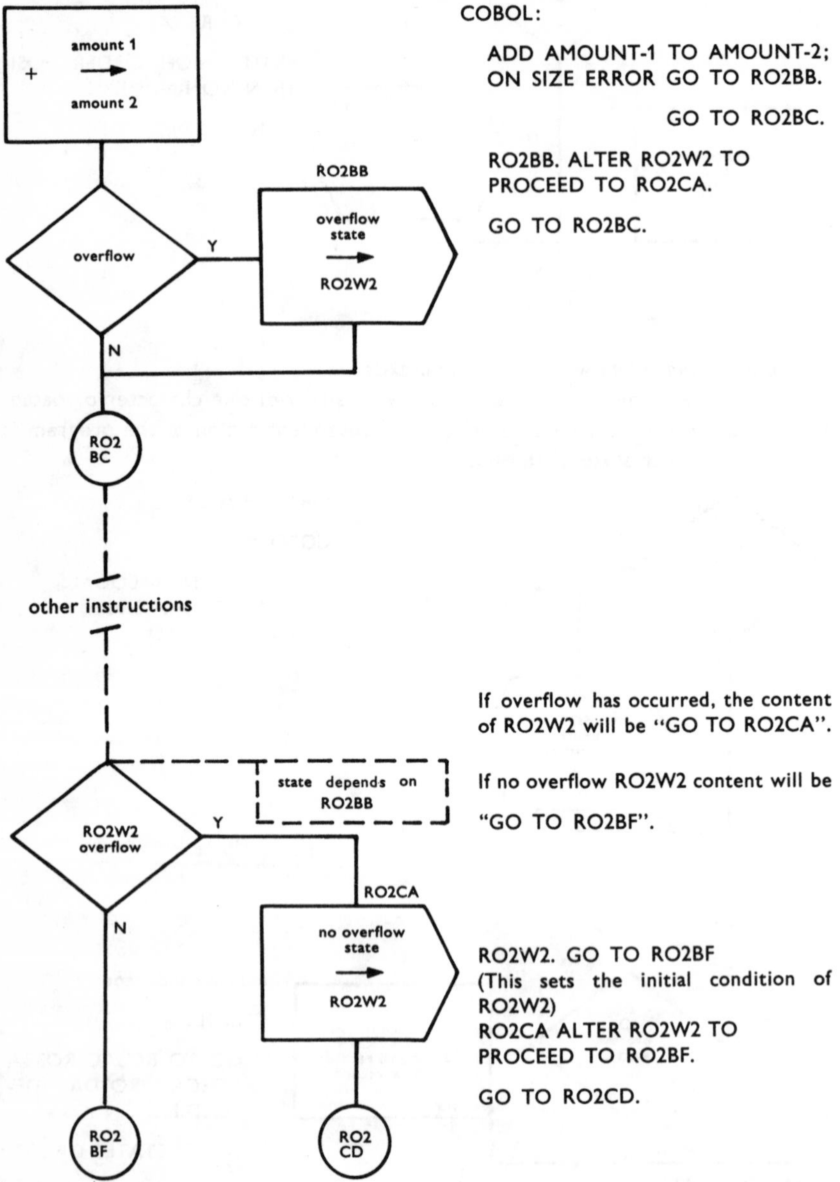

COBOL:

```
ADD AMOUNT-1 TO AMOUNT-2;
ON SIZE ERROR GO TO RO2BB.
                GO TO RO2BC.
RO2BB. ALTER RO2W2 TO
PROCEED TO RO2CA.
GO TO RO2BC.
```

If overflow has occurred, the content of RO2W2 will be "GO TO RO2CA".

If no overflow RO2W2 content will be "GO TO RO2BF".

RO2W2. GO TO RO2BF
(This sets the initial condition of RO2W2)
RO2CA ALTER RO2W2 TO
PROCEED TO RO2BF.

GO TO RO2CD.

Technique 6-6.4: Record key transformation

Purpose

Record key transformation is concerned with the allocation of logical records to addressable locations or areas on direct access storage devices. The purpose of record key transformation is to convert automatically the identification fields (record keys) of logical records into actual (storage) addresses in such a way as to achieve a densely packed file with minimum retrieval time.

The purpose of this techniques chapter is to present the currently available methods of record key transformation and to summarize the advantages and disadvantages of each in order to enable the reader to select the one best suited to any particular application.

Areas of application

Record key transformation techniques are applicable to the activities of file design, development and conversion which are carried out in the design, development and implementation phases of the systems effort.

Types of transformation

Two types of transformation are discussed in this technique chapter; direct and randomized.

The direct type provides a file sorted in the order of the record key. The direct method is the fastest and simplest, but can be used only when the system designer has complete control over record identifiers, and when sequential identifiers are used and re-used (e.g., telephone numbers).

The random type of record key transformation can be used with any key, but requires a detailed evaluation of access time and storage space requirements. A number of methods exist for transforming unique external identifiers — such as part numbers, invoice numbers, etc. — into unique equivalent internal identifiers; all of these, however, can be extremely wasteful of storage area. There is no simple method of transforming a long record key (such as an alphanumeric part number) into a shorter address, while maintaining a reasonably packed file.

Direct transformations

In this technique, each record key numerically equals either the relative, or the absolute address of the storage location containing the record. Since on most random access storage devices the addresses are sequential, the data file is thus stored already sorted in numerical order. The technique needs no indexes, no overflow areas, and no elaborate computational scheme, but it is seldom usable on other than relatively small data files, because of the wastefulness of storage area which results from unallocated keys.

The direct addressing technique usually uses a sequential series (such as 1000, 1001, 1002 1003, . . .) as record keys. The actual memory address A for record key K is given by:

$$A = A_0 + n(K - K_0)$$

where A_0 is the starting address of the file;
n is the number of addressable storage locations or areas necessary to hold the record;
K_0 is the starting record key.

Example
A file uses record keys starting from 1000.
Two records require 1 admissible location of storage, and the initial record is stored in location 26.000.

$K_0 = 1000$
$A_0 = 26.000$
$n = 0.5$
so $A = 26{,}000 + 0.5\ (K - 1000)$
$= 25{,}500 + 0.5\ K.$

The address "A" for selected records "K" are therefore as follows:

K	A
1,000	25,500
1,001	25,500
1,002	25,501
⋮	⋮
2,000	26,000

The file area assigned must include space for the entire set of records represented by the entire range of key numbers, regardless of the number of keys actually left unassigned to records in the file. Efficient use of memory depends on a dense usage of the keys. This is usually possible only when the key represents a physical facility (such as telephone numbers), or when extensive numbering system controls are possible (such as department numbers).

Random transformations

In this technique, a formula is used to compute a storage address from the record key; the records are therefore scattered throughout the allocated storage area, in no particular order. Statistical considerations indicate that the actual storage addresses generated should be capable of holding several records in order to minimize overflow.

In the external file, record keys are usually unique, but the distribution of keys over their total range is far from being either uniform or random. Clusters of sequential numbers and large gaps occur and change as time passes.
The problem is to transform these keys in such a manner as to obtain an as uniform as possible a distribution of keys throughout the range of available storage addresses. A perfect transformation would completely utilize the memory space available, and no overflow would occur. This ideal is unattainable but the method described below can often approach reasonably close to it. A random distribution of keys throughout the available storage area is usually the best performance achievable by means of the technique presented. The table on page 25 of technique 6-4.2 shows the percentage of overflow from storage areas of different record-holding capacity, assuming random distribution of addresses. By the use of this table an estimate of total storage space requirements for a file of given size can be made.

One widely used method of key transformation is performed in two stages: first the record key is changed to a format suited to the arithmetical capabilities of the specific computer (while maintaining, as far as possible, the uniqueness of the record key); and second, the modified key is reduced to the length and range of storage addresses available through division by a prime number, and adjustment for available addresses.

Calculation Procedure
If the number of available addresses is N, and the first address is A_0, then a record key K may be transformed to an address by computing K/P, and adding the remainder to A_0 (all numbers being treated as integers). This calculation produces N consecutive addresses from A_0 to $A_0 + N - 1$.
The value of P should be chosen so that:

- it is a prime number, so that regularly spaced record keys (e.g. multiples of 100) will not convert to the same address;
- it is less than the number of physically available locations (the remaining locations can be used for overflow storage);
- prime numbers are avoided whose form is $aR^m \pm 1$ for $a = 1$ to 9, where R is the radix of the number system used in addressing (usually either 2 or 10), and m is an integer.

The K/P division should always be carried out in the same number system as the computed addresses.

Example
A file averages 160,000 records, and an addressable area will hold ten records. If we assign 20,000 areas to the file, the average number of records per area will be eight. The table on page 25 of technique 6-4.2. indicates that for the random distribution with an 80% loading an average of 5,3% of the records i.e. 8,500 records will overflow and must be stored in overflow areas.
The prime number 19939 which meets all the requirements stated previously

could be used for the calculation described. A record with the key 20711003 would therefore go into area 14321, because:

20711003/19939 = 1038 remainder 14321

Note that the record with the key "20711004" would go into the next area, 14322, so that a long string of sequentially keyed records would contribute to a uniform, efficient distribution.

Folding procedure

Folding is the descriptive term often applied to the process of changing a record key to the format required for the calculations presented in the previous paragraphs.

Most folding is accomplished by splitting the key into sections and adding the sections together. If the numeric and zone portions of zoned-decimal format keys are added during folding, a more even distribution can often be achieved.

The folding method used must be tailored to the specific key set and the particular computer. General guidelines to follow are:

- strive to maintain the uniqueness of each individual key;
- ensure that consecutive input keys produce consecutive folded keys;
- if bit positions are dropped, or if the radix is changed (for example: a character format input key simply used as if it were pure binary), try to remove possible unused series of folded numbers.

Note that a decimal digit used directly in the most significant portion of a binary folded key will waste 3/8 of the file space available because only ten of the sixteen possible combinations of bits are used.

Folding is a critical step in random transformation, and should be tried out on samples of the record keys which will be encountered. The result of the trial should be printed, and then scanned for unforseen effects.

General notes

Computation time and storage space limitations must be considered when selecting the record storage system and key transformation techniques to be used. What is advantageous in one application may not be adaptable to another; for example: a significant reduction in computer time per transaction for one method may not be relevant if only 100 transactions a day are processed.

Advantages of direct transformations

- Both sequential-order and random-order transaction files can be efficiently handled by direct transformation;
- sorting is not required for reports, when data is reported in the same order as it is stored in the file;
- more positive control and checking of the file is possible, since visual scanning of listings is possible;
- extensive key analysis, and file-structure simulation before implementation, are not needed.

Disadvantages of random transformations

- Development of address conversion routines, and simulation of actual files are required before final selection of conversion procedure;
- conversion to a different file organization requires a re-sorting of the entire file;
- dynamic files may require frequent redesign and development of new transformation rules.

Technique 6-6.5: Program conversion

Purpose

The purpose of program conversion is to convert programs from one software/hardware configuration to another.

Areas of application

Program conversion is used during the development phase of an application which is being written in a new programming language. The conversion will be either from assembly language to new assembly or procedural language; or an adaptation of the procedural language for a new computer.

Introduction

The conversion of an existing computer application — such as an accounting system or a stock control system — to a new software/hardware configuration requires the conversion of both the programs and the files. The efficient conversion of large volumes of existing data usually requires the writing of a translation program (or set of programs) capable of producing the new files properly organized and in the proper format. This translation application should be considered a separate systems analysis & design problem, and one to which all the appropriate activities and techniques presented in this manual should be applied. The other aspect of conversion — that of adapting existing programs to the new configuration — can be performed either by "imitation" or by "refabrication".

Imitation

The process of imitation causes the new computer to duplicate the operation of the old, so that no change in existing operational programs is required. The available methods of imitation are simulation, emulation, and identity:

Simulation

Simulation is a technique based on special software alone. A simulator program — nearly always simulating the operation of one of the earlier computers in a given manufacturer's line — is included in the manufacturer-supplied operating system of a number of third-generation computers. A simulator accepts without change assembly-language programs written for the earlier computer — i.e., the computer is simulated — and translates the data-processing operations specified by the old assembly-language programs into functionally equivalent instructions in the target computer's assembly-language, which are then run normally on the target computer.

Emulation

Emulation is a technique based primarily on hardware. Special circuitry provisions of a computer capable of emulation permit its acceptance of "micro-programming" which, in effect, changes portions of its logic circuitry to duplicate the logic circuitry of the earlier, emulated computer. Once the target computer has been thus micro-programmed, it constitutes a functional duplicate of the earlier computer, and is, therefore, capable of accepting, and running without change, assembly-language programs written for the earlier computer.

Identity

Identity, sometimes called "compatibility" is a purely hardware-based technique of which only few computers are capable. Identity-mode operation of a target computer is possible only when that computer incorporates in its entirety the logic circuitry of the earlier (or smaller) computer as a functionally separable subset of its own logic circuitry. When only this separable logic subset is operated, the target computer is functionally identical to the alternative computer, and is thus capable of accepting, and running unchanged, programs written for the earlier computer.

Refabrication

The end-product of the process of refabrication is a new program which performs the same tasks as the old program — possibly with greater efficiency since this process can benefit from the lessons learned during the earlier programming and operation. Reanalysis, reprogramming, recoding, and translation are the available methods of refabrication, differing principally in that they represent varying degrees of duplication of the work which produced the existing programs. The worst case, reanalysis, requires complete application of the activities and techniques described in this handbook. The other extreme — translation — can be applied only if specific software is available from a manufacturer or consulting firm.
The areas of reprogramming and recoding are the main subjects of the section which follows.

Reprogramming

Reprogramming starts with system and program description generated in the course of developing the existing programs. This documentation is used as the basis for new flowcharts, record formats, and coding, which are appropriate to the new target computer.

Reprogramming is called for when one of the following sets of conditions occurs:

- the present system efficiently meets the objectives of the organization, and good, current documentation is available; but the hardware software capabilities of the new computer are sufficiently different to make any exact duplication of the old system's operations inefficient;
- when good, current documentation of the existing programs is not available, so that changes to the present system would entail a prohibitive amount of detective work, discovering the intention of programmers and analysts who are no longer accessible.

The process of reprogramming starts with a detailed review of the available documentation, followed by a refinement and extension of this documentation to include all elements of desirable change discovered during the previous implementation and maintenance. This phase of system design upgrading is completed by the incorporation of these changes into the system development. It is often possible to reduce the development period for a new system to less than half of that previously required, if proper study and analysis of the documentation is carried out.

Recoding

Recoding starts with the flowcharts of the previous runs, and uses the old code as a guide to the production of new programs which are functionally identical with the old. Many descriptions of what is described as "reprogramming" in the literature of computer applications are actually discussing recoding.

Recoding requires that accurate documentation, such as flowcharts and source deck, be available before the effort is started. The first step in converting from the old to the new system is to audit the accuracy and currency of this documentation, in the course of proving out a set of test data that will be used in developing the new program.

Summary

When properly carried out from a basis of good documentation, reprogramming may utilize less than half the man power and computer time resources required for the original programming; while recoding can cut this figure in half again. Most of these savings are achieved during the flowcharting stage — that is, the design of processing logic — and are possible because of the availability of complete reliable documentation; substantial savings in the checkout stage result from the availability of correct logic and audited test data.

Bibliography

Volume 1

Ansoff, Igor H., *The firm of the future*, Harvard Business Review **43** (1965.09/10) no. 5, pages 162-168.

Berkel, P. L. M. van, *Automatisering van de informatieverwerking als deel van de lange en korte termijn planning van een onderneming*, Chapter IX of Management-aspecten van de automatisering, Marka boeken, Utrecht, 1965.

Bruijn, W. K. de, *15 Facetten van administratieve automatisering*, Samson, Alphen aan den Rijn, 1965.

Clive de Paula, F., *The use of computers in business information processing*, M.A.B. (Maandblad voor Accountancy en Bedrijfshuishoudkunde) **40** (1966.1), no. 1, pages 4-25.

Hartman, W., *Automatie en organisatie*, M.A.B. **38**, (1964.1) no. 1, pages 8-13.

Hartman, W., *De omvang van een automatieprojekt*, M.A.B., **38** (1964.10) no. 9, pages 362-369.

IFIP-ICC Vocabulary of information processing, first English language edition, North-Holland Publishing Cy., Amsterdam, 1966.

Johnson, Richard A., Kast, Fremont E. and Rosenzweig, James E., *The theory and management of systems*, McGraw-Hill, New York, 1963.

March, James G. and Simon, Herbert A., *Organizations*, John Wiley & Sons Inc., New York, 1958.

NEN 3386, *Woordenlijst informatieverwerking*, Glossary of information processing, Nederlands Normalisatie Instituut, 1967.

Stogdill, Ralph M., *Basic concepts for a theory of organization*, Management Science **13** (1967.6), no. 10, pages B666-B676.

Vocabulary for information processing, U.S.A. standard X 3.12, 1966.

Wilson, Ira G. and Wilson, Marthann E., *Information, computers and system design*, John Wiley & Sons Inc., New York, 1965.

Volume 2

Blau, Helmut, *Die Planung von E.D.V.-Anlagen, Wirtschaftlichkeits- und Rentabilitäts-Berechnungen*, Bürotechnik + Automation (1966), AR5, pages 218-226.

Brandon, Dick H., *Management standards for data processing*, Van Nostrand, Princeton, N.J., 1963.

Follett, Mary Parker, *Dynamic administration*, edited by Metcalf, Henry, C. and Urwick, L. F., Pitman, London, 1941.

Frielink, A. B. (editor), *Economics of automatic data processing*, North-Holland Publishing Cy., Amsterdam, 1965.

Gordon, Robert M., *Personnel selection*, Data Processing Digest **12** (1966.10), no. 10, pages 1-9.

Luftig, Milton, *Computer programmer, complete preparation for the major aptitude tests*, ARCO, New York, 1966.

Meeuwis, A. and Schaafsma, A. H., *De rol van de interne organisatie-adviseur bij automatisering*, Chapter XXIII of Managementaspecten van de automatisering, Marka boeken, Utrecht, 1965.

Ronayne, Maurice F., *Analyzing the systems analyst*, Data Management (1963.7), pages 29-35.

Volume 3

Ansoff, Igor H., *Corporate strategy: analytic approach to business policy for growth and expansion*, McGraw-Hill, New York, 1965.

Anthony, Robert H., *Planning and control systems, a framework for analysis*, Harvard University, Boston, 1965.

A management guide to IMIS, Document no. E36 Diebold European research program, june 1967.

Bromley, Alan C., *Choosing a set of computers*, Datamation, (1965.8) no. 8, pages 37-40.

Churchman, Ackoff and Arnoff, *Introduction to operations research*, John Wiley & Sons Inc., New York, 1957.

Cooper, W. W., Leavitt, H. J. and Shelley, M. W. (ed.), *New perspectives in organization research*, John Wiley & Sons Inc., New York, 1964.

Corporate data file design, EDP Analyzer, Vista **4** (1966.12), no. 12, pages 1-15.

Dearden, John, *How to organize information systems*, Harvard Business Review **43** (1965.03/04), no. 2, pp. 65-73.

Duyne, U. K. C., *Computerkeuze-factoren en kriteria I en II*, Informatie 1966 nos. 2 and 3, pages 7-11 and 5-10.

Fast response system design, EDP Analyzer, Vista **5** (1967.3), no. 3, pages 1-14.

Forrester, J. W., *Industrial Dynamics*, John Wiley & Sons Inc., New York, 1961.

Frielink, A. B., *Inleiding tot het organisatie-onderzoek ten behoeve van de toepassing van informaten bij de besturlijke informatiebehandeling*, Samson, Alphen aan den Rijn, 1965.

Gatto, O. T., *Autosate*, Communications of the ACM, 1964, **7** (1964.7), no. 7, pages 425-432.

Joslin, Edward O. and Mullin, Martin J., *Cost-value technique for evaluation of computer system proposals*, Proceedings Spring joint computer conference, 1964, pages 367-381.

Kaufman, Felix, *Data systems that cross company boundaries*, Harvard Business Review **44** (1966.01), no. 1, pp 141-155.

Kaufman, Felix, *Electronic data processing and auditing*, Ronald Press, New York, 1961.

Langefors, B., *Theoretical analysis of information systems*, Student litterature, Lund, 1966.

Lease, Rent or Buy; The leasing decision; Parts I and II, Automatic Data Processing Newsletter **12** (1967.11.27 and 1967.12.4), nos. 6 and 7.

Naylor, F. H., Balintfy, J. L., Burdick, D. S. and Kong Chu, *Computer simulation techniques*, John Wiley & Sons, New York, 1966.

Opler, Archer, *Measurement of software characteristics*, Datamation (1964.7), pages 27-30.

Price, Dennis G. and Mulvihill, Dennis E., *Developing systems timing specs*, Datamation (1965.4), no. 4, pages 53-58.

Rapport uitgebracht aan de Commissie van Advies inzake organisatievraagstukken door de subcommissie Administratie en Verkoopleiding, De Accountant **72** (1966.5), no. 9, pages 481-513.

Rosenthal, Solomon, *Analytical technique for automatic data processing equipment acquisition*, Proceedings Spring joint computer conference, 1964, pages 359-366.

Starreveld, R. W., *Leer van de administratieve organisatie, Delen 1 and 2*, Samson, Alphen aan den Rijn, 1963.

Steenbergen, Th. J., *Hoe kiest U de computer*, Doelmatig Bedrijfsbeheer **19** (1967.10), no. 10, pages 498-501.

The corporate data file, EDP Analyzer, Vista **4** (1966.11), no. 11, pages 1-13.

Tucker, Spencer A., *Successful managerial control by ratio analysis*, McGraw-Hill, New York, 1961.

Veen, B. van der, *Introduction to the theory of operational research*, Centrex, Eindhoven, 1966.

Volume 4

Generalized file processing software, EDP Analyzer, Vista **3** (1965.10), no. 10, pages 1-15.

Herman, Donald J. and Ihrer, Fred C., *The use of computers to evaluate computers*, in Proceedings of the Spring joint computer conference, 1964, pages 383-395.

Ihrer, Fred C., *Computer performance projected through simulation*, Computers and Automation **16** (1967.4), no. 4, pages 22-27.

Laden, H. N. and Gildersleeve, T.R., *System design for computer applications*, John Wiley & Sons Inc., New York, 1963.

Martin, James, *Programming real-time computer systems*, Prentice Hall, Englewood Cliffs, N.J., 1965.

New Light on error detection and control, EDP Analyzer, Vista **1** (1963.2), no. 1, pages 1-11.

Starreveld, R. W., *Leer van de administratieve organisatie*, Samson, Alphen aan den Rijn, 1963.

Volume 5

Kennevan, Walter J., *ADP Conversion planning*, DPMA Quarterly, Park Ridge, Ill., **1** (1965.4), no. 3, pages 2-23.

Schwartz, M. H., *Training and education in electronic data processing*, Data Processing Digest **13** (1967.04), no. 4, pages 1-11.

Volume 6

Technique 6-1.1

Special "automation" number, Scientific American **215** (1966.9), no. 3.

PERT Coordinating Group, *PERT-GUIDE: for management use*, U.S. Government Printing Office (0-698-452), 1963, 56 pages.

Technique 6-1.2

Bower, Zlathovitch and Schlosser, a chapter in *Accounting systems theory and practice*, Allyn & Bacon Inc., 1965.

Chapanis, Alphonse, *Man-machine engineering*, Wadsworth and Tavistock, Belmont, 1965.

Crombach, Lee J., in consulting with Hilgard, E. R. and Spalding, W. R., *Educational psychology*, Harcourt Brace & World Inc., New York, 1963.

Krech, D., Crutchfield, R. and Ballackey, E., *Individual in society*, McGraw-Hill, New York, 1962.

Lester, D. and Crow, Alice, *Understanding our behaviour*, Alfred Knopf Publishing Co., New York, 1956.

McCormick, Edward J., *Human factors engineering*, McGraw-Hill, New York, 1964.

Schlosser, Robert E., *Psychology for the systems analyst*, Management Services (1964.11/12), pages 29-36.

Technique 6-1.3

Zelko, Harold P., *Successful conference and discussion techniques*, McGraw-Hill, New York, 1957.

Technique 6-2.1

Boer, H. de (ed.), *Schriftelijk rapporteren; een praktische handleiding bij het samenstellen van rapporten*, Aula boeken, Utrecht, 1961.

Erlich and Murphy, *The art of technical writing*, Bantam books, 1964.

Follet et al., *Modern American Usage*, Hill and Wang, 1966.

Fowler and Gowers, *Modern English Usage*, Oxford University Press, London, 1965.

Technique 6-2.4

Defoort, W. F., *Beslissingstabellen*, Informatie **9** (1967.10), no. 10, pages 206-213.

Fisher, D. L., *Data documentation and decision tables*, Communications of the ACM **9** (1966.1), no. 1, pages 26-31.

Grindley, C. B. B., *Systematics, a non programming language for designing and specifying commercial systems for computers*, The Computer Journal **9** (1966), no. 2, pages 124-128.

How to use decision tables, EDP Analyzer, Vista **4** (1966.5), no. 5, pages 1-14.

Pollack, S. L., *Conversion of limited-entry decision tables to computer programs*, Communications of the ACM **8** (1956.11), no. 11, pages 677-682.

Pollack, S. L., *Decision tables directly into program*, Ideas for Management; Systems and Procedures Association, 1966.

Pollack, S. L., *How to build and analyze decision tables*, talk presented at Air Defence Command Automation Symposium, Colorado Springs (1963.1.12), Published by Rand Corporation, Santa Monica.

Reinwald, L. T. and Soland, R. M., *Conversion of limited entry decision tables to optimal computer programs I and II*, Journal of the Association for Computing Machinery **13** (1966), pages 339-358; part II, **14** (1967.10), no. 4, pages 742-756.

Technique 6-3.1

Bolsky, M. L., *Guide to gathering information for system analysis*, Unpublished note LO-2864, SDC, 1964 (USAF System Command) Project 465L.

Kahn, Robert L. and Canell, Charles F., *The dynamics of interviewing*, John Wiley & Sons Inc., New York, 1966.

Nichols, R. G. and Stevens, L. A., *Are you listening*, McGraw-Hill, New York, 1957.

Technique 6-3.2

Battersby, A., *Mathematics in management*, Penguin Books, London, 1966.

Kaufmann, A. and Faure, R., *Invitation à la recherche opérationelle*, Dunod, Paris, 1963.

Moroney, M. J., *Facts from figures*, Penguin Books, Harmondsworth, 1958.

Wijvekate, M. L., *Verklarende statistiek*, Aula Boeken, Utrecht, 1960.

Technique 6-4.2

Data management; File organization, EDP Analyzer, Vista **5** (1967.12), no. 12, pages 1-13.

Technique 6-4.4

Application packages; Coming into their own, EDP Analyzer, Vista **5** (1967.7), no. 7, pages 1-12.

Technique 6-4.6

Adams associates, *The computer display review*, Adams Associates, Inc., Bedford, Mass., USA, 1967.

Auerbach Corporation, *Auerbach data communications reports*, Auerbach Info Inc., Philadelphia, Pa., USA, 1967.

Code for information interchange, USA standard X 3.4- 1967.

Gentle, Edgar C., Jr., *Data communications in business*, A.T. & T. and Publishers Service Company, New York, 1965.

Beckley, Dudley F., *Check digit verification*, Data Processing **8** (1966.07/08), no. 4, pages 194-201.

Belkum, A. J. en van 't Klooster, J. W., *Administratieve automatisering en controle*, Samson, Alphen aan den Rijn, 1964. 238 pages.

Bijleveld, W. J., *Fouten voorkomen of controlecijfers?*, Informatie **9** (1967.11), no. 11, pages 239-243.

Frielink, A. B., *Een methode voor analyse van de werking van controlemaatregelen bij automatische informatieverwerking*, M.A.B. **41** (1967.2), no. 2, pages 50-55.

Hartman, W., *Beheersing van de invoer bij automatiesystemen*, M.A.B. **40** (1966.4), no. 4, pages 161-180.

Hinds, G. H., *The accuracy of data preparation*, The Computer Bulletin (1960.6), pages 7-9.

Holzer, J. E., *Controls for data processing*, Data Processing Magazine **7** (1965.08), no. 7, pages 28-30.

Joplin, H. Bruce, *An internal control checklist for EDP*, Management Services (1964.07/08), pages 32-37.

Laden, T. R. & Gildersleeve, H. N., *System design for computer applications*, John Wiley & Sons Inc., New York, 1963, 330 pages.

Louwers, P. C., *Enige praktische ervaringen van de accountant bij de geautomatiseerde informatieverwerking*, Managementaspecten van de automatisering, Marka boeken no. 19, pages 393-408.

Matzken, R. H., *Toepassing van leap frog bij computers*, Philips Administration Review, **17** (1963.11), no. 4, pp. 11-16.

Mühring, W. J., *Controles bij geautomatiseerde informatieverwerking*, Kantoor en Efficiency **5** (1966.01), no. 44, pages 1838-1842.

Meyeraan, J. F., *Proeve van een vragenlijst over interne controle*, Bijlage van M.A.B. **40** (1966.07), no. 7, 19 pages.

New Light on error detection and control, EDP Analyzer, Vista **1** (1963.2), no. 1, pages 1-11.

Price, Waterhouse and Company, *Management control of electronic data processing*, 1965, 33 pages (distributed by I.B.M., no. F20-0006-0).

Tyran, Michael R., *Mechanical verification of accounting data input*, Management Accounting **47** (1966.2), no. 6, pages 36-48.

Verhoeff, Dr. J., *Error-detecting and corrective codes*, International Office Machines guide (1966.10), no. 51, chapters 3.1, pages 1-8.

Waller, R. R., *The legal requirements in data processing*, The Computer Bulletin (1966.03), pages 133-136.

Ziessow, Bernard W., *Establishing input/output controls*, Data Processing Equipment Encyclopedia; updating service, 1966, pages 156-165.

Technique 6-6

Martin, James, *Programming real time computer systems*, Prentice Hall, Englewood Cliffs, N.J., 1965.

Subject index

— C —

— Q —

— R —

— S —

— T —

— U —